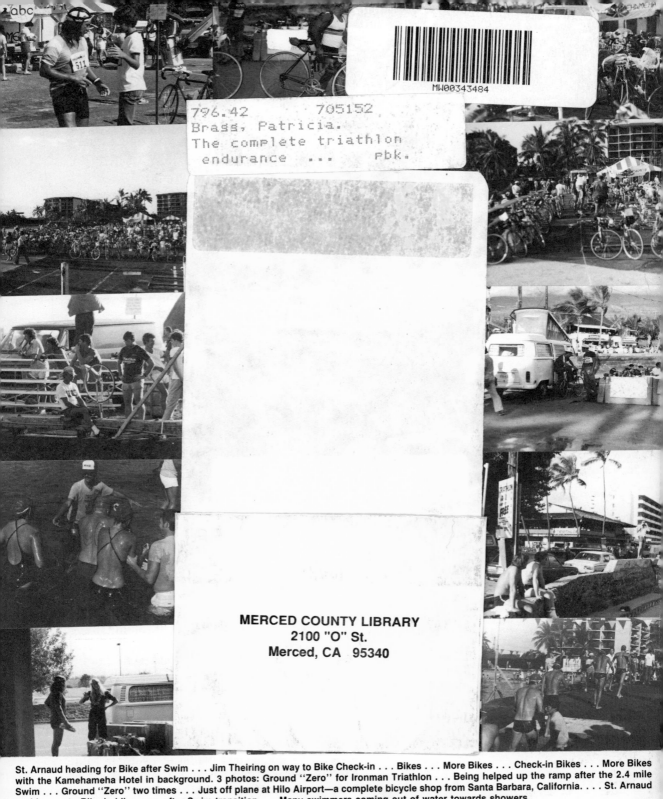

St. Arnaud heading for Bike after Swim . . . Jim Theiring on way to Bike Check-in . . . Bikes . . . More Bikes . . . Check-in Bikes . . . More Bikes with the Kamehameha Hotel in background. 3 photos: Ground "Zero" for Ironman Triathlon . . . Being helped up the ramp after the 2.4 mile Swim . . . Ground "Zero" two times . . . Just off plane at Hilo Airport—a complete bicycle shop from Santa Barbara, California. . . . St. Arnaud on his way to Bike holding area after Swim transition . . . Many swimmers coming out of water towards showers.

TRIATHLON

The Multi-Fitness, Participation Sport of the 80's

The exciting growth of this sports combination, since the advent of the first Ironman Nautilus Triathlon in Honolulu, Hawaii, 1978, is proof that the Triathlon as a multi-fitness participation sport will equal or surpass the running boom of the 70's.

A Triathlete Can Be Anyone

Triathletes come in all shapes, sizes, sexes and handicaps. The sport is a great equalizer of ability and achievement. Athletes that excel in either swimming, bicycling or running are brought down to a common level at the start of their multi-sport training program!

"The Complete Triathlon Swim, Bike, Run, Endurance Training Manual" is a comprehensive, concise, encyclopedia of multi-sport fitness training and covers every conceivable area of over-distance . . . swim, bike and run training, including:

> Mental Spiritual Fitness • Nutrition • Fat Conversion • Muscle Fibre Training • Percent of Body Fat • Breathing • Walking • Race Walking in the Triathlon • Injuries • Stretching • Omega Aerobics Testing Training • Anerobic Intervals • Women Triathlete Training • Nautilus Strength Training • Swim 2.4 mi—Bike 112 mi—Run 26.2 mi— at Speed in 12 Months Training • Cold Water Swimming by Jack LaLanne • Ultramarathon Training for the Triathlete • Combined Swim Bike and Run Training • History and Future of the Triathlon.

A Complete Compendium of Fitness

600 pages, 300,000 words, written in the same perceptive readable style of the 30 volume Bragg Library of health and fitness books. Over 200 live, Triathlon action and technical photographs, plus many illustrative graphs and charts.

Everyone Can Be Physically Fit

This book is must reading for everyone interested in total health, and for anyone who never expects to go beyond walking as their total exercise but who can fantasize the possibility of someday becoming a Triathlete!

$16.95   Soft Cover   USA
$24.95   Hard Cover   USA

Important Message for Readers

The publisher, on its own behalf as well as on behalf of the writers of this book, wishes to emphasize that the contents are intended to inform readers, but are not intended to provide medical advice for individual health problems. Such advice should be sought from your physician

Cover Personalities:

Swimmer — Diane Giebel,
    1968 Olympic Swimmer

Biker — Bob Johnson, Champion
    Triathlete, Over 60 Class

Runner — Max Telford, World Class
    New Zealand Runner

Cover Art: Laurie Sunderland
    of Santa Barbara

Design: Sterling Sasaki, Honolulu, Hawaii

Photo Credits:

Swimmer — Tom Moore, Santa Barbara
Biker — Tom Moore, Santa Barbara
Runner — Carol Hogan, Honolulu, Hawaii

**All photos by Bob Johnson
unless otherwise credited**

THE COMPLETE
TRIATHLON
ENDURANCE TRAINING MANUAL
SWIM • BIKE • RUN

No Sexual Bias in the Triathlon

In this the era of multi-sports events involving both men and women equally, it is important that we set forth our editorial policy from the outset. In the desire to give equal attention to both men and women in writing a text such as this and at the same time alleviate the need for printed clutter such as he/she, him/her and himself/herself, we have taken the masculin gender to include men and women equally where proper and applicable.

The Ironman Triathlon World Championship of Kona, Hawaii, at the suggestion that Ironperson be used for the title of the event, officially set Ironman to mean Iron Men and Iron Women. The Triathlon is the great equalizer between persons of the same sex as well as between men and women. It is possible and entirely probable that a woman will indeed become the Ironman of some future event. This could only happen in the great multi-sport event called Triathlon.

THE COMPLETE TRIATHLON SWIM-BIKE-RUN ENDURANCE TRAINING MANUAL
By Patricia Bragg, Ph.D. and Bob Johnson

Revised 1985

Library of Congress Catalog Number 84-082236

Library of Congress Cataloging in Publication Data
Bragg, Patricia
The Complete Triathlon Swim-Bike-Run Endurance Training Manual
Includes Index.
1. Walking, 2. Running, 3. Swimming, 4. Biking, 5. Sports Nutrition, 6. Sports Injuries, 7. Sports Physiology
Johnson, Bob Joint Author
ISBN: 0-87790-028-0

THE COMPLETE
TRIATHLON
ENDURANCE TRAINING MANUAL

PATRICIA BRAGG, Ph.D.
Life Extension Specialist

AND

BOB JOHNSON
Champion Triathlete

HEALTH SCIENCE
Box 7, Santa Barbara, California 93102 U.S.A.

PAUL C. BRAGG, N.D., Ph.D.
Life Extension Specialist

One of the world's foremost authorities on scientific nutrition and physical fitness. Dr. Bragg was the pioneer Triathlete, and promoted swimming, biking, and running for physical fitness years before the Triathlon became an "in" event.

DEDICATION AND APPRECIATION

Dr. Paul C. Bragg was a good friend. He met with an untimely death in his late 90's, or he would still be with us today! Dr. Bragg was a confidant and health counselor to many top Hollywood celebrities, including names of distinction worldwide and millions of health followers over four continents. Paul C. Bragg was a Health and Fitness Crusader, a Life Extension Specialist, and an Evangelist, one of those rare persons who is able to make us laugh at ourselves. His dedication and crusade for over 70 years was our physical, mental, spiritual well-being!

Dr. Bragg attracted the physically culture-minded and the athlete wherever he went . . . Hawaii, Sydney, London, Europe, New York, Chicago, Hollywood. Through the years, his association with many of the world greats in Business, Films and Athletic achievement had a great impact on Dr. Bragg. He counted these people as his closest friends and they were his. Competitive sports health and fitness was the common denominator in these relationships.

From the voluminous legacy of the written and the spoken word left by Dr. Bragg to posterity, priceless gems of counsel and wisdom on matters of health, mental and spiritual well-being has been drawn.

This book will change your life . . . that is a promise! It will open your mind and heart to a philosophy of life, timelessly old and yet clinically new and sporting. Paul Bragg would have wanted us to consider how priceless good health, mental and spiritual well-being are in our everyday walk through life! Whatever the cost, it is such a small price to pay.

I wish to acknowledge the support and contributions made on the part of the following persons to the compilation of this training manual. Bragg follower and author, **Bob Anderson**, author of *Stretching* has contributed a special chapter on "Stretching for Swim, Bike and Run." **Arthur Jones** and **Ed Farnum** of *Nautilus Sports and Medical Industries* offered the chapter on ''Strength Training for Swim, Bike and Run.'' **Chad Craieen** contributed "Fat Conversion for the Triathlete." **James E. Counsilman**, author of the *Competitive Swimming Manual for Coaches and Swimmers* contributed a portion of the Swimming chapter, the "Muscle Fiber" chapter and the "Interval Training" chapter. **Jack LaLanne** offered the chapter on "Cold Water Swimming", on which subject he is a great authority. **John Marino**, cross-continent bicycle racer and his co-authors, **Dr. Lawrence May** and **Hal Bennett** contributed portions of the chapter on "Bicycling," from their publication, *John Marino's Bicycling Book.* **Max Telford**, World Class New Zealand distance runner, Ultra Marathoner Instructor of Running and Biking class for Triathletes in Hawaii, offered his support of the "Marathon and Ultra Marathon" chapters, and in doing so, reflected the teachings of the Great **Arthur Lydiard** of New Zealand. The late **Percy Cerutty**, through his inspiration and training at Portsey, Melborne, Australia. **Doctors Scaff and Wagner**, of the Honolulu Marathon Clinic, for convincing me and thousands like me that I could run a marathon, if I would follow their 10-month program. To **my parents**, who provided a Christian home environment and, in difficult financial times, provided an abundance of nutritious food for me through my formative years, during the Great Depression. Forming the sound straight bone and muscle that makes it possible for me to compete in the Triathlons today, while most of my peers are inactive spectators. Lastly, to an uncle, **Jerry Melvile Lewis**, who was a very young boy's athletic god and who has been a continuing Christian influence and health inspiration in my life through the years.

Bob Johnson

The oldest and the youngest Ironmen! In the 1981 Triathlon Walter Stack, the oldest at 74 years young, and Robin Tain, the youngest at 14, both finished and became members of the exclusive Ironman finishers!

Photo by Carol Hogan

CONTENTS

BOOK III

Breathing, Walking and Race Walking for the Triathlete

BOOK IV
Preliminary Swim, Bike and Run Training Concepts

BOOK V

Triathlete Strength Training for Swim, Bike and Run

BOOK VI

Swim Training for the Triathlete

BOOK VII

Bike Training for the Triathlon

BOOK VIII

Marathon and Ultramarathon Training for the Triathlon

BOOK IX

Combined Swim, Bike, Run Triathlon Training

BOOK X

History of the Triathlons

Important Message for Readers

INTRODUCTION

I personally considered it a great honor to be selected by Health Science to help compile, and co-author this book. Dr. Paul C. Bragg, founder of Health Science, was my friend. He literally saved my life! I owe him a debt of gratitude far greater than the toil and labor I put into this volume. However, the time spent does have its rewards... if only by reaching out and touching just one life whose lifestyle will be changed for the better by these written words.

I count myself as a typical Bragg student. This is confirmed by the thousands of testimonials in Dr. Bragg's files. I first met Dr. Bragg on the beach at Waikiki (Fort De Russy lawn area) where he was leading his free and famous... "Live Longer, Healthier, Happier Exercise Class," which is now in its 13th year — 6 days a week, except Sunday, from 9-10:30 A.M. — everyone is invited when visiting in Honolulu. My health had deteriorated rapidly from the age of 45 to 50, and I was concerned so I joined in the exercises, and afterwards, I stayed and listened to the free health lecture given by Dr. Bragg. Under his counseling I turned my debilitating health trend around. Day by day, month by month, year by year, I basked in an ever-increasing "new glow" of good health! As stated earlier, this I owe a debt of gratitude beyond any monetary value to Dr. Paul Bragg.

As a result of this new body, new-found vigor, mental awareness, and excellent good health... I looked about for new tests, new goals, new mountains to climb! Running seemed to be catching on as a participating sport requiring only a minimum investment — a pair of good running shoes.

Hawaii is an ideal running paradise... good air, the northeast trade-winds are filtered by 2000 miles of blue sea and sky, climate is an even 85°F or 30°C the year-round with occasional rain showers which are a blessing to a warm, perspiring runner's body... not a curse. Hawaii boasts the largest number of runners in the world by percentage of population — all ages, sizes, shapes, nationalities and in all walks of life.

This running boom in Hawaii was not all by accident. Two men unselfishly gave of their time and talent and formed what has now become the Honolulu Marathon Clinic — Scaff & Wagner, doctors... (naturally, who else would call their creation a "clinic?"). But this clinic has been responsible for a decade of Honolulu Marathons nearing 10,000 participants from around the world annually. Over two-thirds of the participants are "first-time marathoners."

I went from the 10-Kilometer to the Half-Marathon to the 26-mile Marathon to the Ultra Marathon to the "Isle of Maui, Hawaii, Run to the Sun" 37½ miles from sea level to 10,500 feet up Mount Haleakalau Summit, to swimming ¼-mile — 1 mile — 2.5 mile rough open-sea swims, to bicycling 20 — 30 — 50 — 100 miles in competition. Finally at the age of 62 I have found the ultimate "mountain to climb" in competitive participation sports... the triathlon, which combines all three of these events — swim, bike and run.

One Year of Triathlons

Starting in Southern California in the late summer of 1981, I have, to date, completed 8 triathlons of varying distances and presently hold the southern regional championship for the United States Triathlon series having taken first place in the San Diego and the San Francisco Triathlons in my age group.

We have witnessed a humble start of this event in the first 1978 Honolulu Nautilus Triathlon with only 14 contestants, but with exciting promise of competition spreading fast nationwide in seasons to come! The enhancement of one athletic specialty, be it swim, bike or run to include each of the remaining two disciplines is what it's all about. The over-all physiological conditioning brought about by the combined swim-bike-run training for this event was the ultimate mountain on my horizon. The interaction of skills, technical expertise, distance training, spacing out endurance to cover all three events, to find competition in a full 2.4 mile swim, 112 mile bike race, and a 26.2 mile marathon will keep me occupied until I can no longer pick up one leg and place it ahead of the other.

Starting with my first 10 Kilometer competitive run in Finland in 1977, I have climbed several mountains only to arrive at the mountain of them all, the Triathlon. In fact, I arrived there so enthusiastically that I have participated in two Ironman World Triathlons and six of the Tin Man Variety of triathlon of lesser distances. I hold the Regional Championship in the U.S. Triathlon series, having taken two first places in three events in the over-55 age group. The stoker of it all is participating stroke-for-stroke, wheel-to-wheel, toe-to-toe with a wonderful group of dedicated triathletes, young enough to be my children and grandchildren.

This ability is all due to a new youthfulness, a new vigor only made possible through Dr. Paul C. Bragg's techniques and teachings of sound principles of Spiritual, Mental and Physical Philosophy of Life!

We will share this priceless knowledge with you throughout this book. In special areas of expertise, we have enlisted the help of leaders in specialized fields. My co-author is long time friend, Patricia Bragg, daughter of the late Dr. Paul Bragg. Patricia lectured with her father world-wide on health and fitness, co-authoring with her father many of the 30 Bragg Health and Fitness Books now in print. Patricia has her Ph.D. in Health Sciences and Nutrition. An internationally reknown authority on preventive medicine and extending the prime of life, Patricia has been a guest on over 300 radio talk shows from coast to coast in addition to Australia, New Zealand, England and Canada.

The triathlon, Swim-Bike-Run, the participation sport of the '80s, is fast becoming America's and the world's most exciting sport. As evidenced by the ABC-TV Wide World of Sports coverage of the Ironman World Triathlon in Kona, Hawaii. Presently, the triathlon as a sport enjoys the same position that the 10 kilometer marathon did from the late '70s to the time of this writing.

Excellent Training Material for Athletes

Volumes have been written on the subject of marathon running, bicycle road racing, distance rough water swimming and as yet, no one has given a thought to writing a complete training manual on preparing for these three sports "in combination" . . . the Triathlon.

Training instructions from the diet of a distance competitor, to equipment, to clothing, to physiology, to injuries, and on . . . you name it, and you will find printed answers to all of your questions on every subject in this volume.

Much of the material available today is top drawer, up-to-date, clinically proven, documented, and aimed at the top 5 to 10% of the participants in these sports. This select definitive group of genetically endowed, slow twitch, red-muscle distance fiber participants fits a typical mold . . . slim, long of leg, cardiovascular perfect athletic specimen who finds long distance competition training a piece of cake!

We will be able to assist this top athlete in the fast-growing, participant sport of Swim, Bike and Run Triathlon by answering and assisting in training problems in these combining events in a way that no one volume has attempted to do to date.

However, this book does not particularly focus on the top 10%, genetically endowed athlete. Why? Because we feel the 40-minute-mile swimmer . . . the 15-mile-per-hour bicyclist . . . and the 9-minute-mile runner . . . represents the average novice participant in these individual sports. They make up the greatest portion of the field and deserve and need all the help he or she can find to assist and improve his or her performance.

This volume does not pretend to be the final word on each one of these three disciplines, however, it does provide the basics and covers all areas to improve individual performance and open minds to new areas of training never before outlined. This manual also lists an in-depth bibliography of works available for the large and varied area of interest generated here on the subject of swim-bike-run distance training, for the Triathlon.

Triathlon aspirants are for the most part mono-dexterous, excelling in one of the three disciplines but dismally poor in one, if not both, of the remaining events.

Lifestyles, geographical limitations, climatical conditions could appear to make swim-bike-run distance training somewhat restricted. However, we have tried to cover training under all adverse conditions in this work.

Specifically, we wish to emphasize the need to train in combination for all three of these exciting events; to pace oneself properly and to go the whole distance. Most of all . . . to learn to enjoy training for the new quality of physical conditioning of the total body made possible by bringing together three of the best and most popular amateur athletic sports, swim-bike-run, into the greatest multi-sport event called the Triathlon!

This Manual Fills the Need

I have long felt the need for a training manual to more specifically meet the needs of the physical body . . . the slightly overweight; the older age groups; women as well as men; etc. The average or below average contestant has been left out of guided training and of course, left out of media coverage. It is time the "also-rans" should be heard from, given credit for their great accomplishment, and assisted in problems in competition training in these sports.

The triathlon is also called the great equalizer of distance competition. A person could be attracted to the excitement of the triathlon combination if he had excelled in swimming, but is willing to spend the time to train in order to also "go the distance" on a bike or on foot. This is probably the most difficult way to get into triathlon competition. The marathon runner, providing he or she is not deathly afraid of the water, has a little less demanding training regime and a somewhat better chance in tallying up a respectable total time than the swimmer in a full 140.6 mile triathlon.

The bicyclist is best suited for the triathlon (proven by the 1981 winner of the Ironman World Triathlon in Kona, Hawaii, bicyclist John Howard) and the greatest advantage in completeing competition with a low overall final time. John Howard is a world-class bicycle rider, holding a number of national and world championship titles. Even with his proven excellence in bicycling, it was still necessary for him to work extremely hard in training for swimming and running to be able to ward off strong competitors in these fields.

Space is given in the book to the training strategy that creates an interplay with these three events — swim, bike and run — in combination and forms the challenge that has made triathloning the super participating sporting event of the 1980's!

I am proud to be a Triathlete and I know you will be!

Your Triathlete Friend,
Bob Johnson

Sylviane Puntous triumphantly crossing the finish line at the Oct., 1983 Ironman Triathlon World Championship in Kona, Hawaii. Sylviane's winning time of 10:43:36 and that of her twin sister Patricia, 10:49:17, shattered Julie Leach's 1982 women's division record time of 10:54:08. Sylviane won again in Oct., 1984 (10:25:13).   Photo by Noël Black

I

Mental and Spiritual Aspects to Distance Training

Scott Tinley makes the turn from Kawahai Harbor towards Kona, 75 miles into the 112-mile bike segment of the 1984 Ironman Triathlon. He placed second behind Dave Scott, finishing at 9:18:45.

Photo by Carol Hogan

1

Mental and Spiritual Purification for the Athlete

TOWARD PHYSICAL EXCELLENCE
by E. Eugene Greer

THE PURPOSE OF THIS CHAPTER is to challenge our readers in general with a spiritual motivation of maintaining higher levels of personal physical fitness. Such levels will approximate more closely biblical teachings about God's standards and expectations. The first 43 years of my life, I let either my mother, doctor, and/or my wife be concerned about my physical health rather than I. I was very much in error in this attitude. In recent years, however, I have been convicted by the teachings of the Scriptures, by the testimony of others and by my own experience that my physical health is a stewardship matter between me and God.

Also, I have sometimes sensed that many of my fellow Christian workers have somewhat the same attitude toward their bodies which I had for so many years toward mine. This attitude of Christian leaders and laity relates to diet control, regular rest, therapeutic work patterns and meaningful participation in physical exercise.

My prayer for myself and for others is that we will read the Bible in terms of its teachings on physical fitness, and that we will feel a deep conviction to positively improve our personal physical health. Good health habits are not suggested necessarily as a way to lengthen life, although this could well result. What these habits will do is enhance the quality of life and make it much more zestful.

Physically Fit for Eternity

Physical fitness of the human body is magnified many ways in the New Testament. The New Testament is God's new contract with man. Not only is this emphasis remarkably pronounced in the gospels, but also the writings. Examples of this in the general sense are outlined here:

On the physical life...
And if the Spirit of God, who raised up Jesus from the dead, lives in you, he will make your dying bodies live again after you die, by means of this same Holy Spirit living within you. — Romans 8:11

On the life-style of Christian leaders...
Afterwards they preached from town to town across the entire island until finally they reached Paphos. — Acts 13:6-7

On natural world productivity...
My work was to plant the seed in your hearts and Apollos' work was to water it, but it was God, not we, who made the garden grow in your hearts. The person who does the

planting or watering isn't very important, but God is important because he is the one who makes things grow. —I Corinthians 3:6-7

Enlarging on the concepts noted above, the writers of the New Testament point up the Christian's body as a sacrifice, as the temple of God, and as an object of disciplined control, as a source of energy, as a tool of God, and as a model of the church.

"Just As I Am" Won't Do

At salvation time, "Just As I Am" is okay, but it won't do later — spiritually or physically. A Christian is to present his body as a living sacrifice to God. Paul, highly-trained in the meaning of the Jewish sacrificial ceremonies, appreciated the significance of "suitable" and "acceptable" when used to describe an offering to God. To be suitable and acceptable, "Just As I Am" won't do. A Christian must continually work at achieving his maximum potential both spiritually and physically. Paul indicated work and excellence in the following exhortation to Christians: "I plead with you to give your bodies to God. Let them be a living sacrifice, holy — the kind he can accept. When you think of what he has done for you, is this too much to ask?" (Rom. 12:1). He further explained Christian discipleship in Romans by concluding that "we can obey God's laws if we follow after the Holy Spirit and no longer obey the old evil nature within us" (Rom. 8:4).

Paul wrote to encourage his readers to live clean and honorable lives spiritually. However, there is an almost one-hundred percent correlation between the spiritually acceptable life as described by Paul: "Love, joy, peace, patience, kindness, goodness, faithfulness, gentleness and self-control" (Gal. 5:22-23), and the physically conditioned body of persons living such a life.

A physically fit person simply cannot maintain his conditioning and feature the opposite set of qualifications articulated by Paul: "Eagerness for lustful pleasure, hatred and fighting, jealousy and anger, envy, murder, drunkenness, wild parties, and all that sort of thing" (Gal. 5:19-21). Spiritual and physical fitness cannot accommodate in life nor body the practices and qualities which tear them down.

Athletes and everyday citizens who maintain high levels of personal physical fitness avoid physical indulgence. There are a few notable exceptions, but as a rule, trained people, simply out of respect for their pride and achievement, live according to Galatians 5:19-21.

In writing to the Christians at Corinth, Paul considered several other physical relationships toward one's being physically fit and wholesome: "Don't you realize that your bodies are actually parts and members of Christ?" (I Cor. 6:15) he asked. Then in great detail, the matters of diet control and sexual discipline were considered. He summarized these two extended discussions by saying that God has given us an appetite for food and stomachs to digest it. But that doesn't mean we should eat more than we need" (I Cor. 6:13). He further observed that "sexual sin is never right; our bodies were not made for that, but for the Lord, and the Lord wants to fill our bodies with himself" (I Cor. 6:13). He spoke in terms of the physically clean, healthy and wholesome body of the Christian. "Just As I Am" won't do. We must continually work at improvement.

It's a Fabulous Mechanism, That Temple, Our Body

For a Christian, his body is not only the sacrifice, it symbolically and actually is the place of sacrifice. It's the Temple, the dwelling place of the Holy Spirit.

A Christian should recognize that his physical body is the earthly temple of the Holy Spirit. Closely associated with one's body being a sacrifice to God, is the idea that a Christian's body is actually the in-dwelling place for the Holy Spirit. It takes the place of the Old Testament tabernacle and the Temple of Solomon. These were the two dwelling places for the Spirit of God before the coming of Christ. Now the flesh and blood of the Christian is the earthly dwelling place of the Spirit of God:

Don't you realize that all of you together are the house of God, and that the Spirit of God lives among you in his house. If anyone defiles and spoils God's home, God will destroy him. For God's home is holy and clean, and you are that home. — I Corinthians 3:16-17

Care For Your Body; It Is Not Yours

Another reason is added to these two for one's keeping his body clean and pure: "Your own body does not belong to you. For God has bought you with a great price. So use every part of your body to give glory back to God, because he owns it" (I Cor. 6:19-20). Just as God's universe exists to bring honor and glory to him, so do our physical bodies exist to bring honor and glory to him. And only as a body is kept in its highest possible conditioning is it capable of honoring God as it should.

Therefore, for the Christian especially and for others as well the body should be maintained with utmost care. Inside and outside. Mentally, physically, emotionally it should be honed into its best possible performance and production capabilities. It ought to be worthy of God's presence. For not only is God indwelling the body, He also has designs on it for doing His work.

Picked Out — Not Over

In doing his work, God has chosen people as his instruments. And the instruments are the bodies — hands, arms and legs, nervous system, and the like. Therefore, in order to be serviceable in work, the machines, the bodies, must be kept in good repair! They need protection from the indulgences and undisciplined activities that deteriorate capabilities. To provide this protection, a person must look over the available options of things to do, ideas to nurture and goals to pursue. A lot of help is available along this line. Followers of Jesus were picked out — chosen. Jesus explained it this way: "You didn't choose me! I chose you! I appointed you to go and produce lovely fruit always, so that no matter what you ask for from the Father, using my name, he will give it to you" (Jn. 15:15). You have been picked out — not over. The reasonable approach then, is to live as if you know it!

On the other side of the ledger, the Christian is exhorted to work hard like an athlete. One of the many direct challenges leading toward physical discipline, training and commitment is this one, found in Hebrews: "Since we have such a huge crowd of men of faith watching us from the grandstands, let us strip off anything that slows us down or holds us back, and especially those sins that wrap themselves so tightly around our feet and trip us up; and let us run with patience the particular race that God has set before us" (Heb. 12:1). Self-discipline is the note. Discipline to choose the better; to select the best from the good. Whether it is eating, sleeping, exercising or whatever, if improperly done — too little — too much — too often — its undesirable. A Christian should work toward an equilibrium to achieve wholesomeness and health!

This is at least part of the lesson from the scriptures quoted above. The body, to glorify God correctly, is disallowed indulgences that lead in any direction short of complete healthiness, vitality and serviceability. For serving, working and achieving is what life is all about.

Metabolism Alone is Not Enough

A Christian is exhorted to live with a newness and vitality in all that he does. This achievement rests on the promise of one's fitness physically, but suggests far more. The book of Romans contains a section on practical Christianity starting with chapter twelve. Focal in its message are these phrases on physical vitality: "Be a new and different person with a fresh newness in all you do and think"... and "never be lazy in your work but serve the Lord enthusiastically"... (Rom. 12:1,11).

Paul was so involved physically in serving God that he said "I carry on my body the scars of the whippings and wounds" (Gal. 6:17) from his service to God. A vitality, an energetic leadership, a tone of action was partly the descriptive phrases that distinguished his ministry. He was alive and aggressive in his service and life. He was not satisfied just to live — to carry on bodily functions. In fact, in his effort to summarize in a once-for-all illustration of how one should live for Christ, Paul said of himself: "Like an athlete, I punish my body, treating it roughly, training it to do what it should, not what it wants to do" (I Cor. 9:27).

An athlete experiences such tension that he actually does in fact punish his body.

Spiritual vs. Physical Fitness

Training, common to athletes as well as to others who work toward personal physical fitness, was a familiar matter to Paul and he often referred to it. His admonition to Timothy along this line needs to be considered. Listen to it: "Spend your time and energy in the exercise of keeping spiritually fit. Bodily exercise is all right, but spiritual exercise is much more important" (I Tim. 4:7-8). The phrasing above indicates the superiority of the spiritual over the physical, but doesn't leave the impression that physical exercise is unnecessary nor unprofitable. Some commentators imply and others say outright that in this reference Paul was referring to religious ceremonies to which he had alluded in the first part of that chapter. Actually, the ceremonies to which he refers are hardly anything to be compared with "physical exercise." And I think many commentators, not sensitive to the physical teachings of the Bible, miss the point.

Paul's intention in this succinct instruction to his young preacher and ministerial student was very practical. Paul wrote so profusely about the body, physical excellence and discipline that he feared Timothy might get the wrong idea. So, in this reference, he is making a point to clarify priorities. He emphasizes that the spiritual is the foremost factor and leaves the impression that the physical is surely second. He was making sure that Timothy would keep the spiritual and physical aspects of his ministry and life in their proper perspective.

Physical fitness is indeed desirable for one to have a "newness" and a vitality in performing acceptable spiritual service to God. For all the work and service performed in behalf of others and to others come from Christians' hands, mind and feet. They are God's tools.

What You See is What God's Got

The angels God uses are called people. And God's purposes are achieved in "people-to-people" settings. If you're a Christian then you are in his hands. Look in a mirror and you see one of God's tools. You are it! What you see is what God's got.

Two of the events which reflect the physical stamina of Jesus' early followers are recorded in Acts, chapter eight. One simply states that "... Peter and John returned to Jerusalem, stopping at several Samaritan villages" (Acts 8:25). This means of course that these men were traveling a good many miles from home, walking several miles each day and stopping in at villages as they went, preaching the Gospel.

Another reference to the physical strength of a follower tells of Philip's run or jog to and alongside a chariot. Philip was in Jerusalem and God told him to go to a certain road outside Jerusalem where he would see a man in a chariot. And in the context of Philip's finding the chariot, engaging the passenger in conversation and his subsequent getting into the vehicle with the Ethiopian ruler, is implied a rather high level of physical capability (Acts 8:26ff). All of this indicates that Philip was in rather exceptional physical conditioning, especially as it relates to walking and/or jogging.

Duncan MacLean   **Dr. Paul C. Bragg**

Dr. Bragg on a training run in Regents Park, London, with his British running friend,
Duncan MacLean, at 94 years young, is England's oldest champion runner.

And how about those two people who were walking along the road to Emmaus following Jesus' resurrection? The trip from Jerusalem to their home was ". . . seven miles out of Jerusalem" (Lu. 24:13ff). However, as they talked with Jesus after they reached home, they found out who he was. Anxious to tell their friends back in Jerusalem about their experience, ". . . within the hour they were on their way back to Jerusalem" (Lu. 24:33). The indication is that they got back that same night. They must have jogged and hurriedly walked back.

Anyone who runs or jogs knows that a seven-mile jog, even at a nine- or ten-minute pace is quite demanding on the heart and lungs. A person, or as in this case, two persons, do not get out and jog seven miles without some hard training previously. These two disciples, like many other of Jesus' followers, were in an excellent state of physical conditioning. They were ready to do their job, whatever it called for.

In another setting, Paul wrote that "just as there are many parts to our bodies, so it is with Christ's body" (Rom. 12:4). He was referring to the church. In this case the church is pictured as a composite. Each individual Christian is contributing his part, and if that part should be disabled or unable to perform, then to that extent would the whole "body of Christ" be disabled and weakened. The inference clearly therefore, is that the persons who make up this body be individually fit and ready to do acceptable work.

The fit and functioning body was used by Jesus in illustrative ways. Collectively, Christians should be able to carry out their responsibilities successfully. If the church is the body, and Christ is the head of the body, then He knows what's going on.

Parts of the body were brought in for discussion in relating truth about the Christian experience. Jesus spoke somewhat of the "completeness" of physical fitness in referring to the eye as necessary for leaders when he commented that "They are blind guides leading the blind, and both will fall into a ditch" (Matt. 15:14). The point is that physical fitness is the standard in the Bible.

It's a Kinship Friendship

A Christian's physical fitness is known to God and therefore should be a concern of the individual. That God is interested in the spiritual welfare of his people is a preeminent emphasis of the scriptures. However, it is also the major factor in the scriptures, that God is very much aware of His people's physical condition. God relates physical well-being and prosperity to forgiveness of sins. That practice was continued through New Testament times and into current Christian experience as well.

One of the constantly recurring themes in Christian prayer is to ask God's blessing upon those who are physically ill. The scriptures point out that the physical body is of minute concern to God. Jesus said that ". . . the very hairs of your head are all numbered" (Matt. 10:30). God's interest is personal, on the basis of a close friend or a near relative. That is, the New Testament as well as the Old, emphasizes the principle of God's knowing about each person's physical well-being. As a person known intimately by God, each one should be aware that God knows how one's body is getting along.

Some common place observations along this line are: "Oh, my doctor doesn't allow me to eat this but he isn't here . . ." and "whether I get fat or not, this looks good, so . . ." Persons making such observations are acting as if the doctor, and not they themselves were responsible for their health. Far worse is the fact that such a comment rules out God's minute-by-minute surveillance and knowledge of every tissue, every thought and every deed. How could a serious person so insult God with an attitude like that? Because God is so intimately anxious that physical fitness and health be nurtured, honored and promoted, we should be thankful and urgently active in cooperating to please Him.

A Case of Incurable Health

As cited above, Jesus in His resurrected body, reflected a type of physical perfection. He had a case of incurable, non-terminable, eternal health. Although He was indwelling a body drastically different from a body of ordinary flesh and blood, it nevertheless had earthly body characteristics. Also illustrations used by the New Testament writers as well as the words of instructions on the subject from Jesus himself strongly indicate that the believer can confidently look forward to a state of eternal health. The curse on the natural environment is outlined above.

However, a new world, a physically right world, awaits both the people and their environment:

"*For we know that* even the things of nature, like animals and plants, suffer in sickness and death as they await this great event. And even we Christians, although we have the Holy Spirit within us as a foretaste of future glory, also groan to be released from pain and suffering. We, too, wait anxiously for that day when God will give us our full rights as His children, including the new bodies He has promised us — bodies that will never be sick again and will never die." — Romans 8:22-23

A follow-up to the above is the paragraph below from Corinthians. Paul is discussing the resurrection question, and answers two specific points: "How will the dead be brought back to life again?" and "What kind of bodies will they have?" (I Corinthians 15:35). He goes on in the remainder of this chapter to answer the second question. This question has physical fitness implications. Paul's most pertinent comment on eventual physical fitness is quoted here:

. . . *Our earthly bodies* which die and decay are different from the bodies we shall have when we come back to life again, for they will never die. The bodies we have now embarrass us for they become sick and die; but they will be full of glory when we come back to life again. Yes, they are weak, dying bodies now, but when we live again they will be full of strength. They are just human bodies at death, but when they come back to life they will be superhuman bodies. — I Cor. 15:42-44

This section of the Scripture, more than others akin to it, gives a model of the resurrected earthly physical body. It portrays a fitness that is perfection itself. For the Christian, it seems that the New Testament writers outlined how the "new life" on the inside, is to be matched at the resurrection time with a "new life" outside, as it were. Peter wrote that the life passed on to you from your parents "will fade away," but "this new one will last forever, for it comes from Christ" (I Peter 1:23).

The point is this: spiritual fitness, initiated when a person is redeemed from his sinful state by faith in Christ, is to be matched by a type of physical bodily perfection upon the occasion of His resurrection from the dead. This is the ultimate gift of God to an individual. He will completely renew and re-create the body into one of never-decaying, never-failing, ever-healthy, ever-vigorous qualities. A case of incurable health will break out! The complete restoration of both environmental and personal fitness is pictured in Romans to be a great day. Paul said that "God will give us full rights as His children, including the new bodies He has promised us" (Rom. 8:23). This all sounds great. And it is, but there are hordes of people who categorically and systematically turn down the package. The spiritual and the physical are separated in their thinking.

Health Pioneers, Dr. Paul Bragg (on the left) with Bernarr Macfadden. Dr. Bragg, as a young man admired Macfadden for his pioneering Physical Culture and Preventive Medicine Concepts. Bragg became his protege and worked up in the famous Macfadden publishing empire, becoming editor of the Physical Culture Magazine. Dr. Bragg opened the Deauville Club Hotel in Miami Beach, which became America's first World Famous Health and Fitness Spa and was the making of the new Miami Beach years ago. During the Great Depression, these two men developed the famous "Penny Kitchens" throughout the country, supplying a nutritious health meal to millions of hungry people for one cent!

A Whole-Person Affair

Many of my Christian friends give me the very same reasons for their not being physically fit . . . as my unbelieving friends give me for their not being Christians. Rather odd, perhaps. But it's a fact and those reasons go like this:

"How do I know it will work for me?"

For the non-exercising, soft and deconditioned believer, usually a good many pounds overweight, this seems a fairly logical question. It is the very same question that a non-hoping, non-trusting person asks about thrusting himself in faith toward Christ for salvation. The spiritually unregenerate person is hard-pressed to think in terms of trusting the strength of Christ, just as the unconditioned Christian is hard-pressed to think in terms of hard exercise and diet management for himself. How do I know it'll work? The answer for both the Christian and the unregenerate is: It has always worked for everybody who has tried it.

Remember, I'm not talking about "perfect" physical conditioning and I'm not talking about "perfect" faith. In both cases, I'm talking about the everyday practice by ordinary people of faith in Christ and personal physical health, both of which grow in strength as they are practiced. One "practices" faith in Christ and physical fitness habits very much like one practices the piano or medicine. The more able a pianist is, the more he practices the piano. And while the thought sometimes frightens me, the medical doctor in whom I have the confidence to trust my body, is one who is "practicing" medicine. He never arrives, he never finishes the race; like the musician, he is never "perfect," but he is pressing toward the mark. So it is with the practicing Christian; and the individuals practicing physical fitness, they have not arrived, but they enjoy being on their way!

"I'm getting along OK like I am."

The non-Christian thinks the marginal spiritual strength he derives from being "morally good" is all there is. How sad! And the deconditioned Christian doesn't know how bad he feels physically until he is on the way to feel like God intends for him to feel. Fully operational capillaries all over the system, functioning and regularly oxygenated, make a life of difference. He doesn't know this. How sad! The levels of "getting along" are raised immeasurably higher than normal — in both cases when Christ is accepted as Savior and when physical fitness is practiced as a way of life. Trust in Christ leads to a spiritual high, a spiritual plateau of comfort, joy and exhilaration not known in life without Christ. Christians who clean out the waste from the body and replace it with alert, energetic vitality come up to a level of physical exuberance never known before. You have to experience both situations before you know what they are like.

"I know a lot of people it didn't work for."

The Christian says "I know of a jogger who died of a heart attack while jogging." And the unbeliever says, "I know a bunch of church members who are hypocrites." Non-believers tend to think that all Christians are flukes and Christians tend to think that vigorous physical exercise is done only by screwballs.

The facts are: *First,* most practicing Christians, like most practicing physical fitness exponents, are successful. Not champions, Not even contenders for the crown, but participants. They are not Billy Grahams, nor Charles Wesleys, and they are not Frank Shorters nor Charles Atlases. They are main-stream people. A good test for this objection works like this: For every "hypocrite" in the church a non-believer can name, ask him to listen while you list off all those in the church who are not hypocrites.

Second, for every person the Christian knows who died of a heart attack while jogging, ask him to hear you read off the names of all you know who died of a heart attack while *not* jogging. Neither one will want to give you that much time, for this is a weak objection.

Paul Bragg and Bernarr Macfadden in the early 1920's would hike on Sunday afternoons with followers up Mt. Hollywood, California, and would run them down the mountain. This trail was pioneered and built with the permission of Mr. Griffith, who later granted his entire ranch to the City of Los Angeles to become the famous Griffith Park.

After the hike up Mt. Hollywood and the run down the mountain, the "health class" would gather in the park off of Los Felice Blvd. and go through an exercise routine. Mr. Macfadden was in his early 60's in this picture. He flew his own plane and made a parachute jump at the age of 90 years. His publications included romance screen magazines, the famous 5¢ Liberty Magazine and many books on health and fitness.

"I'm too busy with important things."

Many times the non-Christian is of the opinion that Christians live a motley life. He thinks Christians mope around, weary of much Bible study, praying, church-going and funerals. And the Christian is so loaded up with commitments at work, the family, recreation activities and related schedules that he just doesn't see how a person can take time every day to "exercise." The facts are more or less like this: The Christian's schedule is loaded with happy, exciting events that relate to seeing God at work in the lives of people. It's true that the Christian spends time in Bible-reading, prayer and the like, but it's because he likes it. It's no drag. There's plenty of time to do it because it adds zest to his living! And for the busy Christian who doesn't have time to exercise, here's some news. His poor health practices are cutting down on the total number of years he can expect to live at all, whether good or bad. Yet the time it takes to get in great physical condition is not much more than thirty minutes a day, five days a week. You see, you have to bathe every day anyhow, so don't count the whole time of exercising and bathing as all "exercising." All you need is about a half-hour extra. So, both the unbeliever and the Christian are kidding themselves by saying that they don't have time.

Both the unbeliever and the Christian who hangs on to these points of view are missing a life of opportunity. One has no hope for today nor tomorrow. The other has no hope for today. The deconditioned Christian faces the prospects of meeting God tomorrow and being found guilty of irresponsible stewardship of his chief material possession — his physical body. And the unbeliever faces the prospect of meeting God with full guilt of all his sinfulness on himself, not on Christ.

An Exciting Adventure Awaits Us!

Both Christians and non-Christians alike should take these issues seriously. They relate to individual fitness of the body and spirit. One's acceptance and cooperation with these principles help God fulfill his purposes for individuals. Acceptance on the part of people of these two facets of life — physical and spiritual fitness — provides beautiful meaning to the fact that in the future, "God will give us our full rights as His children, including the new bodies He has promised us" (Rom. 8:23). What an exciting adventure awaits!

An Ode to the Training Triathlete

The Lord is my pace-setter, I shall not rush.
He makes me stop for quiet intervals; He provides
    me with images of stillness, which restore my
    serenity.
He leads me in ways of efficiency through calmness
    of mind, and His guidance is peace.

Even though I have a great many things to ac-
    complish each day, I will not fret, for His
    presence is here.
His timelessness, His all-importance, will keep me
    in balance.

He prepares refreshment and renewal in the midst
    of my activity by annointing my mind with
    His oil of tranquility, my cup of joyous energy
    overflows.

Surely Harmony and effectiveness shall be the fruit
    of my hours, and I shall walk in the pace of
    the Lord, and dwell in His House forever.

The amazing Puntous twins (Sylviane, right, Patricia, left) finish first and second respectively in the 1983 Triathlon World Championship in Hawaii. The 23-year-old sisters shattered the previous division record of 10:54:08. Sylviane finished in 10:43:36; Patricia, in 10:49:17. In the 1983 Ironman event, fifteen percent of the participants were women. Winners again . . . Sylviane finished first in the October 1984 Ironman in 10:25:13 and Patricia, second, in 10:27:28.   Photo by Noël Black

Two great competitors, the Dynamic Duo, brothers Scott (right) and Jeff (left) Tinley of San Diego, California, relaxing after finishing second and third, respectively, in the 1983 Ironman Triathlon World Championship. In Spring 1982 the talented pair finished first and third respectively. In the October 1984 Ironman, Scott Tinley finished second.

Photo by Noël Black

The 7 Baths of Purification for Athletes

Power, Strength and Agility are Available to Us Through the Seven Baths of Naaman

The City of Damascus, Syria, considered the oldest city of continuous human inhabitation in the world, owes its time-honored existence to the rivers that flow from the Jordanian Mountains to the west.

A number of these rivers flow through the city only to go underground and to supply the irrigation waters for the fertile soil lying around Damascus. Principle of these are the rivers of Albana and Pharpar ... Together they represent the highest manifestation of this human power that comes out of the unaided efforts of man. Abana means human stability, or knowledge, at its greatest; Pharpar represents human agility, or skill, at its finest. Together they represent the highest efficiency known to man. What more can one ask than strength combined with agility, science with art, knowledge with skill? If Naaman lived today he would probably reply to a modern Elisha, "Why bother to pray when we have at our service marvelously efficient surgeons and hospital staffs, combining all the sound, substantial scientific knowledge of all ages with the most perfect skills the human hand is capable of?"

Israel, in direct contrast with Damascus, means "prevailing with the help of the Lord." The Jordan means an "eternal rhythm or constant pounding," and to bathe in the river Jordan flowing through the land of Israel is to submit oneself to the eternal rhythms of the power that is continually flowing out from the heart of God.

Now, taking all of these hidden implications, "to bathe seven times in the river Jordan" means simply to immerse ourselves in the cleansing, healing power of God's love and to put ourselves completely in tune with the rhythms of its flow.

Let us give thorough consideration to these seven immersions in the Jordan River and how they might apply to our need for healthier lives today:

First Immersion: Washing the Outer Skin

Nine-tenths of us do not bathe as often as we should. Ninety-nine out of every hundred of us do not brush our teeth as long or as thoroughly as we should. We do not wash our hands thoroughly enough before eating.

Shocking as it sounds ... not too many years ago, doctors did not wash their hands before operating. Now it has become a rite. Watch a doctor over the basin before he goes into the operating room. He rolls back his sleeves and washes far up on his wrists and arms, much farther than he ever would need to do as far as contact with the patient is concerned. After he finishes washing his hands thoroughly in soap and water he washes them again in some disinfectant. After all these seven scrubbings and immersings he usually puts on rubber gloves besides! Cleanliness is as much the mark of a good surgeon as godliness is the mark of a good clergyman. To that fact, almost more than to the surgeon's skill with scalpel and knife, we owe most of the marvels wrought by modern surgery.

Second Immersion: Washing the Inner Skin

Washing the kidneys and digestive tract with plenty of pure water is one of the best ways to keep well, and one of the quickest ways to recover health when sick. A sensible internal bathing system recommended to me by a physician years ago is as follows: Drink two glasses of water upon rising, at least an hour before breakfast if possible; again at ten in the morning; and again at two and again at five in the afternoon.

Third Immersion: Cleansing the Blood Vessels

A cleansing of the blood vessels under the skin must be done by washing them, not with water, not with soap, but with blood. Exercise, especially stretching, rhythmical exercise that relaxes every muscle of the body is particularly valuable here. From five to fifteen minutes of stretching and rhythmical calisthenics every day, or better still, twice a day when rising and retiring, and two miles of fresh air "on the hoof" will send the blood on its joyous mission to give this necessary cleansing of the muscles.

To begin the day with ten minutes of calisthenics and end the day with a game of golf or tennis or a two- to five-mile run, swim, or bicycling in the open air would complete the necessary requirements for proper washing of the blood.

Fourth Immersion: Cleansing the Lungs

An hour of fresh air every day is of infinite value in the cleansing process. The two miles "on the hoof" is partly for the blood stream coursing through the muscles, but primarily for the air stream coursing through the lungs. If housewives, shut up indoors all day, should make it a religious rite not to let one day go by, not even the coldest day in winter, without going outdoors long enough for a good lung cleansing, if merely by a walk around the block, they would make much better wives and mothers. Business men who step from their front yards into waiting cars, then from the cars into office entrances; and who, when work is over, reverse the process, are building foundations for hardening arteries and weakened hearts. Let them leave their cars at home for their wives to use, and walk the five blocks to the bus, and if the bus is late, walk five blocks more until it overtakes them. Then let them read a book on the way downtown that will cleanse their souls.

A business executive found himself a complete physical and nervous wreck at the comparatively young age of forty-nine. After the clinics had done all they could do for him with medicine and other treatments, he finally went to a physical culturist who specialized in building up broken people. First of all, the physical culturist demanded that he come faithfully to his office three times a week for one month. The next requirement was that he pay him a large fee *in advance* for these twelve treatments. The treatments consisted of lying supine on the table, taking a deep breath and holding it in the lower part of the lungs while counting four, then with quick motion, lift it to the upper lungs while counting four, then again to the lower for the same length of time, then expelling it and leaving it expelled for the same interval of time. This he repeated over and over again for fifteen minutes. After three days of this the man asked the physical culturist why he couldn't do it at home just as well and not bother to come down to the office.

"Not on your life," exclaimed the other. "You paid me in advance and you have to do it right under my eye. I have found that nine out of ten people are so lazy or careless that they would neglect this unless I supervised them." This lesson was so hammered into him by these twelve "treatments" and by the high price he paid for them, that he formed the habit of going through these exercises every day for the rest of his life. At sixty-nine he was stronger than he was at forty-nine.

Fifth Immersion: Washing the Emotions

I have been informed that Freud was once pestered with a persistent, loquacious woman with an incurable disease. She insisted on coming to him at regular intervals to tell all her troubles, and relate all her emotional upheavals to him. He told her frankly that her disease was incurable, and that further consultation would be a waste of time for him and waste of money for her. She said that it was worth what it cost if only to have the chance to talk out what was "on her chest." So on a strictly professional basis he allowed her to talk to him at so much an hour. After a few months he was astounded to discover that she was getting well. Thus it was that the medical profession stumbled upon a method of healing that has revolutionized both psychology and medicine. To drain out the poison from the emotions, it was discovered, is just as important, if not more important, as to drain out the poison from the body. Indeed, is not infection in the soul much more dangerous than infection in the body?

The important thing seems to be to give expression to these infected centers. A man who swears like a trooper when he is crossed will keep in better health than the polite gentleman who pockets his wrath and smiles outwardly. Safest of all, however, is the man who loves instead of hates, and therefore has no wrath to pocket.

In other words, the most fortunate is he who has no wrong emotions; next most fortunate from the point of view of health, is he who gives vocal expression to his emotions whenever they come to him. Whether this expression be in the form of quiet, controlled confession to some spiritual counselor or be in the form of violent, uncontrolled expresion to the person who caused the emotional upheaval, it does not matter so far as health is concerned.

It is just as bad to lose your temper with yourself and to think mean things of yourself, as to think mean things of others. Indeed, remorse and inferiority complexes are twin causes of many ills. Jesus knew this when He said to the man who was crippled through remorse, "Thy sins are forgiven thee, take up thy bed and walk."

In other words, when one has "dirty" emotions it is better to give them a good scrubbing in the presence of some faithful friend rather than to hide them and hold them in. Only after one has washed his emotions clean can he pray for himself or be prayed for with power.

Take acquisitiveness. When this very valuable trait of human nature gets dusty it becomes covetousness; when muddy it becomes greed; when rusty it becomes miserliness. Cleanse this emotion without destroying it and it becomes a combination of foresight, thrift, and charity — a wonderful trio of virtues!

"Dirty" courage is the gambling poison that has swept many persons into nervous tensions and mental conflicts before their time. "Courage gone to seed" we might well call it. One of the most contagious diseases of our generation today, it is robbing youth and middle age and filling the coffers of gambling barons. Talk of measles and chickenpox! They don't compare with it, either in destruction of morals and morale, or in destruction of life through breakdowns and violent deaths.

Another emotion that requires cleansing in many people is the desire for inspiration, the craving to "step outside oneself," to lose oneself in a power greater than oneself. When properly cleansed, it is the stuff that saints and prophets are made of. When soiled and dragged in the mud, it becomes slavery to drugs and intoxicating liquors. Wash away the deadly craving for fermented *spirits* with the craving for the Holy *Spirit* and we change a common drunkard into a prophet and a seer. Jeremiah called himself a drunkard for God. The one hundred and twenty saints at Pentecost talked with such inspired tongues that those who didn't understand them said, "They are drunk with new wine!"

One emotion that is difficult to keep clean and sweet is the affection for the opposite sex. Wash the selfishness out of "dirty" affections, and lust becomes transmitted into holy love.

Just as blood when washed and cleansed with the life-giving element of water and sunlight brings health to every part of the body, and when sluggish and infected, brings disease, so the emotions when cleansed and in proper circulation, bring health to the body, and when infected and sluggish manifest in illnesses of various kinds.

We should learn in our schools how to scrub our emotions. It is wrong to say that young people have inferiority complexes, or complexes of any kind. No young person has a complex. He may have inferiority *feelings*, but these feelings are not "hardened" into complexes until people become older and get set in their ways. When our feelings gather dirt and become tarnished they become complexes. When we are young a good scrubbing of the emotions fixes us up in a jiffy, but when we grow older these scrubbings may have to be more severe. When one becomes a very old and hardened sinner, a spiritual surgical operation may be required.

Sixth Immersion: Washing the Mind

An active, balanced and disciplined mind is one of the greatest sources of health a person can have! Persons of low mentality but of giant physique do not live as long nor keep as well as men of frailer build, who have well-cultivated minds. President Charles Eliot of Harvard was a "blue baby" but he lived into his nineties, chiefly because he had a well-balanced, contentedly occupied mind. Men of wide interests and absorbing application, like Benjamin Franklin and Thomas A. Edison outlive men of narrower interests. This is true also of Charles A. Dana, Immanuel Kant and others, who outlived great athletes like Frank Gotch and Walter Eckersall who had amazed the world by the strength and endurance of their bodies.

People who do not have enough ideas get sick, people who have too many ideas get sick, but people who have the *wrong* ideas get sickest of all. Indeed no man ever said a truer thing than the old philosopher who wrote the proverb: "As a man thinketh in his heart, so is he!"

The sickest people of all are the very rich people who do not have enough to occupy their minds. A great nerve specialist told me that the most unhappy people in the world were the unmarried women of very wealthy families who had nothing to do. Another group that needs protection are the people who are out of jobs and need them. Men who retire and have no hobbies to occupy them are a pitiful lot. Another unhappy group includes the people who have jobs but who hate the work they are in, seeing in it nothing but deadening drudgery.

We can approach this subject best by considering first, how our minds can be occupied with our work, then with our play and then with our hobbies.

If a person has no work to engage his mind he should get busy at once to remedy the defect, either by getting a job, or by filling his time in creative, health-producing ways. A person who has work that he hates should either change his field at the earliest possible moment, even accepting work at a lower salary, or, if he cannot change his work, he should change his attitude toward it, seeing all the good in his job which he had overlooked before. The value of a vacation is that it separates a man from his job long enough for him to see it in perspective, and when he returns he often finds in it more sources of happiness and more ways of bringing happiness to others, than he had ever dreamed was possible before.

A good, wholesome *hobby* is one of the best safeguards against illness any man could have. A hobby can often do what one's regular work fails to do — enable him to keep happy in spite of the fact that his work may be filled with drudgery and boredom. Gardening, carpentering, painting, sculpturing, writing, are all wonderful sources of health because they give the mind natural, wholesome outlet, drawing off the old pockets of poison, enabling one to return to his work with a washed and sun-kissed mind.

Next to hobbies comes *sports* as a mind cleanser.

The games of life are all health-giving: golf, tennis, bowling, even checkers and chess and bridge. Strange to say there is more danger in sports like bridge or chess or even golf becoming too engrossing, than there is that our hobbies shall become our obsession. One never grows morbid over hobbies, unless it might be over some crazy incongruity like a search for perpetual motion, but it is quite possible to get morbid over one's sports. A dowager who plays bridge as though it were a matter of life and death and who criticizes every false move her partner makes, will soon be on the road to the state hospital — or her partner will be. A golfer who makes the air blue with his misuse of the English language every time he dubs a stroke had better take up gardening for his stomach's sake.

Blessed is the man who loves his work, and who also has a hobby, and who also enjoys a swim, bike ride or run, and who, above all, has opportunity and time to indulge in all three.

One other way to crowd out wrongs and morbid thoughts is to pack one's mind with good books and reading matter. Keep up on current events with a good newspaper and a good weekly news magazine. Keep in touch with the eternal things of life through good books and masterpieces both new and old.

Seventh Immersion: Washing the Soul

The soul is a very inclusive term. It incorporates the mind and heart and the entire being, but in a very peculiar and particular way, for the soul is the point at which one's entire being contacts the Infinite. Your infinite self in relation to which your little three-dimensional, conscious Self is but the outer, visible expression, is always well, always sound, always perfect. The trouble is that you do not "live there" enough. "Tell me where you live and I will tell you what you are," someone has said. If you dwell all day long in a countinghouse counting up your greedy gains, or, if you live in a "nagging house," where you have a constant sense of irritation and antagonism with all those about you, or if you live in a "lonely house" where you think of yourself as separate from everyone else in the world, or, worst of all, if you live in a "hating house" where it is "each man for himself and the devil take the hindmost, then you are exposed to all the poisons, all the infections, all the epidemics that flesh is heir to. If you live in high and exalted contact with the Creator, if you are aware of your sonship to the great Father, and if you have a sense of your corporate relationship to your brothers, then you are giving wholesome circulation to the finest part of your being, and the blood, nerves, and organs of your body will manifest the wholeness and harmony experienced in your soul.

To achieve the cleansed soul is to achieve perfection. To achieve this perfection, yes, to come anywhere near it is not to be hoped for in a day, a week, or even a year. To attain it is well worthy of a lifetime of effort.

Health is an old English way of spelling wholeness. And wholeness is merely a modern, scientific way of spelling holiness. To give oneself wholly to God and to practice continually the presence of God is the only sure short cut I know of to achieve holiness — which in turn is the only short cut I know of to achieve permanent, undeviating health.

You have committed yourself to a sport that will take from your physical and psychological strengths, all that you have to give, and then some. It is important that we go forth into this supreme athletic endeavor, The Triathlon, with the purity of body, mind and spirit that is set forth in this chapter. — from Glen Clark's writings

How to enjoy life: Eat less, exercise more. Talk less, think more. Ride less, walk more. Worry less, work more. Waste less, give more. Preach less, practice more. Frown less, laugh more. Grumble less, thank more. Scold less, praise more. Regret less, aspire more. Hate less, love more.

Paul Bragg leads a portion of the Bragg famous exercise class at Ft. DeRussy, Waikiki Beach, Honolulu, Hawaii. This free class in its 14th year, invites the public to participate every day but Sunday, from 9 to 10:30 a.m. and usually has between 100-200 health-minded participants daily . . . a Living Memorial to Dr. Bragg's unselfish offering of his time and energy for over 70 years of lecturing world-wide on healthful living.

3

The Nine Doctors of Preventive Medicine

These Nine Doctors Are At Your Command!

NATURE'S NINE PHYSICIANS are ready to help you attain radiant, glorious health. They are all specialists in their particular field of health-building. They have had years and years of experience with thousands upon thousands of people. Their cumulative record is one hundred percent perfect. They have never failed a patient . . . patients have failed them, turned their backs on them, and ignored them. But they are kind and understanding, and no matter how many times patients have failed them, they still stand ready to render perfect professional service. They have but one prescription and that is elixir of LIFE.

They are the kindest doctors in the whole universe. They are anxious and willing to help everyone who comes to them for Health . . . their professional services are available to all — the young, the old, the rich, and the poor! They give no operations . . . except bloodless ones. They give no drugs . . . not even the latest "wonder" drugs.

You are familiar with these nine doctors . . . and from time to time many of you have needed their services and called upon them. But, from this day on, I want you to call on these nine doctors frequently . . . they are so anxious to Help You Help Yourself to Health, Long Life, and that extra-special physical condition known as "AGELESSNESS!" That is the Highest Health you can have . . . and I DO want you to have the finest!

These wonderful physicians will never, ever fail you. They not only want to be your personal physicians, but they want to be your friends. It gives me a most secure feeling that I have, at my command every day, the world's great physicians.

Now, it is my pleasure to give you a personal introduction to each one of these physicians, and, from this day on, feel free to call upon them. It is my pleasure to introduce to you the nine doctors. First, I want you to meet the Daddy of them all, the most eminent, the most powerful, the great Healer, the giver of life to everything on the face of this earth.

DOCTOR SUNSHINE

Doctor Sunshine's specialty is heliotherapy, and his great prescription is solar energy. Each tiny blade of grass, every vine, tree, bush, flower, fruit, and vegetable draws its life from solar energy. All living things on earth depend on solar energy for their very existence. This earth would be a barren, frigid place if it were not for the magic rays of the sun. The sun gives us light, and were it not for LIGHT, there would be No You or Me! The earth would be in everlasting darkness. Human Beings were never meant to have pale skins, not even the fair northern races. Man's skin should be tanned by sun and air, and should take on a darker pigment according to his original type. It has been found that under constant sun even red-headed people will tan. Pigmentation is a sign that solar energy has been transformed into human energy. Man can only gain health, vitality, and happiness in the bright, brilliant rays of the sun. The people who are indoors too long have a sallow, ghastly-looking skin. That is why so many women hide their yellow, sun-starved skins with makeup.

And God Said, "Let There Be Light!"

Let's pause to marvel at the role of God's very first creation — light. God said, "Let there be light!" because there cannot be life without it. Every one of his creatures, from fish that swim deep in the sea to birds that fly high in the sky, depend upon it. Light controls life. Either directly or indirectly light enters the organism and enables it to live. For most of us this life-giving miracle enters through the eyes.

Actually, our eyes are gateways to three important glands. When sunlight strikes the retina and the optic nerve, messages are shot to the brain. Thence to the hypothalamus and the pituitary — that tiny master gland which controls the thyroid, our adrenals and our sex glands. All of them critically important to vigor, growth, resistance and sexual health. Scientists say it's for this reason children born blind develop more slowly; that youngsters in torrid climates mature early; that during long months of darkness in the Arctic, explorers often have physical and emotional problems, and Eskimo women don't menstruate or conceive.

It's light that causes birds to migrate and even bestirs them to mate, ornithologists say. Their studies are responsible for the poultry industry's trick of "lengthening" days with full-spectrum bulbs so hens will lay more of those wonderful eggs. In his fascinating book, *Health and Light*, John Ott writes, "The response of the hens is due to the light energy entering the eyes and stimulating the pituitary gland."

Ott, who pioneered in time-lapse photography, was one of the first to discover the relationship of light and body chemistry. It was also Ott who made the connection between sunlight and arthritis. After breaking his glasses on a Florida vacation, he decided to do without even dark glasses for a while. To his amazement, his arthritis improved. "Something was stimulating the glands that lubricated my joints without artificially injecting any of the prepared glandular extracts. The effect was as beneficial as the injection of one of the extracts right into the hip joint."

The Sun and Vitamin D

"The sun," wrote Galileo, "is 92 million miles from the Earth; it is the center of the solar system and by the power of gravity holds every planet in its orbit. Yet that very same sun can ripen a bunch of grapes as though that were all it had to do."

Miraculously, this distant sun "ripens" us as well. For its ultraviolet rays shining on our skin create from the fats there (primarily the cholesterol) the vital substance known as vitamin D. The process is precarious, however. Water, even cold water, will wash it away. (So always take your sunbath *after* your swim.) And once the skin is deeply tanned the sun can't form any more. Also, the winter sun gradually loses its power, so that even a hot sun on a December ski slope is creating about a tenth as much vitamin D as the suns of July.

Curiously, this vitamin has only three food sources: An egg yolk (sun-round and sun-yellow); the seeds of sunflowers, which, mysteriously, always keep their faces lifted to the sun. And, even more mysteriously, saltwater fish like cod and halibut, which swim deep and far from the sun, yet have rich stores of it in their liver, along with vitamin A. Fish like sardines also contain some vitamin D; but it is cod-liver or halibut-liver oil — oils we associate with babies — that are the major sources we have for vitamin D.

Some scientists say vitamin D has been mislabeled since, unlike other vitamins, it isn't found altogether in foods; that it functions more like a hormone. But whatever we call it, we *must* have it; it is absolutely critical to the health of our skin, our eyes and the building of strong teeth and bones.

This was starkly demonstrated during the Industrial Revolution when rickets began seriously to deform the bodies of children working in factories. At first this bone-crippler was blamed on lack of calcium. Then recognized as lack of sunshine — for even when these youngsters went outdoors the air was thick with coal smoke. (Rickets and its adult counterpart, osteomalacia, are not uncommon even today in backward countries where babies are still swaddled and women kept robed, veiled and mostly confined to their homes.) By 1919 it was discovered the disease could be prevented and cured by cod-liver oil. But it was many years before vitamin D was identified as the healing substance in the oil.

Calcium Needs Vitamin D For Absorption

Without this vitamin the body can't utilize calcium. Calcium can't be absorbed into the bloodstream or deposited in the bones. Nor can it be withdrawn from the bones as needed. And although we think of calcium primarily as important to teeth and bones, *calcium is in constant demand for every activity of the body. Vitamin D sees that calcium gets where it's needed, even if that calcium has to be stolen from the very structure of the bones.* When this happens bones begin to weaken, teeth deteriorate — afflictions which do beset the aged, but which are not solely the result of aging. Rather, simply a lack of vitamin D.

Tragically, the two extremes who most need vitamin D are those who are most often deficient in it — the aged and growing children.

Thousands of elderly people are shut up in houses or nursing homes where they get very little sunshine. And unless they are drinking quantities of D-enriched milk or taking fish-liver oils, they are prime candidates for broken hips and other casualties. A great many need more calcium as well; but it's not just calcium they may lack, but the vitamin D which makes the calcium available to the bones.

Mothers, however conscientious about giving babies their drops, usually stop when children get older. Which would be okay if the kids consumed plenty of eggs and milk, and could play outdoors as much as we did, in unpolluted sunshine. But an awful lot can't, or don't. Physicians have been astonished to find rickets among hospitalized children today, often from affluent homes. And even when there is not actual deformity, the deficiency shows up in other ways — bad skin, bad eyes, bad teeth and weak bones.

The rest of us don't come off so well either. Look at how many people work and play and go to school in windowless, air-conditioned buildings, locked away from natural light. How we huddle in sealed-up houses, often in the dark before TV. And when we do get outdoors the sun is often blocked from us by buildings, or the air so choked with smog its rays can't penetrate. To compound the problem, at least half the population wears glasses, and practically everybody slaps on a pair of dark ones the minute the sun is spied. Some people even wear them indoors.

No wonder dentists and eye doctors drive Cadillacs. No wonder millions of dollars are spent just on the *ads* for the pastes that hold false teeth in place. No wonder some 17 to 20 million Americans are tortured by arthritis, and uncounted millions more break hips and other bones every year. We are a nation woefully crippled by too little vitamin D.

Which Vitamin D and How Much?

Adding vitamin D to whole milk is one commendable case of fortifying food. However, the form is the synthetic or vitamin D^2, which is less potent, yet at the same time more toxic, than the natural form found in fish-liver oil — vitamin D^3. Even the vitamin D^2 in whole milk is easily destroyed by light; and there is no vitamin D at all in skimmed milk, used by so many people who are worried about both weight and cholesterol. The vitamin D in fish-liver oils is preferable to any other, because it is the very same vitamin D^3 substance manufactured by the sun. As such, it is far less toxic.

Vitamin D, like vitamin A, is fat soluble, which the liver stores. But reports of the dangers of toxicity from taking too much have been vastly exaggerated. *The Merck Manual*, that classic guide for physicians an pharmacists, says it would take 40,000 IU a day to produce ill effects in babies. (An amount no mother in her right mind would give.) And 100,000 IU a day, taken for months, to cause any trouble for adults. "Treatment consists of discontinuing the vitamin, placing the patient on a low calcium diet, and keeping the urine acid."

A far cry from the warning screams from the FDA about the awful possibilities of too much vitamin D. Furthermore, if the body is also well-supplied with vitamins C and A, any toxicity will be negated.

The person who is starved of the vital rays of the sun has a half dead look. He is actually dying for the want of solar energy. Weak, ailing, anemic people are all sun-starved, and in my opinion, many people are sick simply because they too are starving for sunshine.

The rays of the sun are powerful germicides. As the skin imbibes more of these rays, it stores up enormous amounts of this germ-killing energy. The sun provides one of the finest remedies for the nervous person, who is filled with anxiety, worry, frustration, stresses, and strains! When these tense people lie in the sunshine, its powerful rays give them what the nerves and body are crying out for, and that is relaxation. Sunshine is a tonic, a stimulant and above all, the GREAT HEALER! As you Swim, Bike, and Run in the warm sunshine, millions of nerve endings absorb healing vitamin D . . . and the solar energy, and transform it to the nervous system of the body.

Make this experiment determine the value of sunshine in the matter of life and death. Find a beautiful lawn, where the grass is like a green carpet . . . cover up a small space of that beautiful lawn with a box, small piece of wood or a piece of metal. Day by day you will notice that the beautiful grass that is full of plant blood, Chlorophyll, will start to fade and turns a sickly yellow. Then the tragedy happens — it withers and dies — death by sun starvation. The same thing happens in your body without the life-giving rays of the sun, and when you fail to eat an abundance of sun-cooked foods such as ripe fruits and vegetables.

Life-Giving Vitamin D Rays of the Sun

We must have the direct rays of the sun on our bodies and we must eat at least 50% of food that has been ripened by the sun's rays. When we eat fresh fruits and vegetables, we absorb the blood of the plant, the rich, nourishing Chlorophyll. Chlorophyll is the solar energy that the plant has absorbed from the sun, the richest and most nourishing food you can put into your body. "Chlorophyll is liquid sunshine." Green plants alone possess the secret of how to capture this powerful solar energy and pass it on to man and every other living creature. When you put sunshine on the outside of your body, and eat 50% raw fruits and vegetables in your daily diet, you are going to fairly glow with radiant health.

But these too-powerful, natural medicines must be taken in small doses at the beginning, because your sun-starved body cannot absorb too great an amount at first. When you take your first sun bath, start with short time periods . . . until you can condition your body to take more and more. The best time for a beginner to start taking sun baths is in the early morning sunshine . . . five to ten minutes on the nude body is sufficient at first. Or you may sunbathe in the late afternoon sunshine. The best rays of the sun are in the early morning . . . these have the cooling rays. Between 11 to 3 we have the hot burning rays of the sun. In exposure to the sun, it is quite necessary to use good judgment.

The same caution should be taken in eating sun-ripened foods . . . the raw fruits and vegetables. The average person who has been eating mainly cooked foods will find that . . . if suddenly great amounts of raw fruits and vegetables are put into the body they can cause a reaction. It is wiser to gradually add more and more sun-cooked foods to the diet. In exposure to the sun, it is quite necessary to use good judgment and proceed with caution!

DOCTOR FRESH AIR

Dr. Fresh Air is a specialist, and his greatest prescription is "The Breath of God's Pure Fresh Air." The first thing we do when we are born is to take a long, deep breath and the last thing we do is take a last gasp, before we stop breathing. Between birth and death, life is completely maintained by breathing. Dr. Fresh Air wants you to have a long active life and he feels, as a specialist, that if you follow his simple instructions of breathing deeply, always being conscious that with every breath you take, you are bringing into your body the breath of God, the life-giving oxygen...you will have a long, fulfilling, healthy, happy life!

People who fail to obey the doctor's orders about getting plenty of fresh air day and night, invite some extremely severe complications. Let us examine very closely the function of breathing. First it is invisible food...it is the only food that we cannot be deprived of for over five to seven minutes or death will take us. We not only take from the air the life-giving oxygen that is so necessary to every cell in our bodies, but when we breathe oxygen, it is carried by the blood to the lungs and there a great miracle takes place. The life-giving oxygen is exchanged.........for deadly carbon dioxide in which form the deadly toxins of the body are being released. In other words, in the process of living, we create toxic poisons. They are collected by the blood, and when the blood brings carbon dioxide to the lungs, it is expelled as the new life-giving oxygen enters. In the process of metabolism in the building up and tearing down of the cells of the body, carbon dioxide poison is constantly burned up in the very process of living.

Shallow Breathers Poison Themselves!

If a person does not get enough fresh air, or if he is a shallow breather, and the intake of oxygen does not equal the outgo of carbon dioxide, we are encouraging carbon dioxide toxic poison to build within the structure of the body. This can result in very serious physical problems, because the retained carbon dioxide can be concentrated in some other part of the body and cause intense physical suffering.

Enervation, or the lack of nerve energy, can lower the Vital Force so much that the great bellows, the lungs, cannot pump in enough air to flush the carbon dioxide out of the body. So you see how important it is that you not only breathe fresh air, but you should be always conscious of the fact that you must breathe deeply! I believe we are air machines! I believe that oxygen not only purifies our body, but is also one of the great energizers of the human body. We are air-pressure machines! We live at the bottom of an atmospheric ocean approximately 70 miles deep. This air pressure is 14 pounds per square inch. Between the inhalation and the exhalation of a breath, a vacuum is formed. As long as we continue to have this rhythmical intake and outgo of oxygen, we will live. We know that we can go without food for 30 days or more and still survive, but as I have stated, we can only go without air for a very few minutes. **Air is one of the important energizers of the human body. The more deeply you breathe pure air, the better your chances are for extending your years on this earth! Deep breathing of pure, energizing air is one of the greatest benefits to the triathlete!**

Deep Breathing...Secret of Endurance and Stamina

My father and I had a friend for many years named Alonzo Stagg, the famous football and athletic coach. Mr. Stagg lived to be over 100 years of age. We asked him his secret of long life and his answer was "I have the greater part of my life indulged in running and other vigorous exercise that forced large amounts of oxygen into my body!"

We had a friend in New York, James Hocking, who was one of the greatest long distance walking champions this country has ever had. We asked Mr. Hocking, on his hundredth birthday, the secret of his long, active life and super-health. His answer was "I have always walked vigorously and breathed deeply!"

So you see, *oxygen is a detoxifier. It is like fasting . . . it removes poisons from the body.* I not only practice deep breathing personally, but also believe that people should expose their bodies to a free current of moving air. Air baths are important to good health! You should sleep with your windows wide open with a cross ventilation of air moving across you as you sleep. I find that I sleep better, and have a deeper night's rest, if I don't wear sleeping garments of any kind. Under the covers it is warm and when we pile on extra sleeping garments, we shut off the skin from its supply of oxygen. You must compensate for your hours of sitting down . . . because it is then that your breathing slows down. So if your occupation requires a lot of sitting, you should compensate with swimming, biking and running.

You will also find that you can solve most of your problems on a brisk 2 to 3 mile hike. Whenever I have a problem to solve, I always take a long brisk walk and do some breathing exercises in the fresh air, and by the time I have finished the walk, I most often have solved my problems! I believe that after the evening meal, everyone should make a practice of taking a 2-mile walk (even if it has to be up and down your driveway). Today Americans are a race of sitters! We sit at our desks, at the movies, concerts, and sit watching athletics and television. We are air-starved, we are oxygen-starved. We cannot get carbon dioxide out of our bodies, and so we are full of aches, pains, and prone to premature aging. This is all because we are too lazy, too indifferent about being active, vigorous people. On any city street, you can see nothing but pale, out-of-shape, ghastly people, unhealthy and exhausted, all because of air-starvation and lack of exercise. That is why it is so important to fast, because then you clean some of this concentrated, stored carbon dioxide that failed to leave your body by deep breathing. Fasting is nature's way of helping you to clean your house (your body). When you are fasting, whether it is day or night, and if you have the energy, take a walk, even if it is a short one.

Make it a part of your life to be an active person. That does not mean house-walks, it means getting out in the fresh air and hiking, running, swimming, or biking. You must not allow carbon dioxide to pile up in your body, it can only bring serious consequences. So, along with your fasting program, make it a point every day of your life to have a vigorous swim, run or cycle, which will force you to breathe deeply. Every time you think of it during your waking hours, take long, slow, deep breaths. Remember what I told you . . . the more long, slow, deep breaths you take, the longer you will live, and when you combine deep breathing with fasting, you are adding years to your life. You are building energy and vitality! You are going to break free of many miseries with fasting and deep breathing, so remind yourself every day that Doctor Fresh Air is your constant friend.

DOCTOR PURE WATER

Dr. Pure Water is a fine physician and a splendid friend! It's important to drink pure water. Water makes up about 65% of your body so you need a continuous replacement to keep the water level normal. As you add more raw fruit and vegetables to your diet, you will add a greater intake of natural distilled water. Dr. Pure Water is a friend, and you may enjoy many pleasant hours using the various gains that water gives you. A good warm bath is a tonic and a relaxer which soothes irritated nerves and quiets emotions. Every day of the year in the United .States, people enjoy water at the seashore, in lakes, rivers, streams, and swimming pools. Swimming is one of the best exercises anyone can take. It puts no strain on the human body or the heart. Make it a point to swim as often as you can. If your swimming is lacking style, endurance and speed . . . go to a professional who can help you improve. You will never regret it, because it is one of the most relaxing, and yet, exhilarating of exercises. It can be enjoyed regardless of your age! Don't fear it — learn to love it.

Water and You in the 20th Century

Distilled water is one of the world's best and most pure water. It is excellent for detoxification programs and for cleaning out all the cells, organs, and fluids of the body because it can dissolve and carry away so many harmful substances.

Water from chemically-treated public water systems and even from many wells and springs is likely to be loaded with poisonous chemicals and toxic trace elements.

Depending upon the kind of piping that the water has been run through, the water in our homes, offices, schools, hospitals, etc., is likely to be overloaded with zinc (from old-fashioned galvanized pipes) or with copper and cadmium (from copper pipes). These trace elements are released in excessive quantity by the chemical action of the water on the metals of the water pipes.

So, pure water is essential for health, either from the natural juices of vegetables, fruits, and other foods, or from water of high purity obtained by steam distillation or by one of the new high-efficiency deionization processes.

At the same time, the body is constantly breaking down old bone and tissue cells and replacing them with new ones. As the body casts off the old minerals and other products of broken-down cells, it must obtain new supplies of the essential elements for the new cells.

Moreover, scientists are only now beginning to understand that various kinds of dental problems, different types of arthritis, and even some forms of hardening of the arteries are due to varying kinds of imbalances in the levels of calcium, phosphorus, and magnesium in the body. Disorders can also be caused by imbalances in the ratios of various minerals to each other.

Proper Mineral Balance Essential

Each individual healthy body requires a proper balance within itself of all the nutritive elements. It is just as bad for any individual to have too much of one item as it is to have too little.

It takes appropriate levels of phosphorus and magnesium to keep calcium in solution so it can be formed into new cells of bone and teeth. Yet, there must not be too much of those nor too little calcium in the diet, or old bone will be taken away but new bone will not be formed.

In addition, we now know that diets which are unbalanced and inappropriate for a given individual can deplete the body of calcium, magnesium, potassium, and other major and minor elements.

Diets which are high in meats, fish, eggs, grains, nuts, seeds, or their products may provide unbalanced excesses of phosphorus which will deplete calcium and magnesium from the bones and tissues of the body and cause them to be lost in the urine.

A diet high in fats will tend to increase the uptake of phosphorus from the intestines relative to calcium and other basic minerals. Such a high-fat diet can produce losses of calcium, magnesium, and other basic minerals in the same way a high-phosphorus diet does.

Diets excessively high in fruits or their juices may provide unbalanced excesses of potassium in the body, and calcium and magnesium will again be lost from the body through the urine.

Deficiencies of calcium and magnesium — for example — can produce all kinds of problems in the body ranging from dental decay and osteoporosis to muscular cramping, hyperactivity, muscular twitching, irregular heartbeat, poor sleep patterns, and excessive frequency or uncontrolled patterns of urination. Similarly, deficiencies of other minerals, or imbalances in the levels of those minerals, can produce many other problems in the body.

Therefore, it is important to clean and detoxify the body through fasting and through using distilled or other pure water as well as healthy organically-grown vegetable and fruit juices.

At the same time, it is also important to provide the body with adequate sources of new minerals. This can be done by eating a widely-distributed diet of wholesome vegetables including kelp and other sea vegetables for adults, healthy mother's milk for infants, and certified raw goat's or cow's milk for those children and adults who are not adversely affected by milk products.

But, despite dietary sources such as these, many adults and children in so-called civilized cultures will be found to have low levels of essential minerals in their bodies due to losses caused by coffee, tea, carbonated beverages, and long-term bad diets containing too much sugar and other sweets as well as products made from refined flours and containing refined table salt.

In addition, the body's organ systems can be thrown out of balance by continuing stress, by toxins in our air and water, by disease-produced injuries, and by pre-natal deficiencies in the mother's diet or life style.

As a result, many — if not most — people in our so-called civilization may need to take mineral supplements such as the new chelated mineral preparations as well as a broad-range multiple-vitamin tablet.

Water has been used as a treatment for man's miseries since the very beginning of time and in my travels all over the world, I have found, as a Life Extension Specialist, many types of water treatments. It has been proven that the ancient civilizations of the Egyptians, the Assyrians, Hebrews, Persians, Greeks, Hindus, Chinese, and many other races, including the American Indians, have used all forms of water treatment for the relief of human ailments. Hippocrates, the father of medicine, 400 years before the birth of Christ on the island of Cos in the Aegean Sea, developed a complete system of water treatments. His records state that a cold bath followed by a hot bath and then followed by friction improves the circulation. We cannot surmount that natural philosophy today. The cold, then hot bath, then cold . . . finishing with a coarse friction rub with a towel, is one of the best circulation builders known to man.

Water — More Important Than Food to Triathletes

More than one-half of the human body is water. The bones in your body are even one-third water. To lose a tenth of your body's water supply is dangerous, and to lose a fifth can be fatal. Losing lesser amounts disturbs body functions and impairs chemical and physical processes necessary to good health. Yet, the body itself, can take lots of punishment — half your proteins can be lost and almost all of your fat and glycogen without causing death. Only that important fifty-five percent of your body — water — requires that it be kept at a consistently high level.

A practical example of the body's demand for water can be drawn from mountain climbing histories. In the assault on the Himalayas, men working and climbing in high altitudes cut down on the weight they carried in an attempt to conserve body energy. None were notably successful until the team conquering Mount Everest scientifically considered the effect of the altitude in relation to bodily water metabolism. These men increased their fuel load in order to melt snow and ice into water. They were assured of an average of six pints per day per man, much more than previous teams had considered as adequate rations. While water was not the sole contributing factor to their success, it was recognized as helping prevent the fatigue experienced by former teams during their final assaults!

We triathletes, ourselves, may not need water for anything as demanding as climbing the Himalayas, but this serves as an example of how important water — or the lack of water — in our diets can be.

How Our Body Is 65% Water

Almost every fluid connected with life and living things is based on water. Protoplasm cannot exist without water. Nor can a blade of grass, or a cactus, or an insect, or a bird or a fish. Dry out a living cell and it will stop working. It must have liquid. Human cells are the very same. Even their food is brought to them via fluid — blood. And there are about ten pounds of blood alone in your body. After food is consumed by cells, the waste is washed away in a water-based liquid called urine. Even oxygen canot be absorbed by your lungs except through a moist surface. The same is true of the waste by-product of oxygen, carbon dioxide.

To quote W.B. Cannon: "Water is the vehicle for food materials absorbed from the digestive canal; it is the medium in which chemical changes take place that underlie most of our obvious activities; it is essential in the regulation of body temperature, and it plays an important part in mechanical services such as the lubrication... of joint surfaces..."

Water and Digestion

Food can't be digested without water. There is an actual chemical process that goes on in your body that's known as "hydrolysis." It involves changing proteins, starches and fats into foods that various cells require in order to work properly. But water is also necessary to stimulate gastric glands in the stomach. In the intestines, it helps facilitate the absorption of solids — and the excretion of wastes.

Blood and Water

Sure, blood is thicker than water. But only by about 10%. Blood plasma is 90% water and permits it to circulate through the body freely. It carries all sorts of foods and gases, minerals and products, and items needed for body functions, activity and growth. Everything used by body cells is transported by plasma, including the material the cell is made from. Anything made by these same cells needed in other parts of the body — or to be excreted — is carried by the same plasma. Yet, plasma remains fairly identical in composition at all times at all places in the body. As it absorbs foods and fuels from the digestive and respiratory processes, it has the same foods and fuels taken from it by body tissues — including the kidneys and lungs. A balance is always maintained, and water (the proper intake) is important.

Water Keeps You Cool

Automobiles have water in their radiators to help cool their engines. It's much the same with the human body. The reason is that water absorbs heat readily. In living organisms, where constant internal temperatures are often vital, water acts as a super-efficient coolant. The human body has a constant temperature level. Measured orally, this is 98.6° F. And, it shouldn't vary much despite the climate or temperature surrounding the body. This internal temperature is controlled by external skin evaporation to a large degree. Just about a fourth of the heat created in the burning of oxygen and food by the body is thrown off the body by normal perspiration, and by the process of breathing. But, under exceptionally dry conditions, the body can lose up to a quart an hour through the sweating process alone. Obviously, this water has to be replaced or other functions of the body are impaired. When it's cold, the body can actually cease perspiring and water is further withdrawn into the tissues. The evaporation of water from skin surfaces results in cooling — air-conditioning. It's related to fever. When you sweat and feel hot, perhaps you have a temperature. When your skin is dry and you feel chills, perhaps body temperature has dipped. Signs of illness. And, of course, in humid weather, evaporation is more difficult. So we feel hotter though we're sweating. Our body is having a harder time cooling off, and ends up working harder to keep it cool.

Research has shown that people who run, bike or swim, have an increased need for pure water, for the average man, doing nothing, on a normally humid day will lose about twenty-three ounces of fluid via lungs and skin per day. A long-distance runner, on the other hand, can lose as much as eight pounds. Football players lose almost fourteen pounds of water alone in about an hour's time. Because the body is more than one-half water, and because excretory processes depend so much on water, water is easy to lose and many so-called diets are often based on lower water consumption or higher water loss. This can be very dangerous, especially if protracted over a period of time. Tiredness is one of the first signs of water deficiency. It should be heeded. Take a drink.

Water is a Lubricant

The body, in its own way, is greased and oiled automatically. The basic lubricant is water. It permits organs to slide against each other — such as when you bend down. It helps bones slip in their joints. You couldn't bend a knee or elbow without it. Also, it acts as a shock absorbing agent to ward off injury from blows. Applied hydraulically to various parts of the body, it is used to build and hold pressures. The eyeball is a good example of this function of water.

Muscle tone cannot be kept without adequate water, for the muscles are three-fourths water. This is another reason why fatigue hits the dehydrated body.

Three Sources for Water

Your body has to come by its water somehow. The first way is obvious. You drink it — or a fluid containing water such as fruit juice, coffee, soup, beverages, and the like. Regular foods are sources of water supply, too. Don't forget, your own body is about 65% water ... so little wonder that steak should be about 60% water. An egg is more than two-thirds water. A peach is almost all water — 90%. Something as dry as a hard roll even is a fourth water. The third, important source is metabolism. This water is called metabolic water and it's made by the body from raw materials taken into the body. In other words, it's a chemically made water. It happens when cells convert ingested food to cellular food. A perfect example of this type of water production is that water-factory known as the camel. Now, the camel doesn't store water. It stores fat in the hump on its back. It also eats carbohydrates. In using these foods, the camel creates a great deal of water as a by-product — and uses the water in its body chemistry just as if it had drunk the water! Some insects are able to do this, too, even though they eat exceptionally dry, low-water-content foods.

While the average man only consumes about two and a half quarts of water a day by eating and drinking, he uses up a full two and three-fourths quarts (4.922 grams vs. 5.210 grams). His production of metalobic water is the difference.

Body Thirst

When the body hasn't enough water, it reacts. First, the secretions of glands are drastically cut. Saliva dries up, membranes dry out. We're thirsty. We've been signaled quickly that a drink of water is imperative. After losing more than a little water without replenishing the supply, other symptoms develop. Headaches, nerves, inability to concentrate, digestion problems, lack of hunger are some of these. Water quickly alleviates these symptoms. American soldiers in the artic experienced personality problems when forced into low-water rations because of the lack of fuel. As mentioned elsewhere, to be deprived of water for just a few days can invite death. It is needed continuously.

Water and Waste

While water plays an important role in the excretion of waste through the intestine, most of it is re-absorbed and doesn't leave the body. But the other forms of soluble waste rely on water, too. The kidneys (and bladder), skin and lungs all depend on water to rid themselves of poisons and excretions.

The lung-wall is comprised of tiny air sacs that, in order to function in the intake of oxygen and the expulsion of carbon dioxide, must be moist. The linings of the nose, throat, trachea and bronchial tubes are also always moist — or should be. Because of all this contact with air, the body loses about a pint of water every day solely through exhalation. When the air is very dry, more is lost. Many people replace this moisture by using a vaporizer in their homes. Water lost through the skin can amount to large quantities, but here water is used not only as a vehicle for waste, but for other purposes.

Kidneys use water rapidly, but the amount they use depends on the amount of fluid you drink. For every quart of water passed through the kidneys, one and a half ounces of waste are carried in it. This is normal, but water (as urine) never falls below a level of a little more than half a pint. Kidneys never stop working and constantly demand water, even when none is available. The body is forced to supply it through dehydration as long as there is life. All this occurs without any chemical transformation of the water. It might be named for its contents, but it carries them in solution. The water remains water. Read this informative book.

The book, *Shocking Truth About Water*, by Paul C. Bragg, N.D., Ph.D. and Patricia Bragg, Ph.D., gives you the facts about why to drink pure water. See back pages for ordering.

DOCTOR GOOD NATURAL FOOD

Your body is the most gloriously accurate instrument in this universe. Given the correct fuel, pure air, exercise, sunshine and keeping it internally clean by fasting, your body will last indefinitely and function perfectly. The healthy body of the triathlete is an efficient chemical factory. Given the correct raw materials, it should be capable, except for accidents, of developing strong tissues and good resistance against most bacteria, viruses, and other environmental impacts.

It is the only fine machine I know that contains its own repair shop and can work wonders if you give it the proper tools. It is constantly working for you. Its cells are being destroyed and renewed every second. Biologically, it has no age limit, and, in fact there is no biological reason for man to grow old at all. The body has the seed of eternal life! Man does not die — commits slow suicide with his unnatural habits of living!

Scientists tell us that every cell in our body is renewed within eleven months. Then why should anyone speak of being old? Don't you believe the moth-eaten fallacy that man, as he gets older, must face decrepitude, decay, senility and death. If people knew what to eat and would eat what they should, Old Father Time would shoulder his scythe and walk off in the other direction.

Universally people are suffering from mineral and vitamin starvation. Research shows that thousands of people are victims of malnutrition. The millions of red blood cells in the body are constantly dying and being replaced, some of them being renewed every second. But they cannot be renewed properly without the right substance. The right substance must come from food — good, wholesome, natural food. The person you are today, the person you will be tomorrow, next week, next month, ten years from now, depends on what you eat! You are the sum total of the food you consume. How you look, how you feel, how you carry your years, all of these depend on what you eat!

Every part of your body is made from food — the hair on your head, your eyes, teeth, bones, blood and flesh. Even your expression is formed from what you eat, because the healthy man is a well-fed, happy man. We can begin anywhere in the body but there is some logic in starting with the skeleton which supports all other tissues. Superficially, our bones are largely mineral matter — mostly calcium and phosphate. One might suppose that once the skeleton is formed, nutrition of the bone stops. This is far from true. With "isotopic tracers," biochemists have found that even in an adult body, minerals are constantly leaving and entering the bones. This means that bones are alive; the situation is dynamic rather than static. Bones contain living bone cells which require not only minerals for building bone, but all the other food nutrients that living cells need in order to maintain themselves.

An emergency need for these cells arises when a bone becomes broken. If these cells had ceased to live and function when the adult skeleton became formed, a broken bone would remain broken for the rest of one's life. When a bone does become broken, nourishment of these bone cells is crucially important, they not only need the minerals required for repairing the damage but the cells themselves need to "eat" and keep well.

These bone cells, like all other cells, can be nourished at various levels of efficiency. This is related to the fact that sometimes bones knit slowly and sometimes rapidly. The rate of healing can be retarded by relatively poor nutrition of the cells that do the repair work; it can be stepped up by improving the nutrition of these cells. Good physicians who treat fracture cases, especially those who are nutrition-minded, take pains to see that every possible measure is taken to promote the finest nutrition possible to build new bone cells.

Entire Body Needs Natural Nutrition

The cells in our skin, including the hair-building cells need continual nourishment; this becomes more evident and compelling when we remember that skin is constantly being worn away and replaced, and hair grows continuously, day and night, year after year.

Those who handle farm animals, pets, or racing animals know that skin and hair-sleekness is an important index of health and well-being. If an animal's hair or fur is well-nourished and healthy, this is an indication that the other cells of its body are at least fairly well-nourished. Laboratory experience with mammals and fowl shows that many entirely different nutritional deficiencies will cause the skin and hair, or feathers, to become unhealthy and disheveled in appearance. Nutritionists recognize the appearance of healthy skin and are often able to judge the person's condition on this basis. Several gross vitamin deficiencies in human beings are obvious in the unhealthy appearance of the skin.

That national misery, constipation, is often a manifestation of wrong nutrition of the intestinal tissues. In the intestinal tract, there are many involuntary "smooth" muscles which, when stimulated, cause stomach and intestinal movements. These wave-like motions keep the partially digested food moving along until the residue reaches the large bowel and is eventually eliminated. All the smooth muscles are made up of living cells which must be nourished to a high level of efficiency if the whole process is to proceed with facility. In order to prevent stagnation in the intestinal tract, irritating substances (powerful laxatives) are often used. These stimulate and "drive" the muscle cells, sometimes mercilessly, when usually all that muscle cells need to function efficiently is bulk to work on, coupled with good sound nutrition habits.

"Teach me Thy way, O Lord; and lead me in a plain path . . ." Psalms 97:11

50

The system of arteries, veins, and capillaries which carries blood and nourishment to all parts of the body are not inert pipes; their walls contain indispensable living cells which must be nourished satisfactorily in order to remain alive and well. They do not always stay well, as in the case of so-called hardening of the arteries which results from an unhealthy, "corroded" condition which can certainly be aggravated by improper nutrition.

The Circulatory System is the Athlete's Power Line

The center of the circulatory system — the heart, is very much alive and its continual nourishment is crucially important. It pumps blood all over the body, but the heart is a powerful muscle which utilizes a tremendous amount of energy and the heart-muscle cells need to be "fed" a highly-nutritious, "natural" diet, day in and day out. If an artery supplying blood to the heart becomes unhealthy and corroded, it is more likely to be stopped-up by a small blood clot. In this case, the heart-muscle cells which depend on the artery for sustenance are starved. If the starvation, particularly for oxygen, is extensive and lasts even a fraction of a minute, the victim may die of a coronary heart attack. In this case, the quality of the blood may be satisfactory, but it cannot get through to the heart-muscle cells, and thus cannot carry its benefits to them. The heart cells die and, as a result, all cells in the body finally die.

This is another example in which failure of cells to get what they need on one area can cause severe damage elsewhere in the body.

There are various special organs in the body that have special and distinctive nutritional requirements. All the hormone-producing glands in the body: the thyroid gland, the pituitary, the adrenals, the sex glands, the insulin-producing cells in the pancreas, the parathyroids, are made up of living cells which, like all other living cells, need continuous and complex nourishment. In addition, these cells need raw materials to build the respective hormones.

One of these hormones is particularly interesting because it contains a specific chemical element — iodine. The cells that produce the thyroid hormone are among the differentiated cells in the body. They absolutely need iodine if they are to perform their unique function. In certain parts of the world, such as the Great Lakes region, the Pacific Northwest, and Switzerland, iodine is at a low level in soil and vegetation. As a result, the thyroid glands of animals (dogs) and human beings are starved (relatively) for iodine; they become diseased, and highly swollen, thus calling attention to themselves (endemic goiter). They simply cannot do the job of producing the hormone adequately unless they are furnished enough iodine to put into it. When sufficient iodine is furnished through sea vegetation (kelp, Irish-moss, etc.) or the eating of fish from salt water, the enlarged thyroid gland reduces to normal size and the diseased condition disappears. By limiting the different degrees of the amount of iodine furnished a mammal, it is possible to produce severe simple goiter or any condition intermediate between this and completely normal functioning.

The Effect of Food on the Mind

At first glance, no connection between food and thinking is apparent; yet I assure you that, just as surely as food affects the different parts of the body, it also affects our thinking, for the very same reasons that pertain to the body. Our thought processes are influenced directly by what we have eaten; perhaps not from what we have last eaten, but surely from what we eat habitually.

The brain is given credit for the processes of thought, though some profess to doubt this, and maintain that thought originates outside of us, in the ethereal universe. But wherever it originates, the processes are certainly run by some parts of the body. The brain occupies the most strategic position in the body for direction of impulses; it is the logical seat for emotions, motivating impulses, and conscious thinking.

The brain is the great reflex center, from which radiate all the nerves that control motion and sensation; and as the brain must depend on the body for blood and oxygen, surely it must be affected by what we eat; for what we eat determines the sort of blood we have. A brain nourished by blood laden with various toxic acid debris is surely not in a condition or position to function at its greatest efficiency. Toxic states can so befuddle the brain that clear thinking is impossible, and even deep comatose states will result from unusually deep types of intoxication, as we often observe.

To have a crystal-clear, alert, keen, sharp brain you must keep the toxic poisons of the blood at the lowest level and you must eat a diet that will supply every cell in the brain with the proper nourishment. This calls for regular periods of fasting to keep the toxic poisons at the lowest levels and a diet that supplies all the nutrients required by the brain!

Refined and Processed Modern Food
Produces Many Backward Children

To show you the effect of toxic poison and malnutrition on the children of today, I have talked to many educators across the country, who have thousands upon thousands of children between the ages of six to seventeen that just cannot be educated. Their brains are sick from toxic poison and malnutrition because of our so-called standard American diet. These children have been fed on breakfast foods that have had all the nutrients refined out of them. Although the schools are blamed for turning out uneducated students, it is not the fault of the school teacher. The blame lies on the children's parents.

Mothers who buy and prepare food for the children are misled by T.V., radio, magazine and newspaper advertising. They tell the mothers to give the children canned soups which are composed of refined starch, sugar, and fat, that are rich in "empty calories" which quickly satisfies a child's appetite, but contain practically no minerals, vitamins, enzymes, roughage, or protein. They are told to give the children "Blunder bread" and "Ghost toasties" that have been "enriched." This is virtually an admission that essential food values have been extracted in the processing, and that the product needs to be "enriched." The mothers are told to put hot dogs and lunch meats in this refined, bleached bread. Both hot dogs and all lunch meats have two or more chemical additives. Children of today are allowed cola drinks and pop. They are filled with "empty calories" which may give a short surge of quick energy, but which have no basic nutrients such as vitamins and minerals. They eat commercial ice cream which is filled with all kinds of additives and commercial fillers, they eat candy bars, cookies, cakes, rich crackers, and pastries. These foods are called "deprived" foods. They satisfy a child by making him feel well-fed when he is truly being partly starved by spoiling his appetite for better, more nourishing foods.

How in heaven's name can you feed a child's brain on such "junk foods" as potato chips, and French fried potatoes with gobs of catsup smeared over them?

Most American Young Men Unfit

Is it any wonder that a high percent of the young men who enlist for military service are physically unfit? Even though standards have not been raised, there is a worsening condition as it relates to American youth. The percentages of failures due to their inability to meet minimum requirements has been alarming.

The American Journal of Clinical Nutrition flatly stated that: "Nutrition is the most important single factor affecting health. This is true at age one or 101. But too often this fact is overlooked in the development of new health programs. Nutrition is a specific factor in the prevention and in the control of many chronic diseases."

Medical Science: "One out of every 14 boys and one out of every 17 girls under the age of 20 are hospitalized in a course of a year, according to the experience of one insurance company." An editorial in the London Times said, "The food industry, it predicts . . . is in for a turbulent time and had better take steps at once to remedy its shameful neglect of basic research in nutrition."

Dr. G.E. Burch, Prof. of Medicine, Tulane University, New Orleans, La., states . . . "Even in the young age-group, the incidence of neoplastic diseases such as leukemia is increasing. The collagen diseases such as acute arthritis are becoming more common."

Boys made a sad showing in physical examinations; the nutritional status of girls — the mothers of tomorrow — is even more serious. Most nutritionists, doctors, and teachers agree that, basically, two factors are to blame; dietary ignorance and the lack of parental direction. One of the consequences is the inability to resist infectious disease. Childbirth complications are another result of poor nutrition. A girl whose nutrition is not adequate for her own body cannot expect to develop a healthy baby.

Americans consume more chemicals in their food than any other nation. At the same time, American forecasts are the gloomiest in the world about the continued rise of all the degenerative diseases.

The United States leads the civilized world in degenerative diseases, and in chemicalized foods. She also leads the world in high living standards and ample foods, which should reduce instead of increase the degenerative diseases.

The Sad Physical and Mental Condition
of Our Adult Population

If you think school-age children are befuddled in their thinking, let's look at the adult population. If you think the young population is half-sick or all-sick, our adult population is even worse! If we examined our adult population from 25 to 75, what a group of physical and mental wrecks we would find.

If a group of fifteen adults are gathered together in a room for a social evening and the conversation turns to health and disease . . . you can be sure that 99 percent of these people have some chronic ailment eating away at one or more vital organs. It seems that each one has something wrong with him. They talk of the shots they are taking, the operations they have had or are going to have . . . the pills they are taking . . . or the misery they are suffering. They calmly admit to each other that they are mentally disturbed, as if it were natural to be in that condition. The longer the adult person lives on the standard civilized program the worse he gets, mentally and physically. This proves out by the great number of convalescent nursing homes all over the country. These places are packed with prematurely-aging adults who are senile, feeble, forgetful, pitiful humans!

I ask you, is this the way that God and Nature intended us to end our days on earth? If you are going to eat a diet deficient in the essential nutrients and you are going to let your body become loaded with vile, acid poisons, the answer is *yes*. Just because we live a limited number of years, there is absolutely no need that we break down, mentally and physically! Since the mind is supported by purely physical processes, it is not hard to see the connection between foods and thinking; for the physical processes depend so completely on the character of foods eaten that it is not logical to disassociate the mind from foods.

During fasts, when the body nears a purified state, the mind is on such a high level that the subconscious mind becomes very active. Some of the greatest mental feats have been performed during a fast, and a high degree of mental efficiency has been noted for rather long periods following the fast. Because fasting clears the system of much toxic debris, the brain is nourished with a much purer blood stream, and rises to amazing heights of efficiency.

We have achieved miracles in mechanics, invention, and science; but how much more might we have achieved if we had known the simple facts of proper nutrition as a background for thinking more efficiently!

The ancient philosophers of Greece placed proper diet first in training their students, and

Roy D. White, (on the left) at a youthful 106 years young starts a five mile walk with his friend Dr. Paul Bragg. In Dr. Bragg's lifetime of lecturing and writing on health and fitness, he never missed an opportunity to meet and talk with active, long living persons in his over twenty health crusades around the world. It was through this exposure, combined with years of research on the Subject of Life Extension, that Bragg was able to advise and encourage literally hundreds of thousands of his followers and students to live a health regime (a basic, natural nutrition, ample exercise, and 7-8 hours sleep) that put them in superb condition. Bragg stressed this health regime is a daily investment in YOU, and when you stop exercising, etc.... the benefits stop.!

their rigid economy in the use of foods shows clearly the importance of this subject in their philosophy.

Epicurus, Socrates, Plato, and many others, placed great stress on food and its relation to the mind as a background for phlosophic study; and they themselves practiced what they preached.

The philosophy of these sages is still respected today on a very high plane, even after the passing ages; and it has been said that some of the utterances of these men contain wisdom that seemed so far in advance of their times as to appear inspired.

Foul Body - Foul Thoughts
Clean, Purified Body - Clean Thoughts

So much of the responsibility for clear thinking rests on the manner of feeding, however remote this connection may seem to those who have not seen the relationship demonstrated in many hundreds of cases of various types. As the body becomes cleared of toxic acid debris, thinking is at once on a much higher plane; and the baser thinking, the grosser pleasures, seem to be idle and useless during this time.

"*As a man thinketh in his heart, so is he,*" is more than a trite saying, and is capable of active and most convincing proof. When the body is cleared of this waste material, the mind soars to heights not formerly glimpsed by toxic minds, and new worlds seem to open to the fortunate one. Most of the worthwhile things of life, those things that have elevated others, that have lived as great accomplishments for ages, have been achieved by those who placed accomplishment before idle pleasure! Among these benefactors, you will never find gluttons . . . and will seldom ever find people who eat a devitalized, processed, or dead-food diet.

Eating is and should be a science, and one of the greatest importance to everyone, for it is such a fundamental thing. So much depends on it for efficiency, health, happiness, accomplishment, and the length of time we will remain on earth, that it should have much more important aspects in every person's early training.

It is never too late to start a program of wholesome nutrition. The very second you begin a natural diet . . . your body, mind, and spirit start to improve! In just eleven short months, you can build a whole, new, wonderful, youthful-feeling body, by fasting to clean out the half-dead cells and using natural foods to build new youthful cells. This is the great secret of life.

DOCTOR FASTING

Fasting is accepted and recognized as being the oldest form of therapy. It is mentioned 74 times in the Bible. It is the universal therapy used by animals in the wilds the world over. As we study the ancient healers of the world, we find that fasting heads the list for helping Nature heal the sick and the wounded. There has been a misconception about fasting that must be clarified. It must be definitely and positively stated that fasting is not a cure of any disease or ailment. The purpose of the fast is to allow the body full range and scope to fulfill its self-healing, self-repairing, self-rejuvenating functions to the best advantage. Healing is an internal biological function. Fasting gives the body a physiological rest and permits the body to become 100 percent efficient in healing itself. Fasting under proper care or with workable knowledge is probably the fastest and the safest way or means of regaining health ever conceived by the human man.

If I have to repeat myself, I want to make it clear and positive that fasting does not cure anything. Fasting puts the body in a condition where all the Vital Force of the body is used to flush out the causes of body miseries. Fasting helps the body help itself. We who have made a life study of The Science of Fasting and conducted and supervised thousands of fasts, know the miracle that the body itself can perform during the period of complete abstinence from food. It gives the over-worked, over-burdened internal organs rest and time for rehabilitation. It exhilarates the internal power and vitality of the body to flush out toxic poisons and wastes that have been stored in the body for years. It raised the Vital Power to the highest point of efficiency. Thus it promotes the elimination of inorganic chemical accumulations and other pollutions that cannot be flushed from the body by any other means.

The prophets of old fasted for spiritual illumination and a closer contact with God. We know that fasting sharpens and makes the mental facilities keen and sharp. Fasting improves the organs of mastication, digestion, assimilation and elimination of food. The liver, which is known as the chemical laboratory of the human body and the most abused organ, has a chance during the fast to rehibilitate and pick up more Vital energy. Thus, after a fast the liver functions more efficiently. Particularly all the sensory powers possessed by human beings are exhilarated and raised to a much higher efficiency level than normal during and after a fast. No process of therapy ever fulfilled so many indications for restoration of vigorous health as does fasting. It is Nature's very own prime process, her first requirement in nearly all cases. After a fast the circulation is better, food can be assimilated better, vital vigor is greater, and the triathlete will find that endurance, stamina and strength are multiplied. After a fast the mind becomes more receptive to logic and a sensible natural way of living.

After the fast the mind becomes so powerful that it can take full control of the body. It becomes the complete master and if a person does not go back to his old habits, he can carry this mastery of the body for the rest of his life. Fasting gives a person confidence. Fasting gives a person a positive mental attitude. Fasting brings tranquility of mind and a glow of well-being that no other therapy can achieve.

Fasting renovates, revivifies, and purifies each and every one of the millions of cells that make up the human body.

Fasting is the Royal Road to Internal Purity.

Fasting and the Distance Athlete

Much has been written and said about the diet for the athlete, the do's and dont's of food intake. Any day we can pick up the daily paper, take a magazine off the newstand, or at the grocery check-out counter and discover a new diet. The one thing all diets have in common is that you must ingest some substance. Seldom do these fad diets recommend abstaining from any and all foods for any period of time. This is not a popular course of action in today's society. We feel that all cures for what ails us should not be difficult or a sacrifice. Just take a pill, take a dose of chemicals, and treat the symptom, not the disease.

Man through the ages has enjoyed the therapeutic and health restoring benefits of the fast. The periodic cessation of all consumption of solid matter accompanied by an adequate intake of water, not fruit juices . . . is known as a water fast.

We are primarily concerned with the general physical well-being of the athlete and the beneficial effect fasting can and does have on his power and endurance in his sport. It has been estimated that the triathlete, training in swim-bike-run consumes an average of 500 calories per hour . . . or the equivalent of one full day's calorie consumption for a four-hour training period. If this intake is made up of empty calories, high in saturated fats, processed and devitalized white flours, and sugars devoid of all vitamins and live enzymes, this same triathlete will soon be running on an "empty fuel tank."

Distance, endurance sports training and participation taxes the total body! The blood stream traveling through miles of arteries, veins, and blood vessels serves the athlete in many ways. Primarily much need oxygen is transferred from the lungs to hard-working muscle issue, exchanging oxygen for carbon dioxide and lactic acids from the muscle tissues and transferring it back to the lungs, to be exhaled. This is an over-simplification of just one of the blood stream's life sustaining functions. It is absolutely essential that the blood stream be pure and free from toxic poisons before starting your distance training program.

The Miracle of Fasting for Super Endurance

This segment on fasting is a must for all triathlon aspirants. The fast is nature's operating table; fasting has been known for centuries as a natural rejuvenation for mankind. Basically, man is the walking, talking result of the food that he consumed yesterday. If the quality of food substance is nutritionally correct, he is an active, happy, productive, healthy, mentally alert individual. If the quality of food consumed is not nutritionally balanced, he lacks energy, has the "life is a bore" attitude, his work suffers, he seems susceptible to everything going around, and he is constantly complaining of aches and pains.

The purpose of this chapter is to start a house-cleaning of our bodies . . . not nutrition or dieting. It is important to know that we are what we eat or ingest into our bodies. Our skin is renewed periodically, as is our hair, and our bloodstream is replaced every six to eight weeks. Our bodies contain trillions of cells (over three trillion, scientists tell us). These cells are being bombarded and destroyed daily, by solar rays, air pollution, water pollution, and the poor quality of our food. To retard the destruction of these cells, the body must have the proper enzymes available only in "live foods," food that is fresh and essentially alive. These cells cannot survive on dead, devitalized, devitaminized, or overly processed foods.

Back to our house-cleaning. We live in an age of pollution; our water supplies are exposed to every imaginable contamination known to man. If this were not bad enough, man proceeds to further contaminate his water supplies deliberately by selecting a menu for you, from a pantry of 240 body polluting chemicals, all in the name of purification. Then, "big brother" steps in and insists that we all inject a dose of poison florides with every drop of water we drink, supposedly in the name of fewer cavities for our children. These contaminates are all "heavy metals." A few years or a lifetime of this "chemical diet," and we are all candidates for cancer.

These ingested chemicals never leave your body. They form sedimentation in our fat deposits, joints, and extremities. Combining this with increasingly higher, heavy, inorganic mineral substances and quantities of calcium chloride, (salt) intrusions into our water supplies . . . and we can end up with arthritis, kidney stones, eye cataracts, hardening of the arteries, and high blood pressure.

Our Creator has endowed us with a wonderful mechanism; the human body. As athletes we have a better knowledge of our bodies, a greater respect for this priceless gift which enables us to "go the distance." We learn to listen for signs of illness or injuries. We know that properly trained, our body becomes like a fine-tuned violin. The slightest discord is noticeable . . . and when all the strings are in perfect harmony, all systems are "go." We enjoy the supreme sense of superior activities that comes only from the feeling of well-being and superior athletic achievement.

To maintain this excellent, complete harmony, our body has to be free of all contaminants. This body purification process is only possible through the fasting process. The body possesses superior healing powers if left to its own devices. Our problem is that we do not give the body opportunity to "clean house." We are constantly bombarding it with food, drink, and polluted air.

The triathlete has a vested interest in maintaining an absolutely pure body. The demands that will be made on his powers of strength and endurance are above and beyond anything imagined in any athletic endeavors! True flexibility, strength, and endurance comes only from a body, internally clean, fueled by the proper food and drink, and trained to perfection!

Fasting is "house cleaning." Start at the beginning, make fasting one-day-a-week part of your training schedule. Plan your day fasts after a major event, in preparation for a future event.

For a complete book on fasting read THE MIRACLE OF FASTING, which is the "Bragg Bible of Health" (see back pages for order blank). The superior sense of well-being, physical power, mental and spiritual awareness, will reward you beyond all measure at the finish line of the triathlon and the game of life!

Benefit From the Joys of Fasting

by Allan Cott, M.D.
"Fasting As A Way Of Life"

- Fasting is easier than any diet.
- Fasting is adaptable to a busy life.
- Fasting is the quickest way to lose weight.
- Fasting gives the body a physiological rest.
- Fasting is used successfully in the treatment of many physical ills.
- Fasting can yield weight losses of up to 10 pounds or more in the first week.
- Fasting lowers cholesterol and blood-pressure levels.
- Fasting is a calming experience, often relieving tension and insomnia.
- Fasting leads to improved dietary habits.
- Fasting frequently induces feelings of euphoria, a natural "high."
- Fasting increases the pleasure of eating.
- Fasting is a rejuvenator, slowing the aging process.
- Fasting is an energizer, not a debilitator.
- Fasting often results in a more vigorous sex life.
- Fasting aids in the elimination process.
- Fasting helps to eliminate or modify smoking, drug, and drinking addictions.
- Fasting is a regulator, educating the body to consume only as much as needed.
- Fasting produces "found" time — all the hours spent in marketing, preparing, and consuming food and drink.
- Fasting rids the body of toxins, giving it an "internal shower."
- Fasting does not deprive the body of essential nutrients.
- Fasting can be used to uncover the sources of food allergies.
- Fasting is used effectively in schizophrenia treatment and other mental ills.
- Fasting under proper supervision can be tolerated easily up to 4 weeks.
- Fasting does not accumulate appetite; hunger "pangs" disappear after a day or two.
- Fasting is routine for the animal kingdom.
- Fasting has been a commonplace experience for man almost since existence.
- Fasting is a rite in all religions; the Bible alone has 74 references to it.
- Fasting under proper conditions is absolutely safe.
- Fasting is not starving, it is nature's own cure! (Patricia Bragg)

Fasting Heightens Spiritual Awareness

As the body cleanses and heals itself by fasting, keener mental concentration and clearer spiritual perception develop. Remember, the brain is the physical instrument of the mind. When the mucus and toxic poisons are flushed from the brain cells, worries and frustrations are also flushed from your mind. It becomes free and clear. You can think intelligently and logically. Your memory is sharp and keen. Your creative powers are expanded. You are able to face reality and yourself . . . to view your problems objectively and find definite answers — and solutions!

The elimination of toxic wastes releases the mind from physical bondage. The freedom from the necessity of procuring, preparing, eating, digesting and assimilating food releases a tremendous amount of nervous energy which invigorates the mental and spiritual processes. You attain new levels of tranquility, serenity and peace of mind. You become spiritually perceptive and receptive.

You can become at one with the Infinite . . . "Be still, and know that I am God."

"Fasting does not change God, but man. A cleansing process takes place. The awareness of the purification of the heart builds faith, and faith in God means authority with God." So states Rev. Charles F. Stanley, Atlanta, Georgia, in a recent article. (*Fasting,* MOODY MONTHLY, May 1975).

In *God's Chosen Fast* (Christian Literature Crusade, Ft. Washington, Pa.), author Arthur Wallis says:

"Without doubt there is a very close connection between the practice of fasting and the receiving of spiritual revelation. Many non-Christian religions such as Buddhism, Hinduism, Confucianism and Islam (also) practice fasting because they know its power to detach one's mind from the world of sense, and to sharpen one's sensibility to the world of spirit."

Great Spiritual Leaders Practiced Fasting

It was after fasting for forty days and forty nights that Moses received the Ten Commandments on Mt. Sinai. Jesus spent forty days and forty nights of fasting in the desert before starting His ministry.

The founders of the world's four religions of today — Christianity, Judaism, Buddhism and Islam — taught fasting as a means of communication with the Divine through purification of body, mind and spirit . . . to be carried out with dedication and in private.

Many who tried to travel with him fell by the wayside from heat and exhaustion. But Ghandi was inexhaustible. I have been an athlete all my life and a high mountain climber . . . but I have never seen a human who had the physical staying power and limitless energy as Ghandi. He walked and talked until sundown before he stopped for a rest.

In the days that my father was a member of the Ghandi party we had many talks with him on the power of fasting. Of the number of things we learned from him this statement seems to be the summation:

"All the vitality and all the energy I have comes to me because my body is purified by fasting."

Walking mile after mile from village to village, he gave the people hope and courage that a better life was coming to them. His internal strength was so powerful that weak people felt strong after seeing him and hearing his words. He gave of his unlimited strength to the discouraged and the sick. He brought bright light where there was darkness.

Ghandi told the people to fast and purify their bodies, and regardless of their circumstances they would find peace and joy on earth.

"Fasting will bring spiritual rebirth to those of you who cleanse and purify your bodies," he told those who thronged to hear him. "The light of the world will illuminate within you when you fast and purify yourself."

This trip with the great Mahatma Ghandi is an experience I will never forget. This physically small man was a spiritual giant. He led the millions of people on the sub-continent of India to independence from the mighty British Empire without striking a single physical blow. And yet, with all his power and influence, he was completely without arrogance. Characteristically, on the day of India's independence, Ghandi took no part in the celebrations that went on throughout the country . . . but spent the day in fasting and prayer.

The Grotto Where Jesus Fasted

On one of our trips to the Holy Land, my father and I were in the area of Jericho on an archeological research project. It was near the Mount of Temptation, the mountaintop where Jesus is said to have been tempted by the devil after his fast of forty days and forty nights, and we determined to climb it. It was a long but easy ascent. From the top, which was still 200 feet below sea level, we looked down upon the terrible, hot, bleached bareness of the Jordan Valley.

On our descent, halfway down the mountain, built partly within the rock itself, we came upon a monastery where ten elderly Greek monks were living in poverty. Following the ancient custom of greeting any stranger as if he might be the wandering Christ, these monks welcomed us with beautiful courtesy. We were taken on a tour of the monastery. It was a fantastic place . . . parts of it jutting out over deep, brutal chasms . . . other rooms carved out of the solid rock.

One of these was a grotto which, the guide told us, was "the very spot where Jesus fasted forty days and forty nights, and was tempted by the devil."

The monks told us that they fasted two days every week, and once a year fasted forty days and nights in the grotto. They felt that this fasting had not only given them great spiritual enlightenment, but had also added many vigorous years to their lives.

Their appearance bore them out. Although far along in calendar years, these men had great flexibility in their bodies. It required a lot of physical stamina to keep the monastery in good condition in this rugged, barren wilderness and oven heat. All were lean and muscular, with the glow of health to their skin and bright, keen eyes — none wore glasses.

Looking back, as we descended the long, stony trail, I saw him watching solicitously. We waved to each other, and I carried a warm glow of friendliness in my heart from that barren rocky land.

Here again was proof of what I have learned from my own experience . . . that one of the spiritual benefits of fasting is a genuine sense of the kinship of all humanity.

The Fast of 40 Days and 40 Nights

There is a significance to the "forty days and forty nights" of fasting of the great spiritual leaders and of those who seek the highest spiritual enlightenment. This is the practical limit to which the disciplined body can exist without food before it begins to consume itself. The cleansing process has been completed . . . toxic wastes and excess fat have been "incinerated," burned up into energy. When this limit is reached, starvation begins . . . the body will have to feed on sound living tissue . . . and this is harmful to body, mind and spirit. The fast should be terminated before this point is reached!

The Benefits of Fasting for the Distance Athlete

Aside from the spiritual implications and motivations, there are several reasons for fasting. Many of us are grossly over-trained to eat three square meals every day, and succumb to this habit according to the clock — for excessive eating habits are mostly time oriented, or related to tension. But in truth, overeating contributes more to excess tension as a direct cause of physical stress, than it contributes to relief of stress as a temporary placebo.

Fasting flushes poisons from the body. When you fast, the portion of your metabolism that is usually used to convert food into energy and body tissue is no longer burdened by the demand to digest unneeded food, and focuses on removing toxicity from the system, eliminating inorganic chemical deposits, and purifying cellular structure.

Fasting prepares the body for healing, regimenting your vital energy so that healing is a natural, internal function of the body. Frequent illnesses make a person feel like stopping eating altogether. Fasting is demanded by nature. It is a part of natural healing. In the USSR, fasting is considered a "cure-all," as it is by many cultures around the world, both modern and primitive.

Fasting for Weight Control

Fasting is one of the most reliable known forms of weight control, far superior to any diet. Regular fasters' bodies find their own proper weight level.

- Fasting has been known to eliminate abnormal growths from the body.
- Fasting sharpens the taste buds.
- Fasting relaxes you, by removing much of the unnecessary garbage that has been imbalancing your metabolism, giving you a new outlook on life, based on renewed health and unhindered happiness.

Through the purification of the body, the mind also becomes sharper, increasing both sensory and extrasensory perception.

As religious faith is a personal matter, so is fasting, yet the idea and principles of fasting seem to overlap into almost every religion in the world. Fasting is a very spiritual experience, for the purer one's body becomes, the more at-one a person becomes with the spirit of life that is within every human soul.

Dr. Paul Bragg's positive dictums should be kept at the heart of your fasting experience, and some of his most succinct truisms follow:

★ "I have this day put my body in the hands of God and Nature. I have turned to the highest power for internal purification and rejuvenation.

★ "Every minute that I am fasting, I am flushing dangerous poisons out of my body that could do great damage. Every hour that I am fasting, I am happier and healthier.

★ "Hour by hour my body is purifying itself.

★ "In fasting I am using the same method for physical, mental and spiritual purification that the greatest spiritual leaders have used throughout the ages. Exercise relates to the body, nutritional eating to the mind, and fasting to the spirit."

Fasting has been prominent as a means for intensifying prayer. Those who have found spiritual value during times set aside for prayer and fasting are found both in Scripture and throughout church history. Those who knew the values and secrets of fasting as a vital dimension in God included: Jesus Himself, the Apostle Paul, the early church leaders, Daniel, Elijah, Ezra, Esther, David, Hannah, Isaiah, Nehemiah, Zechariah and others. Prominent fasters in the annals of church history include John Calvin, Martin Luther, John Knox, John Wesley, David Brainard, George Muller, Rees Howells, and many more.

They discovered that abstaining from food not only freed them to focus upon God with fresh intensity, but opened avenues of spiritual perception and understanding that were not available during the rush of routine living. They found as they focused upon God by deliberate discipline, God focused upon them in clarity of direction and quickening of spirit. They could partake of God more easily with all else set aside.

So we fasted and besought our God for this, and he listened to our entreaty. — *Ezra 8:23*

DOCTOR EXERCISE

Dr. Exercise makes these statements, *"To rest is to rust"* and rust means decay and destruction! In other words, the good doctor tells us that activity is Life, stagnation is death. The good doctor further tells us that if we do not use our muscles, we lose them! In order to keep muscles firm, strong, vigorous, and youthful, they must be continually used. Activity is the Law of Life! Action is the Law of Well-Being. Every vital organ of the body has its specialized work, upon the performance of which its development and strength depend.

When we use the body, we build endurance, strength, and vigor. When we become lazy and do not use our muscles, we bring on decay and death. Daily exercise quickens and equalizes the circulation of the blood, but in laziness, the blood does not circulate freely and the changes in it that are so vital to life and health do not take place, and we have poor muscle tone. The muscles become flabby, sick, and unable to take vigorous activity.

People who do not exercise regularly have poor skin tone. In exercise, we bring on healthy perspiration in the 96 million pores of our body. The skin is the largest eliminative organ in the entire body. If someone would shellac or gild your body and thus clog the pores, you would die within a few minutes. With exercise, you bring on healthy perspiration. Impurities and toxic poisons are expelled when you are exercising and perspiring freely, and you are allowing the skin to perform its natural function of eliminating poisons. If you do not exercise daily to the point of perspiration, all the work that the pores are not doing throws a double burden on the other eliminative organs and then you get into trouble physically. **Vigorous exercise helps to normalize blood pressures; it helps to bring a healthy pulse. Vigorous exercise is an anticoagulant which means that it keeps the blood from clotting (called a "thrombus") which often brings on a heart attack.**

Every creature, human or otherwise, seeking to eliminate the internal waste, does so by means of muscular action. Inside your intestinal tract there are 3 muscular layers which undergo a rhythmic, wave-like action called peristalsis. If you allow the internal and external muscles, through inactivity, to become flabby and fat instead of muscular, a serious condition results. The muscles lost their tonicity and power to contract, and the result is intestinal clogging. The abdominal muscles play an important role in the evacuation effort. What happens when the internal and external muscles become flabby, soft, sick and infiltrated with fat? They refuse to work, so we pile up intestinal waste that should have been eliminated. This brings about autointoxication, or the building of large amounts of toxic poison. I repeat that inactivity is the fruitful cause of many diseases.

Fasting and diet are allies in your struggle for long-lasting youth, health, and symmetry! When it comes to fighting fat . . . diet and fasting come first, but when it comes to keeping fit, it is exercise that matters most. However, they all help each other, for by taking exercise you may be more generous in your diet, and, up to a certain point, your food increase will make for increased vitality. The human machine should work at the highest pitch of efficiency. As with all machines, it improves with intelligent use, and nothing betrays its weak spots like inactivity and rust.

Running, Biking, Swimming for Life

I believe in all of the many forms of exercise, but without hesitation, I will tell you that running, biking and swimming . . . are the best all-around exercises.

Vow to become a wonderful runner, biker or swimmer, and make the day's exercise a fixed item in your health program all the year round, and in any kind of weather. Go at your own stride with your spirit free. If the outer world of nature fails to interest you, turn to the inner world of the mind. For, as you run, bike or swim, your body ceases to matter and you become as near a poet and philosopher as you will ever be. Each to his taste, but to my mind these are better than golf. Life has so much to teach us that it is a pity to waste big chunks of time trying to get a ball into a hole in a stroke less than the other fellow. The importance of exercise is the same — healthily-functioning muscles and quickened blood circulation with its attendant sense of harmony and happiness.

Gardening, too, is a marvelous form of exercise. It will give you enough exercise in the open to keep you in the pink of physical condition. But you can get fat while gardening, because there is too little movement, and you are bent over instead of being erect. For this reason, I prefer running, biking and swimming. Satisfy your conscience by applying your energy productively in your garden, then take the kink out of your back with the healthy triathletes.

In my personal life, I combine a system of calisthenics, plus brisk walking, running, biking and swimming.

Importance to the Abdomen . . .
Running, Biking and Swimming Exercises

I believe the most important exercises are those that stimulate all of the muscles of the human trunk from the hips to the armpits. These are the binding muscles which hold all of

Dave Scott's number 1 proved prophetic as Scott captured his third Ironman crown at the 1983 Ironman Triathlon World Championship in a record time of 9:05:57.

the vital organs in place, for, in developing your torsal muscles, you are also developing the vital muscles. As your back, waist, chest, and abdomen increase in soundness and elasticity, so will your lungs, liver, heart, stomach, and kidneys gain in efficiency.

The widened arch of your ribs will give free play to the lung bellows, your elastic diaphragm will let the heart pump and function more powerfully; your rubber-like waist will, in its limber action, stimulate your kidneys and massage your liver. Your abdominal muscles will strengthen and support your stomach with controlled undulations. All of this hard, clean development of your torso will stimulate the sound walls of your house, which fortify the interior to resist the ravages of time. Trunk exercise is like a massage of the vital organs, and, for that reason, it has an influence over the whole organism that cannot be underestimated.

The more you fast, the more poison you will clean from your body and, as your body increases in internal cleanliness, so will your muscles have more tone and vitality.

You will find after a fast that the old lazy feeling will leave you and, in its place, there will be a desire for more action and more physical activity.

DOCTOR REST

Dr. Rest is another specialist always at your command to help you win Vitality Supreme. I believe the word "rest" is the most misunderstood word in the dictionary. Some people's idea of resting is to sit down and drink a cup of strong stimulant, such as alcohol, coffee, tea, or soft drinks. This is so well portrayed in the modern coffee break for employees. To me, rest means repose, freedom from activity, quiet, tranquility. It means peace of mind and spirit, it means to rest without anxiety or worry, and it means to refresh one's self. Your rest should be a general refresher of your whole nervous system.

It does not mean sitting with one leg crossed over the other, because when you sit in this position, you are putting a tremendous burden on the artery which supplies the feet with blood and also cuts off nerve energy. So if you sit with one leg crossed over the other, you are not resting, you are giving the heart a tremendous load of work to do. Don't cross your legs when you sit down — keep both feet on the floor!

To rest means to allow a free circulation of blood in the entire body. If your shoes are too tight, if your collar is too tight, if your hat is too tight, if your belt or any of your undergarments are too tight, if stockings are too tight, you are not resting when you sit still or lie down. The best rest is secured when all of the clothes are off the body. Any clothes you are wearing should be comfortably loose and never binding.

Why do we rest? You often hear people say, "I must have a rest." But when they sit down to rest, they nervously thump their fingers on a table or desk, or they squirm or move restlessly. The art of resting is something that must be acquired and concentrated upon. Among the various ways you can rest is to lie down on a firm bed or couch unclothed or with as few loose clothes as possible. One of the finest ways to rest is a sun bath, because, if there is anything that will relax the muscles and nerves, it is the soothing rays of the sun. As you rest, you must learn to clear your mind of all anxiety, worries, and emotional problems. When the muscles and nerves are relaxed, the heart action slows, and especially when you take long, slow, deep breaths. This will bring deep relaxation and total rest.

"Come Ye and Rest A While . . ."

Another form of resting is a short nap, and in taking this nap, you should command your muscles to become completely relaxed. Your conscious and subconscious mind control the muscles and the nerves, so you must be in complete command of your body when you rest. *Jesus and His Disciples, when worn and weary, said "Come Ye and Rest a While."* The Master did not lead them into the busy streets of Jerusalem where there was noise and clatter.

He didn't even take them into the synagogue, but into the quiet of the wide open spaces, under the blue sky. Here he could rebuild, relax, and revivify every organ of their exhausted bodies, and revitalize, refresh, and invigorate their weary minds. Under the blue sky in the clean, fresh air is the greatest place to relax and rest, and renew your Vital Force.

To me, sleep is the greatest revitalizer we have, but so few people get a long, peaceful, and refreshing night's sleep. Most people habitually use stimulants; tobacco, drugs, coffee, tea, alcohol, and cola drinks. All of these whip the tired nerves, so that people who use these stimulants never have complete rest and relaxation, because their nerves are always in an excited condition. Most people do not earn their rest; rest is something that must be earned with physical and mental activity, because they go hand in hand. So many people have come to me, telling me what poor sleepers they were, and how they roll and toss all night long. Today, thousands of people are forced to take some type of drug to induce sleep, but this is not true sleep. No one can get restful sleep with a drug. You may drug yourself to unconsciousness, but you cannot drug yourself to a restful, normal, healthful, and satisfying sleep.

A body full of toxic poisons is a continual irritant to the nerves. How is it possible to get a good night's rest with irritated nerves? I have found in my years of experience with fasting, that when people discard their stimulants while on a fasting program, they become deep, restful sleepers. You will notice as you purify your body that you will be able to relax more readily. You will be able to nap often, and you will enjoy the benefits of a long, restful, night's sleep. Rest is important! The Bible tells us that God appointed one day of rest every week for man. In this act of God Almighty, we have plenty of support for our contention that frequent change of activity is an important factor in the maintenance of super-health. Along with our busy days, we must add some form of recreation to our activities. We have all heard the trite saying "All work and no play makes Jack a dull boy."

Today we live in a mad, competitive world which in business parley is called "The Rat Race." In our civilization, it is dog-eat-dog, so we build up tremendous pressures, tensions, stresses, and strains. This is the reason why people turn to tobacco, drugs, coffee, alcohol, and other stimulants. There is not only competition in the business world, but status must be upheld. People are always trying to impress one another, and trying to create an image. Thus a false image is created and it takes a tremendous amount of energy to portray a false image! There is competition among women, who have been told that gray hair makes them look old, so they spend hours having their colored, to constantly keep up with the latest fashions, which also calls for energy. Our whole modern civilization is one that "whip-drives" and pushes us.

Life is to be Enjoyed!

It is no wonder that we have created twenty million chronic alcoholics and untold millions of drug addicts. Have we completely forgotten that life is to be lived, to be enjoyed? Leisure living is something few people in our modern society enjoy. Life is rush, rush, and more rushing; where are we rushing to? Where? To the hospital or the graveyard?

To be able to relax, rest, and sleep, your day must be programmed to have time for rest, recreation, exercise, and a good night's sleep. You cannot get a good night's sleep if you overload your stomach. You cannot have a good night's sleep unless you have had some vigorous out-of-door exercise such as running, biking, or swimming. I do not consider housework or the daily occupation as the way to get exercise and activity. Let your body be nourished by pure, natural food and distilled water . . . let it have plenty of fresh air and sunlight. Have a balanced program of exercise and repose and let Nature do the rest; treat yourself as if you were a fine beast of pure-bred stock, and as surely as it will win prizes for superiority, so will you! It is all too easy to sneer and laugh at the *"back to Nature"* people, but we who believe in Nature will always have the last laugh.

Natural Way of Living Reaps Huge Benefits in
More Peace, Joy, Health and Happiness!

One of the predominant suggestions of this chapter, then, is a gradual return to a more natural way of living. In food, clothing, exercise, rest, sleep, and a simplicity in living habits, try to reach a nearness to Nature and God . . . that makes you almost one with Him. When you feel that the same pure forces that express themselves in a pine tree are expressing themselves in you, you have made a big stride toward a health ideal.

Begin to live as Mother Nature wants you to live. Seek to feel that she claims you and that you are part of glad, growing things. Put yourself into her hands and let her have her way with you. Leave to the young the smog-filled, air-polluted, microbe-infested cities. You will find that in the quiet beauty of hill and meadow, you will rekindle your own youth. If you would grow young, begin by believing you can, and that Nature is eager to aid you. Better than any human, she can run that ill-used machine of yours, and, if it breaks down while in her hands, it is because its usefulness is really at an end.

If you are a prisoner of a city, make it a point to get out in the country or the seashore where you can really find true rest, tranquility, and serenity. In a sisterly way, I have tried to stress these points. First, you should demand of yourself a higher standard of health and happiness. You cannot receive higher health unless your body gets its rest periods to develop new vitality and energy. Second, you should regard your body as a machine under your care and control, and every machine must have rest periods. If not, you will build up too much nerve irritation. Third, with increasing years, you should draw closer and more intimately to Nature and God. You should cease to look for thrills and over-stimulation, and instead, seek a life of serenity and peacefulness. By living in simplicity and purity, you will be as healthy as a carrot in the Bragg organically-grown garden.

Let health, air, sun, exercise, and complete rest work for you. With a serene, clear eye, and confidence, put yourself in Nature's hands. Let her run your machine, heal your hurts, comfort you in sickness and adversity. Then, when you have lived a long life of usefulness and happiness, let her call you back home. Make Nature and God your partners, and when you are resting, relaxing, and recreating new energy, Nature and God will always be there with kind hands on your shoulder. So be a child of Nature, don't look for sophisticated thrills, but find your fun and diversion in relaxation and other pursuits that are simple, down-to-earth, and one with Nature. Your rewards will be many, in renewed health, a calmness of spirit, and a new awareness of the perfect natural beauties that Nature and God have bestowed upon us so generously!

Relaxation Complements the Triathletics

In our American culture, we are prone to look down on the person who wants to relax, or live a leisurely life. It seems that we must be doing something constantly. We must be reading, talking, listening to music, or watching television. We have to attend dances, parties, movies, programs, and athletic sports. We are constantly pushing and driving our bodies. No wonder so many people have emotional problems, and no wonder the psychiatrists and the psychologists are overworked. It is because we ourselves are overworked.

Please do not be ashamed to sit down or lie down and rest, or relax to get off the treadmill. It is not only fun to just do nothing, it is healthy and necessary.

You have a natural, built-in, tranquilizer system located throughout your body in the muscle cells, which you should be using. Don't expect to take sedatives and yet become skilled in relaxation. Barbiturates and true relaxation are not bedfellows. On the other hand, I have known persons who have needed sedatives for six months or longer and were able to discard them after going on a fasting program.

To relax yourself to sleep, first darken the room to some extent, turn off the T.V. or radio, and lie flat on your back with your hands down at either side without touching your body, to reduce sensory stimulation to a minimum. Let your hands rest, palms down, on the bed. Legs should be extended with the feet approximately a foot apart. Your head may rest on a small pillow or directly on the bed, whichever is more comfortable. Permit your eyes to remain open at first, looking at an area, not at a point directly in front of you, that is, on the opposite wall or ceiling, not up or down, or to either side. After the movements of your eyes have ceased, blinking movements of the lids may continue for a while. These will not interfere with the relaxation of the eye muscles.

Thinking is always accompanied by eye movements. By relaxing your eyelids and eye muscles, you are slowing down your thought processes — and the end result of relaxation of the eyes and of other parts of the body is a natural, quiet, and restorative sleep.

If you have insomnia, reading just before going to sleep, or reading to put yourself to sleep, is not helpful, because, in all likelihood, your eye muscles are already over-fatigued. Reading will tire them more, increasing the eye muscle tension, and interfering with the process of relaxation, which if interrupted, would inevitably lead to sleep.

Avoid Interruptions

Disregard all minor muscular discomfort while lying perfectly still, and permit all of your muscles (you have 625 voluntary muscles) to relax without interruption. Do not tighten or move any muscles unless absolutely necessary. Movements of an arm or leg, or a change in your position, will interrupt the entire relaxation process, and those muscles which have already attained a certain degree of relaxation must begin the process all over again. Muscles that are overly tense may be uncomfortable, but if you move them you will only prolong their discomfort. Permit them to relax and, in most instances, the distress will disappear within ten to fifteen minutes. A relaxed muscle is a comfortable muscle and if you are relaxing efficiently, you will feel comfortable. Discomfort in a muscle or muscle group is an indication that it is tense, that you are not permitting it to relax.

False Notions

In the practice of relaxation, beginners have told me many times that they cannot possibly lie on their backs and go to sleep in that position. In observing the training of several hundred individuals, I have yet to prove the truth of their statement. If this is your belief, disregard it, for no matter how deeply entrenched this idea may be in your mind, you will be able to prove it is fallacious.

"I always have to sleep on my right side." "I always sleep on my stomach." "I must curl up when I sleep." "I have to change my position frequently." "I cannot sleep at night if I have a nap in the daytime." "I must have my hand resting on my stomach." "I can go to sleep when I go to bed, but I wake up around 2 or 3 A.M. and can't go back to sleep." "I sleep right through until 5 A.M., but then I am wide awake until I get up at 7 o'clock — and then I am tired out by afternoon." These are common complaints — but I have yet to find a person willing to devote 15 minutes a day in training himself to relax who cannot learn to break these habits, if they live by the natural system of living and a fasting program.

Insomnia usually responds to relaxation techniques within 10 days to two weeks, and then sweet, beautiful sleep will be yours every night and you will wake up in the morning as bright and fresh as a healthy newborn baby.

Your fasting program is going to help you secure complete rest, relaxation, and sound, sweet sleep. Toxins put pressure on nerves and muscles. Fasting releases these pressures and allows them to relax.

DOCTOR GOOD POSTURE

Why should emphasis be placed upon such a simple thing as the pull of gravity? This is very easy to explain. As long as your muscles are stong enough, they hold your skeleton in proper balance with its many points and sections free from strain or discomfort. However, the muscles of people who do not exercise adequately gradually lose the battle with gravity. They become prematurely older, or heavier, and an enforced rest will weaken their muscles just enough for an uncomfortable state of balance.

Such a sagging stretches the ligaments of their back and causes backache. Ligaments that are unduly stretched are painful. Ligaments are meant to serve only as check reins for the joints and they cannot be forcibly stretched without pain. When the ligaments in their back are made uncomfortable by stretching, it is only natural for their muscles to try to oppose the sagging of their back which results from the pull of gravity. However, their muscles are too weak to do their proper job, so they rapidly become exhausted and develop the rankling misery of fatigue, making their back even more uncomfortable.

Check your own symptoms! Do you notice a deep aching and soreness along your spine due to stretched ligaments? Are your back and shoulder muscles achy and tired? Is yours a postural backache due basically to weak muscles? If it is, it's about time you did something sensible to relieve it — like strengthening those weak muscles by proper exercise — running, biking and swimming!

Look at yourself in the mirror. Do your shoulders slump? Is your upper back round? Have you a potbelly? Are you a sway-back? Can you see the reasons, now, why your back has the right to ache? The bending, slumping, ligament-stretching force of gravity has finally taken charge. But even though you may be presently a hapless sufferer of backache due to poor muscles and bad posture, do not despair. You can regain back comfort if weak muscles and poor posture are at fault!

It has been said that backache is the penalty man must pay for the privilege of standing and walking upright on two feet. Although man's ancestors are believed by some to have been four-footed creatures, there is no doubt about the fact that man himself is definitely two-footed. Every infant struggles instinctively to stand on his own two feet and walk. He need not be taught. He will attempt this bi-ped gait even if left alone most of the time and never instructed. It is natural for a human being to stand and walk in this manner. This is interesting, because there are no animals which spend all of their standing and walking hours on two feet — not even the chimpanzees or the gorillas.

These higher apes use their hands and arms to help them move about. The world's strongest gorilla would be unable to follow a fragile housewife about, walking as erectly as she does, for more than a short time. This is because human beings are meant to walk erect, and other animals are not.

The spines of human beings have normal curves which enable the muscles to oppose gravity and hold their backs erect. As long as the muscles are strong enough to maintain the balance of these curves and prevent sagging, the back is comfortable. When the muscles are too weak to do their normal work, the back sags, ligaments are stretched, and backache enters the picture.

To maintain one's self in a healthy state involves many factors: right, natural food; rest; exercise; sleep; fasting; control of emotions and mind; and last but not least, good posture. For the body of a well-nourished triathlete, good posture is not a problem. When the body lacks any of the essentials, poor posture is often the result. Once poor habits have been established, one must resort to definite and corrective measures, such as proper exercises and deliberate postural habits.

Fit as a fiddle health boys keeping youthful ... Dr. Paul Bragg and his disciple Jack LaLanne pose for People Magazine photographers beside Jack's pool at his Hollywood, California home. Jack often tells the dramatic story of how he attended a Bragg Health Crusade at the age of 15 which dramatically changed his life from sickness to vibrant health! ..... He has often repeated how he owes his long healthy life to Paul Bragg.

How to Stand, Sit and Walk for Strength and Health

When in a sitting position, see that the spine is well back against the chair and, again, that the abdominal cavity is not relaxed, but well drawn in, shoulders back, head high and never forward. The position can be with arms folded or the hands clasped in the lap.

When walking, one should imagine that the legs are attached to the middle of the chest and that gives long, sweeping, graceful, springy steps, because when one walks correctly with this swing and spring, he automatically builds energy. Habit either makes or breaks us, and good posture habits make graceful, strong bodies. "Just as the twig is bent, the tree is inclined."

When in a sitting position, never cross one leg over the other. Under the knees run two of the largest arteries, carrying nourishing blood to the muscles below the knee and to the thousands of nerves that are found in the feet. When you cross your legs, you immediately cut down the blood to almost a trickle. Therefore, when the muscles of the leg and knee are not nourished and do not have a good circulation, we go stagnant in the extremities which can lead to varicose veins, or broken capillaries. Look at the bare ankles of people 40 and over who have made it a habit of crossing their legs and see all the broken veins and broken capillaries. When the muscles and feet do not get their full supply of blood the feet become weak and poor circulation sets in. Cold feet torment the leg-crosser.

A well-known heart specialist was asked once, "When do most people have a heart attack?" The heart specialist answered, "At a time they are sitting quietly with one leg crossed over the other." So you can see that when you sit down you should plant both of your feet squarely on the floor and never cross your legs. People who are habitual leg-crossers always have more acid crystals stored in the feet than those who never cross their legs while sitting. Crossing the legs is one of the worst postural habits of man. It throws the hips off balance, throws the spine off balance and throws the head off balance and can become one of the most prolific causes of a chronic backache. Poor posture of any kind can bring an unbearable pain across your upper back, fatigue in your drooping shoulders . . . as well as soreness shooting from the base of your neck to the back of your throbbing head and downward to mingle with stiffness in the belt area of your lower back. Poor posture causes weakness in your hips and loins, a numb feeling at your tail bone, and a shooting pain down your legs. Bad posture can develop aches and pains not only in the back, but all over the body.

One very simple habit, but most beneficial one to establish, is to stand tall, walk tall, sit tall, never crossing one leg over the other. This does not require an exaggerated position, and when one stands tall, walks tall and sits tall, a correct posture is assumed and all of the sagging, dropped and prolapsed vital organs will assume normal position and function; that is, if all other natural habits of living are practiced every day.

DOCTOR HUMAN MIND

Man a Trinity

There is an old German saying: "Alle gute Dinge sind Drei." Or, "All good things are three."

We worship a God represented by a trinity, the Father, Son and Holy Ghost.

The soul is the head man, the first man, the ego, the individual, the personality, which makes each of us individuals.

The mind is the second man, through which the soul or the first man expresses; the soul's only means of expression.

The body is the third man, the physical, visible part; the means by which the mind expresses, also its only means, and its only mode of contact with environment.

These three are one, just as the God is one, each making up a part of this individual called man.

"The body is composed of many members, yet is one body."

"If one of the members suffer, all other suffer with it."

We recognize the body as an indivisible unit, a community of closely grouped and interrelated organs, tissues, and cells, each individual, yet so closely related that not one of them can exist apart from the whole.

The public has too long viewed these various organs as unrelated, or loosely related, units, and has been inclined to treat each more or less individually, not realizing that if one indivisible unit suffers, all the rest suffer with it.

The body is the most wonderful example of widely diversified functions in one indivisible whole that was ever conceived, and it must be treated always as a unit. What is good for one part is good for all; what is bad for one part is bad for all.

If the toe is affected by gangrene, does not the whole body suffer with it? Not only is the pain reflected to the whole man, but the absorption of decaying material has to be taken care of by the whole man; the loss of appetite, the headache, the nausea, the fever, and the chills; yet the toe is the only affected member that can be seen.

In the science of fasting, we are concerned with the whole man . . . the soul, mind and body.

Right Thinking and Health

In the book of Proverbs, the ancient Wise Man tells us, "For as he thinketh in his heart, so is he." (Proverbs 23:7)

When a sick person constantly convinces himself that he will never get well . . . it becomes almost certain that he will carry his troubles to the grave.

FLESH IS DUMB. I never want you to forget that statement. That is the reason I use it over and over again. Your mind is really the controlling factor in your entire makeup.

Flesh cannot think for itself because only the mind does all the thinking. That is why you must cultivate only Positive thinking.

Your mind must rule your body with a will of iron. The mind must always be in command of the body.

From this day on you must learn thought substitution . . . when a negative thought such as "I am losing my sight because when you get older you start to lose sight" enters your mind . . . substitute it for a positive thought that says "Age cannot in any way affect my sight. Age is not toxic."

Keep in mind always that what the mind tells a dumb flesh, that is exactly what the flesh is going to believe and act upon. Mind influences flesh.

Let your mind make all the decisions for your body, because if your body rules your mind, you face a life of misery and slavery.

The "dope fiend" is the extreme example of the body ruling the mind. The body's craving for dope can force the mind to command the body to commit any crime of violence so that it may satisfy the body with the dope that it craves.

The same applies to alcohol, tea, coffee, and any other stimulant. The body does the ruling and not the mind.

We maintain most of our bad habits simply because our minds are enslaved by our bodies.

The body rules by the false philosophy of "Eat, drink and be merry, for tomorrow you die."

This is false. You don't die tomorrow, but you continue to live by this philosophy, and five, ten or twenty years later you are burdened into a sick, weak, premature-aging body that tortures you day and night.

Remember always, you are punished by your bad habits of living. Not for them, but by them. That is the law.

Sickness, aches, pains, and physical suffering are ills that YOU are responsible for personally. YOU committed the crimes against your body because you did not use your God-given reason and intelligence to rule your body with your mind, by living by the natural laws.

What has your psychology to do with Health and long life? Far more than the majority of men and women realize. Think of your thoughts as powers, as magnets, as entities which have the ability to attract or repel, according to the way they are used.

A great majority of people lean either to the positive or the negative side mentally; the former phase is constructive and tends in the direction of achievement, while the negative side of life is destructive, leading to futility and failure. It is self-evident that it is to everyone's advantage to cultivate a positive mental attitude. With patience and persistence this can be accomplished.

There are many negative or destructive forms of thought which react in every cell in your body. The strongest is fear, and its child, worry, along with depression, anxiety, apprehension, jealousy, envy, ill-will, covetousness, anger, rancor, resentment, revengeful-ness, and self-pity. All of these bring tension to the body and mind leading to waste of energy, enervation, and either slow or rapid poisoning of the body; rage, intense fear, and shock are very violent and quickly intoxicate the system; worry and other destructive emotions act more slowly, but, in the end, have the same effect. Anger and intense fear stop digestive action, upsetting also the kidneys and the colon. These are scientifically-demonstrated, physiological truths.

Fear and worry, as well as the other destructive phases of thought, muddle the mind. A crystal-clear mind is needed to reason to the best advantage, thus enabling us to make sound decisions. A beclouded mind must necessarily make inferior decisions, assuming it is able to reach any conclusions at all.

A Healthy Mind in a Healthy Body

What are the positive mental forces or expressions? They are the ones that lead to peace of mind, to inner relaxation, as opposed to the destructive ones which cause tightening-up of the entire system.

This very second, let your mind take over your body.

In your mind, form an image of the person you want to be. Now, with nature's nine doctors as your helpers, you can make yourself exactly what YOU want to be. Believe in the power of positive thinking. Practice thought-substitution . . . never ever let a negative thought take over your mind. In this way, you set your own pattern of living, and you make your mind a powerhouse of constructive thoughts. Strengthen your mind so thoroughly that if any of your weak, fearful, relatives or friends tell you that fasting is starvation, and that something harmful can come out of your health program . . . let your remarks slide out of your mind like water off a duck's back. Feel sorry for these poor, weak, fearful, ignorant people because you will live to see them perish and go to their graves long before their time.

- Each time you fast, you will make your mind stronger, and more positive.

- Each time you fast, you will eliminate fear and worry.

- Fasting helps you to a higher life. That is why the greatest spiritual leaders were ardent fasters.

- Fasting elevates the soul, the mind, and body. What greater rewards can you desire in life?

By fasting, you can create the person you have always longed to be. That is, if you demand only the best life can offer.

Only when the body and mind are in harmony will there be opportunity for proper spiritual development; never forget that the spiritual man is first, the mental, second, and the physical, the third man; and that only when the second and third are in harmony, can there be a proper spiritual life!

Spirituality depends far more on proper harmony of the rest of the man than is generally thought; and we all have it in our power to create this harmony through proper understanding of the relationship of these three entities, and the means necessary to keep them in harmony.

Use your mind to help you attain your desires by developing a constructive philosophy of life.

Think constructively about health, know what the requirements of wholesome living are, employ your mind and will power to live accordingly, and your determination to continue in that way, and health in soul, mind, and body will be yours.

Join hands with nature in making yourself a true living Trinity.

Fasting and a constructive program of Healthful Living can take you to the heights of true living that very few experience on this earth.

Let your mind take control of your body this instant. New doors will open for you. You will be leaving the darkness and living in the light. Darkness is death, light is life, so let in the brightness of the light of a good life, today!

Laws. If we follow them, we will be rewarded with Super Health! Nature demands by strict laws that you keep your body clean inside and there is no better way to keep the body clean inside than by periodic fasting.

Make Mother Nature your personal friend. She is a friend that will never, ever fail you if you will work with her and not against her.

If after reading this book it sounds reasonable and intelligent — follow it. Live by it and let no man keep you away from living by these Natural Laws.

Which Person are You?

There are only two kinds of people in the world. Which kind are you? The real person thinks for himself. The imitation person lets others think for him.

It takes courage to live your own life. Fasting and Living the Health Life takes courage in this sick, poisoned world. Set a high standard of living for yourself. Demand the best health. Let no weakling drag you down to their level. It is the survival of the fittest. Be fit, be strong, live long and vigorously!

Let this book be your guidepost to a Long and Healthy Life. May the knowledge and wisdom in this book bring YOU a New Life; a Life Free From All physical suffering, a Life with Youthful Energy, Peace of Mind, and the Joy of Living.

Spiritual and Mental
Bibliography

I Will Lift Up Mine Eyes, Glenn Clark. Guideposts Associates, Inc. Carmel, New York, 1937.
Jesus Wants You Well, C. S. Lovett. Personal Christianity, Box 549, Baldwin Park, Ca 91706, 1981
Jogging with Jesus, C. S. Lovett. Personal Christianity, Box 549, Baldwin Park, Ca. 91706, 1982
The Miracle of Fasting, Paul C. Bragg and Patricia Bragg. Published by Health Science, Santa Barbara, California, 93102.
Towards Physical Excellence, E. Eugene Greer. 11317 Earlywood Dr. Dallas, Texas 75218.

John Howard receiving the 1981 Ironman Triathlon first place overall award from Valerie Silk, who organized and has guided the Ironman Triathlon to what it is today — The Leader in Triathlons. Valerie Silk has built the Ironman's reputation as a safe, enjoyable, superbly organized triathlon. She is respected in the sports world as a tower of strength for prompting fairness and world-wide triathloning!

II

Nutrition and Physiology in Distance Training

From right to left, Paul Bragg, front row, Patricia Bragg, Percy Cerutty, world renown distance trainer, kneeling lower left, Bob Johnson co-author of this training manual, and guests at "Ceries", The Cerutty Running Training Camp at Portsey, Melbourne, Australia.

Dr. Paul Bragg, Percy Cerutty and Bob Johnson, discuss the pros and cons of "Training The Cerutty Way," at Cerutty's Portsey Runners Training Camp. Percy trained over 30 gold medal winners in various Olympic Games from a population of only 6 million persons, this in itself is a record and a tribute to Percy's ability to instill ability, direction and determination in his students.

1

The Importance of Nutrition in Distance Training

Fresh, Natural Foods Give Power

NUTRITION IS VITALLY IMPORTANT both to optimum athletic performance and day-to-day functioning! You can improve your overall athletic ability by eating sensibly, but good nutrition is no guarantee that any particular training session or race is going to be successful. Although professional nutritionists are not in agreement about a training diet, your best bet is to follow a sensible diet, concentrating on fresh, natural foods, especially grains, legumes, and vegetables, and to avoid processed, refined foods which have little or no nutritional content and contain preservatives and other additives.

Two of us may respond differently to the same regimen, so each of us must discover individually how our own body works and which foods seem to help our performances. As Roger Bannister said, "What applies to one person doesn't necessarily apply to another . . . I think the essence of a good performance is doing it the natural way."

Yet there are a few general principles worth heeding, as they apply to almost everyone, especially in view of recent studies which indicate that dietary deficiencies may be surprisingly common.

Fact!
Shift From Protein to Carbohydrates

Paul C. Bragg pioneered high-protein, meatless, vegetarian cuisine over sixty years ago. He had seven health restaurants way back in the early 20s. They served delicious whole wheat bakery items, whole wheat pasta, etc. . . . to honey-pure cream-fresh fruit ice cream . . . to delicious vegetarian entrees. See back pages for ordering Bragg Hi Protein Vegetarian Cook Book. He was the granddaddy of the health movement, not only to health restaurants but originator of health stores. He pioneered vitamins and minerals and encouraged his health devotees to take them for added health insurance!

Myth!
Athletes Needed Excessive Quantities of Protein

Athletes ate steak, chairmen of the board ate steak, presidents of the United States ate steak, even astronauts ate steak, squeezing it out of toothpaste tubes in outer space. You were certainly doing okay if you were eating steak. The ambition to eat and even to look like a well-marbled piece of USDA Prime beef was masculine, dominant, winning. On the other hand, the ideal female ate chicken, cottage cheese, water-packed tuna fish and liquid Metrecal — and politely refused starch.

Then something changed.

It was not so much that protein lost its status as that starch began to be admitted to the ranks. The beginning of this trend dates back at least 10 years, though the effects are now just beginning to be noticed. Around that time, in 1971, a potential crank named Frances Moore

Lappe published a little nutrition manual with recipes, called *Diet For a Small Planet*, with the curious subtitle, "How to Enjoy a Rich Protein Harvest By Getting Off the Top of the Food Chain."

Efficient Protein

Lappe explained how to put together meals of wheat, rice, corn, potatoes, beans and peas (plant foods usually considered carbohydrates in the meat-dominated scheme of things) to make the most of the protein they contained. In effect she redefined the category of starch by showing that a lot of things called carbohydrates shared the vital and energetic properties of protein. Meat was expensive to produce, she argued. Why feed grain to fatten animals when half the world didn't have enough grain to eat? It was an attack on the privilege of meat-eaters, but couched in the positive philosophy of protein. Lappe wasn't by any means the first apologist for plant food, but to judge by the success of her book (it sold well over two million copies in 24 North American printings), plant food was an idea whose time had come! Cereals and legumes, it seemed, were to be accorded their culinary equal opportunities.

Infinite Variety of Carbohydrates

Ten years later, carbohydrates have made their way to the middle of the plate. Remember when bread came in white and rye? Bread, released from its standard boxy prison, has risen up in all sizes and shapes and cereal hybrids, from the winged croissant to the neat sourdough French baguette to the stoneground seven-grain loaf. Spaghetti now comes in yellow, green, pink and brown, not only in spaghetti squiggles but in waves of fettuccine, linguine, sheets of lasagne, ravioli, cappelletti, tortellini. Cream of Wheat? How about whole wheat, cracked wheat, corn meal, rolled oats, steel cut oats, buckwheat, brown rice, millet, barley and the granola combos? Boston baked beans? You can also have soy beans, bean sprouts, tofu, black beans, kidney beans, pinto beans, split peas, lentils and chick peas. Pilau, risotto, tabouli, kasha, polenta, couscous, Chinese dumplings, you name it. Ten years ago you probably never heard of it.

While the marketplace of carbohydrates was rapidly expanding, the medical academy had also begun to question the carnivorous prejudice of the American diet. Doctors who once might have fussed in the face of a diet that did not feature meat in large identifiable chunks, have now gotten interested in the complex carbohydrates. Medicine began to study the proposition that the American diet was contributing to the high rates of obesity, diabetes, heart disease and cancer. Research began to implicate the fat in meat and dairy products in heart disease. A diet low in complex carbohydrates was linked to cancer.

Science has by no means put its imprimatur on the shift to starch — as a matter of fact, diet is an area of hot controversy. But while medicine weighs the evidence to establish the law on what's healthy, the average American is already making the symbolic shift.

Simple Carbohydrates Gain Popularity

In a recent survey half the population said they thought it was "healthy" to eat more carbohydrates such as pasta and less protein such as red meat. The Pritikin high-carb diet now attracts the glossy trend-setting reducers, while Dr. Tarnower's high-protein Scarsdale plan is looking a little tarnished. Steak has lost some of its grip on the imagination. The mad carnivore now seems a little ridiculous, a beefy plutocrat in the age of the streamlined executive. (Anyway, true imperial gluttony passed away with the majestic appetite of Diamond Jim Brady — who used to dine on two or three dozen oysters, half a dozen crabs, six or seven lobsters, two plates of terrapin, two canvasback ducks and a large sirloin steak, followed by a tray of French pastries and a couple of pounds of chocolates. And that was just one of his six daily meals!) The stodgy carbohydrate is starting to look sleeker, more fit, active and energetic . . . after the image of the new athlete, the life-long fitness expert who combines vigorous physical exercise with a high carbohydrate, moderate protein, health regime.

The Distance Athlete's Go Power

Today nutritionists agree that what you do need more of, particularly before a long distance event, is carbohydrates. The reason lies in the body's way of converting the chemical energy in food into the mechanical energy needed to Swim, Bike, and Run. As important as it is for other purposes, protein doesn't count much for energy production. Studies have shown that diets low in carbohydrates and high in fats produce remarkably less energy; while the opposite diet . . . high carbohydrate/low fats . . . increases available energy. One reason is that about 10% less oxygen is needed to metabolize a given unit of carbohydrate energy. Another is that a high carbohydrate can pack the muscles with more than the customary amount of glycogen. Glycogen, which the body converts into glucose, is oxidized and subsequently converted to energy.

All this doesn't mean that when you are choosing food during training, it is best to lean toward carbohydrates, especially complex carbohydrates, and steer away from fats.

Aside from the process of carbohydrate loading, which will be covered further in this chapter, athletes can eat as much as other people do. You should eat plenty of green and yellow vegetables and fresh fruits in order to metabolize carbohydrates and fats.

The other precaution that athletes need to take is to eat only lightly before a long training session or before competition. What you eat on a certain day won't affect the energy you will have that same day . . . it will only weigh you down and leave you uncomfortable.

The Pre-Event Meal

The menu for the day of competition depends on both the athlete and the time scheduled for that competition. Many experienced long-distance runners eat little or nothing before a marathon race, despite the apparent energy demands that such an event should have on their systems. The facts are, however, that you normally obtain energy from the foods you ate *prior to* the day of the event rather than *on* that day.

In recent years, race directors have become wise to the dangers of the environment, and now schedule many distance races in the early morning during warm-weather months to avoid mid-day and late-afternoon heat. Because the pre-event meal should be eaten at least 4-6 hours before an event to permit the stomach and upper bowel to be empty at the time of competition, few runners rise during the middle of the night to consume pre-race meals.

If the event is scheduled for the afternoon or evening, however, and the athlete feels that pancakes or spaghetti will help performance, these foods can be eaten.

Digestion Rates Vary

Different types of foods leave the stomach at different rates. Fatty foods — such as butter, french fries, steak or cream pie — may delay the stomach's emptying. Carbohydrate foods — such as cereal, fruit, fruit juice or bread — normally empty from the stomach in 3-4 hours. Pre-event nervousness may slow the digestion of many athletes . . . particularly before important events. There is no substitute for experience in planning what to eat before competition.

The energy intake of the pre-event meal should be adequate to prevent hunger throughout the performance. Intake of food or fluid also may be necessary *during* an endurance event to maintain adequate hydration and blood glucose! The best energy source is a solution of glucose in water.

"Teach me Thy way, O Lord; and lead me in a plain path . . ." — *Psalms 97:11*

Loss of Liquid Slows You Down

Athletes also need to be concerned about their intake of liquids. A loss of a quart can slow you down, and a loss of two quarts can do real physical damage! It's important to replace fluids promptly with cool (not ice-cold) liquids. Water is your best bet, but fruit juice or special electrolyte solutions are fine if you prefer them, and they don't upset your stomach while you are exercising.

What about alcohol? Many serious runners enjoy an occasional beer, but few are heavy drinkers. if you want to become really serious about training, you may decide to stay away from alcohol altogether. As for smoking, as little as 15 puffs on a cigarette can cause as much as a 31 percent decrease in the body's ability to handle oxygen. If you are serious about training in order to lower your times, giving up smoking is absolutely essential!

Cigarettes are Killers!

According to John A. Yacinda, who runs a smoking withdrawal clinic for the Ventura County Health Department in California, the question teenagers most often ask about smoking is "How long does it take for cigarettes to harm you?" His answer: "About three seconds." Or less. The fact is that the instant you inhale cigarette smoke, that rich country flavor goes to work — on your heart, your lungs, your whole body! It starts your heart pounding an extra 15 to 25 beats per minute, raises your blood pressure by 10 to 20 points. It corrodes the delicate membranes of your lips and palate. In your lungs, it chokes the airways and rots the air sacs, leaving a residue of cancer-causing chemicals. It deposits these and other dangerous poisons in your stomach, kidneys, bladder. All of this happens with *every* cigarette you smoke; no smoker is immune!

And when you exhale, up to 90 percent of that true tobacco taste stays with you . . . in the form of billions of microscopic particles comprising 1200 chemicals. In this balanced blend of aromas are acids, glycerol, glycol, alcohols, aldehydes, ketones, aliphatic and aromatic hydrocarbons, phenols. None is a health food; many will do you harm.

Cigarette Smoke . . . Insidious Lethal Carbon Monoxide

For years some scientists scoffed that it wasn't possible for one substance — smoke — to attack so many parts of the body in so many ways. Research has proved, however, that tobacco smoke isn't a single substance. At least 50 percent of the country-fresh flavor you inhale is gas . . . 20 different noxious vapors, including acrolein, hydrocyanic acid, nitric oxide, nitrogen dioxide, acetone and ammonia. And now science is zeroing in on one that's even deadlier: colorless, odorless, *lethal carbon monoxide (CO)*.

Present in cigarette smoke in a concentration 640 times the safe level in industrial plants, this insidious poison has 200 times the affinity for your red blood cells that life-giving oxygen does . . . and those cells are designed to carry oxygen throughout your body. Therefore, in a smoker, blood is transporting five to ten times more life-denying CO than is normal. His body is forced to compensate by making more red cells.

Emphysema: the Struggle for Oxygen

Chronic bronchitis and its steady companion, emphysema of which the U.S. Surgeon General says, cigarettes are the most important cause . . . kill over 30,000 Americans a year. There is good reason to believe that 99 percent of heavy cigarette smokers (more than a pack a day) have some emphysema, a disease that destroys the lungs' air sacs. Recently a pathologist studied the lungs of some 1800 deceased men and women and classified them by the amount of emphysema apparent. More than 99 percent of those who had smoked heavily had the disease, and in 19 percent it was far advanced; 90 percent of the non-smokers had no emphysema, and there wasn't a single advanced case among them. Even among coal miners and others exposed to lung-damaging dust, smoking plays a significant part in death from emphysema.

Smoking and Cancer

"Lung cancer is a comparatively merciful death," says one doctor. "With emphysema you start gasping, and you may gasp for 15 years." It creeps up on smokers. We all start with about 100 square yards of interior lung surface. But we almost never need all of this; most of us live on a small part of our lung capacity (about 20 percent of it). The first hint a smoker gets of emphysema is when he finds himself out of breath after a small exertion. He may think this is an early warning; it isn't! It means that most of his lung reserve has been destroyed!

Even when warned, many smokers bravely refuse to give up cigarettes until it is too late. Visit the respiratory ward of your local hospital and you'll see them . . . never more than a few yards from their oxygen tanks and respirators, their entire lives devoted to one thing: breathing!

From Smoking . . . the List of Killers Goes On . . .

The list of smoking-related diseases goes on yet further. Smokers have more gastric ulcers than non-smokers, and take longer to heal; more peridontal disease, which attacks teeth and gums, and more trench mouth; more severe upper respiratory infections. And evidence is beginning to show that cigarette smoke attacks the central nervous system.

The damage is "dose-related." Each cigarette does some harm. Each additional smoke repeats the insult. Eventually these incessant attacks on the body may turn into disease. With about one million puffs, or 100,000 cigarettes . . . a pack a day for 15 years . . . smokers edge into the lung-cancer danger zone.

There's no such thing as a safe level of smoking! But since the harm *is* dose-related, research shows that cutting down on the number of cigarettes, and smoking those with efficient filters and less tar and nicotine, will reduce the risk of serious illness. However, the real payoff comes from quitting.

Name of Play: Nutrition

This is a charming scene including all the processes by which the cells of the body are nourished. There are six acts, each one equally important:

ACT ONE — DIET
You alone (with some few, obvious exceptions) are responsible for your diet. Your diet is what you consume. It consists of food, water, and miscellaneous substances such as booze, cigarettes, drugs and the like, and the involuntary intake of such things as hydrocarbons, lead, etc., in our environment. These substances affect the metabolism of the cell itself and the organism as a whole.

ACT TWO — DIGESTION
Digestion is the process whereby: Protein is broken down into amino acids; Carbohydrates are broken down into simple sugars; Fats are broken down into fatty acids.

Unless the digestive process takes place properly and efficiently, nutrients will pass through the body. Nutrition can be interrupted in this scene and your good health can be impaired. A fast look at all the digestive remedies promoted on radio, TV, and newspapers, will give you some idea of how prevalent this particular inadequacy is. The tools the body utilizes in the digestive process are: Chewing; Hydrochloric Acid; and Enzymes. If any of these are inadequate your play might slow down or even stop right here.

ACT THREE — ABSORPTION

It has been said that absorption is the result of proper glandular activity. The various glands and organs of the body produce and secrete the substances that aid in the absorption of nutrients. The liver produces bile, the stomach secretes hydrochloric acid and pepsin, the pancreas gives us insulin and pancreatin, etc. Absorption is the proper mixing of all the ingredients of our diet with the chemicals our body produces to break them down for entry into the blood stream and eventually into the cell itself.

ACT FOUR — CIRCULATION

It should be obvious that even if we are sure that our diet is proper, our digestion adequate, our absorption mechanism working; we still must be able to transport the vital ingredients to their targets around and about the body. Proper exercise plays a great part in this scenario, it should be vigorous enough to raise the pulse rate to 120 beats per minute. We have found the use of the mini-trampoline to be one of the most effective such exercises, although there are many others such as skipping rope and we just recently viewed a computerized bicycle which was fantastic. Triathletes are the most exercised group among athletes, and should have no worries about circulation.

ACT FIVE — ASSIMILATION

Equally obvious, all the foregoing processes will be for naught if, after all is said and done, the assimilation of the digested and circulated nutrients cannot be taken into the cell when needed. The cell is the basic building block of all living tissues. Surrounding each cell is a membrane about one-half millionth of an inch thick. The membrane is very selective and has the capacity to permit the nutritional elements to enter the cell and waste products of metabolism to exit and be excreted. It also assists in keeping biochemical invaders from getting into the cell. If the cell membrane becomes impermeable, it loses its ability to do these functions and the cell becomes toxic and nonfunctional. Some reasons for this are an imbalance in sodium-potassium ratios, inflammatory processes, etc.

FINAL ACT — ELIMINATION

Many of today's doctors agree that one of the principal causes of human illness is due to auto-intoxication, in which the waste material of the digestive process is not properly eliminated but remains in the lower bowel for excessive periods of time and reabsorption of toxic wastes occurs. The large number of laxatives used by our population is proof enough that elimination function is frequently less than perfect.

And so you have our little play about life. When you play your scene, make sure it is perfect, because every step is equally important.

Vegetarianism and the Triathlete

Many leading triathletes and top competitors in Swim, Bike and Run are indicating a growing preference for the Lactovegetarian diet. This diet includes fish, poultry, eggs and dairy products, but no red meat.

Vegetarian diets are fine for athletes, and are much more likely to be more nutritious than diets based on meat. Vegetarians claim that their way of eating gives them more energy . . . citing the cases of Murray Rose, who won two Olympic swimming medals in 1956; of the distinguished Australian runners, Herb Elliott and John Landy; and of swimmer, Johnny Weismuller, who set six world swimming records after becoming a vegetarian. Jack LaLanne eats no red meat and has super energy for his daily physical workouts.

Plant Protein Sufficient

Meat itself, say vegetarians and others, isn't good for you anyway. It is high in fats and contributes to heart disease and — in animals at any rate — to cancer. It is a breeding ground for bacteria, and isn't digested as easily as plant foods. Furthermore, the popular aged meat is really partly putrified. A well-balanced, varied vegetarian diet is much better for your body, and when planned correctly, will provide you with all the nutrients and calories you will need to maintain your training schedule. Many people think that without meat, they won't get enough protein, but plants provide protein. Cereals are 10% protein, common varieties of beans are 25%, and soybeans are 40%. Raw, unsalted nuts and seeds are also a protein source.

You Must Have All the Amino Acids

When planning a vegetarian diet, be sure that you get all of the amino acids. It's the amino acids which become the protein of your body. Eggs and dairy products are complete proteins, which means they contain all the essential amino acids in the correct proportions.

All but eight of the known amino acids can be synthesized by your body from other sources. They are, therefore, not called essential. The eight which you must include in your diet because the body cannot make them, are: leucine, methionine, phenylanine, valine, lysine, isoleucine, threonine and trytophan.

The three great building blocks of protein are lysine, methionine and cystine. The soy bean is the most perfect of all the vegetarian foods and should be eaten several times a week. Bragg Liquid Aminos (from soy beans) is a delicious way of getting more amino acids into your daily diet — just add a few dashes for more zest to casseroles, soups, rice, beans, salad dressings . . . even to pop corn, etc. Bragg Aminos are reasonably priced, available in 16 oz. and 32 oz. at all fine health stores. This has been a favorite with thousands for over fifty years.

Vegetarian Foods that are Rich in Amino Acids

When avocados, seeds and nuts are eaten with raw, green leafy vegetables, they provide a complete amino acid pattern that is well-utilized by the body. Raw and roasted peanuts are a wonderful source of vegetable amino acids. A sandwich made of 100% whole wheat (toast all bread), with natural, unhydrogenated peanut butter (contains no salt, sugar or preservatives) from the health food store, lettuce, tomato, sunflower seeds and sliced raw mushrooms supplies practically all of your amino acids.

BARLEY AND GROATS: Millet is a good high protein cereal which every vegetarian should include in his diet. So are buckwheat groats, whole unpearled barley, natural whole grain brown rice, natural corn meal, and soy beans, which come closest of all the plant foods to being a complete protein.

B-12 Supplement Essential in Vegetarian Diet

The major deficiency which must be guarded against in a vegetarian diet is Vitamin B-12, an essential in the B-complex and considered crucial in preventing anemia. As previously stated, there is no known practical plant source that supplies an adequate amount of Vitamin B-12. Kelp, as noted, is the best plant source, Comfrey leaves have a small amount of B-12. Yeast, wheat germ and soy beans also have traces.

Eggs and milk products contain some Vitamin B-12. But none of the components of a vegetarian diet contain enough.

Let me warn you that folic acid (another member of the B-complex vitamins), which is

Health is not quoted in the markets because it is without price.

plentiful in green vegetables, can make the blood analysis often appear normal — and thus prevent the detection of a Vitamin B-12 deficiency before nerve damage occurs.

To be nutritionally safe, it would certainly be wise for everyone on a vegetarian diet, and especially vegans, to include a daily B supplement that is rich in B-12 — and thus avoid the possibility of a nervous condition which may not show its symptoms for 10 years. B-12 is made from molds, not synthetic and not of animal origin.

Carbohydrate Loading the Sensible Way

The question of carbohydrate loading is one that concerns most serious athletes who participate in long-distance events. There is no question that for most people, endurance can be increased and times decreased by following some variation of this regime.

A long, hard, depleting run on the first day, followed by three days of high-protein, high-fat consumption is observed while in regular training, during which time, theoretically, the body's glycogen reserves are totally depleted. For the next three days, the diet consists of high-carbohydrates, low-protein, low-fat meals, though in regular-sized portions. The term "loading" can be mistakenly interpreted as meaning "gorging," which you definitely don't want to do! The idea is to accumulate a huge supply of accessible fuel (glycogen stores in the muscles) on the day of the race, the seventh day of the planned regime.

Most athletes have experimented with this plan or some variation. Many skip the depletion phase, but increase the ratio of carbohydrates that they consume during the three days prior to competition because the depletion phase makes them feel so sluggish and toxic . . . that they are unable to continue training or their mental confidence is shaken. We recommend that you experiment, find out what seems to work best for your body, although you shouldn't be doing this every week of the year. Use loading only for the most important or longest races of the year, trying to limit it to a total of three "loads" annually.

The secondary, and probably one of the most valuable side effects of carbohydrate loading is the accumulation of water in the muscle cells. This takes place when, for every gram of glycogen stored in the muscle tissue, each cell takes with it from 3 to 4 grams of water. This factor accounts for the excessive increase in body weight. During the 1980-81 Ironman World Triathlon in Kona, pre-carbo loading weights were taken. On the last day of the loading process a Triathlete of 160 lbs will have taken on over 6 lbs. of extra weight, mostly water. This is the liquid that carries the athlete through the first portion of the event . . . as it is utilized first.

An Improved Way to Load Carbohydrates

One of the biggest mistakes made with loading is during the carbohydrate phase . . . many athletes turn to refined flour, commercial pasta, white bread, and sugary desserts to add carbohydrates to their diet. This is not necessary, and can undo the foundation of good nutrition that your whole training schedule has been based upon and that your body has come to expect. Instead, concentrate on vegetables with a high carbohydrate content . . . they are the ones we think of as being "starchy" . . . corn, peas, lima beans, garbanzo beans, kidney beans, potatoes; legumes — dried peas and beans such as green peas, lentils, and pinto beans; and grains such as buckwheat, barley, and brown rice. These foods will offer the same high-carbohydrate content as some of the "junkier" foods, without poisoning your body with additives, preservatives, and sugars which, though providing a quick burst of energy, are always followed by a corresponding low, draggy feeling which will impede training or racing as well as being psychologically damaging!

The following are sample menus for the two phases of carbohydrate loading. You may of course modify them to fit your preferences, but they should give you an idea of the variety of healthful foods available to you for this purpose.

Healthful Cooking and Eating

The Bragg family for four generations has lived a life of health through the utilization of "Live Foods"... that is, foods that are still alive and with proper preparation could live again through sprouting or planting. These foods are the only healthful alternative to dead foods: foods that never lived. Foods that would not reproduce themselves due to the fact that the essential germ of life or garden freshness are gone forever. This damage to these devitalized foods came about through the excessive processing with heat, chemicals, preservatives, flavor enhancers, aging, exposure to air, canning, freezing, and removes the vital nutrients and vitamins that are lacking in our diets today. The Bragg Health Food Cook Book, 448 pages packed with methods of preparing food the health way is a must for Triathletes... also the Hi Protein Vegetarian Cookbook with delicious, healthful carbohydrate recipes (see order blank in the last pages).

DAILY FOOD PLANS

	Phase I (Days 6-4 before event)	Phase II (Days 3-1 before event)
Meat, fish, poultry eggs, cheese*	12-18 oz. or exchanges Calories: 900-1350	6-8 oz. or exchanges Calories: 450-600
Breads and cereals**	4 servings or exchanges Calories: 280	8-16 servings or exchanges Calories: 560-1120
Vegetables**	2 servings or exchanges Calories: 50	4 servings or exchanges Calories: 100
Fruits and juices**	2 servings or exchanges Calories: 80	4 servings or exchanges Calories: 160
Fats and oils*	4-12 tbsp. or 12-36 exchanges Calories: 540-1620	2-4 tbsp. or 6-12 exchanges Calories: 270-540
Milk***	2 servings or exchanges Calories: 160 (whole milk)	2 servings or exchanges Calories: 160 (whole milk)
Desserts**	1-2 servings, unsweetened Calories: 400	2 servings, sweetened Calories: 800
Beverages	unsweetened*** unlimited Calories: 0	sweetened Calories: 0-360
Water	8 or more servings Calories: 0 Total Calories: 2410-3940	8 or more servings Calories: 0 Total Calories: 2500-3840

*Fat and protein sources
**carbohydrate sources
***avoid artificially sweetened beverages

They who provide the food for the world, decide the health of the world. You have only to go on some errand amid the taverns and the hotels of the United States and Great Britain, to appreciate the fact that a vast multitude of the human race are slaughtered by incompetent cookery. Though a young woman may have taken lessons in music, and may have taken lessons in painting, and lessons in astronomy, she is not well educated unless she has taken lessons in preparing healthy meals. For women can either prepare health or sickness with their two hands. Proper nutritional planning is a must for the family. The right fuel (food) produces good performance.

SAMPLE MENUS

DEPLETION PHASE

Breakfast	Lunch	Dinner
1. 2 eggs fruit or juice ½ slice toast, butter	1. vegetable soup 4 small crackers cooked green vegetable	1. whole wheat pasta with cheese and butter salad with dressing
2. fruit yogurt ½ bran muffin, butter	2. green salad with cheese or tuna, salad dressing fresh fruit	2. ½ avocado stuffed with shrimp or crab green beans, milk
3. mixed nuts, raw, unsalted sliced tomatoes & cucumbers, cottage cheese	3. peanut butter open-face sandwich with honey, raw vegetables with dip	3. broccoli/tofu casserole with cheese fruit juice mixed nuts, raw, unsalted

Snacks: raw vegetables with yogurt dip; mixed nuts raw-unsalted or sunflower or pumpkin seeds; cottage cheese with fruit

LOADING PHASE

Breakfast	Lunch	Dinner
1. Buckwheat pancakes honey or maple syrup butter, fresh fruit	1. Sandwich-cheese & vegetables whole grain bread, toasted corn, milk or juice	1. Whole wheat pasta with tomato and zucchini sauce baked potato with butter whole wheat fig bars
2. Hot whole grain cereal milk, butter, honey fruit juice, bran muffin	2. Split pea soup fresh whole grain toast, butter tossed salad with dressing	2. Lentil & brown rice casserole corn and lima beans fruit yogurt
3. eggs scrambled with potatoes and mushrooms tomato juice whole grain toast	3. peanut butter and honey on whole wheat bread, toasted banana, juice or milk	3. bean tostada on whole wheat flour or corn tortilla topping: onion, celery, lettuce tomato, cheese, avocado, olives fresh fruit

Snacks: bran muffins; unsalted popcorn*; fresh fruit

INCREASE FLUIDS WHEN CARBOHYDRATE LOADING

Another precaution you should take when carbohydrate loading is to increase your intake of liquids during the "loading" phase...water, fruit juice, herb tea.

This is because the increased glycogen supply being stored in the muscles causes fluids to accumulate in the muscles, and you must keep the other tissues of your body in relative balance with that fluid build-up.

TRAINING RECIPES

The following is a collection of recipes you may find helpful in protein depletion and carbohydrate loading, for alternate foods refer to the **Carbohydrate Calorie and Protein Chart** in the end of the chapter. These recipes can also improve the level of nutrition that you give your body.

BUCKWHEAT RECIPES

Very few people know that buckwheat is an excellent source of high quality protein and that it tastes good. In the hands of a good cook, it can be a delicious and nutritious food. Buckwheat is an inexpensive and nutritious main or side dish. It is very low in calories for a food with starch content. Buckwheat has fewer calories than wheat, barley, rye or brown rice. Buckwheat is a superior source of protein and is high in manganese, iron, magnesium, thiamine, and riboflavin. It has almost all the food values of a thick, juicy beef steak and can appreciably lower anyone's food budget.

"To preserve health is a moral and religious duty, for health is the basis for all social virtues. We can no longer be useful when not well." —Dr. Samuel Johnson, Father of Dictionaries

EUROPEAN BUCKWHEAT (GROATS) RECIPE

In an iron pot or heavy stainless steel pan place one cup of groats. Add three cups of water, three tablespoons of oil, and two beaten whole eggs. Cover lid and let cook for 30 minutes over a medium flame, or until the mixture is thoroughly absorbed in the groats.

This is a standard recipe used in Romania, Bulgaria, Czechoslovakia, Russia, Yugoslavia and Poland.

BRAGG BUCKWHEAT PANCAKES

¾ c buckwheat flour
¾ c raw wheat germ
¼ c wholewheat flour
3 tbsp honey
¾ tsp double acting baking powder
2 eggs, lightly beaten
3 tbsp cold pressed oil such as soy, peanut, corn or safflour
Water or milk, preferably certified raw milk

In a bowl mix the buckwheat flour, raw wheat germ, whole wheat flour, honey and baking powder. Stir in the eggs, oil and enough milk or water to make a batter the consistency of thick, heavy cream. Ladle the mixture onto a hot, oiled griddle. when holes appear on the surface of the pancakes, turn to brown second side. Makes about 8 large pancakes.

BUCKWHEAT GROATS OR KASHA WITH MUSHROOMS

1 c buckwheat groats (often referred to as kasha)
2 raw eggs, beaten
1 c mushrooms, sliced
2 tbsp oil (cold pressed)
2 c water
1 or more cloves garlic (use garlic press)
1 tsp Bragg Aminos

Beat the eggs well and add the groats. Mix thoroughly to coat the grains. Brown mixture gently in oil (use a heavy skillet). Add the sliced mushrooms. Bring water to a boil and add the mixture together with the Bragg Aminos. Mix well and cook very slowly, covered, until all the liquid is absorbed and the kasha is light and fluffy.

―――――――――

TIME

I have just a little minute,
Only sixty seconds in it,
Just a tiny little minute,
Give account if I abuse it;
Forced upon me; can't refuse it.
Didn't seek it, didn't choose it,
But it's up to me to use it.
I must suffer if I lose it;
But eternity is in it.—Unknown

SOYBEAN RECIPES

SOYBEANS

The soybean is one of the richest of all foods in protein and in minerals, and it also makes a delightful addition to good meals. It has an ancient heritage, having been used for thousands of years by the people of the Orient, but only in recent years have Americans and Europeans become awakened to its possibilities as a meat substitute and also to its great value as a food staple.

HOW TO MAKE SOYBEAN SPROUTS

Bean sprouts can be obtained either from soybeans, mung beans, and other listed beans, and are equally delicious and nutritious. The sprouts can easily be made at home, and their preparation is not difficult.

It is very important to have the finest-quality bean for sprouting. These beans can usually be found at your health food store. They should not be over a year old.

Learn to sprout seeds, beans and grains to reap more protein, vitamins, minerals, amino acids and live enzymes compared to their dry state.

My favorite Sprouts are: Alfalfa Seeds, Soybeans, *Brown Lentils, *Aduki Beans, *Blue Peas, *Mung Beans, Navy Beans, Sunflower Seeds...also experiment with others to see what you enjoy!!! The * ones are a perfect combination that provides a complete protein that contains all the essential Amino Acids and is not only nutritious, but delicious added to salads, sandwiches, and garnish over casseroles, potatoes, vegies, etc. Mix equal amounts (dry) in a jar and then when you want to sprout some they are ready...sprout small amounts in jar - no lid - takes 2-3 days, rinse twice daily, when sweet, tender, ½ sprouted, refrigerate and enjoy as needed!!!

GREEN SOYBEANS

Allow soybean pods to stand 10 minutes in boiling water. Drain and shell beans.

For each cup of the shelled beans, and ½ cup of boiling water. Bring to a boil and cook until beans are tender (10 to 15 minutes). Drain and season in any manner desired.

HERBS TO SAVOR SOYBEANS

Anise	Oregano
Basil	Paprika
Bay	Parsley
Celery Seed	Poppyseed
Chervil	Rosemary
Chives	Sage
Dill Weed	Savory
Garlic	Sesame Seed
Marjoram	Tarragon
Mint	Thyme

Italian Herb Seasons

HOW TO COOK DRIED SOYBEANS

2 c (1 pound) dried soybeans, green or yellow
1 tbsp Bragg Aminos.

Wash beans well and place in a bowl with water to cover. Soak for 24 hours. As the beans expand up to three times their bulk on soaking, make sure that the bowl is large enough and the water level is 2 or 3 inches above the beans.

To cook the beans, place in a heavy kettle with soaking water and extra water, if necessary, to almost cover. Add Bragg Aminos, bring to boil and simmer over low heat 3 or 4 hours or until tender.

Soybeans will not cook into a soft mushy mass. They will remain firmer and hold their shape better than the ordinary dry beans.

SOYBEAN AND VEGETABLE STEW

4 potatoes, sliced	4 large tomatoes, sliced
2 large onions, sliced	1 tbsp Bragg Aminos
2 celery stalks, diced	½ tsp Italian herbs dash of cayenne
1 green pepper, sliced	2½ c soybeans, cooked
4 tbsp soy oil	

Place soy oil in heavy skillet then add potatoes (skins too), onions, celery, green pepper. Sprinkle Bragg Aminos and cayenne over vegetables then add beans and tomatoes. Cover and cook very slowly about an hour or until done, adding liquid from soybeans or water if needed.

The Natural Substitute for Soy Sauce, Bragg Liquid Aminos
ADDS DELICIOUS FLAVOR TO MANY OF YOUR RECIPES!

For extra hi-protein flavoring and zest to your meals Bragg Liquid Aminos is delicious to enhance the natural flavors.

All vegetable source — with natural flavoring, contains no preservatives. It has a meat-like, savory flavor, yet contains no meat or meat products.

WHAT ARE AMINO ACIDS? They are the link between the protein you eat and your body tissue. They are carried by your bloodstream to every part of your body where they set to work repairing, building and maintaining all the important body tissues.

Be sure your high protein food is a quality one by checking these points:

- It must be completely natural.
- It must list the number of Amino Acids on the label.
- It must taste delicious for added zest to the diet.
- It must be made under strict standards to preserve its natural amino acids.

Bragg Liquid Aminos meets all these high standards and is an outstanding addition to many of these meatless recipes for it gives you extra nutrients and delicious flavoring. Available at all fine health food stores.

Bragg Liquid Aminos has a way of making these foods taste just a little better: vegetables, brown rice, beans of all kinds, vegetable burgers, soups, casseroles, gravies and sauces, salad dressings.

Bragg Liquid Aminos contains the following Amino Acids, the building blocks of the body:

Lysine*	Serine	Valine*
Histidine	Glutamic Acid	Methionine*
Arginine	Proline	Isoleucine*
Tryptophan*	Glycine	Leucine*
Aspartic Acid	Alanine	Tyrosine
Threonine*	Cystine	Phenylalnine*

*Essential Amino Acids in naturally associated amounts as derived from a specially formulated liquid-form of vegetable protein from Soy Beans.

Our mental make-up is suited to a life of very severe physical labor. I used, when I was younger, to take my holidays walking. I would cover 25 miles a day, and when the evening came I had no need of anything to keep me from boredom, since the delight of sitting amply sufficed. . . .

When crowds assemble in Trafalgar Square to cheer to the echo of an announcement that the government has decided to have them killed, they would not do so if they had all walked 25 miles that day.
—Bertrand Russell, Nobel Prize Acceptance Speech

"Living under conditions of modern life, it is important to bear in mind that the preparation and refinement of food products either entirely eliminates or in part destroys the vital elements in the original material."
—U.S. Dept. of Agriculture

The Doctor of the future will give no medicine but will interest his patients in the care of the human frame in diet and in the cause and prevention of disease. —Thomas A. Edison

VEGETARIAN CHILI NO CARNE

½ c minced parsley	1 c chopped tomatoes
1 c diced celery	
½ c cold-pressed oil	1 c diced onions
1 can tomato sauce	2 c cooked basic kidney beans (see next recipe)
2 garlic cloves, diced	
½ tsp chili powder	1 tsp Bragg Aminos

Saute the onion, and garlic in oil until golden brown. Combine in large saucepan with the beans and remaining ingredients and cook for 10 minutes. Serve with 1 c grated cheddar or Jack cheese.

PINTO BEANS

Soak 1 c pinto beans overnight. Next morning add enough water to make 1-inch above the beans. Add to beans:

1-3 cloves garlic	1 tbsp Vegetable Broth Powder
1 onion, chopped	
1 tsp chili powder	1 bayleaf

1 tbsp Bragg Aminos

Bring the beans to a rolling boil, add seasonings, garlic and onion, and cook for 2 hours or until beans are tender. Then mash the beans and add ¼ pound of natural Jack cheese, grated. Stir well and slowly saute in vegetable oil.

Serve the beans with the enchiladas and the salad. This makes a perfect Mexican meal, topped off with sliced pineapple, either fresh or canned, unsweetened.

ENCHILADAS

First you make an enchilada sauce. It is very simple to prepare:

3 tbsp chili powder	3 tbsp cold-pressed soy, safflower or corn oil
2 c water	
1 small can tomato sauce	
1 tsp Bragg Aminos	1 tbsp yellor or white cornmeal

Brown cornmeal slightly in oil. Add the rest of the ingredients and cook for 10 minutes, stirring constantly to avoid lumps (this is enough sauce for 12 cheese enchiladas).

When sauce is done, dip the tortilla in the sauce, then remove it and place on a plate. Continue until all tortillas have been dipped.

Chop very finely 1 cup onions, either green or dry. Grate 2 cups natural cheddar cheese. Remove the tortillas from the plate (one at a time) and spread on the chopped onions and grated cheese. Roll the tortilla and place in baking dish.

Pour the remainder of the sauce over the enchiladas in the baking dish and sprinkle with more grated cheddar cheese. Place baking dish in 300° oven until cheese has melted.

(In Mexican restaurants enchiladas are served with a tossed green salad and refried pinto beans.)

VEGETABLE BARLEY SOUP

1 c chopped onions	1 c diced carrots	2 tomatoes
1 c chopped celery	½ c unpearled barley that's been soaked one hour	1 tbsp Bragg Aminos
1 c minced fresh parsley		2 qts water
1 c sliced mushrooms	2 c diced yellow squash	½ tsp Italian Herb Seasonings
	2 c cauliflower florets	

In a large soup kettle saute onions, celery and garlic in oil for 3 minutes. Add mushrooms and continue to saute. Add water, barley and other ingredients. Cook for 45 minutes or until done. Serve in soup bowls and garnish with sunflower and sesame seed meal. This garnish adds deliciousness and also fortifies the soup with protein.

MUSHROOM SOYBEAN PATTIES

1 c chopped mushrooms
1½ c cooked soybeans
2 eggs, lightly beaten
½ c finely chopped onions
½ c non-fat dry milk solids
½ c raw wheat germ
¼ c cottage cheese
1 tbsp Bragg Aminos
⅛ tsp dry mustard
½ c sesame seeds

Mash soybeans to a fine pulp in a mixing bowl. Add all other ingredients and mix well. If mixture is too dry, add small amounts of hot water until it can be shpaed into patties. Before sauteeing, dry for 15 minutes; then saute patties until both sides are brown.

HI-PROTEIN MUSHROOM STUFFING FOR BAKED POTATO

Makes 4 stuffed halves

½ c finely chopped sauteed mush-rooms
⅓ c natural cheddar
½ c finely chopped green onions with stems
1 tbsp oil or unsalted butter per potato
½ tsp kelp seasoning
½ tsp Bragg Aminos

Bake large Russet potato or potatoes. (Scrub thoroughly so that skins can be eaten as many important nutrients, and particularly protein, are contained in the skins of potatoes.)

When baked, cut in half, with a spoon scoop out the inside, leaving ¼ of the potato against the skin. In a mixing bowl mash thoroughly the potato, or potatoes, and add the remainder of the ingredients, allowing 1 tbsp. of cold-pressed oil or 1 tbsp. unsalted butter for each potato. Replace this mixture in the potato shells, sprinkle with paprika and bake 10 minutes or until cheese has melted.

TOFU RECIPES

SOY BEAN CURD
Rich in Vegetable Protein

Tofu goes with everything. It has a neutral flavor, is very porous and absorbs the flavor of any food with which it is combined. Therefore, it can be mixed in with any casserole. For instance, if you are steaming broccoli, when almost done add 1 c. tofu cut into ½″ squares.

Tofu can be cooked with string beans, tomatoes, peas, carrots, celery; in fact, any vegetable. The tofu will fortify the cooked vegetable. Remember, soybeans pack into their little round shells the most and the highest quality of protein of just about any vegetable food. Nutrition-wise, soybeans are the greatest.

Learn the art of blending tofu with cooked vegetables, brown rice, seeds and nuts to make non-meat foods nutritionally and taste-wise as good as meat. Beans, natural brown rice, and tofu are a great protein combination. As a good guide to food combinations for high quality protein, blend in one meal as many vegetarian proteins as you can. For instance, to your casseroles, cooked vegetables and scrambled eggs you could add sunflower seeds.

TOFU CHEESCAKE

Prepare a 9-inch Graham Cracker crust

2 lb drained tofu
3 tbsp Lemmon
   Juice
1 tsp Vanilla
⅓ c cold-pressed oil

½ c Honey
½ c Turbano or
   Brown Sugar
   Soy milk or water
   as required

Combine all ingredients in blender, mixture should be thick and creamy consistency. Pour into partially baked crumb crust, bake about ½ hour at 350° or until Tofu is set in the middle.

TOFU CASSEROLE SUPREME

1-2c tofu cut in 1″
   squares
1 c peeled fresh
   tomatoes
1 c chopped green
   pepper
1 c sliced celery
¼ c cold-pressed oil
   or
1 tbsp unsalted
   butter

1 c zucchini or
   crook neck
   squash
1 c chopped onion
1 tbsp Bragg
   Aminos
½ c chopped parsley
2 cloves chopped
   garlic (optional)

Combine ingredients. Place casserole and bake 45 minutes or until almost done, in 375° oven. Then add 1 or 2 c. tofu and gently stir with wooden spoon, not breaking tofu squares, and bake 10 minutes longer. Serve with grated parmesan cheese.

TOFU AND SCRAMBLED EGGS

3 eggs
½ c sliced onions
   (dry or green)
2 cloves garlic
   (optional)
½ c chopped parsley

1-2c tofu cut in ½″
   squares
1 tsp Bragg
   Aminos
⅓ c parmesan
   cheese

In heavy skillet place 3 tbsp. cold-pressed oil or 1 tbsp. unsalted butter. Saute garlic and onions until onions become transparent. Add 3 well beaten eggs into which you have gently stirred the tofu, parsley and Bragg Aminos. Gently cook on one side, then turn with spatula to cook on the other until both sides are a golden brown. Sprinkle on parmesan cheese when served.

A physician recommended a lady to abandon the use of tea and coffee. "O, but I shall miss it so," said she. "Very likely," replied her medical adviser, "but you are missing health now, and will lose it altogether if you do not."

RECIPES FOR LEGUMES

LENTIL-RICE SURPRISE

1 c dried lentils
¼ c water
1 onion, chopped
1 clove garlic,
   pressed
3 celery stalks,
   chopped

1 lg. can tomatoes
   (28 oz.)
1 tsp dill weed
3 c cooked brown
   rice
1 c whole wheat
   bread crumbs

1 tbsp Bragg Aminos

Cover lentils with water, bring to a boil, cover and simmer over low heat about 1-1½ hours until tender. Drain off liquid—reserve ½ cup liquid.

Heat ¼ cup water in a large pot, add onion, garlic and celery. Cook over medium-low heat until tender, about 15 minutes. Add tomatoes, drained lentils, ½ cup lentil water, cooked rice and dill weed. Mix well.

Lightly oil a 3 quart casserole, sprinkle a few bread crumbs over the bottom. Pour lentil-rice mixture into casserole. Sprinkle the rest of the bread crumbs over the top. Bake at 350° for 45 minutes.

This dish may be made ahead of time and refrigerated until ready to put in oven. Add 15 min. to baking time. Serves 6.

MILLET STEW

1 c millet
8 c water
2 onions, cut in
   wedges
2 potatoes, large
   chunks
2 carrots, large
   slices

1 c celery, large
   slices
½ lb. mushrooms,
   chopped
2 bay leaves
½ tsp basil
½ tsp thyme
1 tbsp Bragg Aminos

Place large pot over medium heat. Add millet, stir constantly to toast for about 5 minutes. Add 8 cups water to the pot, all the chopped vegetables and seasonings. Cover and simmer for 1 hour. Stir occasionally while cooking.

Other grains may also be used; try barley, bulgar, brown rice.

Variation: use 2-4 cups more water to make a delicious grain soup.

CURRIED PEA SOUP

1 onion, grated
½ tsp celery seed
½ tsp curry powder
2 c cooked brown
   rice

2 c dried split peas
10 c water
1 carrot, grated
2 potatoes, grated
1 tsp Bragg Aminos

Place split peas in a large soup pot with 10 cups water. Bring to a boil, cover and cook over low heat about 1 hour. Meanwhile, grate the vegetables.

After peas have cooked about 1 hour, add the grated vegetables, the celery seed and curry powder. Cover and cook for 30 minutes. Add the cooked rice. Cook about 30 minutes more before serving. Serves 6.

Accuse not nature, she hath done her part; do thou but thine. —Milton, *Paradise Lost*

BEAN RECIPES

Sort through beans and rinse well. Presoak beans overnight or cover beans with water, bring to a boil, remove from heat, cover and let rest for one hour. Bring to a boil, lower the heat, cover, and let simmer until tender. Add more water if necessary.

Beans (1 cup)	Water	Time	Yield
Lentils & split peas*	3 cups	1 hr.	2 cups
Pinto beans	3 cups	2½ hrs.	2 cups
Red beans	3 cups	3 hrs.	2 cups
White beans	3 cups	1½-2 hrs.	2 cups
Garbanzos	4 cups	3 hrs.	2 cups
Black-eyed peas	3 cups	1 hr.	2 cups
Black beans	4 cups	1½ hrs.	2 cups

*pre-soaking not needed

Turn a bean soup into a stew—add chunks of vegetables during last 30 minutes of cooking.

Use lemon juice for seasoning. Try dill, celery seed and bay leaf or chopped onions and green pepper, chili powder, cumin and garlic. Add ½ tsp Bragg Aminos.

MORE ASSORTED RECIPES

BAKED EGGPLANT CASSEROLE

1 large green pepper, sliced in rings
1 jar pimiento, chopped
4 c tomato sauce
1 tsp basil
½ tsp oregano
2 medium or 3 smallish round eggplants
½ c cornmeal
¼ tsp garlic powder
1 large onion, sliced in rings
1 tsp Bragg Aminos

Slice eggplant ½ inch thick. Mix cornmeal and garlic powder and dip the eggplant slices in this mixture until both sides are well coated. Place breaded slices on a dry baking sheet. Bake at 400° for 30 minutes. Meanwhile prepare onion, pepper and pimiento. Combine the tomato sauce, basil and oregano. Arrange baked eggplant slices in the bottom of a 9 x 12 baking dish. Lay the onion and pepper rings on top of the eggplant, scatter the chopped pimiento over all this. Pour the tomato sauce mixture over the vegetables. Bake, uncovered, in a 375° oven for 45 minutes.

May also be made in a smaller casserole dish—make it in 2 layers: eggplant, onions, peppers, sauce—then repeat again. Serves 6.

An intellectual feast — Professor Louis Agassiz in his early manhood visited Germany to consult Oken, the transcendentalist in zoological classification. "After I had delivered to him my letter of introduction," he once said to a friend, "Oken asked me to dine with him, and you may suppose with what joy I accepted the invitation. The dinner consisted only of potatoes, boiled and roasted; but it was the best dinner I ever ate; for there was Oken. Never before were such potatoes grown on this planet; for the mind of the man seemed to enter into what we ate sociably together, and I devoured his intellect while munching his potatoes."

STUFFED PEPPERS

8 large green peppers, stemmed and cored	2 c tomato sauce (1 c for topping)
1 onion, diced	3 c cooked brown rice
½ c celery, chopped	¼ tsp thyme
½ lb mushrooms, chopped	¼ tsp sage
¼ c water	¼ tsp basil
	¼ tsp garlic powder
1 tsp Bragg Aminos	

Cook onions, celery and mushrooms in the water for about 15 mintues, until tender. Mix in 1 cup of tomato sauce, the rice and the seasonings. Pack the mixture into raw green peppers that have been stemmed and cored. Place in baking dish. Pour the remaining 1 cup of tomato sauce over the peppers, a little on each. Add about 1½ cups of water to the bottom of the baking dish to prevent peppers from drying out. Cover and bake at 375° for 45 minutes, uncover and bake for 15 minutes longer.

May be prepared ahead of time. Keep in refrigerator until ready to bake. Add 15 minutes to baking.

Variation: use 1 cup of corn, fresh or frozen, in place of 1 cup of rice. Serves 8.

GRAIN PILAF

¼ c water	2 c whole grain (bulgar, buckwheat, millet)
2 onions, chopped	1 tsp cumin
2 carrots, chopped	4 c water
1 green pepper, chopped	½ tsp coriander
½ lb mushrooms, chopped	1 tbsp parsley flakes
1 bunch green onions, chopped	1 tsp Bragg Aminos
	¼ tsp garlic powder

Place the water in a large pot. Add the chopped vegetables and saute for 15 minutes. Add the grain to the pot. Stir and cook for 5 minutes longer. Add the water, spices and Aminos. Bring to boil. Reduce heat to low, cover, and cook 15 mintues. Place the mixture in a casserole dish. Bake, covered, at 300° for 45 minutes.

May be prepared ahead—up to final baking time.
Serves 8.

HOW TO STEAM VEGETABLES

1. steamer basket—collapsible, opens to fit any size pot
2. vegetables—these are especially good ones for steaming: broccoli, cauliflower, snow peas, zucchini, carrots, brussels sprouts, potatoes, green beans and eggplant

Add about 1-2 inches of water to your saucepan. Place the steamer basket in the pan. Bring the water to a boil. Add the vegetables to the basket. Cover pan and reduce heat to medium-low. Cook until tender, usually 10 minutes or less.

Many people go throughout life committing partial suicide—destroying their health, youth, beauty, talents, energies, creative qualities. Indeed, to learn how to be good to oneself is often more difficult than to learn how to be good to others. —Patricia Bragg

HUMUS GARBANZO PUREE

¼ tsp garlic powder
1 tsp onion powder
½ tsp ground cumin
1 tbsp parsley flakes
3 c cooked garbanzo beans
1 tbsp lemon juice
¼ tsp basil
1 tsp Bragg Aminos

Puree the beans and mix all the ingredients together. May be done in a blender. Also some water or bean cooking liquid may be added to make it a creamy consistency.

Helpful Hints: Let stand an hour at room temperature to blend flavors. Use as sandwich spread. Use to fill "pocket bread" (pita). Use as a dip for crackers, pita or corn chips.

MASHED POTATOES

4 medium potatoes, cut into large chunks
2 medium onion, chopped
1 tsp Bragg Aminos
2 cloves garlic, crushed
2 tbsp parsley flakes
⅛ tsp basil
⅛ tsp thyme

Place potatoes, onions, garlic and spices in a large saucepan. Add water to cover. Bring to a boil. Cover and cook over medium heat until done, about 30 minutes. Drain and reserve the cooking liquid. Add one cup hot cooking liquid back to the pot. Beat with electric mixer until smooth.

Serve with gravy or sauce. Also good plain. Use to top the Peasant's Pie for a change in flavor. Save remaining cooking liquid to use in gravy recipes. Serves 4.

TAMALE PIE

3 c cooked pinto beans, mashed
1 onion, chopped
1½ tsp chili powder
¼ c tomato sauce
1 c frozen corn
1 green pepper, chopped
1-2 chopped green chilis
1½ c cornmeal
2½ c water
½ tsp chili powder
1 tsp Bragg Aminos

Place onion in a large pot with ¼ cup water. Saute about 10 min., add green pepper, corn, green chilis, tomato sauce and chili powder. Cook 5 min. Add mashed beans and cook about 10 min. over low heat. Remove from heat.

Combine cornmeal and water and chili powder in a sauce pan, cook over medium heat until mixture thickens, stirring constantly with a wire wisk or cornmeal will lump.

Lightly oil an 8x8 pan, spread ½ of the cornmeal mixture over the bottom. Pour the bean mixture over this and spread it out. Then spread the remaining cornmeal mixture over the top.

Bake at 350° for 45 minutes, or until it bubbles. Serves 8.

Health in a human being, is the perfection of bodily organization, intellectual energy, and moral power.

CALORIE, CARBOHYDRATE, AND PROTEIN GUIDE

			(in grams)	Proteins (in grams)
DAIRY PRODUCTS				
CHEESE				
American, pasteurized				
processed	1 oz.	107	.5	6.5
Cheddar	1 oz.	112	.36	7
Cottage cheese, 4% fat				
large curd	1 cup	235	6	28
small curd	1 cup	220	6	26
Cream cheese	1 oz.	100	1	2
Monterey Jack	1 oz.	106	.2	7
Swiss	1 oz.	107	1	8
CREAM				
Half and half	1 cup	315	10	7
Sour cream	1 cup	495	10	7
	1 tbsp.	25	1	trace
Whipping cream,				
heavy unwhipped	1 cup	820	7	5
EGGS				
Egg (raw)	1	82	.5	6
Scrambled or in				
omelet	2 eggs	190	2	12
MILK				
Buttermilk	1 cup	99	11.7	8.1
Goat	1 cup	168	10.9	8.7
Human	1 oz.	21	2.1	.3
Low-fat	1 cup	121	11.7	8.1
Whole	1 cup	159	11.4	8.5
Nonfat instant dried	1 cup	244	35.5	24
Nonfat dried	1 cup	435	62.4	43.4
YOGURT				
Whole milk, plain	8 oz.	139	10.6	7.9
Low-fat, plain	8 oz.	144	16	12
Low-fat, fruit	8 oz.	225	42.3	10
BUTTER				
one cube	½ cup	815	1	trace
about ⅛ cube	1 tbsp.	100	trace	trace
FISH AND SHELLFISH				
Bass	4 oz.	118	0	21
Crabmeat, steamed	4 oz.	105	0.6	20
Fish sticks,	4 oz. or			
breaded	4 sticks	200	8	20
Halibut	4 oz.	113	0	24
Lobster	4 oz.	103	0.6	19
Salmon				
fresh	4 oz.	246	0	25
canned, pink	½ cup	155	0	22
Shrimp, fresh	4 oz.	103	1.7	20

Whatsoever was the father of a disease; an ill diet was the mother. —Herbert, 1859

		(in grams)	Proteins (in grams)
Tuna			
canned in oil,			
drained .... ½ cup	157	0	23
canned in water .... ½ cup	127	0	28
MEAT AND POULTRY			
BEEF			
Chuck roast.................... 4 oz.	226	0	20
Ground beef, lean............... 4 oz.	203	0	23
Heart, beef, lean and			
braised .... 3 oz.	160	1	27
Liver, beef, fried in			
butter...................... 3 oz.	195	5	22
Steak, lean sirloin,			
T-bone, porterhouse			
or rib, broiled .... 4 oz.	462	0	25
LAMB			
Lamb chop, rib,			
broiled.................... 3.1 oz.	360	0	18
Lamb leg, roasted.............. 3 oz.	235	0	22
PORK			
Ham, light cure, lean,			
roasted .... 3 oz.	235	0	18
Luncheon meat/			
boiled ham .... 1 oz.	65	0	5
1 slice			
Pork chop .... 3 oz.	310	0	21
POULTRY			
Chicken breast, fried .... 2.8 oz.	160	1	26
Chicken livers,			
simmered .... 4 oz.	187	3	30
Drumstrick, fried .... 1.3 oz.	90	0	12
Half broiler, broiled .... 62. oz.	240	0	42
Turkey			
roasted dark meat .... 4 pieces	175	0	26
roasted light meat .... 2 pieces	150	0	28
chopped or diced .... 1 cup	265	0	44
VEAL			
Cutlet, broiled................... 4 oz.	265	0	30
Roast, rump .... 4 oz.	267	0	31

Surely if living creatures saw the consequences of all their evil deeds, with hatred would they turn and leave them, fearing the ruin following. —F'shuing Tsan K'ung

Society is always taken by surprise at any new example of common sense. —Emerson

CLASSIFICATION OF FOODS
ACCORDING TO CARBOHYDRATE CONTENT

VEGETABLES

3 PERCENT	6 PERCENT	15 PERCENT	20 PERCENT	25 PERCENT
Asparagus	Beans, string	Artichokes	Beans, dried	Rice, boiled
Bean sprouts	Beets	Beans, Kidney	Beans, Lima	Potato, sweet
Beet greens	Brussel sprouts	Hominy	Corn	Yams
Broccoli	Carrots	Oyster plant	Potato, white	
Cabbage	Chives	Parsnips		
Cauliflower	Collards	Peas, green		
Celery	Dandelion			
Chard, Swiss	greens			
Cucumber	Eggplant			
Endive	Kale			
Lettuce	Kohlrabi			
Mushrooms	Leeks			
Mustard	Okra			
greens	Onions			
Radishes	Parsley			
Sauerkraut	Peppers, red			
Spinach	Pimento			
Squash	Pumpkin			
Tomatoes	Rutabagas			
Turnip Greens	Turnips			
Water Cress				

FRUITS

3 PERCENT	6 PERCENT	15 PERCENT	20 PERCENT	25 PERCENT
Cantaloupe	Apricots	Apples	Bananas	
Rhubarb	Blackberries	Blueberries	Figs	
Strawberries	Cranberries	Cherries	Prunes	
Watermelon	Currants	Grapes		
	Gooseberries		Kumquats	
	Grapefruit	Loganberries		
	Guava	Mangoes		
	Melons	Mulberries		
	Lemons	Pears		
	Limes	Pineapple		
	Oranges	Pomegranates		
	Papayas			
	Peaches			
	Plums			
	Raspberries			
	Tangerines			

If a man can convince me that I do not think or act right, gladly will I change, for I search after truth. But he is harmed who abideth on still in his ignorance. —Marcus Aurelius, Roman Emperor

Ruts long traveled—grow comfortable.

Sources of Complex Carbohydrates
Recommended for Athletes

Proteins build and repair the muscles and complex carbohydrates supply energy for the continuous and repeated muscular contractions that occur during prolonged exercise. Carbohydrates are stored in the muscles and also in the liver in the form of glycogen. Once these stores are depleted the muscles cannot perform to their best ability.

Whole-grain flours: Whole wheat, buckwheat, cornmeal and rye.

Grains: Brown rice, buckwheat groats (kasha), barley, bulgar (cracked wheat), millet, oats, wild rice.

Dried Legumes: Peas, beans, lentils, corn, seeds and nuts.

Whole-grain Cereals: Rolled oats, shredded wheat, muesli, granola (plain, low in sugar), bran, wheat germ.

Fresh fruits and vegetables

Potatoes: Not french fries or potato chips.

Bread and crackers: Made with whole grain or 100 percent whole wheat flours.

Pasta: Made with whole wheat, soy or semolina flours.

Do not eat refined sugars and starches found in such things as white bread, cakes, pies, potato chips and soda. They contain little or no nutrition.

The night before a game or race many athletes eat a bowl of whole grain spaghetti, a couple of slices of whole wheat bread and vegetable juice, especially tomato (no salt) because it is a good source of potassium.

On the morning of the event most athletes have a high carbohydrate breakfast. Example: buckwheat pancakes, whole wheat french toast, a peanut butter sandwich, bran muffins, fruit and low fat yogurt or a bowl of cereal with fruit. (Read the labels and make sure the products do not contain excess sugar, honey, molasses, corn or maple syrups.)

Sugars do give a short burst of energy but they also trigger fatigue, dizziness and hunger pains within a few hours.

Most top athletes get 80% to 90% of their calories from complex carbohydrates and no more than 10% meat protein.

Wheat Germ Oil . . . a Special Energy 'Fuel'

Wheat germ oil may be another powerful anti-fatigue factor. Not much has been reported about wheat germ oil recently and, as far as we know, there are only a handful of wheat germ oil experts around. The patriarch among them is Thomas K. Cureton Jr., Ph.D., professor emeritus and director of the Physical Fitness Institute at the University of Illinois, who spent 22 years, from 1950 to 1972, studying the energy-producing effect of the nutrient on athletes as well as older adults and boys. In 1972 he published a landmark book on the subject, *The Physiological Effects of Wheat Germ Oil on Humans in Exercise* (Charles C. Thomas).

"Wheat germ oil is a kind of a fuel," Dr. Cureton said. "It aids the production of energy in the muscle cells."

He has found that wheat germ oil stabilizes the nervous system, lowers the pulse and increases the rest interval of the heart during work or exercise. These changes indicate better resistance to stress.

In his book, Dr. Cureton writes: "We have found that in 22 years of working with people who have taken wheat germ oil (WGO), or the related substances, there are measurable benefits and, unquestionably, benefits that cannot be measured, and no narmful effects have ever been observed . . . WGO and octacosanol (the active ingredient of wheat germ oil) taken in moderate amounts will enable most human subjects to bear stress better.

"And you don't have to be an athlete to benefit from it," Dr. Cureton says today. "In fact, we saw more improvement among people not in training, people who weren't at the top of the fitness ladder." In one of his experiments, wheat germ oil "helped the endurance of middle-aged men running the all-out treadmill test, and produced significant gains over a matched (but unsupplemented) group that took the same course of conditioning exercises for eight weeks."

Dr. Cureton and my father, Paul Bragg, both admired each other for their continuing work with athletes and nutrition. I recently found some early correspondence of years ago between the two pioneers. Dr. Bragg pioneered wheat germ and vitamin E and inspired another young man in the importance of wheat germ and that is how Viobin Corp. got started and they are still the major wheat germ oil producer.

Wheat Germ Users Excelled in Olympic Swimming

In what might be the most dramatic demonstration of wheat germ oil's power, Dr. Cureton points to the results of the swimming events at the 1956 Olympic Games in Melbourne, Australia. Four American swimmers who started taking wheat germ oil six months before the Games all did well: One won a gold medal in the 200-meter men's butterfly, another set a world record in the 1500-meter swim, and two more placed first and second in the women's 100-meter butterfly. The other Americans who didn't use the supplement did poorly.

The gold medalist in the 200-meter butterfly was Bill Yorzyk, M.D., and, amazingly, he still attributes some of his stamina to wheat germ oil . . . and he still uses it. Now an anesthesiologist in Springfield, Massachusetts, Dr. Yorzyk said, "I feel strongly that wheat germ oil has helped me. I notice a difference if I forget to take it for a few weeks and I notice a difference when I start back on. But I have no scientific evidence to back that up. It's purely anecdotal." Dr. Yorzyk said his wife and children also take wheat germ oil daily. Clint Eastwood's two children were nursed on mother's milk, then they had goat's milk with a few drops of wheat germ oil added to it. They are beautiful, healthy children, and they live by health principles.

Dr. Cureton advises that wheat germ oil doesn't work overnight. He estimates that you will feel a difference in four to five weeks. The dosage in his experiments was about a teaspoonful a day. When wheat germ oil is sold in capsules, it is often measured in "minims." In that case, the daily dose would be 60 minims.

The oil is best absorbed when taken on a relatively empty stomach directly after exercise, Dr. Cureton says. Now past 80, he swims and trains with weights for two hours a day, and takes the supplement while he's still warm from exertion. Raw wheat germ, if it is very fresh (vacuum packed in tin, sold in health food stores), works almost as well as the oil, he says, and suggests a half cup of it a day. Add to Blender Drinks, juices or sprinkle over cereals, salads, soups, etc.

There also seems to be a link between pantothenic acid (a B vitamin) and fatigue. It's known that from pantothenic acid the body builds coenzyme A (CoA), a catalyst necessary for the conversion of food to energy. Low levels of CoA can be dangerous. In one experiment at the University of Nebraska, Hazel Fox, Ph.D., and colleagues compared two groups of men — one group received the vitamin and the other was totally deprived of it. After 10 weeks, the deprived men were listless and complained of fatigue (*Journal of Nutritional Science and Vitaminology*, August 1976).

That was an extreme case, but Dr. Fox has found that most Americans consume barely as much as the lower end of the National Research Council's recommended daily allowance of four to seven milligrams. "The intake of pantothenic acid by Americans is decreasing," she said.

"In 1955, when I first measured the intake of the vitamin by college women here in Lincoln, the average was about seven mg. a day. We rarely get figures that high now. The average is four or five. People just don't eat three square meals the way they used to. People aren't choosing the right foods. There are too many processed foods.

"Fatigue has been described as a symptom of pantothenic acid deficiency," she added, "and I would make a guarded statement that the evidence shows a relationship between fatigue and low pantothenic acid intake. It's something we need to look into."

Although the current recommended allowance for the vitamin is only four to seven mg.; it wasn't always that low. In 1963, a researcher in Hungary reported that "a healthy adult person requires about 15 mg. of Pantothenic acid daily and he went on to say that physical work, surgery, injury, liver disease, allergies and sometimes the side effects of drugs, can double the need for pantothenic acid."

An athlete should make doubly sure that his intake of this essential nutrient is adequate by eating pantothenic acid-rich foods. Those foods are beef, chicken, potatoes, oat cereals, tomato products and whole grain products.

Nutritionally Improved Dietary Program

The success of any program of nutritional therapy is often founded upon a sound daily diet. In the case of disease or deficiency conditions, this is especially important since the body must receive substantial quantities of high quality "building blocks" such as protein to facilitate the vitamins and minerals in their action. The principle underlying the following nutritional recommendations is the elimination of food items which contribute little or nothing to nutritional or physical status and placing emphasis upon those which are beneficial.

Items to Eliminate

- Catsup, mustard, worcestershire sauce, pickles or olives that contain salt, sugar, preservatives, etc.
- Salted foods, such as potato chips, salted nuts, pretzels, crackers or sauerkraut that contain salt
- White rice and pearled barley
- Commercial dry cereals such as cornflakes and others
- Fried foods
- Saturated fats and hydrogenated oils — enemies of your heart!
- Food which contains cottonseed oil. When a product is labelled vegetable oil . . . find out what kind it is before you use it.
- Oleo and margarines — saturated fats and hydrogenated oils
- Peanut butter that contains salt and hydrogenated oils
- Coffee, decaffeined coffee, tea and alcoholic beverages
- Tobacco
- Fresh pork and pork products
- Smoked fish of any kind
- Smoked meats, such as ham, bacon and sausage
- Lunch meats, such as hot dogs, salami, bologna, corned beef, pastrami, and any meats containing sodium nitrate or nitrite
- Dried fruits which contain sulphur dioxide (preservative)
- Do not eat chickens that have been injected with stilbestrol, or fed with chicken feed that contains any drugs.
- Canned soups (read labels, look for sugar, starch, white flour and preservatives)
- Food that contains benzoate of soda, cream of tartar (preservative)
- White flour products such as white bread and wheat and rye bread that has a mixed wheat-white flour in it; dumplings, biscuits, buns, gravy, noodles, spaghetti, pizza, ravioli, sago,

Men do not die, they KILL themselves —Seneca, Roman Philosopher

pies, pastries, cakes, cookies, prepared and commercial puddings, and ready-mix bakery products.

- Bleached and unbleached white flour products
- Wheat flour is a mixed white-wheat flour. If you use wheat — it should read whole wheat, thus you know it contains no white flour.
- Day-old vegetables, pre-mixed salads, warmed-over potatoes
- Self drugging, no aspirin, buffered aspirin, antihistamines, milk of magnesia, sleeping pills, tranquilizers, pain killers, strong cathartics, or fizzing bromides. You are not qualified to prescribe drugs for yourself (results can be serious).

Items to Increase or Feature

Dairy Products: Milk (2%, skimmed, raw, powder), buttermilk, yogurt (unflavored), cottage cheese, cheddar and other non-processed cheeses.

Grain Products: Wheat germ, bran, whole-grain cereals and bread, full fat soyflour, and other items prepared from whole oats, rye, barley, etc. Brown rice.

Meat: All forms may be liberally consumed provided all visible fat is removed prior to cooking. Organ meats, fowl, eggs are excellent. Ham, sausages, weiners and most canned meat should be avoided if possible.

Seafood: All types of fish. Clams, oysters and other shellfish are excellent.

Nuts & Seeds: Nuts and seeds of all varieties may be consumed daily in moderate amounts provided they are unroasted, unsalted, and without added oil. Especially good are toasted soybeans, raw almonds, cashews, pumpkin and sunflower seeds.

Vegetables: All vegetables except those under "Eliminate" should be used regularly and in abundance. Maximum benefits are obtained from fresh or frozen rather than canned varieties. Emphasis should be placed on leafy green vegetables and the regular use of salads.

Fruit: All types except those under "Eliminate." Use regularly.

Beverages: All fruit and vegetable juices except those with added sugar or salt.
Herbal teas and the beverages listed under "Dairy Products" are acceptable.

NOTE: Food.should be well-chewed, eaten slowly and consumed in smaller amounts. Light between-meal snacks and before-bed snacks are advisable. Avoid as much as possible any "instant" foods and products with chemical additives, colorings or personally allergenic compounds. Care should be exercised in the preparation of foods; fry only in poly-unsaturated vegetable oils and minimize consumption of fried foods. Vegetables retain maximum benefit if quick steamed or prepared in a wok. Brewer's yeast, wheat germ, lecithin, and bone meal are very useful supplements which may be liberally and imaginatively added to enhance the nutritive value of many foods. Medications should be taken only on the advice of a physician.

What About Bran?

Is there a correlation between a long term dietary intake of low fiber refined foods, such as white flour and sugar, and illnesses such as: benign and malignant tumors of the colon and rectum, appendicitis, hemorrhoids, constipation, diverticulosis, gallstones, hiatal hernia and coronary artery diseases?

Current newspaper and magazine articles, and an article in the *Journal of the American Medical Association*, written by three prominent English physicians, Drs. Burkitt, Walker and Painter, have brought a new concept to preventive medicine which is really very old.

Many of us in Western civilizations would live longer, and we would be a great deal healthier, *if we ate coarser diets that would send more indigestible dietary fiber through our digestive tracts.*

The doctors recommend that we eat breads made of 100% whole grains and that we add *unprocessed* bran to our diets. Bran can be mixed into our regular breakfast cereals. We should try to avoid such foods as canned fruits, in favor of raw fruit with the skin or peel.

Bran has little or no food value. We do not digest and absorb it. As it passes through our digestive tract it accumulates liquid and swells up, providing a good amount of soft bulk that speeds bowel movements. Soak 1 to 2 Tablespoons of unprocessed raw bran in 2/3 glass of prune, apple, cranberry or fresh orange juice when you need better elimination! You can also add 1 Tablespoon of Brewer's Yeast to add B-complex, Vitamin C crystals or protein powder to this health cocktail.

Bee Pollen — How Useful Is It?

Bee pollen has received much attention lately from both food faddists and serious nutritionists; and many athletes are convinced that bee pollen increases the quality of their performances. Bee pollen is amazing because it contains a great many of the essential nutrients we must include in our diets.

Bee pollen is useful in the strict vegetarian (vegan) diet because it provides vitamin B-12 . . . which is not found in any plant foods; and it may help your performance if you initially have a nutritional deficiency which the bee pollen corrects.

A very few people are violently allergic to bee pollen, usually those who are allergic to ragweed pollens. If you have this problem, avoid bee pollen. Even if you have no known allergies, you might want to be sure you have access to medical care before you try bee pollen for the first time.

Health food stores can give you more information on Bee Pollen if you want to try it . . . Paul Bragg felt it had good merits and often added it in his Pep Blender Drink or sprinkled 1/3 teaspoon over his vegetable or fresh fruit salads. It also adds a tasty flavor!

The Not-So-Wonderful World of the Aromatic Brew — Coffee

Both socially and privately, coffee drinking is indisputably the drink and choice among Americans. Eight out of ten adults drink it each and every day. We sip three times more of it than we do soft drinks, four times more than beer. We drink 50 times more of it than hard liquor. We take it black or creamed, sweetened or bitter, hot or iced. So much of it washes down the national gullete that the electric coffee-maker is expected to displace the trusty iron as the hottest-selling small appliance.

The beverage's place in American social life is without peer. No other drink — not even coca-cola — approaches coffee as a universal beverage in the American way of life. Coffee houses, coffee cake, coffee break are all words which have been coined to accommodate the universal addiction to this brew. It has been used to substitute for other addictions — Alcoholics Anonymous members have an average intake of 20 cups per day — although you don't have to be an ex-alcoholic to consume that much daily — many who are opposed to alcohol on religious principles see no wrong in the drinking of this beverage which can be just as addicting and health-destroying as alcohol.

Caffeine is a Poison

Evidence of such addictive properties are not difficult to come by. Just ask any coffee drinker what happens when he abstains for a day — the answer will usually be headaches, fatigue, stomach pains, etc. The major addictive factor in coffee is caffeine, a white crystalline alkaloid that stimulates the brain and artificially lessens fatigue. Caffeine is a poison. A sizable concentration injected into an animal's skin will kill within minutes. Injected into human muscles, it will cause paralysis. Ten grams of caffeine (the amount in 100 cups of coffee) accumulated suddenly in the human body would be lethal — resulting in death.

Fortunately, coffee ingested in the common manner is not fatal, since the kidneys work overtime to eliminate this toxin from the body and prevent its accumulation. But even these smaller caffeine doses make things happen which might cause some to reconsider.

Coffee and Alertness

Many drivers depend on coffee to keep them alert and awake when driving. That practice can be very dangerous according to Dr. Nelson Hendler, assistant professor of psychiatry at John Hopkins University School of Medicine. He says that coffee affects the heart and the brain. The caffeine speeds up the heart rate and the release of brain chemicals which excite the brain. But what happens is that within 30 minutes to an hour, the stimulation wears off and you crash down from the caffeine "high." "You artificially excite until there's nothing left to excite. You stimulate release, then you crash." In addition to all of this, coffee is the major dietary source of cadmium, a toxic mineral which has been linked with heart disease and high blood pressure. Coffee also increases the stomach temperature 10 to 15 degrees, increases the secretion of hydrochloric acid, causes the salivary glands to double their output, makes the lungs work harder, increases metabolic rate, and causes the kidneys to manufacture and discharge up to 100% more urine. ENOUGH SAID?

The nervousness and peevishness of our times are chiefly attributable to tea and coffee. The digestive organs of confirmed coffee drinkers are in a state of chronic derangement which reacts on the brain, producing fretful and lachrymose moods. —Dr. Bock, 1910

The more natural the food you eat, the more radiant health you will enjoy and you will be better able to promote the higher life of love and brotherhood. —Patricia Bragg

Let food be your medicine, and medicine be your food. —Hippocrates

Ponce de Leon,

Searched for the "Fountain of Youth".

If he had only known —

— it's within us...

Created by the food we eat!

"Food can make or break you!"

A team effort finishing the Honolulu Marathon

Scene of the Annual "Clam Bake" following the Honolulu Marathon. "Pot luck" lunches from many nations fill the air with sweet aroma.

2
Vitamins and Distance Training

In the Beginning . . .

IN THE "GARDEN" (Gen. 1:29 and 2:8), man had the choicest of foods. "And look! I have given you the seed-bearing plants throughout the earth, and all the fruit trees for your food," and "Then the Lord planted a garden in Eden, to the east, and placed in the garden the man he had formed. The Lord God planted all sorts of beautiful trees there in the garden, trees producing the choicest of fruit" (Gen. 2:8-9).

These fruits, free of any sort of debilitating additive and preparation pitfall, provided man nourishment to complement and enhance his magnificent state of physical fitness. It was pure, naturally good and without government inspection!

There is considerable opinion among various Bible scholars that man was originally a vegetarian. Whether or not this be true, this fact remains: God set in motion processes to supply needed ingredients to foster the physical health and well-being for His highest creation — man. Consider how the apple suits man's needs:

Apples are a very ancient fruit. Most living things enjoy apples and eat as many as they find. They are rich in natural sugars and fiber which are essential for the health of the digestive tract. They contain lots of pectin. Apples are also the finest tooth cleanser there is. Eating only one small apple after every meal will clean teeth far better than any toothbrush, or toothpaste can. And apples have a built-in guarantee against eating too much. (You can say the same about most fruits.) You're not likely to eat more than you want, for down through all the ages this bulk has been one of the ways human beings have known how much to eat and when to stop! The bulk is extremely important in regulating digestion and excretion.

Take your favorite fruit, whether it be oranges, bananas, grapes, cherries, peaches or whatever you like. The same applies to good, wholesome, nutritional vegetables of all varieties.

There is abundant evidence that we would enjoy better health if we would eat more of nature's unadulterated foods. These foods are rich in the necessary minerals, vitamins and acids needed for healthful living. Practically every one of them is free from saturated oils and other materials that debilitate physical health. That is God's provision for physical fitness!

But food of good quality, fresh, nutritious, and un-processed in our day is a continuing challenge to find. The situation for us is almost treacherous with many problem areas. The United States Food and Drug Administration passed a ban on the use of DES (diethylstibestrol), a livestock growth drug, because it leaves "illegal residues of the cancer-causing chemical" in edible beef and poultry tissue.

The DES Drug Issue — Bureaucracy at its Worst!

Since this ban was passed, the FDA has reversed the decision and allowed ranchers to continue to use it. Why? The meat industry enjoys a substantial profit by accelerating the growth of meat animals, by about one-third through the use of this dangerous hormone. The problem still exists although the substance is still classified as a potential cancer-forming agent by the FDA. But lobbying power and pressure from the agriculture and meat-processing industry has forced the FDA to dump these toxic poisons right back into the supermarket meat case.

It is extremely difficult to understand how the Federal Food and Drug Administration can justify such decisions. Bear in mind that the agency was formed during World War II, by President Harry Truman "to protect the health" of the people of the country against just such foolishness. This is only just one small, but serious, example of what takes place in the Government agency daily. Industries with vested financial interests, disregard the nation's health and the well-being of the consumer, by means of millions of dollars made available to Washington lobbyists.

Other banned but later approved chemical substances appearing on our grocery shelves are a number of food dyes and colorings, and sodium nitrite and sodium nitrate. These latter two are extremely dangerous and are used to prevent deadly botchulism bacteria from occurring in processed meat products and allowing processors to handle meat products in an unsanitary manner without contamination even after months of shelf-life.

How to Detect Danger on the Grocery Shelf

If you would like to know more about the dangers lurking on your grocery shelf, visit your neighborhood health food store. These health enthusiasts make it their business to keep the public aware of the injustices taking place daily in our food supply! (I am proud to mention that Paul Bragg originated the first health food store and gave it its name.)

Foreign countries including Japan depending on America for finished meat products, prohibit the importation of DES meat . . . a wise decision to safeguard their citizens' health from any potential harm! As a direct result of the continued use of this hormone, children have ingested meat products containing residue DES and show an increasing tendency to mature faster. Girls are capable of becoming pregnant at an increasingly early age, 10½ to 11 years, and are taking on a more masculine body development including broad shoulders, narrow hips, large hands and excessive body hair. On the other hand, boys have a tendency to take on a feminine shape — narrow shoulders, wider hips, small, narrow hands and little, if any, body hair.

Has your Family Doctor warned you about DES in your food supply? If not, ask him, "Why not?"

A group of Australian researchers report that they "can prevent the transformation of the polyunsaturated vegetable fats of seed oil into animal fats by coating the feed grain with formaldehyde-treated casein, a milk cheese protein," thus sharply increasing the "ratio of polyunsaturated to saturated fat in the animals." As a result, they claim the meats from animals so fed would contribute less to the build-up of cholesterol in persons who eat them. Such manipulation could turn into a dangerous food source problem rather than a help . . . such as the DES growth drug!

On another front, quite in another quarter is a difficulty faced by the grocery of obtaining wholesome, untreated peanut butter. The best peanut butter to buy is the natural unhydrogenated, raw or lightly-roasted peanut butter found in your health food store. In many stores, they now have their own grinder, and they will make fresh peanut butter right before your eyes . . . a taste delight! Most popular brands of peanut butter in the regular, or should I say, "anti-health" food markets, are hydrogenated. The hydrogenation process increases the tendency of the natural peanut oil to remain undissolved in the body. The natural, flowing oil of the peanut, rich in polyunsaturates, is made solid, therefore rendering it less desirable from a health point of view when hydrogenated!

More Go Power With Vitamins

Another area in which we face problems in food choices is the confusing one of vitamins. Vitamins now are added to almost everything . . . from bread to milk to breakfast cereals to artifical eggs. This should not present confusion to a consumer with an average mentality. Just read the label on these so-called "fortified substances." All potencies of vitamins added are scaled on the MDR (Minimum Daily Requirement) as set forth by the government. There is also an ever-increasing number of vitamins available. They are heavily advertised and readily available.

How can you equate daily good health and well-being offered by any substance, that has been proven beyond a question of a doubt to prevent disease, and provide bounding vitality and general well-being. If the price still presents a problem check out the cost of hospital beds, surgery and your most recent doctor bills! I am sure you will never question the price of preventive health measures again. An ounce of prevention is worth a ton of cure!

Why are Vitamins a Touchy Topic in the Doctor's Office?

You may have been stymied in your efforts to get your doctor to take any interest in your nutrition beyond advising you to "eat a balanced diet" and to "get all the vitamins you need with your knife and fork." You may have been unable to find a dentist who not only fills the holes in your children's teeth but fills you in on dietary do's and don'ts that will prevent the need for the dentist's drill.

No matter how well you get along with the physician who watches your blood pressure and appraises the systolic beat of your heart, you have learned that vitamins are a "touchy" point in your relationship. The very mention of them makes the conversation take on an edgy tone.

Either you become annoyed because the doctor simply dismisses the notion that vitamins are worth talking about, or he gets upset because he interprets your interest in vitamins as a lack of faith in him.

The most prestigious journals published by and for the medical profession regularly carry reports of studies showing the wide gap between the average person's need for certain nutrients and his actual supply. Other journal articles demonstrate the values of vitamins as preventives or treatments for specific physical problems. Government health agencies frequently assail the nutritional status of the average citizen. Obviously nutritional concern is not synonymous with faddism. Yet most doctors seem to think of it in that way.

It may fall to those outside the medical profession to foster a change in the doctors' negative attitude toward using nutrition as a specific weapon against disease. In recent years government agencies have become aware of increased nutritional inadequacies in the general population and the relationship of this situation to rising disease rates. Several presidential committees have formally recognized the need for change; and Senator Richard S. Schweiker, Republican of Pennsylvania, has been particularly active in advocating a more realistic and useful approach to nutrition by medical men. In 1972 he wrote:

Many diseases are related directly or indirectly to nutritional factors. In a follow-up report to the White House Conference on Food, Nutrition and Health, the panel on Advanced Academic Teaching of Nutrition pointed out that: "Atherosclerosis (including coronary heart disease), obesity, diabetes mellitus, hypertension, and osteoporosis are representative of many disorders in which nutritional factors are either of principle or contributory importance. In addition, new trends in food processing and environmental concerns require a great expansion of research in the area of trace minerals, 'secondary vitamins,' pollutants, and involuntary and voluntary food additives. Much of the research directed toward these problems must be conducted by individuals who have received (or should receive) advanced academic training in nutrition."

Because of the importance of sound nutritional practices to the maintenance of health and prevention of medical disorders, doctors must have enough knowledge of the relationship between nutrition and good health to advise his patients how to help prevent medical problems from occurring. As the ranking minority member of the Health Subcommittee, I am very conscious of the great need for much more emphasis on preventive medicine in our health care system today. we should not just treat medical problems after they have become serious, but should use nutritional dietary practices as a key means of preventing these medical problems from arising in the first place.

In addition, many doctors today have not been given sufficient knowledge of nutrition to deal with the nutritional aspects of diseases patients already have. The White House panel said, for instance:

Few Doctors Are Fully Informed About Nutrition

"The effectiveness of physicians in providing optimal care for the many patients who have diseases with an important nutritional component, is dependent in considerable part on the kind of nutrition teaching offered them at medical school and thereafter. **At the present time, nutrition teaching in medical schools and in teaching hospitals is woefully inadequate.**"

Therefore, I believe it is essential that the fundamentals of nutrition be taught early in the medical school educational program, with follow-up courses which are more detailed and sophisticated. A study by one medical school indicated that physicians questioned were more knowledgeable about theoretical aspects of nutrition than practical uses of nutrition in our daily lives. The study indicated that younger doctors did not know as much about nutrition as they should but would like to know more. In contrast, many older doctors did not know much about nutrition, but did not feel that education in this area was needed.

Food faddism and "folk medicine" are becoming more popular today, and many people are turning away from physicians to obtain information about nutrition. I believe part of the problem is that many doctors simply are not in a position to provide nutritional information patients need and desire for the maintenance of good health. We urgently need more scientific information about nutrition and health. We need more and better nutrition research but we will not get it unless our medical schools are able to provide nutritional training and can impress upon young doctors the need for emphasizing good diets to help prevent illness or disease.

Nutrition For Athletes Needs Top Priority

Only a few medical schools have separate divisions or departments of nutrition. Special courses in nutrition are rare, particularly in applied nutrition as opposed to the biochemical aspects of nutrition. There is a significant shortage of trained people in this field, and grants to stimulate the teaching of nutrition education in medical schools will help to develop an adequate supply of medical personnel who can help people become aware of the importance of good nutrition to their health and well-being.

The White House Conference Panel on Advanced Academic Teaching of Nutrition made the following recommendation about teaching nutrition:

"In each of the professional schools in a university such as medicine, dentistry, and dental hygiene, nursing, public health, food science, and technology or applied health sciences, an individual or committee should be assigned responsibility for the surveillance of nutrition-teaching in that school. In some professional schools, it will be desirable to teach nutrition in a designated course dealing with basic scientific principles of nutrition and their application to human health. In many schools, nutrition-teaching will be incorporated in courses such as biochemistry, physiology, and certain clinical specialties. Regardless of the plan of instruction, basic nutrition should be part of the required, or core, curriculum. In schools where trained nutrition personnel are not available because of financial restrictions, grants should be established to support nutrition for teaching in the categories listed above."

In 1972 Senator Schweiker introduced legislation toward meeting that goal: the "Nutritional Medical Education Act of 1972" provided for five million dollars for each of the next five fiscal years for grants by the Secretary of HEW to public or nonprofit private schools of medicine to plan, develop, and implement a program of nutrition education; the grants to be structured by HEW to assure that properly trained faculty members are available. The purpose of the program is to provide a single focus on applied nutrition education in our medical schools.

Our national health is at stake! Each person's individual health and life are at stake! We must take every step possible to ensure that all citizens are aware of the importance of their diet and of maintaining a proper nutritional balance in their food on a regular basis. By educating our future doctors about nutrition, we are helping to ensure that future generations grow up knowledgeable about the great importance of nutrition. Our doctors hold the key to our health and that key must include nutrition. Nutrition must become a top health priority.

Three Approaches to Vitamin Use

There are almost as many ways of using vitamin supplements as there are people, which is the way it should be. We are all different, not only in the way our faces and bodies look but also in the structure and function of our internal organs. Each one of us has a pattern of metabolism that differs in significant ways, causing us to react uniquely to food, to exercise, to threats of disease, to vitamins, minerals, and other aspects of environmental exposure. So to say that there is one vitamin program that suits everyone would be going against natural principles. It would be almost like saying that there is one dress or suit of clothes or dinner menu that would please everyone all the time.

Yet despite our built-in diversity, there is need for some pattern of vitamin usage. While we have our differences as individuals, we also have important similarities. We need to consider basic principles of nutrition that apply to everyone in developing personal plans for improving and supplementing our diet.

Insurance Approach

Most people follow one or the other of three basic vitamin-use plans:

NUMBER ONE PLAN . . . might be called the "insurance" approach. The general underlying idea is to take only enough of each important vitamin per day to ensure against deficiency disease. Users of that method tend to choose supplements that contain dosages that are usually modeled closely after the Recommended Daily Allowances of each nutrient. The amounts of each vitamin and mineral contained in these formulas are somewhat in excess of what you would get in a typical diet containing a good selection of natural foods.

The insurance approach was born out of the conviction that vitamins are primarily important as substances that prevent scurvy, pellagra, rickets, beriberi, and other horrible examples of total nutritional breakdown. Getting one of those diseases is no picnic, and preventing them by taking insurance doses of food supplements costing pennies a day makes good sense. That insurance concept of vitamin use is the oldest! In fact, the vitamin pioneers espoused supplementation as insurance against disease, especially when there was doubt about the quality of food.

Starting about 30 years ago, another point of view on vitamin usage began to be expressed. A subtle but extremely important switch in the outlook of some nutrition scientists was at the root of this change. Instead of looking at vitamins only in a negative way — as the cause of terrible disease when they were absent — these research workers began focusing on vitamins as tools for creating greater human efficiency! The evidence that vitamins were central to the structuring of a healthful diet was so apparent to these people they could not rule out the possibility that vitamins served a much greater function in our welfare than the prevention of deficiency disease! They began looking for positive effects of greater-than-normal vitamin usage!

A step toward the recognition of that new vitamin concept was the discovery of the effects of *subclinical* vitamin deficiencies. Scurvy is the very bad effect of an almost total lack of vitamin C in the diet, and for years that was thought to be the only result of inadequate vitamin C intake. But as nutritional science and medicine became more sophisticated, other effects of less serious vitamin C lack were noted. Wounds didn't heal as fast when the vitamin C level was low — even though it wasn't low enough to cause scurvy. Infections didn't heal rapidly in experimental animals kept on slightly low C levels. From those and many similar observations, not only with C but other vitamins, a much broader concept of vitamin need began to be recognized in the scientific literature. To this day, many questions about subclinical vitamin deficiencies remain to be answered, but the door has been opened to a view of vitamin need and function that was almost totally ignored a few decades ago.

Maximum Positive Benefits

Awareness of the positive value of larger amounts of vitamins led to other approaches to vitamin supplementation.

NUMBER TWO PLAN . . . for vitamin supplementation calls for the use of vitamins and other food supplements to produce maximum *positive* benefits. This plan focuses on the positive (improved health and efficiency) rather than the negative (insurance against outright deficiency disease). *This suggests an intake of vitamins considerably in excess of the Recommended Daily Allowances.* These amounts are needed to be sure of getting most of the benefits of supplement use — particularly the extra efficiency and health mentioned earlier. People taking these amounts of vitamins really do feel better and enjoy many benefits . . . especially if they also cut down on refined foods!

Much of the benefit achieved by this program is long-range as well. Preventing degenerative disease is a long-time proposition, and is the fruit of years of wise living and enlightened nutrition!

Scientists are just waking up to the tremendous importance of the long-term view of nutrition. For years they were handicapped by the fact that there was no money available to support experimental work that lasted for more than a few years. They themselves didn't want to hamper their career possibilities by working on a project that might take several decades to begin to produce results. So they kept busy on the abundant short-term challenges of nutritional science.

Now they have suddenly realized that all of human life for the past 40 or 50 years in the United States has been a gigantic experiment in nutrition. Over that time there have been very significant changes in the kinds and amounts of food that most people eat. According to Jean Mayer, Ph.D., of Harvard's School of Public Health (*Science*, 21 April 1972), in 1941 only 10 percent of our foods were highly processed. "Today," he wrote, "that amount has risen to 50%." And while processing of food has increased so drastically, chronic, degenerative disease has increased too!

Refining of foods is only one of the changes which has affected our diet on a national scale, but it is extremely important to long-term health. When food is processed, there is almost always a change in the amount of nutrients. Usually the recognized and important nutrients, such as protein, are preserved. But other facets of food that contribute to its nutritional value, including vital trace elements, are sacrificed in the name of such values as shelf-life, cost, appearance, and flavor. And since not all of the nutrients of value have been discovered, it is almost a certainty that processing of food takes out elements which will someday be found to be of value over the long term.

Present Day Foods Do Not Supply Adequate Vitamins and Minerals!

The obvious solution to that problem is to avoid eating processed foods. But that's not always easy, or even possible. Many people choose processed foods for some of their meals because they're in a hurry, because they can't unhook themselves from the taste of foods they're used to, or because nothing else is conveniently available. **More and more, the answer to ensure getting the vitamins and minerals you need for long-term health points toward food supplements!**

The experiment in long-term nutrition that the American diet has become has already attracted scientists who have begun to tabulate results, draw up charts and graphs, and make recommendations for corrective action. One of the most significant of such efforts is reported in a publication titled *Human Nutrition: Report No. 2, Benefits from Nutrition Research*, authored by C. Edith Weir, Ph.D., for a joint task group of the U.S. Department of Agriculture and the State Universities and Land Grant Colleges. The book, issued in August 1971, lists all the diseases and conditions that can be prevented by improved nutrition and is a real eye-opener. It states in blunt terms that almost all of the health problems of our day can be corrected to some degree by better nutrition — especially if maintained for many years.

Concerning cancer, Dr. Weir writes: "There is a small but growing body of data suggesting that chronic, low-level intake of some nutrients is a factor in the incidence of cancer in man. There is evidence that vitamin deficiency plays a role in the occurrence of cancer of the oral cavity and the esophagus. "Chronic vitamin B complex deficiency, due to inadequate supply of vegetables in the diet, appears to be incriminated. There is recent evidence, March 1970, that dietary iodine deficiency may contribute to breast cancer, at least in rats. Demographic studies reveal that human breast cancer incidence is high in iodine-deficient areas."

Dr. Weir concludes in another section of her report that if everyone improved his or her diet to get the right amount of nutrients, there would be a 20 percent reduction in the incidence of cancer. She also lists similar figures for other diseases. Here are her estimates:

Improved Nutrition Will Reap Huge Benefits

	Infants (0-12 mo.)		Children under 4 years		Adults and children 4 or more yrs.		Pregnant or lactating women	
Vitamin A	1500	IU	2500	IU	5000	IU	8000	IU
Vitamin D	400	IU	400	IU	400	IU	400	IU
Vitamin E	5	IU	10	IU	30	IU	30	IU
Vitamin C	35	mg	40	mg	60	mg	60	mg
Folic Acid	0.1	mg	0.2	mg	04.	mg	0.8	mg
Thiamine (B₁)	0.5	mg	0.7	mg	1.5	mg	1.7	mg
Riboflavin (B₂)	0.6	mg	0.8	mg	1.7	mg	2	mg
Niacin	8	mg	9	mg	20	mg	20	mg
Vitamin B₆	0.4	mg	0.7	mg	2	mg	2.5	mg
Vitamin B₁₂	2	mcg	3	mcg	6	mcg	8	mcg
Biotin	0.05	mg	0.15	mg	0.3	mg	0.3	mg
Pantothenic acid	3	mg	5	mg	10	mg	10	mg
Calcium	0.6	g	0.8	g	1	g	1.3	g
Phosphorus	0.5	g	0.8	g	1	g	1.3	g
Iodine	45	mcg	70	mcg	150	mcg	150	mcg
Iron	15	mg	10	mg	18	mg	18	mg
Magnesium	70	mg	200	mg	400	mg	450	mg
Copper	0.6	mg	1	mg	2	mg	2	mg
Zinc	5	mg	8	mg	15	mg	15	mg

Improved Nutrition Could Reap Huge Benefits

Human Nutrition: Report 2, Benefits from Nutrition Research — joint task group of the U.S. Dept. of Agriculture and the State Universities and Land Grant Colleges.

Health Problem	Potential Savings
Heart and vasculatory	25 percent reduction
Respiratory and infectious disease	20 percent fewer incidents
Mental health	10 percent fewer disabilities
Infant mortality and reproduction	50 percent fewer deaths
Early aging and lifespan	10 million people without impairments
Arthritis	8 million people relieved of afflictions
Dental health	50 percent reduction in incidence, severity, and expenditures
Diabetes and carbohydrate disorders	50 percent of cases avoided or improved
Osteoporosis	75 percent reduction
Obesity	80 percent reduction in incidence
Alcoholism	33 percent reduction
Eyesight	20 percent fewer people blind or with corrective lenses
Allergies	20 percent people relieved (90 percent for milk and gluten allergies)
Digestive	25 percent fewer conditions
Kidney and urinary	20 percent reduction in deaths and acute conditions
Muscular disorders	10 percent reduction in cases
Cancer	20 percent reduction in incidence and death
Improved work efficiency	0.5 percent increase in on-the-job productivity
Improved work and development	25 percent fewer deaths and work days lost
Improved learning abililty	Raise I.Q. by 10 points for persons with I.Q. of 70 to 80

Quantity-Based Measurements

Unit of Measure	Equal to	Used to Measure
microgram (mcg)	1/1,000,000 gram	Other vitamins and minerals in smaller amounts
milligram (mg)	1/1,000 gram	Other vitamins and minerals in moderate amounts
grain (gr)	about 65 mg	Other vitamins and minerals in larger amounts
minim (min)	about 1 drop water	Vitamins and minerals in liquid form

That is a spectacular listing of health benefits, all predicted to result from better nutrition. No wonder drug could approach that kind of record for health improvement. In fact, many of the benefits on that list are beyond the reach of drug medication as we know it today, and it is likely to be the same in the future.

Of course, it would be wrong to imply that the use of food supplements, even the best natural kinds, could achieve all the benefits that Dr. Weir and her co-workers list for improved nutrition. In many cases, she says, these benefits will result only if you *don't* eat certain things, and food supplements can't help you there. But a great many of the improvements she lists are within the power of food supplements to achieve because they require only the assurance of adequate amounts of nutrients over a long period of time.

The long-term necessity for good nutrition is stressed emphatically by Dr. Weir. "Major health benefits are long-range," she says. "Minor change in diet and food habits instituted at an early age might well avoid the need for major change, difficult to adopt in later life." The best course of all is to start an improved diet routine with young people, even small children, but a start at any age is better than ignoring the importance of these nutritional findings!

Megavitamin Therapy

NUMBER THREE PLAN ... approach to vitamin supplementation is best labeled megavitamin therapy. Another less-familiar name is orthomolecular medicine. This branch of healing, used primarily by physicians, is rapidly gaining in popularity and use, and will probably become a major influence on health in the future, if the promise indicated by present research is realized.

The phrase megavitamin means the use of large amounts of vitamins — so large, in fact, that they bear little reference at all to the quantities normally found in foods. In this approach, vitamins are used to get the effect drugs might normally achieve. Some megavitamin concepts are preventive, but many are curative. If you take large amounts of vitamin C when you have a cold, you're using megavitamin therapy. Some people have said that when you cross over from milligrams of vitamin C to a gram or more per day, you're moving into the area of megavitamins.

Mental illness has been the first great testing ground for megavitamin therapeutic concepts. There are important and obvious reasons for that. First, the need for a new approach was painfully apparent. Increasingly, psychoanalysis was being attacked as an elitist technique that pays no attention to the human organism's greatest environmental exposure, food. The drugs being so widely used to treat mental illness don't cure, they merely put patients into a state bordering on suspended animation. Finally, the vast number of victims of mental illness was itself a major factor in the move toward megavitamin concepts. There are in this country today at least 10 million people considered mentally ill who are not treated. They are a source of serious trouble to their families, friends, and to society. Ultimately, many become a burden on the state. And worst of all, the number of mentally ill appears to be expanding.

Schizophrenia was the first target of large-scale megavitamin therapy. Abram Hoffer, M.D., Ph.D., and Humphry Osmond, M.R.C.P., D.P.M., in 1952 began using high levels of niacin and other vitamins, especially vitamin C., to treat patients suffering from what was then called the "split-personality" disease. They reported that about three-quarters of these sufferers from schizophrenia were improved, and their book *How to Live with Schizophrenia* (Secaucus, New Jersey: University Books, 1974) became an important introduction to their techniques of treatment.

Many articles have been published about the work of Doctors Hoffer and Osmond. Allan Cott, M.D.; David Hawkins, M.D.; and others who have made important contributions to the treatment of mental illness with vitamin therapy. One of the most important people on that scene is Linus Pauling, Ph.D. He's important not only because of his advocacy of megadoses of vitamin C for prevention and treatment of the common cold, but he has coined the phrase "orthomolecular psychiatry" to describe an even broader effort to attack mental problems using natural methods. Dr. Pauling says his concept involves "the treatment of mental disease by the provision of the optimum molecular environment of the mind, especially the optimum concentrations of substances normally present in the human body."

Those last six words are important. Most drugs are "abnormal" substances, synthetic compounds created in laboratories and factories and totally foreign to the natural scheme. To use those substances in large amounts to try to treat disease creates large risks. Seeking to create a healthful environment within the body is a far safer procedure. It is also eminently logical.

Clearly, the megavitamin concept is attractive and not only to people with schizophrenia or other mental illness. Rapidly accelerating work in the field is opening up other areas, ranging from treatment of learning disabilities in children to treatment of alcoholism, depression, a wide range of heart problems, and possibly even cancer (which may be shown someday to be preventable through regular use of moderate dosages of vitamin A). Considerable research work is already pointing in that direction.

Preventive Medicine Through Megavitamin Therapy

The potential for the use of larger-than-normal amounts of vitamins and minerals to *prevent* disease logically far exceeds their potential as curative agents. We know — almost everyone today knows — that the most troublesome diseases of modern life have their origin in a lifetime of unhealthy living and eating habits. Problems like heart disease, cancer, arthritis, and similar failures of the human organism don't just happen suddenly when you get to be a certain age. Unfortunately, they are being programmed into many people's lives by habits and actions that start early in life and have continued for decades.

It is even more unfortunate that each year fewer people are able to live the kind of totally natural life which is the best preventive of chronic disease. We are exposed to pollutants of constantly expanding variety. Each year hundreds of new and entirely different kinds of chemicals are created and introduced by industry. Self-inflicted pollutants like tobacco and alcohol take a bigger toll of health each year. Widespread use of drugs is a very important cause of long-range insult to the health integrity of the human body, and this does not refer primarily to the use of drugs for thrills, which is a problem all its own. What is doing the most damage is the routine use of tranquilizers, antibiotics, pain killers, sleeping pills, laxatives, and literally hundreds of other types of drugs, each dragging the body down with side effects.

The standard, old-time advice on health is not enough to combat those mounting insults. The "balanced diet," if there ever was such a thing, has been lost for most people among a welter of convenience foods packed with sugar, white flour, colorings, preservatives, and other additives. Eating normal food and getting enough sleep are not going to prevent the serious diseases which right now are getting a toehold in the bodies of many millions of Americans. We are, in fact, facing a crisis in future disease which has the potential to wreck our society.

Can vitamins, in large amounts, really be our salvation? Of course, there is no absolute guarantee you will never get sick even if you come from the healthiest family, eat the best food, never smoke or drink, and follow a good vitamin plan your whole life. But it is also true that people who do those things, on the average, have a much better record of health. They also report subjectively that they feel better, are "more alive," and generally enjoy life more than those who move hardly a finger to try to improve their health on their own.

To some, vitamins are still controversial. The main problem is that almost all doctors still adhere to old ideas about vitamins, thinking of them only as preventers of those terrible deficiency diseases which are seen today primarily in the pockets of poverty. Doctors are also reluctant to embrace vitamins as a basic health-building tool, perhaps because they lack the mystery and exclusiveness of the prescription drug. Gradually that will change, and vitamin supplements will become accepted as a desirable and even necessary part of life in our modern world.

How to Read Your Vitamin Label

If you've ever been bewildered by the information on labels of the vitamin supplements you take, you aren't alone. Most people don't understand why one vitamin, say B^1, is measured in milligrams, while another is sold in International Units and a third in micrograms.

Yet it really isn't so difficult. Once you've mastered the system, you'll be able to compute your vitamin intake quickly, accurately, and confidently. Very simply, the standards of vitamin measurement fall into two categories: activity-based and quantity-based.

The activity-based measurements are International Unit (I.U.) and the United States Pharmacopeia unit (U.S.P.), which many may recognize as commonly used with vitamins A, D, and E.

The quantity-based measurements are used when the vitamin has a standard strength. They come in two types: metric and apothecary. Many of us learned the metric system in school — liters, meters, and grams — and that same measurement is on vitamin labels. Milligrams (mg), equal to 1/1000 gram, are used to measure vitamins and minerals which we need in moderate doses; micrograms (mcg), equal to 1/1,000,000 gram, are used when we're talking about those nutritious substances which are needed and supplied only in microscopic traces. For example, some vitamin B-complex preparations may contain 14 *milligrams* (mg) of vitamin B^2 but only 25 *micrograms* (mcg) of vitamin B^{12}. When dealing with smaller quantities, you measure them on the smaller scale — micrograms: moderate quantities, moderate scale — milligrams.

Understanding the RDA and the MDR

Once you understand the standards of vitamin measurement, how can you tell what doses of vitamins and minerals you should be taking? Every supplement label has a listing of the amount of each nutrient in the container. Along with the dosage, you will find a column showing what percentage of the MDR or the RDA of that particular nutrient the dosage is. The MDR and the RDA are standards of average nutritional needs established by the federal government.

The MDR, which stands for the Minimum Daily Requirement, is the very smallest amount of a particular nutrient that must be consumed daily by the average person to prevent an actual deficiency disease. The MDR is also sometimes listed as the MDAR, or the Minimum Daily Adult Requirement. The MDR has not been established for all the known essential nutrients but only a few of the better known vitamins and minerals which have been more extensively researched.

Originally established by the Food and Drug Administration in 1941, the MDRs are now considered obsolete and have been replaced by the more up-to-date RDAs.

When you see RDA on a supplement label, it is referring to the United States Recommended Daily Allowances (U.S. RDA). The U.S. RDAs are amounts of 19 vitamins and minerals established by the Food and Drug Administration in 1973 to replace the MDR. While it is a more complete listing than the MDR, human requirements for many nutrients have still not been officially established. Although the U.S. RDAs are broken down into three age groups and one group for pregnant or lactating women, only one listing of the RDA's appears on supplement labels. This listing refers to the allowances set for adults.

VITAMIN CHART

VITAMIN	FOOD SOURCES	BODILY PARTS AFFECTED
A fat soluble	green and yellow fruits and vegetables, milk, milk products, fish liver oil	bones, eyes, hair, skin, soft tissue, teeth
B Complex water soluble	brewer's yeast, liver, whole grains	eyes, gastrointestinal tract, hair, liver, mouth, nerves, skin
B1 thiamine water soluble	blackstrap molasses, brewer's yeast, brown rice, fish, meat, nuts, organ meats, poultry, wheat germ	brain, ears, eyes, hair, heart, nervous system
B2 riboflavin water soluble	blackstrap molasses, nuts, organ meats, whole grains	eyes, hair, nails, skin, soft body tissue
B6 pyridoxine water soluble	blackstrap molasses, brewer's yeast, green leafy vegetables, meat, organ meats, wheat germ, whole grains, desiccated liver	blood, muscles, nerves, skin
B12 cobalamin water soluble	cheese, fish, milk, milk products, organ meats	blood, nerves
Biotin B complex water soluble	legumes, whole grains, organ meats	hair, muscles, skin
Choline B complex water soluble	brewer's yeast, fish, legumes, organ meats, soybeans, wheat germ, lecithin	hair, kidneys, liver, thymus gland
Folic Acid folacin B complex water soluble	green leafy vegetables, milk, milk products, organ meats, oysters, salmon, whole grains	blood, glands, liver
Inositol B complex water soluble	blackstrap molasses, citrus fruits, brewer's yeast, meat, milk, nuts, vegetables, whole grains, lecithin	brain, hair, heart, kidneys, liver, muscles
Niacin niacinamide B comp. water soluble	brewer's yeast, seafood, lean meats, milk, milk products, poultry, desiccated liver	brain, liver, nerves, skin, soft tissue, tongue
Pantothenic Acid B complex water soluble	brewer's yeast, legumes, organ meats, salmon, wheat germ, whole grains	adrenal glands, digestive tract, nerves, skin
Para Aminobenzoic Acid paba B comp. water soluble	blackstrap molasses, brewer's yeast, liver, organ meats, wheat germ	glands, hair, intestines, skin
Pangamic Acid B15 water soluble	brewer's yeast, brown rice, meat (rare), seeds, (sunflower, sesame, pumpkin), whole grains, organ meats	glands, heart, kidneys, nerves
C ascorbic acid water soluble	citrus fruits, cantaloupe, green peppers	adrenal glands, blood, capillary walls, connective tissue, (skin, ligaments, bones), gums, heart, teeth
D fat soluble	egg yolks, organ meats, bone meal, sunlight	bones, heart, nerves, skin, teeth, thyroid gland
E tocopherol fat soluble	dark green vegetables, eggs, liver, organ meats, wheat germ, vegetable oils, desiccated liver	blood vessels, heart, lungs, nerves, pituitary gland, skin

VITAMIN CHART (Cont.)

VITAMIN	FOOD SOURCES	BODILY PARTS AFFECTED
F unsaturated fatty acids; fat soluble	vegetable oils (safflower, soy, corn), wheat germ, sunflower seeds	cells, glands (adrenal, thyroid), hair, mucous membranes, nerves, skin
K menadione fat soluble	green leafy vegetables, safflower oil, blackstrap molasses, yogurt	blood, liver
P bioflavonoids water soluble	fruits (skins and pulp)—apricots, cherries, grapes, grapefruit, lemons, plums	blood, capillary walls, connective tissue (skin, gums, ligaments, bones), teeth

MINERAL CHART

MINERAL	FOOD SOURCES	BODILY PARTS AFFECTED
Calcium	milk, cheese, molasses, yogurt, bone meal	blood, bones, heart, skin, soft tissue, teeth
Chromium	brewer's yeast, clams, corn oil, whole grain cereals	blood, circulatory system
Copper	legumes, nuts, organ meats, seafood, raisins, molasses, bone meal	blood, bones, circulatory system, hair, skin
Iodine	seafood, kelp tablets, salt (iodized)	hair, nails, skin, teeth, thyroid gland
Iron	blackstrap molasses, eggs, fish, organ meats, poultry, wheat germ, desiccated liver	blood, bones, nails, skin, teeth
Magnesium	bran, honey, green vegetables, nuts, seafood, spinach, bone meal, kelp tablets	arteries, bones, heart, muscles, nerves, teeth
Manganese	bananas, bran, celery, cereals, egg yolks, green leafy vegetables, legumes, liver, nuts, pineapples, whole grains	brain, mammary glands, muscles, nerves
Phosphorus	eggs, fish, grains, glandular meats, meat, poultry, yellow cheese	bones, brain, nerves, teeth
Potassium	dates, figs, peaches, tomato juice, blackstrap molasses, peanuts, raisins, seafood	blood, heart, kidneys, muscles, nerves, skin
Sodium	salt, milk, cheese, seafood	blood, lymph system, muscles, nerves
Sulphur	bran, cheese, clams, eggs, nuts, fish, wheat germ	hair, nails, nerves, skin
Zinc	brewer's yeast, liver, seafood, soybeans, spinach, sunflower seeds, mushrooms	blood, heart, prostate gland

Sample Vitamin-Mineral Stress Formula
for Training Athletes

			% RDA
Vitamin B1 (Thiamine Mononitrate)	75	Mg.	5000
Vitamin B2 (Riboflavin)	75	Mg.	4412
Vitamin B6 (Pyridoxine Hydrochloride)	75	Mg.	3750
Vitamin B12 (Cobalamin Conc.)	75	Mcg.	1250
Niacinamide	75	Mg.	375
Folic Acid	100	Mcg.	25
Pantothenic Acid (d-Calcium Pantothenate)	75	Mg.	750
Biotin	75	Mcg.	25
Choline Bitartrate	75	Mg.	*
Inositol	75	Mg.	**
Para Amino Benzoic Acid	75	Mg.	**
Calcium (Di-Calcium Phosphate, Egg Shell, Oyster Shell	250	Mg.	25
Phosphorus (Dicalcium Phosphate)	90	Mg.	9
Vitamin D (Ergocalciferol)	266.6	I.U.	66.7
Iodine (Kelp)	0.1	Mg.	66.7
Magnesium Gluconate	500	Mg.	6.8
Potassium Gluconate	100	Mg.	*
Manganese Gluconate	10	Mg.	*
Zinc Gluconate	100	Mg.	86.7
Betaine HCl	325	Mg.	**
Vitamin E (d-alpha tocopheryl acetate	400	I.U.	1333
Soya Lecithin	600	Mg.	**
Wheat Germ Oil (from Wheat Germ)	600	Mg.	**

One small gelatin capsule contains:

Viatmin A (Fish Liver Oil)	25,000	I.U.	500
Vitamin C (Ascorbic Acid with Rose Hips)	1,000	M g.	1667

(specially processed vitamin C to release to the body over a period of time)

Iron (Chelated)	37	Mg.	206
Predigested Protein (Protein hydrolysate)	600	Mg.	

Amino Acid Composition:

Essential amino acids: Isoleucine, Leucine, Lysine, Methionine, Phenylalanine, Threonine, Tryptophan, Valine.

Non-essential amino acids: Alanine, Arginine, Aspartic Acid, Cystine, Glutamic Acid, Glycine, Histidine, Hydroxyproline, Serine, Proline, Tyrosine. No sucrose, coloring or flavoring added.

%RDA: Percent Recommended Daily Allowances
  *: Recommended Daily Allowances not established
 **: Need in human nutrition not established

"Why not look for the best — the best in others, the best in ourselves, the best in all life situations? He who looks for the best knows the worst is there but refuses to be discouraged by it. Though temporarily defeated, dismayed, he smiles and tries again. If you look for the best, life will become pleasant for you and everyone around you."

What Do the RDA's Tell Us?

Just what do these standards mean to the consumer? Many people wrongly assume that the U.S. RDAs are all that anyone needs to fulfill nutritional requirements. Actually, the U.S. RDAs are based on averages of different population groups to determine how much of a particular nutrient is needed to maintain good health in the average healthy person.

However, in a world comprised of individuals, one would be hard pressed to find an *average* person! According to the Food and Nutrition Board of the National Research Council, the organization which establishes the more detailed figures on which the U.S. RDAs are based, "... it is only within the framework of statistical probability that RDA can be used legitimately and meaningfully. . . . One individual with low requirements might have a high intake of a specific nutrient, and another with a high requirement might have a low intake — but the average would give no indication that one of the two had an inadequate diet." (*Recommended Dietary Allowances*, Eighth Revised Edition, National Academy of Sciences, 1974.)

Furthermore, the statistical averages of nutritional intakes do not take into consideration nutrient losses due to food storage and processing, the adverse effects of illness or any type of stress which can increase nutritional demands, or what the Food and Nutrition Board calls the "unrecognized nutritional benefits of foods." These unrecognized benefits include any kind of nutritional program designed for *maximum* health benefits or *preventive* health measures.

It is indeed unfortunate that the American Consumer should be subjected to this line of reasoning. Studies by specialists have proven time and again that the MDR and RDA are borderline malnutrition! The vested interests in the food industry have used this government scam to try to convince the consumer they are being well fed if they will buy products that have been "fortified" with the MDR or the RDA of vitamins. Using Vitamin C as an example, the 60 mg's established by the RDA is bordering on scurvy. Our bodies are constantly being bombarded by stress, water and air pollution, without an intake of fresh nutritious fruits and vegetables to replace this deficiency naturally! The sad part about this travesty is that the medical profession either does not know the difference or could care less! Preventive medicine is now being demanded by the American public, who are tired of the high cost of medical and hospital bills!

What About Minerals?

Minerals are synergistic, i.e., they work better together than individually; they work in partnership with hormones, enzymes and vitamins.

Minerals are most important than vitamins because vitamins cannot function with minerals, and are required to build and maintain the bony structure of the body.

Organic minerals are more easily assimilated than synthetics. Minerals are necessary for carbohydrates, proteins and fats to be broken down in digestion and built into cells and transformed into energy.

Currently considered essential for human nutrition are calcium, phosphorus, iron, potassium, sodium, iodine and magnesium. Trace minerals (they occur in only traces in food and soil) are vital to human needs. These include: copper, zinc, cobalt and manganese. Processed or refined foods (example, white flour and white sugar) reveal that practically all the trace minerals are removed.

CALCIUM: Calcium deficiency is more prevalent than any other. The adult body contains three to four pounds of calcium, 99% of which is in bones and teeth. (From the age of nine, the diets of girls and women may lack as much as 25% to 30% of the calcium needed.)

Symptoms of calcium deficiencies are: stunted growth, decayed teeth and nervousness. Without sufficient calcium in the bloodstream, nerves cannot send messages and become tense. Finger-tapping, impatience and quick temper can be signs of calcium deficiencies. Calcium can only be assimilated by getting plenty of phosphorus, iodine, vitamin B, vitamin F and vitamin D. Adequate hydrochloric acid in the stomach must be necessary to absorb calcium.

IRON: Iron is the second most deficient mineral in the human body. Women need more iron than men, because iron is lost during menstruation. Iron is the prime factor in anemia prevention. Copper, cobalt, manganese and vitamin C are necessary to assimilate iron. B complex vitamins, such as B^1, B^6, Biotin, Folic Acid and B^{12} all work with iron to produce rich red blood. Inorganic iron or ferrous sulfate destroys vitamin E. The two should be taken eight hours apart. Organic iron is in the form of ferrous gluconate, ferrous citrate or ferrous peptonate.

COPPER: Copper works as a catalyst in the formation of red blood cells and is present in the hemoglobin molecule. Copper must be present before iron can be utilized. Copper is needed to prevent anemia.

SODIUM: Sodium helps to balance the acid-base relationship in the body and is needed to keep calcium in solution.

POTASSIUM: Potassium, aided by sodium, assists the cells in the selection of food particles. Both potassium and sodium help to pull them out of the blood, and both aid the cells in the elimination of wastes. Potassium attracts nourishment that the cells need from the bloodstream. Because diuretics wash out the potassium from the system, many doctors prescribe potassium in conjunction with diuretics.

CHLORINE: This mineral works with sodium and potassium to set up conditions for the irritability and contractility of the muscle tissue and the sending of messages throughout the nervous system.

ZINC: Zinc is a constituent of insulin, which is necessary for the utilization of sugar. It is found in human tissues such as the thyroid, sex glands and prostate gland in males. Zinc is the prime element in male hormone production and also assists food absorption through the intestinal wall.

MAGNESIUM: Dr. Hans Selye of McGill University calls this mineral the anti-stress mineral. He has saved animals under great stress by giving them protective amounts of magnesium. Those animals without the protective mineral, died of heart damage. Calcium and magnesium are found in perfect balance in nature for optimum absorption in a substance called Dolomite. In controlled studies of rats, it was found that magnesium was necessary to prevent calcium deposits, kidney stones and gall stones.

MANGANESE: This mineral functions in blood formation and is an activator of certain enzyme systems. Manganese is necessary for the formation of the urea.

SULPHUR: This mineral is a blood conditioner and cleanser. It aids the liver in absorbing the other minerals. Referred to as the beauty mineral, it has been known to make the difference between stringy or shimmery hair, brittle or beautiful nails; and coupled with vitamins A and D, plays a major part in skin texture integrity.

IODINE: The most important fact about iodine is that a deficiency can cause goiter — a swelling of the thyroid gland. A good source of natural iodine is kelp, and seafoods are very high in iodine.

FLUORINE: An element that helps protect teeth from decay.

The Importance of Potassium Balance to the Distance Athlete

Potassium is an essential mineral, the same as calcium and phosphorous. It is needed in quantities somewhat similar to magnesium. Potassium is needed in many functions, but especially for heart rhythm. There must be a proper balance between sodium, calcium and potassium. There are some drugs which are commonly used that deplete the potassium. In theses cases especially, a special potassium supplement is needed. The right kind of potassium is important.

Organic potassium is preferred. Natural sources for potassium are primarily green leafy vegetables and bananas. Most people do not eat enough of these. Unfortunately, they are not an adequate source for any potent supply. Inorganic potassium "salts" are the sulfate (alum), the chloride, the oxide, and carbonate, etc. "Organic" potassium refers to the gluconate, the citrate, the fumerate.

Ninety percent of the total body potassium is found inside the cells, while the remaining two percent is distributed between the bloodstream and other body fluids. Potassium depletion is common in long fasts, chronic disease characterized by weight loss and muscle atrophy. Major trauma or major surgical operations also cause potassium loss. Example: burns, fractures, severe muscle damage and severe diarrhea. Symptoms of potassium loss are: fatigue, muscle weakness, paralysis, and frequent urination.

Potassium deficiency should not be confused with the loss of salt from our body or sodium chloride through perspiration although the greatest loss of these substances occur during periods of extreme exertion, leading to prolonged perspiration.

Excessive Salt is Passed On to Us in Processed Foods and Meats

The normal everyday diet of fresh fruits, vegetables, seeds, nuts and grains provides 10 times more sodium chloride than the body needs in an organic form which the body can assimilate. Normal everyday table salt is an inorganic substance from a salt mine or the residue of the evaporation of sea water. This is an unnecessary substance to introduce into the human body, the exaggerated use of which will lead to arthritis, eye cataract, kidney stones, and hardening of the arteries or high blood pressure. Unfortunately, the meat industry forces the animal to consume excessive quantities of salt before slaughter. The mercenary purpose of this practice by feed lot operators is to encourage the animal to ingest excessive quantities of water due to the abnormal salt-induced thirst. The water-and-salt combination goes right to the cells of the animal and produces endema or water retention, to an excessive degree.

This high incidence of salt and water in the cells of the animal is carried through to the processing of the finished product. Ah hah! . . . Now you know why your meat cooking pans contain a Residue of Fat and Water and the barbeque fire spits at you (the cooking pulls out excess water) and you have an unquenchable thirst after eating meat. Unfortunately, the water content of the animal was sold to you at the meat counter for $3 to $5 per pound or more, and there is not one thing you can do. In some health circles, common inorganic table salt is considered a poison substance! There is no law against the use of salt.

Consumer Group Seeks Mandatory Salt Warnings

The government should warn Americans to go easy on the salt shaker, a consumer group said, citing the risk of heart attack and stroke.

The Center for Science in the Public Interest asked the Food and Drug Administration to require warning labels on salt packages as a means of reducing the 10 to 35% of the average American's sodium intake coming from salt added at the table or in the kitchen.

The proposed label would state:

"The surgeon general has determined that for many people a diet high in sodium or salt may produce high blood pressure. High blood pressure increases the risk of heart attack and stroke. The public is advised to limit salt consumption by cooking with only small amounts and refraining from adding salt to food at the table."

The group said the surgeon general's advice came from a health report published two years ago.

The FDA is already at work on the problem. It has asked the processed foods industry to voluntarily reduce added sodium, and the agency says the response has been favorable.

But the FDA earlier rejected a request from the same consumer group for a regulation that would have set sodium limits in food or provided for package warning labels on foods high in sodium content.

"We're asking the FDA to put its money where its mouth is," said Michael Jacobson, director of the consumer group.

Zinc for Zing!

Hypogonadism is a dirty word!

Hypogonadism means retarded genital development, and/or diminished or total loss of ability to perform the sexual act.

People have been looking for a cure ever since the beginning of time. Cassanova and Don Juan, who were legends in their own time, started a great many myths and superstitions with regard to virility that exist to this day. When Ponce de Leon went bopping off to Florida, it wasn't the Fountain of Youth he was *really* looking for — (though that is what he told the queen). He was looking for the source of the amazing sexual vitality that seemed to be characteristic of the native Indians. Several of them were brought back to Madrid, ostensibly to be baptised, but actually for exhaustive research into the secret of their sexual prowess.

Had Ponce de Leon only known what doctors know today, he would have found his "Fountain of Youth" in a liberal supply of whole wheat — for this was in the days before wheat was "milled," "enriched" and otherwise loused up, robbing it of its valuable *zinc*.

Zinc Turns Mice Into Men

Yes, *zinc* is the magic ingredient that can turn mice into men, turn Milquetoasts into studs. The doctors have known for a long time about zinc. *They knew that it is necessary to the growth of living creatures, needed for the transport of blood and the removal of carbon dioxide from the lungs; that it's also vital for the digestion of proteins, the utilization by the body of the lactic acid that builds up during exercise.* They even found a direct relationship between the amount of zinc in a man's body and the way he could hold his liquor.

Then one early doctor, who should have become a folk hero, discovered that zinc deficiency almost invariably caused a decrease in the size of the sex organs of the deprived animals, and a lessening of their interest in the opposite sex.

Zinc Assists in the Storage of Glycogen, the Triathletes' Fuel Supply

The scientists began putting two-and-two together. *Zinc is present in all tissues, but is especially concentrated in the thyroid gland.* It is a constituent of insulin, made in the pancreas for the normal storing of glycogen. The livers of infants are about three times as rich in zinc as the livers of adults; *a deficiency results in slow growth, inability to absorb food through the intestinal walls and general emaciation and lack of energy.*

And, what is most important of all, it was discovered that *the male hormone cannot be produced without zinc!*

Any man who is haunted by the specter of impotency might well examine his diet. Zinc is notably deficient in the American diet. And — according to the "Complete Book of Minerals for Health," zinc is absolutely necessary to a man's love life. There is a *very high and active concentration of zinc throughout the entire male productive system; prostate, seminal fluid and especially in the sperm (which, incidentally, contains the highest concentration of zinc of any type of cell in the human body).* Zinc is essential to normal sex activity. "No zinc, no activity," as the above book warns succinctly.

Zinc and Fertility

Another sad negative aspect of the absence of zinc in the male system is *infertility*. It was reported at the World Congress of Fertility and Sterility held in Stockholm in 1967 that as much as 50 percent of the time, the male may be the infertile partner in a childless marriage. Three years earlier Dr. M. Leopold Brody of the Weiss Memorial Hospital, wrote, "It is frustrating to explain the absent or diminished fertility of so many healthy-appearing males, and this infertility is on the increase. . . . There are more than five million infertile husbands in the United States and a much higher number who are only marginally fertile. The reason is a mystery."

What can we do to remedy this situation?

Zinc is Stripped From Our Food By "Processing"

What can we do to remedy this situation?

We know that zinc is concentrated in the bran and germ portion of cereal grains. But unfortunately, all this is removed in our "civilized" milling and enriching processes — we are being so "enriched" that we are starved!

Much of the fault also lies in modern farming methods with their use of artificial fertilizers and poisonous insecticides which deplete zinc in our food plants, which deficiency, in turn, transmits itself to the cattle and other animals we consume.

Zinc is the Mineral for Men

It is possible to raise the zinc levels in various organs and parts of the body by taking zinc supplements. If one wants to theorize on which parts of the body seem most dependent on a goodly supply of zinc, it is wise to take a look at where the trace mineral is concentrated.

Interestingly enough, *the male prostate gland contains more zinc than any other organ of the human body, 102 micrograms per gram — almost twice as much as the liver and kidney.* All body muscles, including the heart, store zinc, indicating that this mineral is *apparently very important to the healthful operation of muscles and heart.* The pancreas, lung, spleen, brain, testes and adrenal glands also contain appreciable amounts of zinc.

The male sex organs of mammals are extraordinarily high in zinc, especially the prostate gland which is where the male sperm is stored. The sperm cells themselves are high in zinc.

Zinc supplements have been given to people suffering from *hardening of the arteries*. In one study, some of the patients showed considerable improvement. Others were so greatly improved that they could return to their usual activities.

Today prostate gland troubles are almost universal among older men in our part of the world and are becoming increasingly common among younger and younger men. Doesn't it seem possible that deficiency in zinc, either partial or extensive, may have something to do with this epidemic of disorders?

Most American men are brought up on diets in which processed cereals, white bread and other foods made of white flour are staples. Since the zinc has been removed from all these *and never replaced*, could not this single factor explain why prostate gland problems are so prevalent in Western society and almost unknown among more "backward" people who are still eating unprocessed, unrefined cereal products?

Reversing the Aging Process With Zinc

Says Dr. F.N. Demertzis, "Working recently with zinc, I was impressed with the effect of zinc supplements on apparently healthy animals. So I decided to take zinc myself. The result was surprising. *First, the long hairs of the eyebrows (a sign of the aged) disappeared, and new, short and thin adolescent-like eyebrows took their place. The hair became more healthy and shining, its color darker, and every trace of dandruff disappeared.* In the comb in the morning there was not a single hair anymore. Finally *the greasy skin (full of acne at the time of my adolescence) became dry and better than I had ever had it.* After my experience, the same effect was noted in three other people I know who took zinc."

Writing on zinc in his regular syndicated column, Dr. Jean Mayer of Harvard School of Public Health, tells us that, in the light of zinc deficiencies that have been uncovered, "we are going to have to take another serious look at our diets and particularly at our methods of milling and enriching grain products. For zinc, like iron, is present in whole wheat. And, like iron, zinc is mostly eliminated by milling. But unlike iron, it is not being replaced by enrichment.

Why We Need Calcium

Just as iron is important to blood so calcium is vital for proper bone formation. The adult body contains about three pounds of calcium (1-1/3 kilograms) and 99 percent of this is found in teeth and bones. It is not surprising, therefore, that the development of the skeleton is affected by the supply of calcium received during the growing period.

Calcium and Stature

The tallest races in the world are found among those who have a high intake of calcium in their diet. These are usually the people who eat a considerable amount of dairy produce, particularly milk and milk products. The Scandinavian and Germanic races are usually tall. The climate and geography of their countries are ideal for dairy farming. Farther south, where the climate is dryer and pasture land is scarce, the natural diet does not include so much fresh milk, butter, and cream. The southern Mediterranean races are shorter in stature.

Recognizing Calcium Deficiencies

The early stages of calcium deficiency can be difficult to detect. The small amount of calcium needed by the blood and soft tissues, only one percent of the total, is extremely important for the proper functioning and well-being of the body. If calcium is in short supply, it is drawn from the store in the bones. If this continues, the bone becomes rarefied and growth is stunted. These changes in bone structure will show on an X-ray if they are very severe, but the early stages may not be easy to diagnose. X-rays cannot penetrate bone, but they can penetrate the tissues at the end of the long bones. In healthy growth, the cartilage at the end of the growing bone becomes calcified and replaced by bone. When calcium is lacking, the tissues will not register on the radiograph. This type of diagnosis is unlikely to be used unless symptoms are severe.

Lesser deficiencies may be indicated by nervousness and irritability in children. Muscle weakness accompanies the bone deficiencies, and children with rickets are often slow in sitting and walking. When blood calcium falls to a low level a form of tetany or muscle-twitching may become evident. Cramping is another symptom of calcium deficiency. This is often seen in older children and adults when there is a lack of calcium in the diet or if there is a pronounced malabsorption due to some stomach trouble, diarrhea, or vomiting. Experiments on isolated animal hearts show that calcium is vital to proper functioning of the heart. Heartbeats cease altogether if the specimen is placed in a calcium-free medium.

Absorption of Calcium is Vital

Absorption of food is a factor so important in nutrition that it cannot be over-emphasized. To see that there is sufficient calcium in the diet is not enough. Calcium must be able to pass through the intestinal wall and into the bloodstream before it can be of value. The problem with calcium is that it is capable of forming insoluble compounds with other foods. When this happens, it cannot enter into solution with the digestive juices to pass through the intestinal wall. The insoluble complex passes out of the body in the feces. The foods which appear to promote calcium absorption most successfully are proteins and milk sugar (lactose). For this reason, milk and cheese are two of our best calcium foods.

Fat is also important in calcium absorption. Although it does not help calcium directly, fat is vital for the absorption of vitamin D from the gut and this, in turn, helps in the absorption of calcium. At one time, it was thought that phosphorus improved calcium absorption, but this has been found to be incorrect. The calcium/phosphorus ratio in the blood is controlled by the amount of phosphorus that is excreted or retained by the kidneys.

Calcium Balance is Important

The balance between the calcium in the skeleton and that in the blood and soft tissues remains constant whether or not there is adequate calcium in the diet. If the diet is rich in calcium some of this excess will be stored in the bone, but there is a limit as to how much is needed; and, when this optimum is reached, the rate of absorption from the gut will be slowed down. Some dietary calcium is lost in the feces, and some, in the urine. When this amount is equal to the amount that is eaten, the body is in calcium balance.

Wheat and rye contain an enzyme, phytase, which splits the phytic acid during the leavening process. Once this has happened, the calcium-binding properties are lost, and the calcium in the bread becomes "available" again as a nutrient. Oats contain very little phytase so they should not be thought of as a good source of calcium. However, oats in hot cereal are usually eaten with milk, and this provides plenty of calcium. A cup of milk provides about a quarter of the daily requirement of calcium.

Oxalic acid is another substance that binds with calcium, making it insoluble. Tea and coffee have a high concentration of oxalic acid, and some fruit and vegetables contain it (particularly rhubarb and spinach). There is no need to restrict these foods from your diet, but they should not be thought of as a rich source of calcium.

Regular Heartbeat Requires Vitamin D and Calcium

The fact that vitamin D plays an indispensable role to both deposit and withdrawal of calcium gives to this vitamin a much more important role than was formerly recognized because besides being necessary to bones, teeth, and nerves, calcium is absolutely essential to every beat of the heart. If for some reason your calcium pool becomes dangerously low, your heart will flutter and fibrillate (twitch) and send out an SOS for more calcium. Vitamin D must be on the job before this calcium can be withdrawn from the bones to come to the aid of your heart.

Calcium is one of the major factors in regulation of the heart. Dr. Winifrid Nayler of the Baker Medical Research Institute describes the process in *Heart Journal* (March 1967). It involves an electrochemical process which takes place in the heart with every beat and within every cell. On the outer surface of each heart-tissue cell there is a thin filament called actin. The actin reaches with a kind of magnetic attraction toward the center of the cell, thereby shortening its length. The result of many cells shortening at one time brings about contraction of the muscle; and it is calcium, fed to the actin by the bloodstream which provides both the stimulus and the means by which the actin does its work. A shortage of calcium must inevitably result in a weakened heartbeat or an irregular heartbeat or an arrhythmia. So vital is calcium to the heart, that when the heart is short of calcium, the bloodstream will withdraw calcium from the bones and carry it to the heart. But, if vitamin D is lacking, the blood is unable to complete this lifesaving maneuver.

The amount of calcium in your bloodstream is small but critical. The body strives simultaneously to keep the heart muscle supplied and at the same time to keep the bones well mineralized and strong. But, to sustain all these delicate adjustments and readjustments, you must have enough vitamin D going for you.

Vitamin Antagonists

Are you a victim of vitamin antagonists? The following chart will give you a basis for deciding that. If, through some good fortune, you have managed to side-step many or most of the threats to your vitamin stores, you may be one of the lucky few who can do without supplementary vitamins. If, on the other hand, your daily habits take their toll in nutrition, this chart will help you decide how to meet your basic vitamin needs.

Vitamin Antagonists

Vitamins	Prominent Antagonists	Primary Allies
Vitamin A	mineral oil	protein
	nitrates from high nitrogen fertilizers	vitamin E
	ozone, nitrogen dioxide (air pollutants)	
Thiamine B_1	heat (cooking)	entire B complex
	Excess sugar consumption	vitamin C
	antibiotics	vitamin E
	stress conditions (pregnancy, lactation, fever, surgery)	
Riboflavin B_2	exposure to direct light	entire B complex
	heat (cooking)	vitamin C
	antibiotics	
	alcohol	
	oral contraceptives	
Niacin B_3	excess sugar consumption	entire B complex
	heat (cooking)	vitamin C
	antibiotics	
	alcohol	
	during illness, niacin absorption by the intestines is decreased	
Pyridoxine B_6	steroid hormones	entire B complex
	(cortisone and estrogen)	magnesium
	aging (after age 50, pyridoxine levels	vitamin C
	decline rapidly)	
	heat (cooking)	
	food processing	
	high protein diets (B_6 intake must also be increased)	
Folic Acid	severe stress situations	complete B complex
	(surgery)	vitamin C
	oral contraceptives	
	vitamin C deficiency	
	alcohol	

Vitamin Antagonists (cont.)

Vitamin B₁₂	iron-deficiency . . . .
	  (prolonged)
	oral contraceptives
	stress situations
	  (pregnancy)
	vegetarianism (if all
	  animal products and by-
	products are avoided)
		complete B complex
		vitamin C

Biotin	heat (cooking) . . . .
	avidin
	  (found in raw
	  egg whites)
	antibiotics
	sulfa drugs
		complete B complex
		
		vitamin C

Choline	alcohol . . . . excessive sugar consumption	complete B complex vitamin A
Inositol	antibiotics (by destroy-. . . . . ing intestinal bacteria)	complete B complex vitamin E vitamin C
Pantothenic Acid	methyl bromide (insecti- . . . . cide fumigant for foods	complete B complex calcium vitamin C

Vitamin C	aspirin . . . .
	corticosteroids
	indomethacin
	stress situations
	  (surgery)
	smoking
	alcohol
	diabetic state
		vitamin B complex
		vitamin P
		  (bioflavonoids)

Vitamin D	insufficient exposure to . . . . ultraviolet light	calcium vitamin A vitamin C
Vitamin E	oral contraceptives . . . . food processing inorganic iron (ferric) compounds rancid fats and oils mineral oil	vitamin A vitamin C B complex selenium manganese
Vitamin K	antibiotics . . . . intestinal illnesses (diarrhea, colitis) anticoagulants mineral oil radiation	
Vitamin P (bioflavonoids)		vitamin C

Vitamin Bibliography

Earl Mindell's Vitamin Bible, Earl Mindell, Rawson Wade Publishers, New York, N.Y.
The Complete Book of Vitamins, Rodale Press, Emmaus, Pennsylvania 18049.

View of Castaic Lake and the crowd of spectators.

Splashing into Cold Lake water, 51 degrees for the 2000 meter swim.

3

Excessive Weight and the Distance Athlete

Empty Calories are the Culprit

WITH OBESITY APPROACHING epidemic proportions in the United States, many people could benefit from an exercise program that includes diet control. Exercises such as running, swimming or bicycling can keep you slim, trim and fit while you enjoy other pleasures. If you're not already slim, trim and fit, one of these sports will help you reach your weight reduction goals.

At least one out of every five adults is overweight . . . that is, from 10-20% over the desirable weights. Most physicians and nutritionists concerned with weight control (along with most overweight persons) agree that those ugly, unhealthy pounds result from overeating!

Foods when measured in calories represent fuel the body turns into heat or converts to energy. The number of calories a body needs to stay even varies according to body weight, sex, age and activity level. During early adulthood, daily intakes of 3200 and 2300 calories represent averages for men and women, respectively. Table B defines other calorie allowances for men and women at different body weights and three ages.

Continued Daily Exercise Effective

Exercise works the same way. You need not run, swim or bicycle several hours a day to lose weight. A modest exercise schedule that shucks off 200 calories each day will reduce your weight by about 21 pounds within a year — even if you don't diet. A half-hour of hiking on level ground (see table C) will just about accomplish that goal.

While this chapter is not aimed at developing a full program for dieting and weight control, look at the numbers in table D. This table shows the relationship between one sport, bicycling, and weight reduction. If you want to lose just one pound of body weight by hopping on your bicycle and riding at a moderate speed of 9-12 miles per hour, you would have to pedal nearly 42 hours. This is why so many weight watchers lose enthusiasm for exercising away extra pounds. But if you reduce food intake by an average of 200 calories per day and ride your bicycle at moderate speeds for one hour each day, you lose one pound in about 5½ days.

One pound of body weight equals 3500 calories. While bicycling at a slow 5-7 m.p.h., a man weighing about 150 pounds burns up only about 2½-3½ extra calories per minute (table C). A woman weighing about 125 pounds burns less, about 2-3 calories per minute, for two reasons: more energy is consumed by the heavier man because he is bigger; women use about 8-10% less energy because their systems work more efficiently.

Table C shows net calories per minute; that is, the calories consumed are due to the physical activity and are in addition to the calories used to maintain normal body functions at rest.

As you would expect, the number of calories burned goes up as the speed or effort at which you bicycle, swim or run increases. Further, since calories used are net, they increase at a faster rate than speed increases. Table C shows that as your cycling speed increases from 5.5

to 13.1 m.p.h. or 138%, calories used increase from 2.5 to 11.6 per minute, or 364%. Thus, if you intend to derive full benefit from bicycling to lose weight, pedal faster within the same time frame and cover greater distances.

The figures in table C represent bicycling along relatively level roads. If you ride on roads with hills that have up to a 5% incline and similar decline, the caloric consumption figures increase by 20-50%. Add another 6% for each 10 pounds of body weight over the 150- and 125-pound averages for men and women, respectively. If you should be riding a bicycle with heavy-tread balloon tires, add one calorie per minute to each of the figures to account for the added rolling resistance.

Proper Gearing Important in Bicycling Weight Loss

Changing gears affects caloric consumption less than you might expect. Important variables are distance and speed. Within the same time spans, the amount of work accomplished in traversing a set distance of level road or of climbing a specific hill relates only loosely to which gear you may be using. If you shift to a high gear, you will pedal at a slower cadence, to be sure, but the force on each pedal revolution will be greater than if you use a lower gear. A very fast cadence in a low gear will use more energy but not as much more as you might expect. The actual differences have not been tested rigorously. However, unless you pedal with an excessively fast cadence or a very slow cadence, the average numbers shown in Table C will remain representative.

The figures for running, swimming and hiking (or other fitness activities not included, such as cross-country skiing or racquetball) are different, but the principles remain the same.

Editor's Note: We do not believe in the continued use of sugared, caffeined soft drinks . . . we prefer natural juices and beverages.

When a person embarks on a regular exercise program, his basal metabolism rate may increase as much as 10%. Maintenance of normal body functions throughout the 24-hour day uses the bulk of the 3250 calories burned by the average man in his 20s. So by increasing the basal metabolic rate, exercise burns up additional calories.

TABLE B: CALORIE ALLOWANCES FOR INDIVIDUALS

Desirable Weight   **Calorie Allowance**

Men

Pounds	25 years	45 years	65 years
110	2500	2350	1950
121	2700	2550	2150
132	2850	2700	2250
143	3000	2800	2350
154	3200	3000	2550
165	3400	3200	2700
176	3550	3350	2800
187	3700	3500	2900

Women

Pounds	25 years	45 years	65 years
88	1750	1650	1400
99	1900	1800	1500
110	2050	1950	1600
121	2200	2050	1750
128	2300	2200	1800
132	2350	2200	1850
143	2500	2350	2000
154	2600	2450	2050
165	2750	2600	2150

Offsetting the increase in basal metabolic rate, however, is the training effect noted earlier. As you get better at any sport, your muscles also become efficient. After cycling along a road for an hour each day for 30 days, you won't burn up as many calories on the 30th day as you did on the first day. This rise in efficiency would affect the figures in tables C and D slightly. However, since these figures already average out a number of variables, and the increase in basal metabolic rate uses up more calories between exercise sessions, they remain a useful guide. Combining bicycling or other exercise with lower caloric intakes makes for weight loss within a reasonable time period. And it can be enjoyable, too.

TABLE C: CALORIC EXPENDITURE DURING EXERCISE
(in calories per minute)

	Men (150 lbs.)	Women (125 lbs.)
Bicycling**		
5.5 m.p.h.	2.5	2.1
9.4 m.p.h.*	7.2	6.0
13.1 m.p.h.	11.8	9.5
Running		
12-min. mile (5 m.p.h.)	10.0	8.4
8-min. mile (7.5 m.p.h.)*	15.0	12.4
6-min. mile (10 m.p.h.)	20.0	16.1
5-min. mile (12 m.p.h.)	25.0	20.0
Swimming		
25 yds./min.	6.0	5.1
50 yds./min.	12.5	10.4
Hiking		
Level road (3½ m.p.h.)	7.0	5.6
Downhill (2½ m.p.h.)	3.6	3.5
Uphill, 5% (3½ m.p.h.)	8.0	6.5
Uphill, 15% (3½ m.p.h.)	15.0	12.5

*Activity level used in computing number of minutes equal to food calories in Table E.

**On level roads. Add 20-50% for grades up to 5%.

(Sources: *Food: The Yearbook of Agriculture,* 1959, USDA; R. Passmore and J.V.G.A. Durnin, *Physiological Review,* 35 (1955): 801; Jean Mayer, *Overweight* (Englewood Cliffs, N.J.: Prentice-Hall, 1968); and Brian J. Sharkey, *Fitness and Work Capacity,* Forest Service 315, USDA, 1977.

TABLE D: BICYCLING DAYS TO LOSE 5 - 20 POUNDS
(in combination with less foods*)

Bicycling (Minutes/Day)	Less Food (Calories/Day)	To Lose 5 lbs.	To Lose 10 lbs.	To Lose 15 lbs.	To Lose 20 lbs.
30	200	41	83	124	165
30	400	28	56	84	112
30	600	21	42	63	84
30	800	17	34	51	68
30	1000	14	29	43	57
45	200	33	65	88	130
45	400	24	47	71	94
45	600	19	37	56	74
45	800	15	31	46	62
45	1000	13	27	40	54
60	200	27	54	81	108
60	400	21	41	62	82
60	600	17	33	50	66
60	800	14	28	42	56
60	1000	12	24	36	48

*Calculated at 7½ Calories/minute for about 10 m.p.h. with slight grades up and down; 3500 calories equal one pound of body weight.

Swimmers elbowing and kicking for swimming space and heading for the first buoy.

Castaic Lake, California, Nautilus Triathlon, Spring '82, start over 700 contestants.

4

Fat Conversion and Metabolism
For the Triathlete

Fat Metabolism

WHAT IS FAT METABOLISM? It is a metabolic process in the body which converts fat into fuel for energy.

Why is it important? Fat is the primary fuel for athletes engaged in long endurance aerobic work, such as triathlon events. Performance in this type of physical activity requires the economic working of fat metabolism. Top marathon runners, during their 26-mile race, will burn approximately 70% fats and 30% carbohydrates as fuel. Studies show that at the end of a marathon, top performers have the highest free fatty acid levels in their blood. So, as a triathlon participant or a long-endurance-type athlete, it is helpful to understand how this process works . . . to train your body's fat conversion for efficiency.

Understanding ATP — Adenosine Triphosphate

ATP (Adenosine Triphosphate) is the energy source needed for all muscle contractions. Stored fuels such as fat and carbohydrate assist in the production of ATP. Every time we have a muscle contraction in our body (i.e. when swimming, biking or running) we break down the ATP. So, there has to be a process to rebuild ATP as fast as it is broken down or there will be no more muscle contractions and a halting of activity.

What is this rebuilding process? ATP rebuilding comes from combining adenosine diphosphate (ADP) and phosphate (P). However, this is not the complete formula, for energy is needed to combine ADP and P. This energy comes from the stored fuels of carbohydrates and fats. These fuels do not change into ATP molecules, but release energy to liberate ADP to combine with P. In short, ADP + P + energy (fats and carbohydrates) = ATP. Inversely, when ATP is used, ADP and P produced.

Where and How is Fat Stored?

Most fat and excessive calories of carbohydrates and proteins are stored as a triglyceride, which is a 4-part molecule made up of 1 molecule of glycerol and 3 molecules of fatty acids. Triglycerides are stored primarily as subcutaneous fat, or fat that is surface flesh. The fatty acids split off the triglyceride molecule to form free fatty acids (FFA). It is primarily the FFA which assist in the production of ATP. When called upon, the FFA are transported by the blood to the muscles and are broken down by beta oxidization. Beta oxidization is a long complicated process and will not be covered in this topic. More importantly, the result of beta oxidization is the production of ATP.

In general, free fatty acids are stored in muscle cells and in the blood. The triglycerides are stored near the surface of the skin. The FFA are made available to the blood from the triglyceride molecules and are then transported to the working tissues.

Advantages and Disadvantages of Fat

The advantages and disadvantages of fat are shown in relationship to the other primary fuel — carbohydrates. Protein is not considered a primary fuel because it only provides a minor contribution to ATP production and is spared as long as fats and carbohydrates are available.

Advantages of Fat:

1) 147 molecules of ATP can be produced from one, 18-carbon fatty acid molecule, whereas, only 38 molecules of ATP are produced from one, 6-carbon glucose (carbohydrate) molecule. Or, per carbon atom, fat metabolism is 30% more efficient in the production of ATP than carbohydrates.

2) 1 lb. of fat can supply more than twice the ATP than 1 lb. of carbohydrate. Carbohydrates are a very heavy fuel because they have to be stored with water.

3) Fat reserves are much greater on the body than carbohydrates. It has been estimated that the total calorie store of a trained individual is approximately 50,000 Kcal or 20 times greater than carbohydrates.

Disadvantages of Fat:

1) The main disadvantage of fat as a fuel, is that it produces less ATP per unit of oxygen consumed than carbohydrates; i.e. 6 oxygen molecules are required to produce 38 ATP molecules during the aerobic breakdown of a molecule of the six-carbon glucose, whereas, 26 oxygen molecules are needed for the breakdown of the 18-carbon fatty acid molecule to 147 ATP molecules. By this, carbohydrates are 12% more efficient in the production of ATP in relationship to oxygen. So, an athlete can expend more energy with less oxygen when utilizing carbohydrate metabolism.

In summary, carbohydrates are more efficient than fats as a fuel in terms of the amount of ATP produced per molecule of oxygen consumed. However, fat has basically unlimited reserves, is a lighter fuel and can produce more ATP per molecule. Any athlete engaged in long duration aerobic events must rely on fat metabolism to conserve the limited body reserve of carbohydrates.

What Does Distance Training Do?

Are you ready to expend over 12,000 calories, endure 3 marathons back to back and supply your moving body with oxygen and fuel for anywhere between 10 and 24 hours? This is approximately what it takes to complete the triathlon in Hawaii. Your training better be sufficient and complete or you won't complete the task.

The most important factor is that when a person trains long distance in biking, swimming or running they use fat preferentially for ATP production more than carbohydrates. This is a very significant point because, as noted earlier, the reserves of fat are plentiful, whereas the reserves of carbohydrates are very limited. Unless the body is trained to utilize fat as a fuel, very little fat is converted until it is really needed. This would parallel the typical marathon runner who "hits the wall" after approximately 2 hours of running. He or she has depleted the reserves of carbohydrates and is now dependent on fat as a fuel. However, because fat metabolism has not been trained sufficiently, it is inefficient and performance suffers. This fate can be avoided by proper training. Remember, we are not concerned with the amount of fat underneath the surface of the skin but, the concentration of FFA in the muscular fibers and how well these FFA are oxidized.

What Physiological Adaptations Occur With Distance Training?

1. There is an increase in the capacity of the oxidative enzymes located on the muscular fibers to oxidize FFA. By this, the muscles of trained individuals can oxidize more fat at a given concentration than those not trained.

2) With training, a lower body-fat ratio can be expected due to the increase in calorie expenditure. In one study done on animals, it shows that the animals with a lower body-fat ratio (after adaption to exercise) have a greater turnover and metabolic activity of fat.

3) Training produces a greater maximal oxygen uptake or higher state of physical fitness. Maximal oxygen uptake (Vo_2 max.) is simply the amount of oxygen that can be used by the tissues of the body. The more physically fit a person is, the greater the amount of oxygen that can be consumed. To calculate this, one must know the difference between the inspired and expired air. The ratio is usually expressed as volume/weight/time. An average Vo_2 max. for college men is approximately 48 ml/kg/min and for women is 40 ml/kg/min.

The workload also defines what type of fuel is going to be utilized. The heavier the workload, the increase in carbohydrates burning and decrease in fat metabolism. Research indicates, the higher the level of carbohydrates used as fuel, the more lactate is produced as a consequence. When lactate is formed, this interferes with the release of FFA, so less fat utilization. By this, at the same workload the physically fit person with a high Vo_2 max. has an advantage over a less fit person in long endurance events. So, in long duration events, such as the triathlon . . . a well-trained athlete will have better performance because this individual can compete at a faster pace without an increase in the comparable workloads. Note, at all workloads carbohydrates are burned, however, in long endurance aerobic work . . . the critical factor is the percentage of carbohydrates used. Too great of a percentage will cause a reduction in performance later on.

4) The capillary transport capacity for triglycerides is increased. With any type of training, capillary density is enhanced, so the transport system is better.

5) The concentration of FFA is increased in the blood. Training promotes easier splitting of the fatty acids from the triglyceride molecule and makes the availability better to the working tissues.

How to Train Fat Metabolism

According to recent studies, it seems there are two main methods to train your body to convert fat economically and efficiently. They are: a) achieve a higher maximum oxygen uptake and b) train at submaximal workloads for extended periods of time.

Oxygen uptake can be increased by training at workloads from light intensity to heavy intensity. The lightest workload should be at least 70% of one's maximum heart rate to get a training effect. What's the best training workload to achieve the most rapid increase of oxygen uptake? Every coach has his own view, but research indicates that by stressing the system with the greatest amount of intensity, the organism will adapt faster. However, the athlete has to weigh such factors as psychological well-being and if there is an increase in injuries. As noted earlier, with an increase in maximum oxygen uptake, this allows the athlete to perform at a faster pace without increasing the comparable workload. In other words, by being more physically fit, an individual who used to run a 7:00 minute mile at 70% effort might be able to run a 6:00 minute mile at 70% now. Just as important, that individual who used to run a 7:00 mile pace might only have to use 65% effort and will be able to endure longer, because he is burning more fat. An athlete who is training for maximum oxygen uptake should include in his or her training program; intervals, fartlek or tempo training.

The other method to train fat metabolism is to train at submaximal workloads for extended periods of time. By doing prolonged work, the body is influenced to convert fat as an energy source. Thus, the rate of fat oxidization is increased by the capacity of the tissues to oxidize fat, and there is an increase of FFA in the blood plasma. Training should be geared toward long slow distance and continuous training.

A third method to assist in adapting the body to fat metabolism is periodic fasting. There is very little information on this subject, but research shows that when an individual fasts, the body is forced to utilize fats as an energy source. This could help as an adaptability factor. Studies by Basu, Passmore and Strong showed that men who fasted and walked at 4 mph. for long hours, had higher FFA levels than men who did not fast. For more information on fasting, read the chapter on The Nine Doctors of Preventive Medicine in this book. For another Health Science life-changing book read . . . *Miracle of Fasting for Physical, Mental & Spiritual Rejuvenation*. See back pages for ordering.

Are Women Better Suited for Triathlon and Distance Events?

Apparently there is no significant difference between women and men in long endurance aerobic events. A study by D.R. Bransford and E.T. Howley showed that the metabolic response of women is similar to men during exercise, before and after training. Many people figure that, just because women generally have more fat on their bodies, they would be better suited for long distance races. However, we are not concerned about how much body fat is near the flesh, but how efficiently that fat is oxidized by working tissues. True enough, in a survival test, a person with 21% body fat would survive longer than an individual with only 10% body fat.

Fat Metabolism Summary

Fat metabolism is a relatively new area of study and some exciting results are being found. As a long-endurance-type athlete, it is imperative that you utilize fat metabolism for a successful completion of triathlon events, or any other type of endurance event. In preparing for a triathlon, your training schedule should include methods to adapt your body to being able to sufficiently utilize the vast resource of fat as a fuel.

Most Americans have over 20% of their body weight in the form of fat. And as you would expect, athletes have a smaller percentage of fat than non-athletes.

RELATIVE BODY FAT VALUES (%) IN VARIOUS SPORTS*

Sport	Male Fat (%)	Female Fat (%)
Baseball/softball	12-14	16-26
Basketball	7-10	16-27
Football	8-18	
Gymnastics	4-6	9-15
Ice hockey	13-15	
Soccer	9-12	
Swimming	5-10	14-26
Distance running	4-8	6-12
Tennis	14-16	18-22
Weightlifting	8-16	
Wrestling	4-12	

*Values represent the range of means reported in various published and unpublished studies.

TABLE E: EXERCISE TIME TO LOSE CALORIES
(Number of minutes to equal food calories for exercise selected)

Food	Cal.	Running M	Running W	Bicycling M	Bicycling W	Swimming M	Swimming W	Hiking M	Hiking W
Beverages									
Cola, 12-oz.	145	10	12	21	23	12	14	21	26
Fruit flavored, 12-oz.	170	11	14	24	27	14	16	24	30
Ginger ale, 12-oz.	112	8	9	16	18	9	11	16	20
Beer, 12-oz.	150	10	12	21	25	12	14	21	27
Wines, table, 3 oz.	75	5	6	11	13	6	7	11	14
Wines, dessert, 3 oz.	125	8	10	18	21	10	12	18	22
Whiskey, 80-proof, 1½ oz.	95	6	8	14	16	8	9	14	17
Whiskey, 100-proof, 1½ oz.	125	8	10	18	21	10	12	18	22
Cereals									
Bread, slice, ¹⁄₁₆-lb.	75	5	6	11	13	6	7	11	14
Muffin, 2¾-in. dia.	140	9	11	20	23	11	13	20	25
Bun, hamburger	120	8	10	17	20	10	12	17	21
Sweet roll	135	9	11	19	23	11	13	19	24
Saltine crackers, 2	35	2	3	5	6	3	3	5	6
Doughnut	125	8	10	18	21	10	12	18	22
Pancake, 4-in.	60	4	5	9	10	5	6	9	11
Waffle	210	14	17	30	35	17	20	30	38
Bran flakes 1 cup	105	7	8	15	18	8	10	15	19
Corn flakes 1 cup	95	6	8	14	16	8	9	14	17
Farina, cooked 1 cup	105	7	8	15	18	8	10	15	19
Rice, puffed, 1 cup	60	4	5	9	10	5	6	9	11
Macaroni, plain	115	8	9	16	18	9	11	16	20
Spaghetti, plain	115	8	9	16	18	9	11	16	20
Dairy Group									
Milk, whole, 1 cup	160	11	13	23	27	13	15	23	29
Milk, skim, 1 cup	90	6	7	13	15	7	9	13	16
Sour cream 1 cup	505	34	41	72	84	40	48	72	90
Yogurt, 1 cup	120	8	10	17	20	10	12	17	21

The first wealth is health. Sickness is poor spirited and cannot serve anyone. —Emerson

TABLE E: EXERCISE TIME TO LOSE CALORIES *(Cont'd)*
(Number of minutes to equal food calories for exercise selected)

Food	Cal.	Running M	Running W	Bicycling M	Bicycling W	Swimming M	Swimming W	Hiking M	Hiking W
Malted milk, 1 cup	280	19	23	40	47	22	27	40	50
Ice cream, ½ cup	145	10	12	21	23	12	14	21	26
Cheese, cheddar, 1-oz.	115	8	9	16	18	9	11	16	20
Cheese, cottage, 2 tbsp.	30	2	2	4	5	2	3	4	5
Desserts									
Cake, 2 in. sect. 10″ dia. with icing	345	23	28	49	58	28	33	49	62
Gingerbread, 2-in. sq.	170	11	24	24	27	14	16	24	30
Yellow cake, 2-in. sect., 18″ dia., no icing	205	14	17	29	34	16	20	29	37
Caramels, 3 med.	115	8	9	16	18	9	11	16	20
Chocolate mints, 2 small	90	6	7	13	15	7	9	13	16
Hard candy, 1 oz.	110	7	9	16	18	9	11	16	20
Chocolate bar, 1 oz.	150	1	1	2	3	1	1	2	3
Sugar, 1 tsp.	15	1	1	2	3	1	1	2	3
Cookies, 3-in.	120	8	10	17	20	10	12	17	21
Apple pie, ⅙ 9-in.	300	20	24	43	50	24	29	43	54
Custard pie, ⅙ 9-in.	250	17	20	36	42	20	24	36	45
Pecan pie, ⅙ 9-in.	430	29	35	61	72	34	41	61	77
Fats and Oils									
Butter or marg. 1 pat	50	3	4	4	8	4	5	7	9
Salad dressing, blue cheese, 1 tsp.	75	5	6	11	13	6	7	11	14
Mayonnaise, 1 tsp.	100	7	8	13	17	8	10	14	18
Salad dressing, low cal., 1 tsp.	15	1	1	2	3	1	1	2	3

William James, American philosopher, coined the phrase, "The great American frenzy." He meant the frenzied push of so many people to acquire money and possessions as if they were the chief aim in life. We must lay aside the frenzy of possessions and seek the peace of mind only God can give.

TABLE E: EXERCISE TIME TO LOSE CALORIES *(Cont'd)*
(Number of minutes to equal food calories for exercise selected)

Food	Cal.	Running M	Running W	Bicycling M	Bicycling W	Swimming M	Swimming W	Hiking M	Hiking W
Meat and Protein Group									
Beef & veg. stew, 1 cup	185	12	15	25	31	15	18	26	33
Beef pot pie, 8-oz.	560	37	45	80	94	45	54	80	100
Chili with beans, 1 cup	170	11	14	24	27	14	16	24	30
Hamburger, broiled, 3-oz.	245	16	20	35	41	20	24	35	44
Meat loaf, 3 oz.	170	11	24	27	14	16	24	24	30
Roast beef, 3 oz.	375	24	30	54	63	30	36	54	67
Steak, broiled, lean, 3-oz.	175	12	14	24	29	14	17	25	31
Bacon, 2 thin slices	60	4	5	9	10	5	6	9	11
Ham, cured, lean, 3 oz.	160	11	13	23	27	13	15	23	29
Pork sausage, 2-oz.	270	18	22	38	45	22	26	39	48
Frankfurter, 1	155	10	12	22	26	12	15	22	28
Chicken, fried, ½ breast	155	10	12	22	26	12	15	22	28
Fish sticks, breaded, 5	200	13	16	28	33	16	19	29	36
Egg, fried, 1 large	100	7	8	13	17	8	10	14	18
Baked beans, ½ cup	155	10	12	22	26	12	15	22	28
Snacks									
Popcorn, popped in oil, 1 cup	40	8	9	16	18	9	11	16	20
Potato chips, 10 med.	115	8	9	16	18	9	11	16	20
Pizza, plain cheese, slice	185	12	15	25	31	15	18	26	33
Vegetables									
Carrot, 1x5½ in.	20	1	2	3	3	2	2	2	3
Celery, 2, 8-in. stalks	10	1	1	1	2	1	1	1	1
Lettuce, 2 large leaves	10	1	1	1	2	1	1	1	1
Tomato, l med.	35	2	3	5	6	3	3	5	6

Now I see the secret of the making of the best persons, it is to grow in the open air, and eat and sleep with the earth. —Walt Whitman

The Galley Cafe of Kona has its welcoming banner out for the Triathletes. The galley is owned by Bud and Rita Anderson of Morro Bay, California, where the original Galley Cafe is located. Local merchants including Jackie, the manager of the Galley, are very supportive of the Triathlon.

Another view of Kailua Kona Bay looking down the swimming course, past the Kona Hilton Hotel, across the bay. The Hilton is about one third of the distance of the course.

5

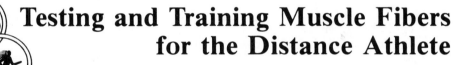

Testing and Training Muscle Fibers for the Distance Athlete

Muscle Power and What it Means to the Triathlete

The study of muscle fibres, their ratio of percentage between red and white, slow and fast twitch is relatively new. The subject is of extreme importance to the athlete as it will determine the genetic composition of his body's muscle tissue, therefore his innate ability to perform certain types of sports.

The triathlete should be aware of this fact as the results of a jump test will determine how best to train for the Swim, Bike, and Run distance events.

It is possible to train muscles to function in a way that they were not intended as we will see later in this chapter but first we must understand the meaning of muscle power.

Muscle power is one of the most misunderstood of our physical traits. It is often considered to be synonymous with strength . . . but while it is related to strength, it also involves speed. Speed more appropriately termed Explosive Power Strength . . . termed another way is stamina and endurance.

Muscle Fiber Test for Triathletes

The vertical jump has long been considered to be a good measure of explosive power. I found the sprinters attained average scores of 28 inches, while the distance runners averaged only 14 inches. The range of the scores on the vertical jump ranged from 9 to 31 inches. The technique used then and still used today involves the jump and reach.

The subject stands sideways and next to the wall against a graph or a yardstick and raises one hand, reaching as high as he can (with his dominant hand). He then moves about 6 inches to 1 foot away from the wall and, without taking a step, jumps upward as he would in jumping for a basketball and reaches as high as he can with his dominant hand. The differences between his standing and jumping reach is noted and recorded. He is given three trials, with the highest score being taken as his final measurement. There is a positive correlation between the height a swimmer can jump and his sprinting ability.

Below are listed the vertical jump scores of some swimmers, including data gathered at the 1975 National AAU Outdoor Meet:

Sprinters:

Mark Spitz . . . . 26 in.
John Trembly . . . . 28 in.
Ken Knox . . . . 27 in.
Chris Woo . . . . 29 in.
Rick Hofstetter . . . . 30 in.
John Murphy . . . . 27 in.
Jim Montgomery . . . . 25 in.
Joe Bottom . . . . 26 in.

Distance Swimmers:

James Kegley . . . . 16 in.
John Kinsella . . . . 18 in.
Bruce Dickson . . . . 19 in.
George Breen . . . . 14 in.

Others:

Greg Jagenburg . . . . 22 in.
John Naber . . . . 18 in.
Mike Stamm . . . . 24 in.
Gary Hall . . . . 25 in.

Swimmers Greg Jagenburg and John Naber
Present Two Very Interesting Cases:

Greg won the World Championships in the 100-meter butterfly and didn't do as well in the 200 butterfly in that particular meet. At the National Outdoor Championships, after Greg had done only fair in the 100-meter butterfly, they tested his vertical jump and found he had a score of 22 inches. On the basis of his score, they prdicted he should swim a better 200-meter butterfly than a 100. He then won the 200 fly in near world-record time!

John Naber, who won the 100- and 200-meter backstroke, probably has the lowest vertical jump of any male swimmer who has ever won a national title at the 100-meter distance. John is not basically a sprinter and would better qualify as a distance swimmer, as evidenced by his win in the 500-yard freestyle in 4:20 plus, and in the National AAU Indoor 1650-yard freestyle in 15:05 plus, both American record times.

Paul Anderson, Olympic weight-lifting champion and considered by many to be the strongest man in the world, weighed 330 pounds, had a vertical jump of 31 inches. Sprinters in track run 60 and 100 yards (6 to 10 seconds) and sometimes 220 yards (21 seconds). In swimming, especially in international competition, the shortest event is 100 meters, which compares to a 400-meter running race in terms of elapsed time. We do not have a truly explosive swimming event as they do in track unless we consider the 50-yard race in indoor competition. It is therefore doubtful that we will see many explosive athletes in swimming, particularly in the long-course competition.

What Makes One Athlete
More Explosive than Another?

For over one hundred years physiologists have been aware of the distinction between *red* and *white* muscle fibers. In humans and most animals both red (slow-twitch) and white (fast-twitch) fibers are found in nearly every muscle. The white (fast-twitch) fibers are adapted to contract quickly, but they tire easily, while the red (slow-twitch) fibers contract more slowly but are capable of greater endurance. For many years it was believed that the main difference in the two muscle fibers was the difference in the level of myoglobin. Myoglobin is a protein material in the muscle that has a strong affinity for oxygen and gives the red color to the muscle fibers. The red fibers, having considerably more myoglobin than the white fibers, consequently display the difference in color. The higher myoglobin in the red (ST) fibers permits them to have a high metabolic capacity for carrying on aerobic oxidation, which results in better endurance. These are the muscle fibers a swimmer would use primarily when swimming a long race. White (FT) muscle fibers are capable of fast release of energy and are the fibers a swimmer uses primarily when swimming a sprint.

Exactly how the slow-twitch fibers are used or recruited in a sprint event, if they are, or how the fast-twitch fibers are used in a distance swim, if they are, is unknown, and the question is a source of controversy. Humans, as well as the various species of animals, show variations in the percentage of slow-twitch and fast-twitch fibers they possess in the various muscles. For example, members of the cat family, such as the lion, cheetah, and even the common house cat, have a predominant number of fast-twitch muscle fibers. They catch their prey by slowly stalking it and then finally capturing it with a fast spring effort. If they don't catch it within ten to fifteen seconds, they give up and walk slowly away with the slow-twitch fibers because their fast-twitch fibers are out of gas.

Members of the canine family, such as wolves, wild dogs, or hyenas, are different from the cats in that they have a higher percentage of slow-twitch fibers and they catch their prey by running it down and wearing it out.

How can this information be used by a coach in his selection and training of swimmers?

Inherent Variability Among Humans in
the Proportion of Fast-Twitch and Slow-Twitch Fibers

Before we make an application to actual coaching methods, let us discuss several important physiological principles concerning slow-twitch and fast-twitch fibers.

The proportion of slow-twitch to fast-twitch fibers is genetically established and apparently cannot be changed by training. The proportional percentage of the two types of fibers that make up a muscle is determined by taking a small biopsy of the athlete's muscle (usually the thigh or calf). The muscle sample is sliced, stained, and examined with a microscope. There is no great deal of discomfort from this procedure, with the athlete's performance not being detrimentally affected. The thigh muscle is usually a mixture of these two fibers in a ratio of 50/50, and good distance runners have a higher percentage of slow-twitch fibers.

**Here are a few examples of the distance runners' results,
as measured in the gastrocnemius muscle:**

Runner	Slow Twitch	Fast Twitch
Ndoo	80%	20%
Prefontaine	82%	18%
Shorter	75%	25%

Sprinters usually have a higher percentage of fast-twitch fibers, some having as high a proportion as 90 percent of white fast-twitch fibers. That this proportionally is an inherent characteristic seems to be an accepted fact. Bengt Saltin reports that identical twins, one a weight lifter and the other a distance runner, were identical in their porportion of fast-twitch and slow-twitch fibers. They tested a father and two sons (Stetina), all three promiment bicyclists, and found the father had 60.5 percent slow-twitch fibers, one son had 60.8 percent, and the other son 61 percent. From the few samples taken of fathers and sons, there is some evidence to believe that sons tend to inherit this trait from their fathers.

A More Recent Classification of Muscle Fibers

Physiologists no longer classify muscle fibers simply as red or white, but rather as fast-twitch or slow-twitch fibers.

What Happens When Fast-Twitch Red Fibers are Converted to Fast-Twitch White Fibers, or Vice Versa?

If we take a sprinter and train him as a distance swimmer, what will happen to his speed and what will happen to his fast-twitch white fibers? Some research plus an application of the physiological adaptation principle would seem to indicate that with distance training the athlete would change some of the fast-twitch white fibers into fast-twitch red fibers. It would also seem logical to believe that, once these fast-twitch white fibers are converted into fast-twitch red fibers, they increase their endurance but lose some of their speed. If you train a runner who runs the 100-yard dash on primarily the same schedule as a marathon runner he will lose much of his speed. This explosive runner cannot train as hard as a marathon runner; his muscles are not physiologically adapted for this type of training. He literally cannot take the work.

In the past they have gotten by with training what we call sprinters and distance swimmers on essentially the same program and with some success because, as mentioned before, we do not have a true sprint event in swimming, our shortest international event being the 100 meters which compares to the 400-meter run in terms of time. As competitive swimmers become more advanced in their performances we can expect to see more variation within a training program as swimmers, in order to win a single event, are forced to specialize in training either for the shorter distance, the middle distance, or the distance events.

Comparisons in Animal Endurance and Speed

To avoid the endurance-type predators, such as hyenas or Cape Town wild dogs, zebras must count on their superior speed in the sprints to save them when the hyenas are near. Eventually the persistent hyenas will wear out many of the zebras because of their superior endurance. The perspicacity of the zebras can be seen by the fact that they will allow the hyenas and wild dogs to get much closer to them than they will allow the cats.

They believe the majority of athletes would fall into the zebra category, being average in endurance and average in speed and not excellent in either. Over the years coaches have always seemed to have one or two swimmers who can't work exceptionally hard and can't swim distances very well but who are able to sprint well. These athletes have always had an above-average vertical jump of 27 inches or more. Such athletes are commonly called *drop-dead* sprinters.

A swimmer is born with a given amount of potential for sprinting and a given amount of potential for endurance work. If they develop him to his fullest potential in endurance, it is impossible to develop him to his fullest potential at the same time for sprinting. Coaches who make such brash statements as "anyone who comes out for my team becomes a distance swimmer" had better re-examine their training programs and be aware of the fact that not only do dogs, cats, and zebras vary in their endurance and speed potential but that humans also vary in the same traits and in their ability to handle hard training!

Hormonal Influences on Power

Gutmann, a German researcher, states that certain muscle fibers are sensitive to the influence of sex hormones. The transition from red fast-twitch fibers to white fast-twitch fibers under hormonal influence has also been observed. The implications here are obvious. If a girl were to be given a male hormone, such as testosterone or the anabolic steroids, her speed would improve, but her endurance would be detrimentally affected. Little work has been done with biopsy studies of females. On the basis of their performances at the various distances women appear to be better suited for endurance activities. If we were to take a large group of world-class women swimmers and give them male hormones, we would expect them to perform well and possibly to set world records in the spring events, but to do less well in the distance events.

Does a High Power Factor in the Legs
Also Mean a High Power Factor in the Arms?

The swimmer receives most of his propulsive force to pull him through the water from his arms. Wouldn't it be better to measure the power in his arms? The answer to this question is a definite yes. At the present time it is difficult to measure arm power. Eventually we will have an electronic digital analyzer that will attach to the Mini-Gym Swim Bench and which will be able to analyze the power factor in the arms. In the meantime we will continue to use the vertical jump.

It is highly unlikely that a person could have endurance-type muscles in his legs and speed-type muscles in his arms, any more than we would expect a cat to have slow hind legs and fast front legs. In the next few years we will see the birth of all sorts of electronic analyzing isokinetic equipment that will be capable of measuring the power output of almost any muscle group. At that time I hope to be able to report to you on the use and effectiveness of this type of equipment.

I think at this time, however, it is safe to say that the power of the muscles in the leg is indicative of the potential power in the rest of the muscles of the body.

Slow Twitch - Fast Twitch
(Percentage of Muscle Fibers in Track and Field Athletics)

Event/Athlete	Percentage of ST Fibers
Sprinters (100-400)	8 to 24%
Middle Distance Runners (800-2 mile)	40 to 65%
Distance Runners (500M +)	80+%
Distance Runners (Dallas study mean)	79%
Middle Distance Runners (Dallas mean)	61.8%
Untrained Men (Dallas, lean somatotype)	57.7%
Throwers	40-50%
Jumpers	40-50%
Lynn Davies (long jumper)	45%
Gary Tuttle (distance)	98%
Jeff Galloway (distance)	96%
Paul Geis (distance)	79%
Don Kardong (distance)	50% (overall equals 75%)
Kenny Moore (distance)	83%
Steve Prefontaine (distance)	77%
Frank Shorter (distance)	80%

Muscle Fiber and Training

The increasing knowledge about muscle fibers and their reactions to training re-emphasizes the knowledge acquired from the energy systems and the principle of event specificity of training. The important considerations in training for specific events are duration and intensity of the training exercise in relation to the event. Fast twitch fibers have very low aerobic potential, high anaerobic and intensity potentials, and respond to very intense anaerobic work. They are characteristic of sprinters. Fast twitch fibers can, through training, increase their aerobic enzymes and utilize aerobic energy sources, and act as endurance fibers (ST). Still, they contract quickly and respond to intense activity. Slow twitch fibers have a high aerobic potential and respond to less intense, long duration work. They are characteristic of distance runners. This indicates that the duration and intensity of the training must both be similar to the event to create the proper training response in the muscle fibers. Slow exercise movements do not affect the FT fibers, and intense, anaerobic movements do not affect the ST fibers.

Muscle Fiber Training Responses:

Just as the energy systems respond to training so do the muscle fibers. The following training responses, or adaptations to stress have been observed:

(1) All fibers grow in thickness. FT fiber responds with more growth than ST fiber, but both grow.

(2) All fibers grow stronger.

(3) Trained muscle fibers store more energy than the untrained.

(4) Training increases the ability of muscle fiber to tolerate fatigue and it increases the endurance characteristics of the fiber.

(5) The type of training that is done determines which fibers, FT or ST, will undergo the greater training response. You cannot train both fibers, or types of ability, with a single training method. Sprinters who only do distance training grow slow. This emphasizes the old standby: "If you don't use it, you lose it!"

How to Change Muscle Fibers by Training

Every person varies from every other in the proportion of red to white fibers that exists in their muscles. Each is born with this proportionality and it cannot be changed through training or by any other means.

The fibers do not change from red to white, or white to red, but the quality in the fibers can be changed somewhat, depending on the type of training to which they are subjected.

How Can the Red Fibers be Changed?

1. The red fibers can be increased in size (hypertrophied) and strength by exercising with heavy resistance at a slow or moderate speed. This is especially true if negative exercise (letting the weight down) is used. This increase in size of the muscle fibers is due to an increase in the size of the myofibrils (the contractile element of the muscle fiber) and results in a bulkier muscle — actually a larger cross-sectional area. The endurance of the muscle is not improved, because there is no beneficial change in the mitachondrial mass of the muscle. The mitachondria are cellules in the muscle fiber which carry on the metabolism of the muscle, and an increase in their mass improves endurance. The use of a certain piece of equipment — a rocker-arm weight-lifting arrangement — or of weight-lifting exercises with heavy weights at slow speed has limited merit for swimmers and other athletes who are interested in acquiring speed, because they build big, but slow muscles. Because the exercises are done at slow speed, the white fibers are not involved and thus remain unchanged and do not increase in size. The increase in the size of the red fibers with no corresponding increase in the size of the white fibers causes a shift in the proportion of total mass of the muscle in favor of the red fibers. This is another reason for emphasizing to all athletes who are interested in building speed or endurance that they should avoid slow-movement types of exercise, such as that developed by the Nautilus and similar equipment.

Body builders use this type of exercise to "bulk up" since they are not interested in speed or endurance. Competitive weight lifters, because they are interested in speed, avoid this type of work.

2. The red fibers can be improved in endurance by performing many repetitions of an exercise against moderate resistance, such as by doing 300 repetitions on a pulley-weight exerciser. This type of exercise may not improve the size of the muscle to any great extent, but it will improve the muscle's endurance. The improvement results from changes within the red fiber — primarily in the mitachondria — which permit a more efficient enzyme action and improve the muscle's ability to utilize oxygen.

The swimmer, however, builds endurance in the red fibers when he swims overdistance or when he uses interval training and does not need to build a lot of muscle endurance in his dry-land exercise program. The dry-land exercise program is necessary to improve strength, speed, and flexibility.

HRFS Exercise
and How It Can Change the White Fibers

1. The white fibers can be increased in size and strength by exercising against high resistance at a fast speed! The increase in the size of the white fibers is desirable since it increases the white fibers' mass relative to that of the red fibers and therefore increases the speed potential of the muscle.

Another day, another mountain to climb. The author, Bob Johnson, at the base of the Matterhorn, Zermatt, Switzerland.

Johny Kelly, 74, just completed his 51st Boston Marathon. His 1981 time was 4:01. The clock was kept running just for Johny. His best time was 2:38 in 1943. He has won the event 2 times finished 2nd 7 times and in the top ten finishers 19 times. Johny remembers Dr. Bragg, having attended the Bragg Health Lectures.

Dave Bending of Daves Quality Bikes, Santa Barbara, California, straightened over 400 bike wheels averaging 5 minutes per wheel for the spring '82 Triathlon.

If you have to work straightening bike wheels, you could not ask for a better place to work, beside the sea at Kona, hawaii.

This type of exercise (**HRFS — high resistance at fast speed**) can best be done by actually getting in the water and sprinting or by doing isokinetic exercise at a fast speed. HRFS exercise is virtually impossible to do on the Nautilus or the Universal or with barbells. The reason is that these three forms of exercise are all done by lifting weights against gravity. If the weight is lifted at a fast speed it soon becomes ballistic, and the momentum it develops during the first part of the lift carries the weight upward, with the result that the lifter gets little benefit from the last part of the movement. For this reason the makers of the Nautilus and the Universal Gym recommend that the exerciser do the exercises at relatively slow speed. The movements in most athletic events involve speed and are done in a fast, explosive manner.

2. The white fibers can be improved in their endurance through the performance of a lot of distance work. A paradox exists in this area: why do some white fibers change in some of their characteristics and become more like red fibers (they are never *completely* converted into red fibers)? If the white fibers are not involved in slow movements, why should they adapt to distance work and change their characteristics? This change has been noted by so many researchers that it is considered a valid change, and there is no doubt it is compensatory in nature. The fibers that change improve their endurance, but they do so at the expense of some of their speed. The application of this knowledge is that sprinters should avoid excessive over-distance work, especially at the peak of the season when they want to develop optimum speed and explosive power.

6

The Triathlete and the Percentage of Body Fat

The Triathlete and Body Fat

THE TRIATHLETE MUST APPROACH the problem of body weight differently than accepted medical approaches offered by many modern physicians and sports medicine practitioners.

First, we must be reminded that the multi-sport participant is interested in swimming, bicycling and running ... not only as individual sports, but excelling in the total multi-sport event! The biathlon or triathlon combines 2 or 3 of these sports into one continuous endeavor. This affects the optimum weight distribution for a multi-sport participant, as opposed to the preferences of a single sport enthusiast.

A Word of Warning to the Too-Thin Body Type

We are aware of the "Slim Jim" prototype, sub-three-hour marathon runner, many times with envy. In their sinewy five-minute mile strides for the finish line, not one ounce of excess weight is in evidence.

Then comes the avid distance swimmer proudly displaying the powerful upper body of pectorals, trapesus and deltoids ... the one that looks to the long stretches of water, the channels of the world for their goal. The human body, marvelous organism that it is has prepared this person, during long periods of immersion in cold water with an insulation layer of subcutaneous body fat that lies just under the skin, giving protection against the loss of normal body temperature, called hypothermia.

Hypothermia and cold water swimming, is a special important chapter in this book written by our friend, Jack LaLanne. Therefore, the percentage of body fat on the swimmer presents a major training and conditioning obstacle for the runner and at the same time an example of the equalizing effect of the triathlon as a competitive sport. Somewhere inbetween these two extremes lies the cyclist, equipped with sizeable lower body bulk in the form of powerful legs and back muscles. The cyclist is generally devoid of excess body fat. However, biking is the one individual sport that the moderately overweight person can excel in. Contrary to running, the bike can support the excess weight of a contestant. Their success will then depend on their power-to-weight ratio.

It is true that the men and women winners of the 1981 and '82 Ironman World Triathlon events held in Kona, Hawaii were on the lean side. This is a tribute to months of training. Bear in mind that the triathlon as a multi-sport participation event is relatively new: hardly time for the human body to adapt to the varied conditions that the triathlete must cope with in these events. Given a few years of participation in vastly varied climates, we predict the emergence of a physiological build and body composition that will typify the triathlete.

The Composite Triathlete Body Type

Having witnessed the major triathlons of the last 4 years, we can easily envision the triathlete of the future. The one outstanding and lasting impression of any triathlon event, from a spectator's viewpoint, is the display of beautiful bodies, both men and women. The name "ironman" in itself appeals to a certain type of athlete that would go out and "climb the mountain," regardless of the name, providing it was a challenge to his or her physical prowess. The awesome proportions of distance, heat, and sport modes add to this attraction.

Our triathlete of the future will be a composite of the body types mentioned above. The powerful leg muscles of the biker with the running performance of the sub-three hour marathoner, with the subcutaneous body fat layer and upper body development of the distance swimmer. The triathlon event is entitled to boast a body most likely to succeed.

Percentage of Body Fat Computation

Our chapter of percentage of body fat has been included to alert the uninformed of the existence of an alternative method of weight measurement. The traditional system of height, bone structure, and age as the determining factors in arriving at the correct weight are outdated; the percentage of body fat measurement is in. A well-trained triathlete will exceed the norm by from 5 to 7% body fat in any given calculation, man or woman, old or young, thus accounting for the layer of subcutaneous body fat required to spend extended periods of time in cold ocean and lake water in the swimming portion of the event.

The average college-age male and female are approximately 15% and 25% fat, respectively. Essential fat is adipose tissue that is contained in the heart, liver, kidneys, spleen, nervous tissue, cell membranes and in the working muscles and is necessary for the body to function in a normal fashion. Three to five percent fat and 13% fat is considered essential fat in males and females, respectively. It has been theorized that low body fat percentage in females may be a contributing factor to amenorrhea.

Some researchers have indicated that male athletes should not drop below five percent fat unless under medical supervision.

In summary, it is not necessary for all athletes to have an extremely low body fat percentage. In fact, an extremely low body fat percentage may hinder athletic performance.

The Fluctuation of Body Weight in a Triathlete

Distance oriented athletes should be especially interested in the percentage of body fat concept, it is the only true gauge of training weight. During the peak training periods prior to a major event such as the Hawaiian Ironman Triathlon, special attention should be given to weight control: the percentage of body fat will be an accurate indication of the proper nutritional intake required for the three-to-five hours of daily swim-bike-run training schedules.

The 1981 Ironman and prior events required a mid-course weigh-in on the bike and the run. If a triathlete's weight loss fell below 5% of his starting weight he would be required to pull out of the event. In the 1982 Ironman, this requirement was dropped due to the logistics of weighing in 600 contestants two times. However, the problem and the committee's concern still exists and should be taken as a personal concern of each triathlete. See our chapter on training injuries as it pertains to excessive training weight loss.

Body fat can be measured by several methods. The two most common measuring procedures are underwater weighing and calipers. The underwater weighing technique utilizes an Archimedean principle to determine the density of the body vs. the density of the water.

152

The second method is by using calipers. Approximately 70-80% of body fat in Caucasians is immediately under the skin. (Blacks, on the other hand, store fat more often around the gut and in pockets in the joints.) That being the case, we can estimate body fat in Caucasians by measuring skinfold thicknesses. Through trial and error in the laboratory, we have determined a few key places for measurements (again using predetermined equations). If you are interested in making an estimate of your own body fat content, you can obtain a pair of skinfold calipers with instructions at a relatively low price.

Skinfold Calipers —
A Concept Whose Time Has Come

If you have always relied on a scale to tell if you are over or underweight, or a height-weight chart (if you are this tall, you should weigh this much . . .), you are probably not getting the most accurate information. To begin with, an overweight person (as revealed by a table), may not necessarily be obese. Consider these two examples: a 6′2″ and 260 lbs. professional football player may be overweight by a table, yet his percent of body fat, a more revealing number, may prove him to be quite lean. Let's assume, for the moment, that normal percent fat for young men and women is less than 20 and 25% respectively. If he is 18% fat (18% of his total weight as fat), he might be considered "overweight" but hardly obese. How about the professional model who weighs 110 lbs. and is 30% fat? Our football player is quite heavy but lean, while our model is small and fat. No scale or table will give you accurate information on these examples, or, in fact, those of both sexes, regardless of age or occupation.

With obesity demonstrated as a risk factor in heart disease, it would be advisable to monitor and control this variable, usually by modification of diet and activity levels. But how do we monitor the amount of fat in our body? As discussed, height-weight tables do not compensate for an increase in weight due to an increase in lean body mass (i.e., non-fat tissue). Children, adults, males, and females differ in body build and may be poorly assessed. As an example, if you are addressing a wrestler as to the correct weight class to compete in, you had better have more information than a height-weight chart.

Non-athletic Americans' body fat percentages range from 30% for males and 35% for females, plus or minus 5%. The average percent of body fat is a function of both age and sex. As one ages, the body's composition changes, usually because of a more sendentary lifestyle. After age 25 . . .

- One's weight *increases* by a pound a year.
- One's muscle mass *decreases* by half a pound a year.

By age 45, there can be a 30-pound gain of fat. Approximately 70-80% of the body fat is subcutaneous (under the skin); it follows that the thicker the skinfold (a fold of skin and fat, but not the underlying muscle), the greater the amount of fat a person is carrying. To use this method, specially designed calipers are used to measure the thickness of representative sites throughout the body. These measurements are then put in as mathematical equation to estimate the body's density and then converted to percent fat. This technique of measuring skinfolds is less expensive, portable, and appropriate in both laboratory and field settings when used by experienced and skilled individuals, and is proposed for use in school systems, with athletic teams.

Traditional Weight Chart

For those who are tradition bound, we will include the weight chart used for years to determine weight by height and build. This method was made obsolete with the advent of the percentage of body fat method for determining the amount of subcutaneous body fat.

I: What you should weigh

Desirable weights for men and women, 25 and over, from the Metropolitan Life Insurance Company.

Men HEIGHT		SMALL	MEDIUM	LARGE		Women HEIGHT		SMALL	MEDIUM	LARGE
Feet	Inches	FRAME	FRAME	FRAME		Feet	Inches	FRAME	FRAME	FRAME
5	2	111-120	118-129	126-141		4	10	92- 98	96-107	104-119
5	3	115-123	121-133	129-144		4	11	94-101	98-110	106-122
5	4	118-126	124-136	132-148		5	0	96-104	101-113	109-125
5	5	121-129	127-139	135-152		5	1	99-107	104-116	112-128
5	6	124-133	130-143	138-156		5	2	102-110	107-119	115-131
5	7	128-137	134-147	142-161		5	3	105-113	110-122	118-134
5	8	132-141	138-152	147-166		5	4	108-116	113-126	121-138
5	9	136-145	142-156	151-170		5	5	111-119	116-130	125-142
5	10	140-150	146-160	155-174		5	6	114-123	120-135	129-146
5	11	144-154	150-165	159-179		5	7	118-127	124-139	133-150
6	0	148-158	154-170	164-184		5	8	122-131	128-143	137-154
6	1	152-162	158-175	168-189		5	9	126-135	132-147	141-158
6	2	156-167	162-180	173-194		5	10	130-140	136-151	145-163
6	3	160-171	167-185	178-199		5	11	134-144	140-155	149-168
6	4	164-175	172-190	182-204		6	0	138-148	144-159	153-173

II: What the champions weigh

Analysis of height/weight ratio for the top 10 qualifiers for 1980 Olympic Marathon Trial, based on all-time fastest performances prior to the race.

Name	Ht. (in.)	Wt.	Ratio	PR (in 5/80)
Bill Rodgers	68	128	1.882	2:09:27
Jeff Wells	71	140	1.971	2:10:20
Tony Sandoval	68	115	1.691	2:10:20
Frank Shorter	70	132	1.885	2:10:30
John Lodwick	76	156	2.052	2:10:54
Ron Tabb	66	116	1.757	2:11:00
Don Kardong	75	150	2.000	2:11:16
Rick Callison	66	135	2.045	2:11:22
Randy Thomas	72	150	2.083	2:11:25
Herm Atkins	72	138	1.736	2:11:52

A physically fit person manages energy like a financier manages money. The financier pours out his money regularly and it returns to him enlarged. The physically fit person does the same with his energy.

It is always a silly thing to give advice, but to give good advice is absolutely fatal. —Oscar Wilde

To find new things, take the path you took yesterday. —John Burroughs

Nutrition and Weight Control

We can offer some suggestions for triathletes seeking to arrive at an ideal training weight as follows:

1. Learn what causes you to gain weight. Most overweight individuals have improper eating habits: they junk-snack, or they reach for that extra helping at dinner. Triathletes are no different. Find out what eating habits cause you to gain weight and eliminate them. Obese people on weight-loss programs often are encouraged to list everything they eat to discover their weaknesses. That is good advice for triathletes, too.

2. Plan your diet around adequate nutrition. Many people who try to lose weight do so by undereating. But the muscles need nourishment, otherwise they will not function properly. Since runners attempting to lose weight will be exercising while doing so, they need adequate nutrition to avoid excessive fatigue during regular workouts. If you become overly tired and start dragging during training, you may compensate by altering your normal training style, which could result in injuries.

3. Include carbohydrates in your diet. Many people who diet exclude carbohydrates and eat only fat and protein. A number of quick-loss diets show initial success because a low-carbohydrate regimen causes the body to shed water, as though it were given a diuretic. Anyone who has tried the full carbohydrate-loading regimen and watched the scale discovers one loses almost five pounds (mostly water) during the three-day high-protein, high-fat phase. In the final three days of high carbohydrates, this liquid loss is usually regained. But if you are dieting and training you need carbohydrates as the most efficient fuel, otherwise your training may suffer. The fats and proteins are not readily burned and more likely will be stored in the muscles. Carbohydrates, however, will be burned readily. A well-balanced diet for a dieting exerciser might include as much as 70-75% carbohydrate and only 10% protein and 15% fat. This means that someone on a 2,000-calorie diet should obtain about 1,400-1,500 of those calories from complex carbohydrates, such as fresh fruits and vegetables, whole grain breads, and pasta.

4. Chart your pounds as well as miles. If you are keeping a training diary, you should record your weight as well as your workouts and multi-sport events over a period of years; this will help you to judge your ideal participation weight much better than any charts or statistics based on either the general population or even other triathletes. One important reminder is to weigh yourself at the same time each day and on the same scale if possible. Don Kardong weighs in prior to his afternoon run. First thing in the morning upon awakening (and after urination) might be a still better time, assuming you can read the scale through bleary eyes. Weighing immediately after a workout is not as accurate because of fluctuations caused by varying degrees of dehydration. But even weighing post-workout, if you do it consistently, is a good gauge.

5. When you want to lose weight, train slowly. After gaining 17 pounds on his Thanksgiving binge, a triathlete said it took him two months of training to get back to his previous level. This may have happened, in part, because of the intensity with which he trains. Runners who run very fast, say within 90% of their maximum VO^2, burn nearly all carbohydrates. Runners who go slowly, around 60 to 70% of maximum VO^2, probably obtain half their energy from stored fat. Moreover, having turned on their fat metabolizing system by LSD running, they will continue to burn fat for several hours after exercise. So if you are looking for the most efficient means of removing fat, run long and run slow.

6. Don't be fooled by sudden fluctuations in body weight. A lot of people think that any weight loss, even if it is brief and transitory, is good. They don't care whether they lose fat or water, they want to see the scales move. We frequently see people who weigh themselves before and after a workout and feel they have accomplished a great weight loss. But to lose

one pound of fat, you need to burn 3,500 calories, which means running roughly 35 miles — and without increasing your food intake. So when you plan your diet, do so for the long run.

Research indicates that girls and women normally have more body fat than do boys and men. An abnormally great or small amount of body fat is related to poor nutritional status. Standards to aid in determining when the amount of body fat is abnormal are presented. The table also indicates that the amount of fat in the tricep area varies throughout life.

OBESITY STANDARDS FOR CAUCASIAN AMERICANS
Minimum triceps skinfold thickness in millimeters

Age (years)	Skinfold measurements	
	Males	Females
5	12	14
6	12	15
7	13	16
8	14	17
9	15	18
10	16	20
11	17	21
12	18	22
13	18	23
14	17	23
15	16	24
16	15	25
17	14	26
18	15	27
19	15	27
20	16	28
21	17	28
22	18	28
23	18	28
24	19	28
25	20	29
26	20	29
27	21	29
28	22	29
29	23	30
30—50	23	30

Enough of the right kind of physical exercise makes you feel like you have just been created!

III

Breathing, Walking and
Race Walking for the Triathlete

The winner of four Ironman Triathlons in Kona, Hawaii . . . Dave Scott from Davis, California shows how health, fitness and endurance training reaps great rewards!

1

Super Breathing Builds Powerful Triathletes

Breathing, Our Most Important Function

Breathing is one of the most important of all vital functions . . . yet it is the one part of our miraculous metabolism that most of us, triathletes included, take most for granted! Proper breathing can be achieved through breathing exercises, which then has desirable impact on breath control and lung efficiency during athletic training. Posture, the stomach muscles, lungs, and the entire cardio-pulmonary system not only affect breathing, but benefit from improved breathing technique. Let's face it: the more oxygen you consume, the better every bodily system functions. There is no substitute for oxygen!

"The breath of life" means exactly what it says. To breathe is to live. Not to breathe is to die. A human being can exist without food for weeks . . . without water for days . . . but without air he cannot exist for even a few minutes.

This fact is so obvious and breathing is so automatic that most people simply take it for granted. *But do you really know how to breathe?* Stop and think about it for a moment. Do you really know how your lungs function? Do you use these marvelous organs to their fullest capacity?

The way you *use your lungs controls your health . . . your looks . . . the way you feel . . . your resistance to disease . . . your very life span!*

Some people seem to have inexhaustible vitality and stamina . . . creative power and/or athletic ability of the highest quality. They never seem to tire. They can do mental or physical work without strain, tension or excessive emotion. Everything seems to be easy. Above all, these are happy, contented people who always seem to find the humorous side of life. They are full of personal magnetism. They are enthusiastic beyond the ordinary . . .sociable . . . lovable . . . a pleasure to be with. They have bright and happy dispositions. They are free from 'hang ups'' and mental blocks. These are the people who enjoy "the good life".

What is their secret? How does one live at a superior rate of vibration?

The answer is really very simple. Such people consume large amounts of oxygen. They breathe deeply and fully . . . utilizing every square inch of their lung capacity.

The more oxygen you can pump into your lungs, the more energy you will have . . . the higher will be your rate of vibration. It is very much like a fire in an open fireplace . . . the more oxygen the fire gets, the brighter it will burn . . . the less it gets, the less fire and more smoke.

Some people simply do not get enough vital oxygen to give them that extra something to keep going under physical, mental or emotional pressures. Under extreme pressure they "run out of gas" . . . they don't have what it takes to make that additional effort.

Why? Because they are not using the full capacity of their lungs for energy-producing oxygen . . . they can't get their "second wind".

Learn How to Increase Your Energy By Deep Breathing

At age 16, my father was pronounced a "hopeless case" of tuberculosis . . . but by age 18, he had become a successful athlete.

During those two years, he was introduced to and cured by the Science of Natural

Living . . . to which I have dedicated the rest of my life, following my father's teachings, which have already been a way of life for me.

I keep myself in a high state of mental and physical conditioning because I supply my body with the fuel it needs . . . natural live foods . . . and above all, oxygen.

I have helped many people in all walks of life . . . top athletes and active sportsmen to musicians, writers, artists, doctors, lawyers . . . as well as top stars of Hollywood and Broadway . . . to office workers and housewives . . . to achieve the enjoyment of a superior healthy state of living.

Let me emphasize again that the basic source of super-vibration is knowing how to fill the entire lungs with oxygen. Everyone is born with this capacity, but only a few retain it naturally. Others have developed it, as I am going to show you how to develop it . . . by this System of Super Breathing.

Whatever your age . . . it is never too early . . . or too late . . . to learn how to increase your energy by the correct method of deep breathing. *Within a short time* of faithfully following the breathing exercises which I shall give you in this chapter . . . you, too, can learn how to fill your lungs with energy-producing oxygen. You will enjoy the thrill of this great natural stimulation . . . a stimulation far more potent than that of any artificial stimulant such as alcohol, coffee, tea, cola drinks or drugs . . . and with no adverse side effects! In fact, the "side effects" of oxygen stimulation add up to the bonus of a longer, fuller lifetime of living. Bob Anderson, the stretching expert spends 15 minutes daily doing these Bragg Super Breathing Exercises . . . and teaches them in his seminars and lectures. He says everyone should be doing them for more health and endurance.

Value of the "Second Wind"

When you consume your full quota of oxygen . . . you have the capacity for getting your "second wind" . . . and feeling stronger than when you began your effort. That is what makes the great athlete, the great politician, the great statesman, the great professional man or woman, the writer and the go-getter.

When you learn to use the full capacity of your lungs through this System of Super Breathing, you will experience this wonderful stimulation of the "second wind". Just when you think you have run out of energy and vitality . . . this sudden renewal of strength occurs. It is an experience difficult to describe. To feel that you cannot take another step . . . that your brain power is all gone, your thinking befuddled . . . then suddenly a great surge of energy courses through your entire body, and you feel as fresh and even stronger than when you started. What a tremendous sensation it is! And when you breathe correctly, you experience this "second wind".

Shallow Breathers Poison Themselves

Loaded with poisonous wastes, the blood has difficulty in transporting the comparatively small amount of oxygen which it does absorb . . . nor can it carry the necessary nourishment from food. The breaking down of food molecules into digestible elements is impaired . . . all bodily functions are slowed down without an adequate oxygen supply.

The organs of elimination are overworked . . . and underfed. But the accumulating wastes must go somewhere. Some are discharged by overloading the sweat glands, producing unpleasant body odors. Other toxic wastes are deposited as heavy mucus in the sinus cavities, lungs and bronchial tubes . . . along the passages of the ears, eyes, nose and throat . . . and along the digestive tract. Hardened wastes are deposited in the movable joints and spine, where pressure on nerves signals the warning of pain. (Pain is nature's alarm that something is seriously wrong . . . it should be heeded by corrective action . . . not silenced by drugs.)

By robbing their bodies of vital oxygen, shallow breathers are actually poisoning themselves . . . inflicting tortures upon their bodies while committing slow suicide. They are suffering from autointoxication, or self-poisoning . . . dying in their own body poisons.

If someone else deliberately tried to force you to kill yourself in this manner, what would you do? You'd fight back, wouldn't you? In defiance, you would breathe deeply and fully . . . cleansing your blood . . . purifying your entire system . . . making your body tingle with life and energy.

Why not do it now?

The Way You Breathe Is The Way You Live

When you breathe deeply and fully . . . you live deeply and fully!

When a generous flow of oxygen is being pumped into your body, every cell comes alive. The four main "motors" of the body . . . the heart, the lungs . . . the liver and the kidneys . . . operate at peak performance. Your bloodstream purifies itself . . . cleanses every part of the body and transports the toxic wastes to be eliminated as Nature planned . . . and carries fuel-food and vital oxygen to every cell.

Your muscles, tendons and joints function smoothly. Your flesh becomes firm and resilient . . . your skin clear and glowing . . . your hair lustrous. You radiate health and well-being.

Your brain becomes alert . . . your nervous system functions perfectly. You are free from tension and strain . . . you withstand stresses and pressures with ease.

Emotions are under control. You feel joyous and exuberant. When negative emotions try to intrude . . . such as anger, hate, jealousy, fear or grief . . . they are expelled by concentrated deep breathing.

Your Marvelous Lungs

Every living thing breathes. Plants breathe through pores in their leaves. In the marvelous balance of Nature, plants breathe in carbon dioxide and give off oxygen . . . while animals inhale oxygen and exhale carbon dioxide. In natural balance, both thrive. But man has played havoc with this natural balance by destroying forests, covering grass with pavements . . . and to air already thus polluted by an excess of carbon dioxide, he continues to add more pollutants from motorized traffic and industry. Wildlife (the remainder which has survived slaughter by man) suffocates in such atmosphere. Fish die in polluted waters. How long can man survive in the midst of the environment poisons which he creates has become a question of concern.

The lungs are composed of some 800 million alveoli, air cells or sacs, of elastic tissue which can expand or contract like tiny balloons. If these little air sacs were flattened out and laid side by side, the flattened alveoli would cover an area of 100 square yards.

Tiny capillaries (blood vessels) thread the elastic walls of each of the hundreds of millions of air sacs . . . and it is through these that the blood passes to discharge its load of poisonous carbon dioxide and absorb the life-giving oxygen. This cleansing in the body's 5 quarts of blood (average man) must be performed from *1 to 9 times a minute,* depending upon activity from rest to running.

Air inhaled through the nose and/or mouth reaches the alveoli through an intricate system of tubes, beginning with the large trachea, or windpipe, which is kept rigid by rings of cartilage in its walls. The trachea extends through the neck into the chest, where it divides into two branches, or bronchi, one leading into each lung. The bonchi divide into a number of smaller and smaller branches to reach every air sac.

Each lung is enveloped in a protective elastic membrane, the pleura, whose inner layer is attached to the lung . . . and whose outer layer forms the lining of the thoracic cavity, inside the rib cage. Although one end of each rib is attached to the spinal column, the front of the rib cage is open, allowing for expansion and contraction of the lungs.

When you breathe deeply, filling every air sac, your thoracic cavity expands as your lungs fill to capacity with some 6 to 10 pints of air (depending on body build and size), occupying approximately 200 to over 300 cubic inches.

And this marvelous mechanism is yours for free! You are born with it. It functions without conscious effort . . . yet without it, you would not exist.

No invention of man, however ingenious, can equal the human breathing apparatus. The "iron lung" is misnamed . . . lifesaver that it is, it is merely a cumbersome outside contraption to replace paralyzed muscles . . . to enable those marvelous human lungs to function.

Perhaps if human beings had to pay some fabulous price for their lungs, they would use them to full capacity all the time. But did you ever stop to think of the price you pay for *not* using them? Remember, we are always "only one breath away from death"!

Correct Breathing Makes Exercise and Distance Training a Pleasure

Whatever form of exercise you prefer . . . swimming, biking, running, hiking, golfing, dancing, calisthentics, tennis, weight lifting, etc. . . . you will derive greater benefits because of this Super Breathing Program! What's more, you'll enjoy your exercise as never before!

Rhythmic Breathing and Walking

Of all forms of exercise, brisk walking is the one that brings most of the body into action . . . it is the "king of exercise" . . . when the rhythm of your breathing and the rhythm of your stride are in harmony, you feel like a king!

The Super Breathing Exercises in this book, when practiced faithfully, will give you such perfect control of your breathing that you can become a tireless walker. As the oxygen-filled blood courses through your body, your legs will carry you along buoyantly. Walk "tall" with head high, back and shoulders straight, chest out and tummy in . . . arms swinging easily from your shoulders . . . your legs moving smoothly as though they were attached to the middle of your torso.

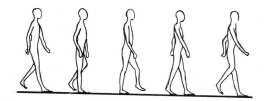

Walking posture.
Always prepare a new base
before leaving the old.

Enjoy your walk. Set your own pace, with a free spirit and a light heart. Watch with interest the things and people you pass . . . or let your walking be an accompaniment to your ideas and thoughts. As you breathe and walk rhythmically you lose awareness of your body, and you become as near poet and philosopher as you will ever be. You can truly "walk your worries away." As the blood courses through your arteries and veins, cleansing and nourishing your entire body, you are filled with a sense of well-being that cleanses your mind of its troubles and nourishes it with positive thoughts. **Often as I stride along on my daily hike, jog, run, etc. . . . I say to myself, "Health . . . Strength . . . Youth . . . Vitality . . . Joy . . . Peace . . . Love . . . Happiness."**

Why Breathing Exercises?

Why put such an emphasis on the exercise of breathing? For one thing, scientific studies show that the greatest susceptibility to sickness and the aging process occurs with the breakdown in breathing capability. All the other metabolic functions deteriorate in ratio to the drop in breathing capacity. Without breathing exercises, statistics show that effective breathing among Americans drops from 100% at birth to roughly 60% during middle age, and to 40% of capacity, or less, during advanced years.

Winner Dave Scott, crossing the 1984 Ironman finish line with a deep breath of success.

Photo by David Epperson

Proper breathing, the utilization of pure oxygen, and the body's resilience and power to heal itself are a result of proper breathing which can help rejuvenate you at any age! ***Regular, daily practice of deep, hard breathing is life-changing and life-restoring.*** The first . . . and last . . . exercise dictated by nature is breathing, followed by stretching!

Aerobics, and exercises designed to improve cardiovascular functioning and the value, power and technique of utilizing oxygen to its utmost advantage, have swept the nation and the world. After breathing exercises, and stretching, go out for a walk, a run, or bike or swim, anything that will get your heart rate up and keep it up, exercising the entire circulatory system along with the hearts and lungs.

George Bernard Shaw, the Irish playwright, who used to speculate about the secrets and wonders of life, looked at a lifetime chart in his day and said, ***"Youth is such a wonderful thing, it's a shame to waste it on young people."*** He refused to believe that it was only for the young. He adopted a program to integrate his body, mind, spirit and lived an active, happy and productive life to 94. He did breathing exercises daily.

To maintain good health the body must be exercised properly (walking, jogging, running, biking, swimming, deep breathing, good posture, etc.), and nourished wisely (natural foods), so as to provide and increase the good life of radiant health, joy and happiness. —Paul C. Bragg

Many people go throughout life committing partial suicide — destroying their health, youth, beauty, talents, energies, creative qualities. Indeed, to learn how to be good to oneself is often more difficult than to learn how to be good to others.

If a man can convince me that I do not think or act right, gladly will I change, for I search after truth. But he is harmed who abideth on still in his ignorance.

— Marcus Aurelius, Roman Emperor

BRAGG SUPER BREATHING EXERCISES

The Cleansing Breath

Find a nice, open spot with plenty of fresh air for this basic breathing exercise. The back yard or patio will do nicely. Stand straight, with your hands at your sides, with bare feet about 18 inches apart, about even with the width of your shoulders. Wear loose clothing.

Raise your arms straight up, reach over your head, and arch backward, taking a deep breath through both nose and mouth . . . and hold it . . . now bend forward from the waist as far as possible . . . keeping the knees bent . . . letting your arms swing between your legs. the idea is eventually to bring the head below the level of the heart. At the same time exhale vigorously through the mouth. Compress the chest and push upward with the diaphragm and abdominal muscles to expel every bit of carbon dioxide from your lungs.

Now slowly inhale through nose and mouth . . . pushing downward with your diaphragm and expanding your chest at front and sides to draw in the air to the full capacity of your lungs . . . as you return to the original standing position, continue to breathe in deeply.

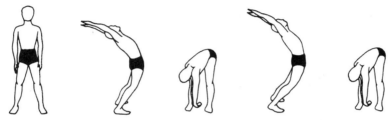

All Super Breathing Exercises begin in this way. As your hands reach the overhead position . . . tighten your diaphragm and hold your breath for 5 to 10 seconds (mentally counting "One thousand and one . . ." etc.) while pulling your abdominal muscles back to "pin your stomach to your backbone." Then exhale vigorously through the mouth . . . bending forward at the waist as at the beginning . . . and inhale as you return to the starting position. do this exercise 5 times.

The Kidney Breath

Locate your kidneys on the lower back, just below the end of your rib cage near the waistline. Get the "feel" of them by placing your palms over this area, fingers and thumbs pointed downward . . . as this is the position you will take during the breath-holding part of this exercise.

Start by exhaling and inhaling vigorously as at the beginning of the Cleansing Breath.

As your hands reach the overhead position . . . tighten your diaphragm and "pin your stomach to your backbone" with your abdominal muscles . . . while holding your breath. Now, still holding your breath, place palms over kidneys . . . exerting a light pressure on the kidneys for a silent count of 10 ("One thousand and one . . ." etc.). Still holding your breath, return to standing position . . . then bend forward, exhaling vigorously through the mouth. Slowly inhale as you return to starting position.

Do this exercise 5 times at the start . . . gradually increasing to 10.

The Liver Breath

Start by exhaling and inhaling as at the beginning of the cleansing breath.

Now bring the feet together and clasp the fingers overhead, palms upward.

Keep legs stiff from the hips down . . . and holding the breath, bend slowly to the right side with as much stretch as possible . . . then to the left with a good stretch . . . alternating these bends to right and left 5 times each . . . while holding the breath. Return to starting position with feet apart . . . exhale and inhale vigorously with the usual forward bend.

Do this exercise 5 times.

Heart-Strengthening Breath

The purpose of this exercise is to expand the aorta, the main trunk of the arterial system which carries the blood from the heart after it has been oxygenized by Super Breathing. It stimulates the circulation of the blood in the heart, as well as throughout the rest of the body, helping to increase the power of the entire cardiovascular respiratory function. This exercise may give relief to those who suffer from angina pectoris, commonly called "choking in the chest," with feelings of suffocation and apprehension.

This exercise starts with the same vigorous exhaling and inhaling as the beginning cleansing breath . . . except that the arms are held forward at shoulder height (not overhead).

When you return to the standing position, holding your breath . . . clasp your nose tightly with thumb and index finger so that no air can escape . . . pretend you are blowing your nose. You should feel some air pressure in your ears.

Now, with knees bent, bend over from the waist . . . getting your head as near to the floor as possible . . . and continue to hold your breath for a silent count of 10.

Return to starting position and exhale and inhale in the usual Super Breathing manner.

Do this exercise 5 times.

Colon-kicker Breath

This exercise should be done in the bathroom on arising each morning . . . and several times within an hour after eating. If you will make this a habit, you will soon find that you will get a bowel movement within an hour after eating. This is as it should be . . . outgo should equal intake.

Start by exhaling and inhaling vigorously as at the beginning of the Cleansing Breath. Now, holding your breath, drop hands to sides in relaxed position . . . and slowly go into a squatting position . . . then strain for a bowel movement for the silent count of several seconds.

Return to standing position and complete exercise by exhaling and inhaling as in previous exercises.

Apex of Lungs

This exercise is to get oxygen into the little used air sacs at the apex of the lungs, down near your waistline.

Exhale and inhale as at the start of the Cleansing Breath . . . but, instead of returning arms to overhead position, drop them relaxed at sides . . . and bring feet together, toes and heels touching.

Holding your breath, bend to the right and try to touch the floor with the fingers of your right hand . . . at the same time bringing the left hand up to touch under the left arm-pit. Hold position for a silent count of 10.

Return to starting position . . . exhale and inhale as before . . . then repeat breath-holding position on the left side, reaching toward the floor with the left hand, and touching the right hand under the right armpit . . . for a count of 10.

Return to starting position . . . exhale and inhale as before.

Do this exercise 5 to 10 times, alternating from side to side.

The Yoga Breath

As in the cleansing breath, start with erect posture, your feet comfortably apart. Place the index finger of the right hand over the right nostril, closing the nostril.

Bend from the waist, knees locked, toward your left knee, forcing out all of your breath as you reach the vicinity of your left knee.

Rhythmically return to the starting position while inhaling through the left nostril, keeping the right nostril closed.

Change over to left hand-left nostril, and repeat, going toward the right knee, exhaling, and inhale upon returning to the original position.

Continue this sequence to at least a count of 20, and increase that number with practice. If your nose runs, just let it go, and continue the exercise.

Finish with four regular Cleansing Breaths.

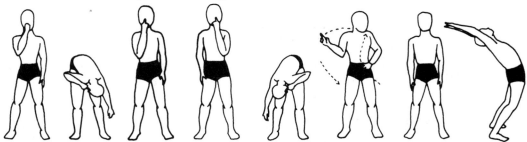

The Super Brain Breath

Start by exhaling and inhaling as at the beginning of the Cleansing Breath.

When your hands reach the overhead position . . . hold your breath and bend forward from the waist, knees bent . . . dropping your head as far forward as you can. Continue to hold your breath to the count of 10 (mentally counting "One thousand and one . . ." etc.) . . . the purpose being to allow the oxygen-filled blood to suffuse the pituitary gland and reach and refresh every part of your brain, as well as cleanse the skull cavities (sinuses, ears, nose, mouth).

Still holding your breath, return to standing position . . . then bend forward, exhaling vigorously through the mouth. Slowly inhale as you return to starting position.

Do this exercise 5 times at the start . . . and gradually increase to 10 times.

NOTE: You may not be able to hold your breath for the full count at first. If you feel dizzy, exhale, return to standing position, drop arms to sides and relax for a minute or two before continuing the exercise. You will gradually build your oxygen tolerance to the full count.

Mental Attitude Is Important

I have already spoken about starting these exercises with pleasant anticipation . . . knowing that the result will be improvement in health and figure, and enjoyment in living a fuller, longer, more youthful life! Remember, your mind must be the boss of your body . . . and a positive mental attitude will bring you greater benefits sooner.

As you exhale, think to yourself, "I am expelling all poisons from my body . . . physical, mental and emotional. I am expelling sickness and fatigue, fear and hatred, envy and grief." Name whatever state of body, mind, emotions you want to get rid of, and feel that you are breathing it *out* of your system.

As you inhale, think to yourself, "I am breathing *in* health and strength . . . courage and self-confidence . . . love and peace of mind." Concentrate on the qualities you want to acquire, and feel that you are drawing these in with the fresh air and oxygen.

After you do this faithfully every day for several months, you will be amazed at how well it works. Your whole attitude towards life will improve. You will feel confident and happy . . . you will get along much better with your family and with other people, both friends and strangers. Petty annoyances will no longer bother you. Your worries and troubles will fall into proper perspective . . . you will be able to face your problems realistically and solve them with courage and ingenuity.

Let your mind and body work together in these Bragg Super Breathing Exercises . . . Let living become a glorious adventure!

CRAWLING AND CREEPING

Wait a minute . . . Crawl?

That's right . . . crawl. Think of a newborn baby, then think of yourself as a newborn babe every day as you awaken. The first exercise dictated by nature is breathing. It's common knowledge, or should be, that every baby sometimes screams and cries to no end . . . for exercise. One of the first things an adult does, upon waking up, is yawn. This is to fill the lungs with oxygen, to get those physical furnaces going. Half the time, it is also why a baby cries: to fill his lungs with oxygen. When you're tired, you yawn, because your body requires more oxygen to supply you with the necessary energy for further activity.

It's the same thing when you wake up in the morning.

Next, you stretch. In fact, you probably stretch before and after yawning, and sometimes simultaneously. Just like any other earth-bound animal, people stretch their muscles because nature demands it, not just because it feels good. (And it *does* feel good, doesn't it?)

Get in the habit of stretching every day . . . in fact, several times per day, if possible. But try to get in at least one good stretching session, preferably in the morning, and especially before exercising, every day. You need only to observe a newborn child to realize that its entire body reaches out, stretches and expands by an inner impulse. From its first inhalation there are movements and the impulse to stretch . . . the entire body . . . vigorously. When the body is stretched, the muscles need more oxygen, and there are compensating automatic functions in other parts of the metabolism. Women find after childbirth . . . crawling and creeping exercises help put the womb and abdomen area back in shape.

Researchers in Philadelphia have concluded that some of the movements we normally attribute to babies are the fundamental basis of health, inherent in breathing, movement, crawling, creeping, and rolling . . . natural exercises which should continue into adult life because they are conducive to improved health and physical fitness. These "outgrown" motions induce tremendous levels of oxygenation in their influence on the respiratory system, in coordinated physiological functioning and in improving endurance and strengthening muscles.

Remember, you're newly born in the morning when you wake. First you breathe a deep breath, then you stretch, moving every muscle you can feel (and a few you may not feel). What's next?

Crawling. Not to be confused with creeping, which is propelling yourself on hands and knees. Crawling is defined as "movement with stomach in contact with the earth," and developing mobility with the use of the arms, legs, and body undulations.

Try to imitate this baby crawl, now that you're an adult, and see how far you can go. You're in for a surprise.

On hands and knees, the sequence is right hand forward, left knee forward, left hand forward, right knee forward. At an accelerated speed, a point is reached where only one hand and one knee are in contact with the earth, which implies a necessary sense of balance.

Many people use this exercise not only for coordination, but as a simple, steady conditioner with cardiovascular benefits at a minimum of stress. Do it slowly and rhythmically. Those who engage in it regularly as a part of their exercise keep it as one of their "secrets of health." Paul Bragg openly recommended crawling and creeping, and billionaire H. L. Hunt practiced it as part of his program to the end of his eighty-five years.

In terms of triathletics, crawling is closely related to the motions performed when swimming. Even swimming, though, requires you to regulate your breathing in a slightly unusual fashion, regardless of the fact that gravity's influence on your body's weight, while floating, is only a fraction of what you're accustomed to carrying around when you're not in the water.

Crawling is much simpler . . . just lie on your stomach on the floor, and start stroking and crawling. I often do these exercises while the news is on, or one of the Bible tapes I listen to daily for spiritual inspiration. If you want to make the time for keeping physically in shape for training . . . the time can be found! I try and make each minute count in each day! When you are healthy and fit — oh! what joy, peace and happiness life offers!

Breathing Bibliography

Bragg Super Breathing For Health and Energy, Paul C. Bragg, N.D., Ph.D., and Patricia Bragg, Ph.D., Health Science, Box 7, Santa Barbara, CA 93102.

I went to the woods because I wished to live deliberately, to front only the essential facts of life, and see if I could not learn what it had to teach, and not, when I came to die, discover that I had not lived.
—Thoreau

A typical scene any morning for weeks prior to the Kona Ironman . . . Triathletes getting in their early morning swim.

View down Alii Drive towards the Kona pier where the Ironman Triathlon takes place.

2

Walking, the King of Exercise

Why a Chapter on Walking in a Triathlon Training Manual

Aside from the fact that walking is the king of all exercises, proper walking can become an important part of the beginning triathlete's transportation modes. It is a rare triathlete who has not felt the need to establish an incremental pace from the start of his running portion of the triathlon, meaning a period of running interspersed with a shorter period of walking.

At this point I wish to make an observation on the whole business of marathon running. Since the advent of TV, we have been psyched into believing that the marathon should be run as a full foot race from beginning to end, without a stop or without walking. Olympic distance runners, world class runners and sub-4 hour marathon runners obviously have the power to achieve this goal of running the distance without a pause. This leaves the rest of the field trying desperately to accomplish something that they are not trained or equipped to do, go the whole distance running, as TV coverage of major marathons show the front runners doing.

This is also true of the triathlete. Coming out of a 2.4 mile swim and a 112 mile bike race, he has gone the equivalent of 2 full marathons in energy expenditure. If he has paced himself properly and thinks he has the strength to complete a full 26.2 mile marathon, an excellent pacing policy at this point would be to take on an ultra-marathon concept: start out with a slow walk, to get the leg muscles used for running into action, then relax and stretch the cycling muscles, slowly increasing the pace until all body signals are go. Now is the time to set your incremental pace. (This is covered more fully in the ultra-marathon chapter).

Walking, A Total Family Exercise Activity

We have included this important Walking Chapter in an effort to round out the readership of this book and to involve the rest of the family, young and old, into the use of leg power. To encourage the children to leave the T.V. set and walk to the store or to school. To encourage parents and grandparents to keep aerobically active, increasing their intake of oxygen, to use their 640 muscles, or they will lose them. Leg muscles are the muscles of the heart in that they work to flex the blood supply back up to the heart against the force of gravity. A healthy heart is one that is owned by an active walking, running, biking owner.

There is one thing that all long-living people have in common, and that is that they all advocate, or have advocated, walking. In no other exercise is movement so natural, to walk straight and balanced, synchronizing our 260 bones, our 640 muscles, our 70,000 miles of circulatory channels . . . every part of the body is strengthened by walking, including (perhaps most importantly) our sensory and extrasensory perceptions.

In Sweden, where the highest average life-expectancy in the world exists — 75.6 years — walking is a national fitness test, and more than three million citizens have received their qualification badges. Other European countries also fare better than the United States, by a difference between one and two years, in the area of longevity and a different attitude toward walking, as a whole.

"I have two good doctors," quotes an adage, "my right leg and my left." Walking is life's most valuable exercise. Synchronized with breathing, walking is the world's most reliable physical therapist for holistic living.

For those triathletes that meet some family resistance to the time and energy that training schedules demand, we feel that walking for exercise for the spouse will encourage the marriage partner to become involved to some degree in the training, even though it is only a brisk daily walk while the triathlete is running down the road. Who knows, the running bug might bite them! This also goes for biking and swimming, both enjoyable sports that can be shared together. Even though speeds and distances are unequal, the spirit of togetherness will go a long way toward cementing a marriage relationship that could be otherwise strained due to stiff training schedules.

Would You Like to Take A Walk?

Years ago, scientists predicted the evolution of a race of men without legs, thanks to the automobile.Today we know they were wrong. We are not losing our legs. But we are losing our figures, our good looks, the use of our senses, our health both physical and mental — and some of us are losing our lives as a result of ills that walking could prevent or keep in check.

Walking is the exercise that needs no gym. It is the prescription without medicine, the weight control without diet, the cosmetic that is sold in no drugstore. It is the tranquilizer without a pill, the therapy without a psychoanalyst, the fountain of youth that is no legend. A walk is the vacation that does not cost a cent.

Walking clears the brain of worry and concern. It rewards you with new peace of mind. Nature is the best possible psychoanalyst, though you must sometimes force yourself to walk in her classroom.

Dr. Paul Bragg, who made walking a basic art of exercise, demonstrated to thousands of people what he meant when he said, "Walk naturally with your head high, chest out, feeling physically elated. Carry yourself proudly, straight, erect, and with an easy action of swinging arms. Go at your own stride and with your spirit free. If the world of nature fails to interest you, turn to the inner world of spirit. As you walk, your body ceases to matter and you become as near to being a poet or philosopher as ever you will be, each step bringing words of positive inspiration."

Many find that this can become a time of communion with God, in prayer and meditation, without interruption. Time and distance fly by and you are at your destination long before you desire to bring this beautiful time of oneness with God to an end.

Some people know this. Some people never give up walking from the day they take their first step. There are more such people than anyone knows, because walkers tend to keep their walking private. When anyone admits that he arrived somewhere not by car, bus, subway or taxi but on his own two legs, people stare at him and exclaim, "You mean you walked?"

Nobody likes to be looked upon as an oddball. But the fact is, more and more people are joining the oddball club of those who would rather walk when they can ride. And a further fact is that there is more talk about walking today, more attention paid to it in the media, more concern about preserving old places and creating new places where people can walk, than there has been in a quarter of a century.

The last time Americans thought very much about walking was when we were at war, and gasoline rationing had slammed the garage doors shut for any but the most necessary transportation. During the war years, magazines blossomed with articles on the joys of walking and the newspapers sprouted columns on walking trails around the cities. People could not take their cars out for a Sunday drive, so they went walking instead. Many of them got together in hiking clubs. Some of those people are still walking, not because they must, but because they found they liked it.

A National Walking Revival

We are again witnessing a walking revival. City planners talk about turning urban centers into pedestrian malls, state authorities talk less about superhighways and more about state parks, and cities and states both look hopefully to Washington for money for these projects. In Washington, meanwhile, Congress is presented with proposals for new park areas, new wilderness and seashore areas, and a giant bill for the rehabilitation of our historic national trails. Some of these proposals come under the heading of wildlife sanctuaries, some are for conservation, some are for recreation — but all, in one way or another, mean more places to walk.

This time we have not a single overriding emergency, such as a world war, but a whole complex of them. We have a health emergency, a population emergency, a recreation emergency. But most intimate and oppressive to us all is the automobile emergency.

We are fed up with our cars. We are sick of getting stuck in traffic whether in a city street or on a highway, sitting trapped and helpless, breathing air befouled by automobile fumes, feeling tempers and tensions rise to the point of explosion. Not long ago a veteran parkway planner argued for a road along a famous island beach, on the ground that families needed this additional place to take a pleasant Sunday drive. He was greeted with derisive laughter. It is a long time since people found any pleasure in a Sunday drive.

Walkers Are Special People

There have always been people — a few — who like to walk. Throughout the half century when the automobile has governed American life, there have been walkers. They have been a small, somewhat secret society, in which each one tends to keep his membership private. Walkers recognize each other by certain signs, like the signs of an underground movement, but most walkers are soloists, each a revolutionary cell unto himself.

Non-walkers sometimes note the signs and ask, "Have you been away? You look tan!" because even in midwinter the walker has an outdoor glow on his face.

People ask how he keeps his weight down and what diet he follows. People who have not seen him for a while remark that he doesn't get any older and ask him what his secret is.

Walkers do not boast of their addition. And generally they do not proselytize, because they know from experience that everyone has to discover the magic of walking for himself.

Dr. Paul Dudley White Prescribed Walking

"Walking," says Dr. Paul Dudley White, "is as natural as breathing." Dr. White, who knows his physiology, may be taken to mean this not as an expression of his known enthusiasm for walking but as a statement of literal fact.

For it is a literal fact. The mechanics of walking are built into the human body in much the same way as the mechanics of respiration, and both are triumphs of mechanical engineering. For sheer efficiency, which means getting best performance at least energy cost, these nature-built mechanisms surpass anything devised by man.

As a locomotor device, the bony structure of the human body is an engineer's delight. It is not built for speed, to be sure. But for carrying its own weight from one point to another on the earth's surface it is a wonder. The body is built poorly for sitting, only a little better for standing, but for walking it is unrivaled.

In plan it is so simple that a child can draw it in a stick figure: a single upright for the spine; two crossbars balanced on it horizontally from which swing a pair each of arms and legs; a knob at the top for a head. But on examination, certain subtleties appear. The spine is not a straight vertical rod but a jointed and double-curved spring. The legs also have springy joints at knees and ankles and springlike arches in the feet, and they swing from the hips on ball-and-socket joints. The crossbar supports for the appendages, furthermore, are not fixed rigidly on the spine but can swing and pivot. At every point the structure is flexible, mobile, clearly built as a dynamic rather than a static support.

The distribution of weight, too, is subtle and at first glance rather puzzling. The body dome of the skull, the bony shoulder girdle and the arms swinging from it all add up to a top-heavy construction. Can this be efficient?

God Designed Us To Walk

Walking, the human design comes into its own. Form blends with function and the result is harmony — and perfect performance. The body is built for action, and the action for which it is specifically built is walking.

Consider what happens to the body structure when we walk. The flexible spine yields and springs back with each stride; the springlike forms of the arched feet dissipate the impact of weight meeting surface as effectively as any fluid suspension designed by General Motors engineers.

And see what use is made of the body's peculiar distribution of weight. The top-heavy torso now reveals its true value in two-legged locomotion: the forward pull of its weight becomes the motive power for its progress. With each stride we are falling forward, and one or the other leg is swinging out on its ball-and-socket hip joint to catch us.

In terms of its mechanics, walking is nothing more than a series of stumbles caught in the nick of time, a continuous, rhythmic loss and recovery of balance. Gravitation, no less, is the force that we harness to our service when we walk. If we need any proof of this, we have only to remember that when the astronauts go "walking" weightless in space, they need a little jet-propulsion gadget to move them — *because they do not have the help of gravity.*

The Miracle of Human Locomotion

Walking is a muscular symphony. More than half of the body's muscular equipment has as its primary function nothing else than locomotion — which in man means walking.

All the foot, leg, and hip muscles, and much of the back musculature, are involved in walking, and abdominal muscles, diaphragm, rib, arm, shoulder, neck and eye muscles play a part as well.

Sooner or later in walking we are using all our muscles except the jaw muscles. And if we have a companion we are using those, too, in conversation.

Yet all of this is unconscious, and without effort. We are not aware of this automatically conducted symphony of muscular action. It is possible to make hard work of walking, but a person who is not actually disabled must fairly dislocate himself to do so — except, of course, if he is grossly overweight.

Because it exercises so many of our body's muscles, walking is an ideal warm up for triathletes.

Nature's Prescription

For walking is indeed as natural to the human body as breathing. No more than a few days after the child has taken his first step, he has mastered the coordination necessary for walking, and barring unusual circumstances, he need never again be conscious of it for the rest of his life. We have to learn how to swim, to skate, to ski; we have to make a conscious effort to run, jump, or climb. But to walk, all we have to do is put one foot before the other. From that point on, the body's singular structure takes over.

And when we hit our stride — the step that is just the right length for our height and length of leg, the speed that is just right for our weight and muscular strength — then something miraculous happens. We become unconscious of weight, of locomotion; we are aware only of rhythm. It is a sensation akin to swimming, in which the water bears our weight. In the right rhythm of walking, the body's weight does in fact float, borne along in a perfect balance between gravitational force and the momentum of forward motion. We do not seem to be carrying our weight at all.

That is walking. To hit your stride is to discover a new sensation, the sensation of moving as effortlessly as the deer bounds, the horse gallops, the fish swims and the bird flies.

Dr. Walking — The Best Physician

For all its economy of muscle and energy, walking is endorsed by medical and health authorities for an astonishing variety of benefits. It is listed as:

- A "best" exercise (by physical fitness experts)
- A preventive of heart and circulatory disorders (by cardiologists)
- A first-rate weight controller (by obesity experts)
- A preventive and a remedy for respiratory disorders (by chest specialists)
- An aid to digestion and elimination
- An aid to sleep
- An antidote to tensions whether physical, nervous, psychological, emotional
- A partial protection, at least, against the damaging effects of heavy smoking on the heart, circulatory, and respiratory systems. Heavy smokers find that walking also cuts down their smoking, at the very least by removing the temptation to smoke while they are enjoying a good walk, probably also by relieving some of the tensions that lead to heavy smoking.

So it is overwhelmingly evident that, according to the experts, walking can be a prime preventive and even a cure for a long list of common nuisance ailments and some of the more serious ones.

This is puzzling. It is even hard to believe. We think of exercise as being effective only if it is strenuous and somewhat punishing.

People think of bicycling, rowing, mountain-climbing, 50-mile-hiking as exercise, but not walking. Walking is so ordinary. How can walking, so mild, so far from strenuous, achieve so many desirable effects?

The answer to this puzzle is that walking is one of the natural functions of the human body. The erect posture and bipedal gait were an early and essential part of human evolution. And so other essential functions developed along with walking, became integrated with it, became to some extent dependent upon it.

Through walking, we can achieve an awareness of our bodies which cannot help but be beneficial to the person training for the swim-bike-run.

Hearts Work Together

Probably man could not have survived except for a second mechanism that is also built into his legs. And that is the mechanism of walking, which in effect constitutes a second heart.

The muscles of feet, calves, thighs, of buttocks and abdomen, all work when we walk. So does the diaphragm, the powerful muscle that forms the floor of the chest and is part of our breathing apparatus. However moderately they may work in the act of walking, all these muscles nevertheless work. And as they rhythmically contract and release, they squeeze the veins, pressing the blood along. Since the venal valves prevent the blood from flowing backward, it goes in the only direction possible. It goes upward, against gravity. As we walk, our muscles literally milk the blood back to the heart.

One Heart Burdened By The Load

When we settle for a sedentary life, and fail to give the circulation that extra muscular push upward, the blood tends to pool in the belly and especially in the feet, slowing the return rate and volume of blood, and forcing the heart to work harder. When we stand still too long, the blood collects in the veins of belly, legs, and feet, and the upper body and the brain are deprived.

But when we walk, the muscles take over their proper share of the work. The circulation speeds up. *And the heart rate and blood pressure go down.*

This has been shown by actual measurement. In people whose pulse was habitually accelerated and whose blood pressure was habitually elevated, a regime of regular walking — not necessarily very far or very fast — brought their resting pulse rate and blood pressure down to normal levels.

Weight Loss Through Walking

Though walking will probably not help you to lose weight, it can help you keep the weight off once you have dieted, or help keep it from creeping up in the first place.

A brisk walk uses up about 300 calories an hour. This does not seem like very much of an expenditure. But as a method of weight control, for most people it is quite enough. Because for most of us, this expenditure of a few hundred calories has a direct relationship to the way in which we gain weight.

Most people do not gain weight suddenly. Most people gain slowly, a little each week, over the years, because they consistently take in as food a little more than they expend as energy.

That is the way most of us gain our excess pounds. Some few people gain weight because of a glandular disorder, and some few because of psychological problems, but both these groups are very small minorities in the overweight class.

For years the Health Department of New York City has conducted a highly successful obesity clinic, and the finding is that most people are overweight either because they are hearty eaters by family tradition or because their way of life has become increasingly sedentary and they have not cut down their food intake. Wherever they begin, both kinds of overweight people end with the same unbalanced equation. They are taking in more supplies than they are using up, and are carrying around with them a million or so little storage warehouses in which the excess supplies are put away in the concentrated form of fatty tissue.

Army Pace, 3 mph Walk

Three miles an hour is the generally accepted average because it suits the average male height. It is the United States Army pace for long hikes, and it is the pace that most men find comfortable for a longish walk, although many can of course go faster if they need to.

Since women have a shorter average height, the assumption must be that their best average pace is something less than three miles an hour. Yet most good women walkers, wearing the right shoes and either a walking skirt or slacks, can let out their stride and do three miles an hour without feeling pushed, even on a long walk. They can do this although they may be inches shorter than the average man, say five feet three or four. At five feet and an inch or two, a woman might find it hard to keep the average pace, because there is a limit to her stride and she must move her legs that much faster to make up the difference.

The average length of stride for a man is two feet from the toe of the back foot to the toe of the front one. The number of steps per minute for a brisk walking pace, according to the United States Army, is 106. This of course has to do not with height or length of leg, but with temperament and energies. On a crisp day an energetic fellow may enjoy his walk at 110 steps per minute or even more. People who like to keep statistics on their walking can do it with the aid of a wristwatch and a pedometer.

The number of steps a walker takes per minute, or the number of miles he covers per hour, is no measure of his enjoyment. Nor is it a guarantee that he has hit his natural walking stride, the easy rhythmic pace that makes walking a pleasure in itself and can take him for miles without fatigue.

That he discovers only by experiment. He discovers it by lengthening his stride, again and again if necessary, until he has stretched the habit-formed, tension-dictated kinks out of muscles and joints.

When he has found it, he will know it unmistakably. And again and again, as he sets out for home after a tense day, he will find himself beginning with the short, stiff-legged walk of old habit until his legs remember and begin to reach. And then he is off and swinging as though he had not a care in the world.

How Far Is a Mile?

Distance is as full of illusion as a magician's bag. A mile sounds like a long way, but a twenty-minute walk is a pleasant prospect. Yet at the average walking pace of three miles an hour, a mile on level ground is precisely a twenty-minute walk.

A mile is an exact measure, 5,280 feet. At an average man's walking stride of 2 feet per step it will take him 2,640 steps to go the distance. And if he slogs through it counting his steps, it will be a very long mile indeed. But if he goes along interested in what he is seeing, thinking, or talking about with a companion, a mile will be hardly any distance at all.

Anyone in ordinary health and wearing comfortable shoes can walk a couple of miles and not know it. The authors and their friends have tried this experiment numerous times with friends who are not walkers. Walker and friend set out together with the implicit understanding that they will board a bus or taxi, or some equivalent conveyance, at whatever point they feel like it. Almost without exception, they arrive at their destination on foot, without the question of taking a bus or a taxi ever arising. The non-walker's action is typically one of surprise that he or she has actually covered so much distance. A mile and a half, two miles, without ever feeling it? They would hardly have thought it possible.

Your Personal Walking Program

First, walk on a measured course. You can use an indoor or outdoor track or you can measure your own course.

Some people mark segments of distance by painting slashes on the curb at various intervals or remembering a tree, house, or some other landmark that is a certain distance from the beginning of the course.

When you walk any measured course, your speed is simply a function of time and distance. To determine your speed, divide your time for a one-milk walk into 60 and you'll arrive at your miles per hour. For a three-mile walk, divide your time into 180. Or you can get your approximate speed from this chart.

Some models attach to your belt or a pants' pocket. Others can be attached to your feet. Since you know how far you've walked, you can use the chart above to determine your speed.

WALKING TIME IN MINUTES

One Mile	30	27	24	22	20	18	17	16	15	13	12
Three Miles	90	80	72	65	60	55	51	48	45	40	36
Speed in M.P.H.	2	2¼	2½	2¾	3	3¼	3½	3¾	4	4½	5

The walker can take advantage of the body's capacity for measuring distances by knowing the length of his own stride. Technically, a stride is composed of two steps. It begins when you push off with one foot and it ends when that same foot hits the ground again. You can count the number of strides you've taken by counting the number of times either the right foot or the left foot (but not both) hits the ground. if the right foot hits the ground one hundred times, that's one hundred strides. To determine the length of your stride, you need to measure a distance of at least twenty-five feet. Then count the number of steps you take within that distance, divide that number into twenty-five (or whatever distance you walk), and multiply by two. The result is your stride length. If you don't feel like measuring your stride, you can assume it's five-and-one-half-feet long, about average for an adult. Once you've settled on a stride length, you need only count the number of strides taken in one minute to determine your speed and distance. You can approximate your walking speed from this chart.

STRIDE LENGTH	STRIDES PER MINUTE						
	40	45	50	55	60	65	70
4 feet	1¾	2	2¼	2½	2¾	3	3¼
4½ feet	2	2¼	2½	2¾	3	3¼	3½
5 feet	2¼	2½	2¾	3	3½	3¾	4
5½ feet	2½	2¾	3	3½	3¾	4	4½
6 feet	2¾	3	3½	3¾	4	4½	4¾
6½ feet	3	3¼	3¾	4	4½	4¾	5¼
7 feet	3¼	3½	4	4¼	4¾	5¼	5½

SPEED IN M.P.H.

After you've determined your approximate speed, it's easy to figure how far you've walked. You just multiply the time walked by your speed in miles per hour.

Time × Speed = Distance

The walker who has a consistent stride is virtually a walking tape measure. Most of you will be satisfied, however, with an estimate of your speed and distance. It's seldom necessary, after all, to know these things exactly. But for those of us who are mathematically inclined, have a lot of time on our hands, or are just curious, here's a short excursion into walker's mathematics.

The first step of the precision walker is to get a precise measurement of his stride.
Here's how:

1. Mark off a distance of twenty-five feet.
2. Count the number of steps required to walk that distance.
3. Mark the position of your last step and measure the distance between that point and the twenty-five-foot line. (See illustration.)
4. Then subtract that distance from three hundred (the inches in twenty-five feet).
5. Divide the remainder by the number of full steps.
6. Multiply by two to convert to strides. The result is the *exact* length of your stride.

Here's how to figure your exact speed once you've determined your exact stride length:

1. Count the number of times in one minute that your right foot hits the ground.
2. Multiply the number of strides per minute by the length of your stride.
3. Multiply by sixty to convert to strides per hour.
4. Divide by twelve to convert inches to feet.
5. Divide by 5,280 (the number of feet in a mile) to get miles per hour.

Calories Consumed While Walking

Every pound of stored fat in your body consists of about 3,500 calories. So every time, through exercise or dieting, you burn up 3,500 more calories than you consume, you lose one pound. If you walk an hour a day and keep your diet at its normal level, you could lose a pound in roughly twelve days. That's a relatively slow rate of loss. But if you cut your calorie intake by an equal amount, or roughly three hundred calories a day, and continue to walk for an hour a day, you could lose a pound every six days. And that's about as fast as you should be losing weight without a doctor's supervision.

The number of calories you burn while walking varies with your speed, your weight, and the inclination and ruggedness of the terrain.

The caloric loss while walking increases with body weight, simply because it requires more energy to move a heavier object any given distance. This is actually good news for overweight people because it reduces the amount of time needed to walk off the pounds. Unfortunately, as you lose weight, the amount of time it takes increases. Researchers also have found that a backpack, worn properly, effects energy cost in the same way an equivalent

The Number of Days Required to Walk Off 1 to 20 Pounds Without Dieting*

Min. Per Day	Miles Per Day	Caloric Deficit	Days To Lose 1 Pound	Days To Lose 5 Pounds	Days To Lose 10 Pounds	Days To Lose 20 Pounds
30	1¾	0	23	117	233	467
30	1¾	200	10	50	100	200
30	1¾	400	6	32	64	127
30	1¾	600**	5	23	47	93
60	3½	0	12*	58	117	233
60	3½	200	7	35	70	140
60	3½	400	5*	25	50	100
60	3½	600	4	19	39	78
90	5¼	0	8	39	78	156
90	5¼	200	5	27	54	108
90	5¼	600	3	17	33	67

*Calorie expenditure is 5 calories per minute, about average for a 154-pound person walking 3.5 m.p.h.
**Your calorie intake should not go below 1500 calories a day.

amount of body weight would. So you can use the chart below to calculate the number of calories you burn while backpacking. Just add the weight of the pack to your body weight. For instance, a 160-pound person, carrying a 40-pound pack, would burn as many calories as a 200-pound person, carrying no pack — or 5.3 calories per minute.

Number of Calories burned by People of Various Weights at a Walking Speed of 3 M.P.H.*

	Weight of Walker in Pounds									
	120	140	160	180	200	220	240	260	280	300
Calories Per Minute	3.6	4	4.4	4.9	5.3	5.7	6.1	6.6	7	7.4
Calories Per Mile	72	80	89	97	106	114	123	131	140	149
Calories Per Hour	216	240	264	294	318	342	366	396	420	444

*Calculated from a formula suggested by Roy J. Shepherd, M.D., Ph.D., in *Alive Man: The Physiology of Physical Activity*, (Charles C. Thomas, Springfield, Ill., 1972).

Speed affects the caloric cost of walking in much the same way as weight. The faster you go, the more calories you're burning per minute, simply because you're covering a greater

Calories Burned By a Person Weighing 154 Pounds*

Speed In M.P.H.	Calories per Min.	Calories per Hour	Calories per Mile
2	3.1	184	92
2½	3.7	222	89
3	4.4	260	87
3½	5.0	299	85
4**	5.6	337	84
4½	7.4	444	99
5***	8.7	519	104

*Calculated from formulae in *Alive Man: The Physiology of Physical Activity*.
**The same energy cost as walking at 2 m.p.h. on a 10 percent uphill grade.
***The same energy cost as walking 3 m.p.h. on a 10 percent grade.

distance. Researchers also have found that at speeds greater than four miles an hour, the energy cost of walking rises steeply because we walk less efficiently at higher speeds.

The figures provided in the charts in this chapter are only approximations, but they should give you some idea of how you can use walking to lose weight.

When you lose weight, you begin to expend fewer and fewer calories for each minute of walking at the same speed. You can somewhat compensate for this by increasing your walking speed and, if possible, the total amount of time you spend walking. Most people who walk for exercise find that their walking speed gradually increases with practice and that their tolerance for walking increases as well. Many people can walk for seven or eight hours without any discomfort. When you reach that point, weight will no longer be a problem.

On Walking and Aging

Walking has long been regarded as a fountain of youth. Charles Dickens noted "certain ancients, far gone in years, who have staved off infirmities and dissolution by earnest walking — hale fellows, close upon ninety, but brisk as boys." Dr. Alexander Leaf, a professor at the Harvard Medical School reported in *Executive Health* in 1977: "These men I have examined around the world who live in vigorous health to 100 or more years are great walkers. If you want to live a long, long time in study health you can't go wrong in forming the habit of long vigorous walking every day . . . until it becomes a habit as important to you as eating and sleeping."

The saying "you're only as old as you feel" is, truly, the gospel. Research into the effects of aging has shown that many of the diseases commonly associated with old age are caused by the way we live, rather than how long we live. For that reason, it's difficult to choose examples of people who have retained their vitality in "old age" by walking. For what is "old age"? It's certainly not the kind of life-style these people, all over seventy, are living.

We live a lot longer now than we did in Charles Dickens's day and the sight of ninety-year-old's who are as "brisk as boys" isn't really all that remarkable anymore. Yet our expanded life-spans do not always mean an equivalent improvement in the quality of life. "The years in later life — particularly those of the post-retirement period — should be happy years," says the President's Council on Physical Fitness and Sports. "But the full promise of this stage of life comes only to those who are healthy, alert, and active."

Your Legs and Arms Are Powerful Pumps for Your Superpump — the Heart!

In an effort to measure the effects of aging, researchers have tested the "physical working capacity" of people of various ages and have found that physical ability declines from 35 to 40 percent between the ages of thirty and seventy. Yet walking can effect this decline. In a study of 109 women between the ages of ten and sixty-eight, researchers at the University of California found that exercise was as important as age in determining their levels of physical deterioration. The researchers found that older women, who had exercised regularly, had a level of physical ability similar to that of nonactive women in their twenties. Another study of the effects of exercise on aging showed that middle-aged men, who exercised vigorously for as much as an hour, two to three times a week, could stop and even reverse the customary decline in their "physical working capacity," despite their increasing age.

A great advantage of walking as an exercise is that you can start young and keep at it throughout your life. It's noncompetitive, largely unskilled, and totally individual. Once people develop a taste for walking, they don't give it up easily.

Unfortunately, many people stop exercising during the middle years of their lives. The pressures of raising families and establishing careers are so strong during those years that, even though we know we should get some exercise, we won't do it. And many of us lead extremely sedentary lives during those years. We sit behind a desk all day, grinding away at the paperwork. We smoke. We drink too much, both to escape from the pressure and to reach the level of conviviality that we think is good for business. At the end of the day, we drive home to our television sets for another stint of sitting, smoking, and drinking. We grow tired and waddle into bed. On weekends, we wonder why our golf game has gone to hell. We try to make up for our lack of physical vitality by living vicariously through our heroes, the professional athletes. One day we reach the age of sixty-five and the corporation that's been the focus of our lives for forty years puts us out to pasture.

It's Never Too Late to Exchange Wrong, Lazy Habits for New, Healthy Habits!

But just because we reach our retirement years in poor physical condition doesn't mean there's nothing we can do about it. As one expert told a White House Conference on Aging: "Man at any age, if he is reasonably healthy, can be physically conditioned. While we may not be masters of our destinies, we can affect the degradation of our bodies." And the President's council again: "Fortunately, even if you have let too many years slip by when good intentions of keeping fit were sacrificed to other demands of life, you still can pick up at some level of physical performance and work yourself up several notches."

A national survey showed that walking is virtually the only exercise taken regularly by men and women sixty-five and over. It's easy to see why. It's safe and effective. Herbert A. de Vries, who has studied extensively the effects of exercise on older people, reported in *Geriatrics* in 1971 that vigorous walking, thirty to sixty minutes a day, would bring about an improvement in physical fitness in all but the most highly conditioned men in that age group. Walking and other forms of exercise also have been shown in various studies to be particularly effective in curing or alleviating the afflictions most often associated with old age: brittle bones, emphysema and other lung disorders, diabetes, arthritis, and heart disease.

Although this book contains a walking program that should work for people of all ages, C. Carson Conrad, executive director of the President's Council on Physical Fitness and Sports, has developed a walking program especially for people over sixty, who have led a sedentary life for many years but still are in good health. The program takes into consideration the fact that some people who haven't exercised for many years may need a graded program for gradually working themselves into shape.

Walking can also help us retain or resurrect another aspect of life that we sometimes lose during the busy middle years: the ability to play. As we grow older, our opportunities for play seem to dwindle, or at least we think they do. We have a tendency to sit around and grumble about our infirmities as if we were in some sort of contest in which first prize goes to the one in the worst condition. This is especially true if we haven't developed or maintained the ability to participate in some lifetime sport, such as golf or tennis. It's possible to take up golf or tennis when you are over sixty, but it's not easy. You have to worry not only about getting in shape, but mastering a new skill as well. The frustration of trying to enjoy a game of golf when every other shot lands in a subdivision or a cow pasture is likely to add to our overall depression about being old. Many elderly people have told me that walking has turned their lives around. it's renewed their ability to play, to have fun. And having fun is as natural as taking a walk.

Walking Schedules

1st and 2nd Weeks	3 sessions on alternate days. Emphasize good walking style, good breathing and posture.	¼ mile
3rd Week	3 sessions on alternate days. Use interval training* and lengthen stride. Practice deep breathing.	½ mile
4th Week	3 sessions on alternate days. Practice deep breathing.	¾ mile
5th Week	3 sessions on alternate days. Practice deep breathing. Lengthen stride. Use interval training.	1 mile
6th Week**	5 sessions. Practice deep breathing. Emphasize posture. Use interval training.	1 mile
7th Week	5 sessions 3 m.p.h.	1 mile in 20 min.
8th Week	5 sessions 3 m.p.h.	1½ miles in 30 min.
9th Week	5 sessions 3 m.p.h.	2 miles in 40 min.
10th Week	5 sessions 3 m.p.h.	2 miles in 40 min.
11th Week	5 sessions 3 m.p.h.	2½ miles in 50 min.
12th Week	5 sessions 3 m.p.h.	3 miles in 60 min.
13th Week	5 sessions 3¼ m.p.h.	3 miles in 55 min.
14th Week	5 sessions 3½ m.p.h.	3 miles in 45 min.
15th Week	5 sessions 4 m.p.h.	3 miles in 45 min.

*Interval training simply means that you increase your speed until you feel uncomfortable and then slow down again.

**The first six weeks of training are intended to acclimate your body to walking. The President's Council suggests that if you don't feel comfortable increasing the distance weekly that you remain at a comfortable distance and increase the walking sessions.

Walking Bibliography

The Magic of Walking, Sussman, Goode; Simon and Schuster 1967, Rockefeller Center, 630 5th Ave., New York, NY 10020.
Walking, Andrews and McMeel Inc., Universal Press Syndicate, 6700 Squigg Road, Mission, KS 66202.

Race Walking Vs. Run-Walk,
The Distance Athletes Rest Pace

Finish A Triathlon in Classic Style

We have discovered that walking, the king of exercise, when accomplished efficiently can be very beneficial to the triathlete. Race walking accelerates the walking pace to a point that, if maintained for a full marathon distance, will come into the four to four-and-one-half hour finishing time range.

In fact, an intermediate speed race-walker will maintain a steady 10-minute-per-mile pace with great ease. This should be a revelation to hurting runners in the last event of the triathlon. Race walking the marathon could easily set a better marathon time split for the four to five hour or longer, finisher than attempting to run and walk the distance. Properly trained, a triathlete could ease through at a good pace what ordinarily might be an ordeal.

Also race-walking offers an alternative sport, long after the desire and the will to participate in running events is past.

Race Walking as an Individual Sport

Anybody who has watched a track meet, be it live or on television, has seen a group of people line up at the start, poised and ready to compete after years and years of practice. Perhaps you chuckled to yourself as these finely tuned athletes begin to walk around the track, as if the track's surface had just been transformed into hot coals. These are the race-walkers, a group of men and women who have had their share of ridicule, from being called "funny-legged geeks" to "tetched" in the head, and who, through it all, have pursued their own particular sport with an avid ferocity. In Hawaii more and more people are discovering race-walking as an enjoyable and rewarding alternative to the jogging fever that has swept the country.

From Walking to Race-Walking

Walking is man's original means of transportation, and still is for millions of people . . . also walking has been both an enjoyable and rewarding pastime. Race walking is essentially not too divergent from normal walking; the basic art to the sport is simply learning to walk more efficiently and at a higher rate of speed. Once learned, race walking will produce the same results physically as jogging, but here's the important part: race walking is much less damaging to the joints. As more evidence comes out regarding pelvic damage in female joggers, this is an important fact to remember. Additionally, race walking utilizes more muscles in the upper torso than jogging, providing for excellent all-around conditioning.

Sound easy? Basically it is, but there is a subtle art to race walking: you can't just go out and walk fast around your complex a couple times. But, by starting out slow and building a conditioning program around the basic steps that follow below, in no time you'll be up to olympic class, walking 26 miles at a time.

As in all conditioning programs, you should get a thorough check-up by a doctor — if all of us were in top shape, there would be no need to exercise. Having done this, the next step is to get the proper equipment. A T-shirt and free-fitting athletic shorts are standard fare, but close attention should be paid to your shoes. The shoes should be light and flat-soled, but it's important they give needed support to the feet. Tennis shoes will do for learning, but as the workouts become extended, better shoes will become necessary. Some walkers prefer to wear quality marathon running shoes, but the optimum shoe is the special race walking shoe which is manufactured by some sporting shoe companies.

Once you have all the proper equipment, you're ready. Begin by walking naturally at a speed and distance which causes some increased breathing and tiredness. Once you've developed your rhythm, you can start to concentrate on the finer aspects of the sport. The feet are a very important part of race walking. The feet should move directly forward, and the toes should point forward and not to the side. Do not swing the feet to the left or to the right. Additionally, before one foot can leave the ground, the other must be in contact with the pavement, or you're running.

Sometime while the foot is in contact with the ground, the leg must be straightened. The better walkers do not land on a straight leg, but lock it into place shortly afterwards. Failing to straighten the leg is illegal and would lead to disqualification if you were being judged. This is called "creeping," and if done, will make you look more like Groucho Marx than a true race walker.

As you start walking, the trunk of the body should be shifted forward, utilizing gravity to help move forward. This may be experienced by standing erect, next raising up on the toes, and without changing the relative position of the upper body, settling back onto the heels. If the head gets tilted forward, the walker will fall. Occasionally while climbing hills or walking into strong winds, a slight lean forward will be necessary, but normally leaning will either cause creeping or will pull the rear foot off the ground too soon. Therefore, the pelvis and trunk of the body should be erect.

Race Walking For Total Body Conditioning

The arms serve a number of useful purposes, from balancing the walker to controlling the length and tempo of the stride. When the walker is moving slowly, the arms should be left down at the sides and swung naturally. As the speed increases, the forearms must be raised. The exact angle will depend upon the individual walker, but normally the upper- and forearms should form a 90° angle. The arms should move from a position over the corresponding toe back and to the side. The further the arms move from front to back, the longer will be the stride of the legs. The quickness of the arms will determine how fast the legs move.

The art of race walking requires concentration and time at first, but good form and style are worth it. No walker is ever so qualified that he can't gain from giving attention to form and style. But race walking is basically an endurance sport, and one or two extended sessions are necessary each week up to twelve or more miles at a moderate speed (depending on the level of development of the walker). After a few weeks, form and style will naturally fall into place, and you'll be on your way!

Brief History of Race Walking

Race walking in the U.S. fell into a state of decline beginning in the late 1920s, and it has showed in our performance in the Olympic games. When Larry Young of Columbia, Missouri, won the bronze medal in the fifty-kilometer race walk in the 1968 Olympic games in Mexico City, he became the first American medalist since 1920. Yet, despite this decline in the international competitiveness of Americans race walkes, every major U.S. team has included at least two walkers and sometimes more. Today's race walkers see this as an advantage of their sport. Less competition for these teams means greater opportunities to compete with the best.

Ron Laird, one of America's top race walkers, writes in his book, *Competitive Race Walking,* that he was lucky to forsake running for walking early enough in life to become a champion. "I see so many runners who have hopes of becoming great and going on to make the Olympic team," Laird writes. "When I was running in my high school days, I also had those dreams. How fortunate I was to have discovered my sport early enough in life (at 17) and then persevered with it through those very trying first couple of years.

An Opportunity to Excell

"The race-walking events are still so wide open today in this country that a person with normal athletic ability, if he has the desire to learn and work, may develop himself into a national champion and/or international team member. I have a closet full of U.S.A. sweatsuits to prove this."

Laird, who has dedicated his life to race walking, recalls that in high school his best time in the half-mile was two minutes, 18 seconds, and in the mile, five minutes and 12 seconds, hardly the makings of a championship runner. But in race walking, he's one of the best.

Martin Rudow, another race-walking author, laments that his is a neglected sport which has been the target of efforts by the International Olympic Committee to pare the number of events in the Olympic Games. But like Laird, Rudow sees that as an opportunity.

"In most national championship race-walks," Rudow writes in his book, *Race Walking,* "the quality thins out after the first few places. There just aren't enough top walkers able to travel to all the big races. This fact opens the way for undertrained and less gifted athletes to pick up medals. Even trial races for major teams occasionally have weak fields. If injuries or layoffs take care of only a few of the best walkers, the race is suddenly wide open and berths on the team may go to 'unknowns.' "

The Olympic Games, a national championship, or first place in a local walking event seem a long way off if you've just started to take regular walks around the block; but those coveted athletic prizes may be more accessible than you think. At least that's what the experts say.

This is especially true for conditioned hikers and joggers, and for athletes participating in other physically taxing sports. Four years ago, Allan Price was a mediocre runner. Today he's in the record books.

Rob Spier says he often uses runners as his "rabbits" when he is training. No walker is going to beat a well-conditioned runner, of course, but Spier finds it an entertaining and helpful training tool to try to pick up as much ground as possible on the runner.

In Chicago, Augie Hirt, who holds American records for 100 and 75 kilometer walks and for the 50-mile walk, enters marathons regularly because there are few walking events in the area. In one race, he finished 240 out of 700. But remember, he was walking. The rest were running. "The runners are a little embarrassed," Augie told a reporter afterward. Similarly, in Washington, D.C., Allan Price keeps in shape for race walking during the winter by running ultra-marathons of 50 miles or more.

So walkers and runners are definitely kindred spirits. That does little, however, to appease the walker who sees thousands of runners every year entering the Boston marathon, but only a handful entering such races as the 100-mile walk in Missouri.

Race Walking Requires Skill & Training

Hirt, sounding slightly bitter, recently told a reporter for the *Chicago Tribune* that "race walking is catching on in other countries, but not here . . . You can go to another country and walk in a race, and they think you are a hero. Here you get no respect at all."

Hirt claimed that running was popularized by television coverage of Frank Shorter's marathon victory in the 1972 Olympics.

"Also, everybody can go out and run, but you have to become very involved and know what you are doing to even start race walking," Hirt said. "The hardest thing is that to most people it looks funny. I can't see something that looks funny being accepted on a large basis."

We have all seen some pretty funny-looking joggers lumbering down the street, so Hirt's assessment of the situation may not be quite correct. Our capacity for change and acceptance seems almost unlimited. Clothing that would have seemed outrageous five years ago is in vogue today. Just think back for a moment to what you and the people around you were wearing, thinking and doing 10 years ago; and you'll have to agree, we've come a long way.

As for the expression; "looking funny," it is sad that a lot of people hesitate to participate in some sport or activity which could enrich their lives just because they are afraid of "looking funny."

Heck, we all "look funny" in our own way. We're short or we're tall or we're skinny or we're fat or we're bow-legged. So forget about "looking funny." If you want to race-walk, do it. If you've got it, flaunt it.

While you're out swiveling your hips, swinging your arms, and walking at a blinding pace, those overweight, grinning, sloths on four wheels are dying at an equally blinding pace, and all because they're afraid of "looking funny."

Be a little odd and feel healthy and alive and youthful, instead of sitting back and watching the superb God-given instrument that is the human body dissipate from disease.

Every walker must learn to handle "looking funny" and one of the best ways to do that is to cultivate a sense of humor. Funny things do happen. For instance, Hirt told Dorothy Collin of the *Chicago Tribune* about an incident in which he saw a passing motorist poke his head out of the car window. "I knew I was in trouble," Hirt said. "They threw something at me, and it hit me on the shoulder. I started to chase them but gave up. Then I noticed my shoulder didn't hurt so I wondered what it was they threw. I walked back and found a marshmallow. I was really laughing when I got home."

The great race-walkers are hardened to this kind of harassment, and it's part of the challenge of their sport. If you can learn to fight the crowd and be your own person while race walking, you'll find that you're more independent in the rest of your dealings with mankind, a personality trait that can be extremely valuable — it can even save your life.

A professor in college, a rugged individualist himself, was fond of telling a story about how buffalo hunters would stampede a herd of buffalo over a cliff, thus eliminating the necessity of picking them off with their rifles one by one. Then imploring his students to avoid the herd (something to contemplate during the Boston Marathon), the professor would say with a grin: "You'll be a lonely little buffalo, but you'll still be alive."

When Larry Young won his first Olympic medal in race walking in Mexico City in 1968, he endured a level of abuse you're not likely to encounter even if you're a resident of Muskogee, Oklahoma, here according to the popular song of a few years back, they don't tolerate unusual behavior. The course for the 50-kilometer walk in Mexico City wound through narrow, city streets where masses of Mexicans were lined up within only a few feet of the athletes. As Young passed the Mexican favorite, a man named Pedrazza, he fell into an ocean of sound.

"The most hideous screaming and shouting blasted right into my ears," Young later recalled in an interview. "The crowd was yelling 'Mex-i-co, Mex-i-co, Pe-dra-za, Pe-dra-za, Mex-i-co, Pe-dra-za' over and over again at the top of their lungs. The sound pierced me. Imagine yourself walking along a street with people at arms' length away hollering right into your ears. That way lies madness. Pulling away from Pedraza was as crucial to me as catching the leaders."

The abuse didn't end with that incident. When Larry was awarded the bronze medal for placing third in the event, an historic moment for American race walking, the crowd erupted into a chorus of boos and jerked their thumbs downward to indicate their displeasure. A true walker, Larry stuck out his tongue at the crowd and returned the thumbs-down gesture. A photographer captured the moment, and it remains a monument to those walkers who aren't worried about "looking funny."

Race Walkers & Runners Have Hecklers

Many runners have written about their problems with hecklers and how to deal with them. Their exposure is similar to that of race-walkers.

"For reasons best known to themselves, some people can't stand the sight of a runner," James F. Fixx writes in his best-seller, *The Complete Book of Running.* "There aren't many of them, but when one comes along, you know it. They shout abuse at you from passing cars, fling objects at you and sometimes drive so erratically that you fear for your life. Others gather in ugly little clots on street corners and mutter about your manhood and the shape of your legs."

Fixx says there are basically three ways to handle hostile humans: stoicism, fighting back by yelling obscenities, making appropriate gestures or throwing "lethal objects" at the offender.

You'll have to work out your own method of dealing with this phenomenon. Either ignore the hecklers or use an appropriate hand gesture, mainly because someone passing in a car can't hear you very well, especially if they're going fast, but they can see you in their rearview mirror. As for hecklers, keep quiet unless you're bigger than they are. There is, of course, some danger of violent retaliation by the heckler. It's a good idea to have a plan to escape should something go wrong.

The old adage, "there's strength in numbers," probably applies here, and I doubt that runners are taking as much abuse as they were a few years ago. You'd have to be a fool to hurl insults at a horde of joggers. You might be trampled. Perhaps as the number of race-walkers increases, that sport, too, will achieve greater acceptance by the public, and non-participants, sensing they're outnumbered, will become less openly hostile.

Tremendous changes have taken place in this country in the last 15 years, and the need for regular exercise has become a widely accepted fact. As we progress farther and farther down the road toward socialized medicine and begin paying for everyone else's bad health, this trend is likely to accelerate. It should be accompanied by greater respect for amateur athletes in every sport, including race walking. Ordinary walkers don't face the level of harassment encountered by race-walkers, simply because there's nothing unusual about regular walking. For all the world knows, the avid walker on a 10-mile hike around his city or town is just going about his business.

Women Race Walkers

Only women have serious problems when they're out for a walk at an ordinary pace. Most men don't understand that women aren't necessarily flattered by compliments yelled from a car window.

The odd gait of race walking presents a special problem for women who train on the sidewalk or in any public place frequented by nonathletes. (True sports persons are seldom intolerant of other athletes). It's sad that women, having hurdled all the cultural obstacles against their participation in strenuous sports, must then be victimized by hostile humans while training. In their case, carring lethal objects may be warranted if only to preserve their hard-earned self-respect as athletes.

At least one woman race-walker, complaining that people "honk their horns, call you names, throw rocks and bottles, and try to push you off the road," armed herself with a heavy bolt to throw at cars that veered too close to her. But if this approach seems a little risky to you (and I think it is), you can always take comfort in the knowledge that you're bothering them a lot more than they're bothering you. As one race-walker put it, "Maybe they feel threatened or something because they're big fat slobs, and we're not." That revenge is as sweet as any.

Women Reap Rewards in Race Walking

Women who take up race walking will reap rewards not available in many sports. The record books are wide open for women walkers. Elsie McGarvey of Kalispell, Montana, set a record in 1978 by becoming the first woman walker to complete 100 miles in less than 24 hours. Researchers have found that based on their weight, women have less muscle and more fat. This puts them at a disadvantage in sports that require great speed and strength. But in matters of endurance, where the body must feed on its reserves of fat, women may even have an advantage. Nowhere is this more true than in walking long distances, and women may someday find themselves breaking walking records set by the so-called "stronger sex."

Another aspect of long-distance race walking tends to equalize the traditional dominance of youth in competitive sports. It is the need for mental discipline. "There's some place in that race where you switch over from muscles to head," Rob Spier said of the 100-mile race in Missouri. "There's no place after 25 miles where you wouldn't want to just sit down and watch.

"I've talked to marathoners about the wall at 18 miles. I've walked a marathon, and there is no wall. That point in a walk is about 1:00 a.m. or 2:00 a.m. (12 hours into the race). "Essentially, you just have to make up your mind to do it. If something hurts, it won't hurt in an hour. Something else will hurt, and you will have forgotten about that other pain. "It's a progression of various aches and pains. It's not a pleasure for everybody. It's an accomplishment."

Paul Hendricks, a 35-year-old high school teacher in San Diego, began race walking at distances over 50 miles in 1976. After only a year of training, he won the 100-mile walk and placed second in the "big test" in 1978. He agrees that youth is less important than the kind of mental discipline that seems to come with age. "What people don't know about walking is that their prime is in the late 30's or early 40's," Hendricks said. "Before that, you don't have the mental discipline. Physically, you've got to get to your best condition, but you have to have the mental discipline to cope with the variations of pain — upset stomach, mental fatigue, sharp leg pains, cramps . . .'"

Spier says any one of a variety of physical aches and pains can drive you out of a long-distance walk if you let them. "Some people drop out year after year at the same point. It's not their physical limit. You can predict when they will psyche themselves out. I know one man who gets diarrhea regularly during the race. It's not the travel or the training. It's just psychological."

Art Fleming also emphasized the importance of maintaining your mental balance. "It's so damn easy to step off the track. The psychological boredom is just phenomenal."

Older Race Walkers Stick To It

Spier says older walkers can't rationalize dropping-out of a race as easily as younger ones. A 60-year-old race-walker knows he has a limited number of years ahead of him in which to meet the challenge of a long-distance walk. Younger walkers, on the other hand, can tell themselves that they have many years in which to finish the race.

It probably boils down to something as basic as patience. Psychologists have long known that as we grow older, our understanding of time changes. When you celebrated your 10th birthday anniversary, you looked forward to a year that represented one-tenth of your life. At your 40th birthday, the ratio has dropped to one-fortieth. This produces a different concept of time, a change that may allow us to deal with long hours of physical and psychological struggle toward a cherished goal, like joining that elite group of centurions.

But whatever the reason behind it, walkers over the age of 30 don't need to be placed in separate categories to achieve victories in long-distance races. They can compete on an equal level and feel confident that the 20-year-old speedster who laps them in the early going is likely to fade away after 35 miles when psychological toughness becomes more important than a young body.

Race Walkers Have An Indefinite Competitive Life

If you still have doubts about the possibility of becoming a first-rate competitor in middle-age, the experience of Larry O'Neil, a lumber executive from Kalispell, Montana, should dispel them once and for all.

When Allan Price set a 100-mile record in 1978 of 18 hours, 57 minutes, and 41 seconds, he broke the record for the 100 set in 1967 by O'Neil when he was 60 years old.

Larry is a prime example of the benefits of walking and the potential for remaining competitive in your later years. There is probably no other sport in which a 60-year-old set a national record, for all age groups, that stood for 11 years. And Larry still walks in the 100, though he doesn't always finish.

He trains about two hours a day in the mountains around Kalispell, wearing shorts until the temperature drops below freezing. He uses hiking as a conditioner as well.

It's easier to train in our area where there are so many beautiful mountains and lakes," Larry says, "I like so much to hike up to the high mountains. There's such beautiful fishing in the lakes."

Larry didn't start race walking until 1964, three years before he set a national record in the 100. Like many other walkers, Larry's interest was piqued by the scarcity, rather than the abundance, of walkers. "A friend of mine and I were watching a junior track-and-field meet when they announced they needed two more walkers. My friend asked, 'You'd enter it with me, wouldn't you,' and I thought he was kidding so I said, 'Yes.' I couldn't chicken-out, so I had to do it. I entered the race that day and took fifth."

So what began on a dare for Larry O'Neil, developed into a record-setting performance and continues to be a way of participating in competitive sports into his 70's.

It's this universality of race walking and its close relationship to walking for exercise, for pleasure, and for health reasons, that some people believe it's the sport of the future — especially long-distance walks.

As Augie Hirt notes, walking has long been a respected and popular sport in Europe where many trends that eventually sweep this country are sighted first. "It's always been popular in Europe," says Paul Hendricks who has walked in the world's longest race, the three day, 300-mile Strasbourg-to-Paris walk. He says it's "not just race walking but walking in general. It's the natural thing you do all your life."

Race Walking, A Worldwide Participating Sport

Martin Rudow reported that "ultra-long-distance walking, until recently an obscure branch of the sport, may yet prove to be its mainstay . . . Already interest is building in these super-endurance affairs."

Rudow notes that distance events of 50 and 100 miles, and 75 and 100 kilometers, are now offered at various sites in this country. And in addition to the Paris-to-Strasbourg, European epic, there is the 28-hour race in Roubaix, France, and the 100-kilometer race in Lugano, Italy. England offers the popular 53-mile London-to-Brighton contest and a 100-mile walk which guarantees membership in a Centurions club for those who hoof the distance in less than 24-hours. "Genuine ultra-long-distance specialists are emerging, especially at the one-hundred-mile distance," writes Rudow. "So far, all these events have been held on tracks. The use of roads has probably been avoided because of officiating and traffic problems. However, such road events have proven to be extremely popular in Europe, and we may see similar races held in the U.S. as interest grows."

Authorities verify the dangers involved in road races. Imagine walkers strung out over a 100-mile course, the stragglers as far as 50 miles behind the leaders. The difficulties are obvious. Somehow, these walkers must be watched by qualified judges to determine if they are following the rules of race walking. Another complication is the need for constant refreshment on long walks. How many people would be needed to man aid stations along a 100-mile course? A hundred or more? Nevertheless, the logistical difficulties of road walks could be solved with proper planning. It's a good idea, most race walkers say, for each walker to bring along his own "handler" to provide him with liquids, food, a change of clothes, and other aid. There's no reason why these "handlers" couldn't follow along in cars, during a long road race, providing help when needed, and at the same time, eliminating the need for numerous aid stations. This would require, of course, that each walker bring a "handler" instead of relying on help from race officials. But walkers who move at about the same speed could team up and use the same "handler."

Race Walk Judging

Judging is a stickier problem. Race walking "purists" contend that poor judging makes a mockery of the sport by robbing it of the important element of technique. But judging is really only important for the top walkers in a long-distance race. Who cares whether those far behind the leaders are meeting technical requirements. If they walk 50 or 100 miles, it's still a marvelous accomplishment that should be encouraged.

As an answer to the problem of judging, only the leaders might be watched carefully by race officials. Let the rest of us amble along at our pace, enjoying our walk and the achievement of our personal goals.

Race Walking Rules

The official AAU rulebook defines race walking as a "progression by steps so taken that unbroken contact with the ground is maintained.

"The advancing foot of the walker must contact the ground before the rear foot leaves the ground. During the period of each step, in which a foot is on the ground, this leg shall be straightened (i.e., not bent at the knee) for at least one moment.

"Competitors may be cautioned once: a second violation of the above shall mean disqualifying, and they must leave the track or road."

If you're starting a new walking program in your area, judging is going to be the toughest obstacle to overcome. Ideally, you should find the most experienced race-walkers around and have them obtain certification through the AAU. The experienced walkers are obviously the ones best qualified to judge a race, except for the fact that they're likely to be walking in the race themselves.

So you need to find someone who is interested in the sport but doesn't want to participate in every race. Have them read the chapter on race walking in this book and the two other books that I have mentioned, and they should be able to do a fairly competent job of judging.

But again, at the risk of offending some race-walking authorities, I recommend that you don't get too hung up on this problem. It will work itself out once you get the program well underway and have a few races under your belt. By then you should have a pretty good idea which of your volunteer judges are able to keep the race under control without taking the fun out of it by disqualifying a lot of people who are just out to have a good time. Besides, you won't need a certified judge until your walking group or track club becomes affiliated with a national track association.

Yet the rules are important to the sport of race walking. Without them, it wouldn't exist. It's a sport of technique as well as endurance.

Judging the walker's technique has without a doubt been the most controversial aspect of the sport over the years. Race walking at short distances was eliminated from the Olympics many years ago, simply because these events were so difficult to judge and the temptation for walkers to violate the rules was so great.

"I can't imagine how anyone could race-walk a mile," said Rob Spier, a certified walking judge. "There's a tremendous tendency just to get up and run." But for the longer distances, most authorities agree, violation of the rules is not a serious problem because the pace is slow enough to allow compliance without great effort.

And don't worry about "looking funny." "Hip motion is physically and even emotionally difficult for many athletes to do," writes Laird. "because of the embarrassment involved, especially when doing it in public, many potential race-walkers never give the sport their sincere efforts or stay with it very long."

Even if you practice race walking in your neighborhood, you probably won't attract that much attention.

Straightening the Leg

The rules require that you straighten the advancing leg as it passes under the body, but you can gain power as well as stay legal if you lock the knee as soon after the foot touches the ground as possible.

The Feet

For maximum efficiency of stride, you should always try to touch the ground with the heel of the advancing foot and leave the ground with the toe of the rear foot. Don't walk flat-footed. "Don't push off from the toe," Rudow writes. "Rather, drive with the advancing knee. In hard sprint walking, the heel is jammed into the ground, and the foot and leg are rolled into a stiff legged departure of the toe from the ground.

Joe Duncan, president of the Columbia Track Club, has wrestled with this problem since the 100-mile walk was started in 1967. Initially, entry in the race was wide open, but eventually it had to be limited to those over 18 years old, because children on the track interfered with serious walkers.

Race judges keep an eye on the leaders, while other walkers are allowed greater leeway. You see walkers listening to portable radios, chatting with friends, and stopping for a rest on trackside cots. As a result, the race has a delightfully informal flavor which allows each walker to set his own goal in the race and go away with a feeling of accomplishment.

It's this kind of informality that could lead to mass participation in organized walks. Every walker who achieves his or her personal goal could be awarded a small plaque or medallion. Such walks are already popular in Germany.

Getting a walking program started in your area shouldn't be that difficult if you are persistent and methodical about it. You should start by contacting the local track club, track coaches and physical education instructors at the colleges and high schools in your area, and any other organizations or persons that might be interested.

Race Walking and the Triathlete

For the Triathlon contestant that is not a front runner in the marathon or one that cannot go the 26.2 mile distance at a full run event of the multi sport, race walking offers a very interesting alternative as stated in the beginning of this chapter . . . It would do well for an aspiring triathlete to have this knowledge and discipline in his bag of tricks. To turn in a four to four hour-15 minute marathon at the Ironman World Triathlon at Kona, Hawaii, would prove a great advantage over about 80% of the field of contestants. It is not necessary that the exact form for the race walk be adhered to. A modified version that would allow a bit of "creeping" movement, the swinging arms and the extended stride, head up, would certainly show up the contestant at the end of this physical ordeal as a strong contender, greatly overshadowing the weak appearance that the plodding walker or the slow tired jogger, gives, as the race walker crosses the finish line in high, brisk style.

An exaggeration of creeping.

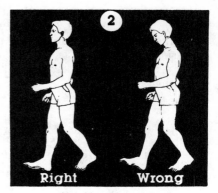

Head bent forward.

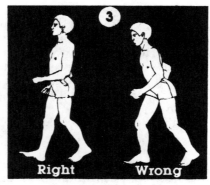

Body leaning forward.

Race Walking Bibliography

Walking, Andrews and McMeel Inc., Universal Press Syndicate, 6700 Squigg Road, Mission, KS 66202.

The Complete Walker, Alfred A. Knopf, New York, NY.

How to Have Strong, Healthy, Happy Feet Through Life!, Paul C. Bragg, N.D., Ph.D. and Patricia Bragg, Ph.D., Health Science, Box 7, Santa Barbara, CA 93102.

Of all exercises walking is the best. —Thomas Jefferson

People love bypaths —Tao Te Ching

In every photographer, there is something of the stroller. —Henri Cartier-Bresson

4

Percy Cercutty's
Race-Walk Training for Triathletes

Walking had a great impact on the restoration of Percy Cerutty's life after his near-fatal physical and mental collapse in 1938. As he began his program of natural diet, weight lifting, swimming and running, he also took long hikes through the Australian wilderness. It was that same year that he founded the Melbourne Walking Club. This was not for serious competitive renners; it was for a small group of fitness enthusiasts who enjoyed hiking and mountaineering. Percy was the "pied piper" of the group, which went on regular long excursions, sometimes as far as 50 miles. To keep everyone's spirits up, he would play his harmonica and recite his prose and poetry.

Walking also played a large role in the formulation of Cerutty's five basic movements. During his trek up Mount Kosciusko, he found that using the galloping method, interspersed with walking, he could travel up the mountain quicker than a fast-moving pack of mules. This is how Cerutty developed the basic movements. During his long hikes, he would walk for a while, then break into a canter and a gallop. He let his instincts dictate which of the basic movements to adopt. At "Ceries", Cerutty's Training Camp at Portsea, on the ocean near Melbourne, he encouraged his athletes to go off on long, solitary hikes, so they could practice the rotation of the basic movements and learn more about themselves at the same time.

Self-knowledge is gained by this solitary practice. When the runner goes off on an even-paced run, his thinking tends to become very uniform. But when he alternates movements and does some walking, his thinking becomes more varied. Percy developed the ideas and many of the actual lines for his poetry in lengthy walk-runs along the beach. He advocated that all distance runners train at a varied pace which sometimes slowed to a walk.

Race Walking Needs Full Lung Usage

Race walking is one of the more neglected events in athletics. Many potentially great race walkers never take up the sport because they cannot give it 100% dedication. "True greatness is never achieved noisily," Percy said. This can be applied to almost anything, but when Cerutty said it, he was referring to race walking. Cerutty himself race walked before his concentration shifted specifically to distance running.

As in running, the area most in need of development in walking is full lung usage. Noel Freeman, silver medalist in the 1960 Olympic 20-kilometer walk, was the athlete who best utilized Cerutty's ideas. The abdominal muscles are especially important in proper striding for the walking events, so sit-ups and hill running should play a large role in the conditioning period. If the abdominals are properly developed, the walker can lengthen his stride and have a lighter foot plant. "As with the long running events, the walker should land with a noiseless 'slithering' footfall," Percy said. "He should not plod along with a noisy thump." The edge of the foot should land first. If this is not happening, the walker should work on it during the conditioning period. Cerutty was opposed to the popular style in which the heel hits first, then the ball of the foot.

The essential breathing technique is acquired only by first developing the proper arm movements and strengthening the upper body with the basic weight lifting exercises. "The runner and the race walker both move on upper-body strength that is transferred to the legs through full, proper oxygen consumption,'' Percy said. ''To fully fill his lungs, the walker cannot move with locked elbows. This immobilizes his oxygen consumption. He should lift his shoulders up high as he inhales. When he exhales, he should throw his arms to his side. The fingers should be pinched together on inhalation and then opened up on exhalation.

''The toes should be pointed slightly inward as the race walker moves. In a relaxed stride that is smooth and flowing, the walker's knees should 'kiss' each other. The race walker, like the distance runner, can only develop full strength when his movements are relaxed. The athlete should never have to force the flow of his pace, as this will abnormally lengthen his stride and in the process cause stress and strain on the entire musculature.

Race-Walk Needs Flowing Movements

''When the athlete's abdominal muscles are strengthened from running on sand hills and doing sit-ups on the incline board, the stride can be lengthened naturally. My experiements here at Portsea with hundreds of athletes have proven to me that calisthenics, mobility exercises and high knee-lifts are useless in lengthening one's stride. All this does is ruin the flow of his movement. The race walker should have flowing movements like a ballet dancer.'' Race walkers usually improve with age. Veteran walkers such as Larry Young, Bernd Kannenberg, Todd Scully, Ron Laird and Vladimir Golubnichiy have all steadily improved as they've matured. Golubnichiy won medals in the Olympic Games from 1960-1972. Many distance runners turn to walking late in their careers. Some who are only good runners find that they are very good walkers!

Race-Walk Training for Endurance

Training for the two basic walks, the 20-kilometer and the 50-kilometer, will obviously be quite different, since the latter is 2½ times longer than the former. Training for the 50-kilometer should involve much more endurance work, particularly in the conditioning period. Typical endurance workouts are a 30-mile walk with a 40-pound pack on the walker's back and cross-country skiing. The 20-kilometer walker also should stress endurance in the conditioning period, but should include some faster walking and less overall volume.

Weight lifting should be done by walkers in both events, using the intensive method and the five basic exercises. Most of the running-walking practice should be on sand, grass or dirt. Once a week, to better strengthen the tendons in the legs and feet, the walker should train barefoot in sand or grass.

The conditioning period. Strength building and proper breathing technique are the important areas to work on in the conditioning period. Using the proper body movements enhances full breathing and lets the walker glide over the ground without ever breaking contact.

The 50-K walker should average 10-15 miles per day in the second half of the conditioning period. The 20-K walker should average 8-10. This should come largely through varied-pace walk-runs at a fast overall rate. The athlete should let his instincts determine when he runs and when he walks. ''It is not the number of miles that is important,'' Percy said, ''but the overall intensity. The walker should concentrate on a fast, but varied overall pace.'' There should be some occasional long overdistance work. The 50-K walker, for instance, should try to work up to 35 miles in training and the 20—k walker up to 20. Long 50-mile hikes are also good to do once a month.

Occasionally, the resistance of a weighted vest or heavy backpack should be used in this period. After each workout, the walker should run in place at a fast rate. This is a speed building exercise and is equally valuable for the 20-K and the 50-K. Gymnastics, hill training and weight lifting should all be practiced regularly in this period.

A Sample Week Midway Through the Race-Walk Conditioning Period Follows:

Mornings
- *20-K:* 3-8 miles at a varied pace.
- *50-K:* 5-10 miles at a varied pace.

Afternoons

Monday:
- An hour of intensive weight lifting.
- Hang limp on the horizontal bar for two minutes.
- *20-K:* Five-mile walk at a varied pace.
- Run in place for 10-15 minutes.
- *50-K:* Eight-mile walk at a varied pace.
- Run in place for 5-10 minutes.

Tuesday:
- An hour of gymnastics.
- *20-K:* Three-mile walk-run at a varied pace.
- Run in place for 10-15 minutes.
- *50-K:* Seven-mile walk-run at a varied pace.
- Run in place for 5-10 minutes.

Wednesday:
- An hour of intensive weight lifting.
- *20-K:* 18-mile walk at a varied pace.
- Run in place for 10-15 minutes.
- *50-K:* 30-mile walk at a varied pace.
- Run in place for 5-10 minutes.

Thursday:
- Six miles at a varied pace.
- Run in place for 5-10 minutes.

Friday:
- *20-K:* Uphill sprints for 45 minutes.
- Three-mile walk.
- Run in place for 10-15 minutes.
- *50-K:* Uphill sprints for 90 minutes.
- Five-mile walk.
- Run in place for 5-10 minutes.

Saturday:
- *20-K:* Walk and run eight miles.
- Run in place for 10-15 minutes.
- *50-K:* Walk and run 12 miles.
- Run in place for 5-10 minutes.

Sunday:
- Rest.

A Sample Week Midway Through the Race-Walk Practice Period Follows:

Monday:
- *20-K:* Sprint up a steep hill for 30 minutes.
- Walk seven miles at a fast, varied pace.
- Run in place for 10-15 minutes.
- *50-K:* Sprint up a steep hill for an hour.
- Walk 12 miles at a fast, varied pace.
- Run in place for 5-10 minutes.

Tuesday:
- *20-K:* 45 minutes of intensive weight lifting.
- Hang limp on the horizontal bar for two minutes.
- Walk four miles with a series of fast 880 intervals.
- *50-K:* 45 minutes of intensive weight lifting.
- Hang limp on the horizontal bar for two minutes.
- Walk 10 miles with a series of fast one-mile intervals.

Thursday:
- *20-K:* Eight miles at a varied pace.
- Run in place for 10-15 minutes.
- *50-K:* 16 miles at a varied pace.
- Run in place for 5-10 minutes.

Friday:
- *20-K:* Two miles at a varied pace.
- *50-K:* Six miles at a varied pace.

Saturday:
- Race or time trial.

Sunday:
- Rest.

In this race-walk practice period, conditioning work should taper off, and the walker should begin doing faster runs, including intervals. The major emphasis of the early race-practice period is to build up a proper neural pattern so that the walker learns to go the full distance at a determined pace. This is done by practicing the race in segments and then connecting them together.

In the second half of this period, the walker should have regular progress tests, in the form of a time trial or race. If the walker feels overtaxed or mentally "stale" in this period, he should cut back on the volume of his training load, but should still get in several intensive workouts each week.

Competition. When the serious competition is underway, the walker's program should be one of continual sharpening. Weight lifting and other supplemental exercises, which should taper down in the early part of the race-practice period, should cease entirely in the final weeks of competition.

There should still be one 10-15 mile stroll a week but it should be at a fast, varied pace. This should fall in the middle of the week if the walker is competing on weekends.

A sample Week During the Serious Race-Walk Competitive Season Follows:

Monday
- *20-K:* Walk six miles at a varied pace, including several all-out surges.
- *50-K:* Walk 12 miles at a varied pace, including several all-out surges.

Tuesday
- *20-K:* Uphill sprinting for 25 minutes.
- Run in place for 10-15 minutes.
- *50-K:* Uphill sprinting for 40 minutes.
- Run in place for 5-10 minutes.

Wednesday
- *20-K:* Two fast three-mile walks.
- *50-K:* Three fast four-mile walks.

Thursday
- *20-K:* Four miles of sprint walking.
- *50-K:* Eight miles of spring walking.

Friday
- Run in place for 10-15 minutes.

Saturday
- Competition.

Sunday
- Rest

Much more than distance running, walking is an event that is far from its full development. "Even with their varied motions, race walkers do not move their arms properly to allow for full-lung aeration," Cerutty said. By raising their shoulders and using the basic movements, walkers will be able to flow through the walk at a much faster pace, moving almost noiselessly. "The best athletes always grunted and fumbled their way to the worlk records at the Olympic Games!" Percy said. "The spectators in the stadium are not close enough to the action on the track to appreciate the masterly efforts of a champion."

Walking-Running Bibliography
Be Fit! Or Be Damned, Percy Cerutty, Sphere Books Ltd., London, England.
Training with Cerutty, Larry Myers, World Publications, Mountain View, CA 94042.

IV

Preliminary Swim, Bike and Run Training Concepts

The first Woman Triathlete to participate in the Ironman Triathlons. Lynn Lemaire went up against 13 men and finished 5th place over all in the *1979* Triathlon, in 12 hrs., 55 min.

1

The Prevention and Treatment of Swim, Bike and Run Injuries

On Preventing Injuries

PAIN IS A PART OF ANY TEST of physical endurance. But there are two types of pain: good pain, the normal, temporary result of hard work; and bad pain, which comes from injuries that hamper continued training and competition. Unfortunately, we sometimes confuse the two which can cause a long stretch on the bench or even permanent disability.

The best way to deal with injuries is to prevent them. By paying attention to the signals our bodies communicate to us, we can reduce significantly the risk of injury.

Some preventative measures are basically just good common sense such as stretching for 20 to 30 minutes before training or competition and not eating for three hours before a race. Balanced nutrition is also essential, avoiding dairy products and foods that have high fat and cholesterol content. Some diets are bad, others just "okay," and a few provide advanced regenerative virtues, such as Dr. Paul Bragg's Toxicless Diet for Physical Rejuvenation which emphasizes raw fruits and vegetables.

Other aspects of triathletics require special attention and analysis, and the most important part of analyzing what needs special attention is to note those little aches and pains that accompany hard training. Many injuries, in fact, most injuries, can be avoided.

Generally, injuries are caused by one or a combination of the following: overuse or fatigue, strain (too much too soon), absentmindedness, such as daydreaming about winning the gold cup only to trip over a sprinkler, or chasing that dog that bit you, only to strain a muscle when you catch the beast and kick it.

The art of remaining even-tempered and maintaining concentration are not covered in this chapter. Here we will focus on aspects of physical mechanics and the prevention and treatment of problems that commonly afflict both runners and cyclists.

When walking or running, one leg swings free while the other bears weight and propels the body forward. Likewise, in cycling, one leg pushes while the other brings up the rear. These actions do not occur in straight lines; a great deal of rotation and angle adjustment takes place automatically in regions of the foot and ankle, the knee, and the thigh. It is through deviations in these adjustments that many small pains grow into big problems. Once analyzed, these deviations can usually be treated with custom orthotic devices and exercises, enabling one to pursue training with notable improvements in both the absence of pain and enhanced performance. Podiatrists use a cast of your foot as a guide to make orthotics. Pedal, seat, and handlebar adjustments are the key to injury-free cycling.

As one foot moves past the body, to take its place in front, the thigh and calf rotate inward, moving the big toe inward midline. When the heel touches the ground, the foot rotates only slightly outward and remains essentially stable. The subtalar joint, between the ankle and the foot, absorbs most of the immediate stress and turns the leg outward for propulsion. The flatness of the foot on the ground, combined with its angle, is called "pronation." It is within this group of movements that most problems involving not only the feet but the rest of the legs find their origin. Pronation directly affects how much the kneecap is pulled by the tendons and muscles connected to it through the calf—as well as other muscles—in the knee and thigh.

The angle of the foot on the pedal has similar implications. As with running, imperfect pronation may force muscles in the knee to over compensate by pulling the kneecap too far to the inside or outside which results in stiffness, a dull ache, and finally painful swelling and causes excessive wear on the cartillage of the knee if left untreated.

The importance of an optimum foot/pedal relationship cannot be emphasized enough. If needed, even seemingly minor adjustments can eliminate unnatural stresses and injury to the knee. Any mechanical changes to a cyclist's equipment, especially shoes, must first be made according to anatomical structure.

Old injuries, dormant during years of inactivity, sometimes surface when a person begins to run or cycle for health. Modern orthotics and exercises can even return a person who has accepted an injury as disabling . . . back to the track of health when combined with a diet . . . which enhances the body's natural healing and regenerative processes!

Heed Basic Training Rules to Avoid Injuries

There are important considerations when participating in any sport which takes on paramount significance when one plans to evolve to longer distances. In conditioning for the Iron Man Triathalon, these considerations should be deemed . . .

• Adjust the equipment to yourself, don't try to adjust yourself to the equipment! Having good footwear is extremely important! So are the heights and angles of your bicycle's handlebars, seat, and especially pedal adjustments!

• Train, don't strain! If your body complains, pay attention. Adjust your equipment and training methods accordingly. Too much, too soon is asking for trouble!

• If you're becoming over-tired, rest! Fatigued tissues have a lowered resistance . . . which increases the risk of injury.

• Take frequent easy days with relaxed training, and occasional days when you don't train at all! Adequate rest is very important!

• Limber up for 20 to 30 minutes before training or competing. This does not necessarily prevent injury . . . but will enhance flexibility, increase oxygen flow, and guard against muscle pain and cramping!

• *Progress in endurance and speed gradually! Most running and cycling injuries come from* trying to do too much too soon! Vary your distances and routes according to personal preferences . . . but take care to avoid long hauls on hills where stress factors increase significantly. Approximately 70% of all track-related injuries are due to overuse! If you consistently push too hard, you're only pushing yourself backwards.

The "Over-Use Syndrome" of Injuries

You know some ways to prevent injury. You have identified your aches and pains as bonafide injuries. Now what? . . . The injuries we are dealing with at this stage are part of the "over-use syndrome." The term simply implies that you are running either too fast or too long for your present level of training.

• *Stop all training.* As long as there is moderate pain with walking, no running should be attempted. During this time, the fallen runner consoles himself with aspirin and ice packs for 15-20 minutes, up to four times a day over the injured area (or as often as he can tolerate). This method promotes increased blood flow to the site of the injury, which promotes healing and carries away the waste products of injury. There are two ways to do this. One is by exercising the muscle involved, thereby making it generate its own heat which in turn increases blood circulation.

The second method is to use ice, which causes surface vessels to constrict in turn, causes deeper vessels near the injury to dilate so much blood reaches the injury. The most effective way to apply ice to injury is simply to rub the area with an ice cube or apply a plastic bag filled with ice cubes.

Myth: "Applied heat is good for running injuries." This may contradict what you have learned, but studies have shown that applied heat does not reach the muscle. It only causes dilation of *surface* vessels. The best healing heat is that generated by the working muscle after the muscle has been exercised. To expedite this healing heat, gentle stretching exercise, not past the point of a little twinge of pain, will help if the injury is to the calf muscle or to one of the large muscles around the upper part of the leg.

Myth: "I'm taking aspirin for the pain." Aspirin some reports claim is actually an excellent anti-inflammatory agent. You are taking the aspirin more to reduce the swelling than for the pain.

This phase, (abstinence, ice and aspirin) generally lasts three to four days, up to, but not exceeding one week. If the pain perseveres, even with the aspirin and ice packs, have your injury checked by a sports-podiatrist or orthopedic surgeon.

• *Go out on a "road test" . . . a 20-minute run to begin again.* When the pain no longer persists while walking, you are ready to try running once more. About half an hour before starting to run, take one aspirin. Remember you are doing this to curb inflammation of the muscle. We emphasize this only to point out to those who will say, "Oh, it doesn't hurt that much. I don't need aspirin." Run on grass if possible. This helps you slow down and is a gentle surface as well. Downhill running and angled surfaces seem to aggravate as well as cause injury, so should be avoided during the healing period.

Shuffle. Slow down as much as is humanly possible for you to endure. Think of this slow running in terms of healing. Your cells are probably healing faster than you can injure them. After five minutes of running to ascertain that any twinges of pain are due to stiffness, continue to run for the remainder of the 20-minute period or until the pain returns or begins to worsen. Stop. Take one aspirin, again for the swelling, pack your injury in ice and rest today and tomorrow. The day after that, you can try again, adding 10 minutes to your run (if the pain does not increase), giving you 30 minutes on the road. Repeat the procedure, adding 10 minutes each time, resting a day between each try, until you are able to sustain one hour of continuous running with minimal or no pain. You may now resume your training program. But *forget it* . . . if, after three running periods, you cannot increase your time on the road at all without the return of pain . . . See a doctor or sports podiatrist.

• *If you have a low grade pain that goes away after warming up,* or which persists to a mild degree after several days of non-running, you can again observe a simple road test. After 20 minutes, if the pain does not increase, or if it even improves, it is probably acceptable to resume running.

The Aspirin Question

Many studies show an adverse side effects of the continued use of aspirin. Aspirin is a toxic substance . . . meaning if taken in large doses it can be fatal. Hundreds of children die yearly of accidental aspirin overdose. The value of this substance in sports medicine has been questioned. Each Triathlete must make his own decision on this personal health matter. Editor's note: We are not in favor of continued aspirin use, but it may be taken for a short term pain aid.

Listen To Your Body

The most important thing you can do is to pay attention to the warning signs your body automatically provides! Doctor George Sheehan, in his *Encyclopedia of Athletic Medicine,* gives a list of "symptoms of overstress," which follow. When these symptoms occur, take a day or two of easy training or complete rest.

1. Mild leg soreness
2. Lowered general resistance (evidenced by sniffles, headache, fever blisters, etc.)
3. Washed-out feeling, or I-don't-care attitude
4. Poor coordination (evidenced by general clumsiness, tripping, poor driving, etc.)
5. Hangover from previous training or race

Whether one has a short big toe, imbalanced arch heights, a short leg, or an old injury that has a habit of surfacing, all structural abnormalities are magnified by running. Seek training methods, exercises, and orthotic aids that are right for you.

While the following contains a great deal of information, it is a rapid reference index and is not intended for use as a complete home treatment manual without professional advice.

The Basis for Treating Athletic Injuries is:

- Correct first aid

- Immediate professional advice

- Sound home therapy and nutrition

- Gradual rehabilitation

MUSCLE CRAMPS

Muscle cramps occur while riding or running and also in the evening after training. Both types are caused by overuse, or pushing harder than you should. Conditioned triathletes can also get cramps from a deficiency in certain minerals which are lost in perspiration. Multi-sport veterans are also careful to keep up their potassium, sodium, and calcium levels by drinking fresh fruit juices, eating bananas, and being on a good health regime . . . and also for added health insurance against having a deficiency of these important minerals . . . by taking a amino acid cheleted multi-mineral food supplement which can be found in health food stores.

STRAIN

A strain is a tear in the muscle-tendon complex graded in first, second, and third degrees.
Unless the complex is **completely torn (a "third degree" strain),** there is no way to tell how severe the tear. A first degree injury heals quickly and allows one to return to training in a few days. A second degree strain is more serious and should be treated with caution. If one returns to running/cycling too hastily, more scar tissue forms in place of muscle which results in decreased flexibility, a greater risk for re-injury, and a longer period of rehabilitation. Stretching exercises are essential to flexibility and without training for limberness as well as strength, the chance for further injury and certainly more pain is enhanced.

SPRAIN

A sprain is a tear in a ligament and according to its severity, is also defined as being first, second, or third degree.
Ligaments are strong, fibrous bands that hold joints together. In runners, the most common sprains occur in the lateral (outer) ligaments of the ankle.

All sprains are treated initially with ice and elevation for the first 24 to 48 hours, followed by at least a two or three day rest and as long as six or eight weeks of restricted activity in more severe cases.

STRESS FRACTURES

Stress fractures are bone damage resulting from stress which with continued stress may become

a complete fracture. Usually involves the lower leg.

A break may not be visible in an initial X-Ray. Sometimes misdiagnosed as "shin splints" which are a musculo-tendenous inflammation, stress fractures do not always require a cast or complete immobilization. But to speculate and continue training when a stress fracture is possible is to court disaster.

TENDONITIS

Inflammation of a tendon or the rubular sheat that surrounds the tendon. Usually, this is caused by a stress tear in the tendon.

A tendon has no blood supply of its own to heal itself and draws from the sheath around it which thickens the sheath and increases the friction between the two, causing secondary inflammation in the sheath. While the tear may heal, the inflammation will continue unless friction desists for a few days, allowing the inflammation to subside. Ice applications help this process, and rest is the primary prescription.

BURSITIS

Bursitis is an inflammation of the protective sacs (bursae) around tendons. Rest and ice are initial treatments unless the irritation persists for a lengthy period of time. In some advanced cases, surgery is required to remove sacs which have solidified with fluid as a result of continued aggravation.

In any acute injury, ice should be applied several times during the first 24 to 48 hours; the injury should be elevated above the heart (example: prop the ankle above the heart level), and the person should rest for a few days at least and allow the initial swelling to decrease.

After the first 48 hours, heat should be applied specifically to the injured area, allowing vessels there to dilate and aid the healing process. Sometimes, in younger people, hot and cold contrast soaks bring excellent results, although this does not seem to benefit older people, in the 40's and beyond as well as their younger counterparts.

Specific areas tend to present special problems. From this point on, we will deal with localized areas of the body and their most frequent predicaments.

Feet

The majority of triathletic complaints can be traced to some problem related to the feet, whether pain is felt mostly in the feet, ankles, calves, or knees. Orthotic devices usually relieve pain and correct imperfect pronation and other common troubles that arise from structural abnormalities. Needing orthotics doesn't mean that you have bad feet: walking or running barefoot on firm sand or grass will readily confirm this. Concrete, other hard surfaces, and ill-fitting shoes cause most foot problems.

First, buy well fitting, high quality shoes! Be sure they have no rough spots, exposed inner stitching, or the like. Take care of your shoes too, so that troubles don't grow out of neglect. And break them in gently; avoid wearing new shoes in a race!

The most common cause of sore feet in cycling is footwear. The soreness is the result of bruising the sole of the foot by pressing against the hard pedal without adequate foot protection. Wear cycling shoes or shoes with firm soles that protect the foot from being bruised by excessive stress against the pedal. Sore feet feel better after a few days of rest and relaxation.

Blisters are caused by heat and/or friction.

1. Keep the area clean, especially if the blister has already broken.
2. DO NOT puncture small blisters immediately. Only those that cause pressure and pain. When necessary, do it with a sterile needle, then squeeze the fluid out gently.
3. Pad with sterile gauze or foam and tape it.

4. Run only if there is no pain.
5. Consult a physician immediately if infection or other complications develop.

Contusions and bruises are usually associated with pounding the feet too hard on pavement, although poor fitting shoes may be given due credit, and may affect any part of the foot (the heel will be dealt with separately).

1. Stop bearing weight on the injury.
2. Place a sponge rubber pad over the area with a hole cut into it to accommodate swelling.
3. Apply ice for the first 24 to 48 hours then heat if so desired.

Stress fractures of the metatarsals are frequently caused by excessive distance when one is not accustomed to it or by fast work on hard surfaces. If you ignore the pain and continue to run, a complete fracture is likely which requires a full three months to heal.

1. Tape the foot for three to four weeks and stop training. Gradually return to running on grass for another three weeks.
2. Wear a cushioned, supportive pad under the toes for the duration of taping and/or pain.

Periostitis of the metatarsals is inflammation of the membranes that surround the bones and supply the bones with blood. Usually it is associated with overuse or excessive stress.

1. Rest for at least four days.
2. Localized heat treatments increase circulation; ultrasonics short-wave diathermy, several times per day, is also recommended.

Tenosynovitis of the extensor tendons is an inflammation of the tendons or tenson sheaths that usually accompanies trauma or excess stress, but can also be caused by a change of running shoes. New shoes should be worn in small doses until they are broken in.

1. Stop training and seek hydrotherapy and/or ultrasonics. Training may be resumed in a few days unless the case is severe.
2. In severe cases, immobilization is mandatory for two weeks followed by a gradual return to walking and running, usually aided by orthotics.
3. If a triathlete refuses to be immobilized, tears in the tendon or sheath may result which as often as not requires surgery.

Arches may have imbalanced heights and can be injured in many ways. There are three arches in the foot: the longitudinal inner (or median) arch which stretches along the inside of the foot from in front of the heel to the base of the first toe joint; the metatarsal arch which runs across the ball of the foot; and the lateral (outer) longitudinal arch which stretches from the heel to the toe joints on the outside of the foot. Imbalanced arches cause deviations in pronation which, in turn, may cause difficulties in the ankles, calves, and knees. Arch troubles are best solved with orthotic devices which balance stress more evenly throughout the foot and, hence, throughout the leg.

1. Arches may fall causing over-pronation, which in turn may cause a stretching of the posterior tibial tendon that runs up the back of the calf.
2. High arches may cause the heel to absorb too much stress at impact and may result in bone bruises or stress fractures.
3. Low arches tend to direct stress toward the forefoot, inviting bone-stress problems in the arch and metatarsals.
4. In event of injury, stop training for at least 48 hours, fit orthotic devices in shoes, and seek hydrotherapy and ultrasonic treatment to relieve immediate pain.

Living is a continual lesson in problem solving, but the trick is to know where to start. No excuses—start your Triathlon Training Program today.

Heel

The heel seems prone to several problems, because of its position between the arches and the achilles tendon, its importance in relation to pronation, and the stress that it bears as a connective point between the foot and the ankle and leg. Also, it receives much heat and friction in shoes, which produces blisters.

Contusions occur from pounding on hard surfaces, low arches and flat feet, and poor fitting shoes.

1. Stop bearing weight for 48 hours or more.
2. Use a "doughnut" pad to relieve pressure and accommodate swelling.
3. Apply ice, if swelling is present, for 24 to 48 hours; then heat to enhance circulation.

Bone spurs may result from continued irritation to the bursae (protective sacs around the heel and tendons), a bony growth on the point of the heel. Left to grow, the spur can cause a tear or rupture in the tendon. As a precaution, shoes with good shock absorbing qualities and orthotic devices which correct deviant pronation are excellent preventative measures. Sometimes, heel spurs respond to rest, orthotics, and taping. Frequently, they require simple surgical removal, performed under local anesthesia. Treating pronation problems early prevents having to treat more serious disorders later.

Neuroma, or nerve damage, may occur because of weight stress or overuse, and often can be relieved through wearing looser shoes. Cyclists who wear narrow shoes frequently have this problem and find quick relief through wearing looser shoes which don't pinch their metatarsal area where most triathletic neuromas occur.

Neuroma pain comes in running, starts with a stinging sensation in the sole of the foot around the arch, this is at about 4 miles into a run. The pain continues in intensity until the 7 mile point where the pain has centralized in the toes causing an increased discomfort in the area . . . to the point that a runner will have to search out relief. The only relief is a quick removal of the running shoe and massage of the toe area. Quick relief is welcome . . . then you are good for about another 4 miles before the next massage . . . from then on it depends upon your paid barrier, as to whether you can finish the run.

There is no amount of shoe adjustment, metatarsal wedges, etc. that seems to relieve this condition. Acupuncture has been considered, and some practitioners have indicated success in this area of therapy.

The pain is caused by the abrasion on the neuroma nerve sheathes that lie between the 3rd and 4th toes. Avoid surgery at any cost!

This is one area that aspirin could give temporary pain relief.

Not all runners are effected by Neuroma . . . however many Bicyclists are. The cause is the same, only in a different way. Relief can be had by flexing the toes on the upstroke, raising the foot against the toe clips. Relief will come quickly . . . but the same relief method will be required periodically.

Heel strains should be treated like any other strain, subject to their severity.

Achilles Tendon

The achilles is the connection between the calf muscles and the heel bone, and has a very heavy work load as both a stabilizer and a propelling muscle. It stabilizes the knee at heel-ground contact and lifts the heel during propulsion. Pain may come from either muscle strain (where the muscle attaches to the tendon) or where the tendon attaches to the bone. Achilles injuries vary according to stress, the length of time that pain has been present, and whether the damage is located within the tendon or the tendon sheath. The achilles tendon sheath is more flexible and has a better blood supply than other tendons, and therefore has better healing properties. However, the susceptibility for injury is also great. Stress, pronation, and still shoes all may cause inflammation.

Achilles tendon injuries are the worse . . . along with knee injuries that a runner can encounter! Once you hurt your achilles, the susceptibility for further damage increases significantly.

Occasionally, cyclists experience pain in the achilles from climbing grades that are too steep for their level of conditioning . . . or from using toe clips that are too short, which forces the tendon to do the work that the muscles were designed to do. A seat that's too low also can contribute to the problem.

Achilles Injuries

There are three main types, or degrees of Achilles injuries:

Tendonitis occurs when one changes training routine with new shoes, different surfaces, altered speed or distance, or when one ignores warning signs and continues to train regardless of pain.

If you suspect tendonities in the achilles, treat it with respect. Reduce training greatly, stay off hills, and don't try to race. Take aspirin before running, and use ice afterward. Stretch before running, after running, and if pain develops during a run, stop and stretch. If pain worsens, stop running completely, and see a podiatrist.

Partial rupture of the achilles tendon may occur when the tendon is already weakened by long standing tendonitis. It is noticeable in the sudden onset of pain and swelling within an hour. Walking is difficult, and jogging is nearly impossible.

Usually immobilization is mandatory for about two weeks, followed by stretching exercises, heel lifts or other orthotics, and a gradual return to walking, then running. Cycling is hindered less by this than running.

Complete rupture of the achilles is big trouble, requiring surgery and/or a cast for twelve weeks. This is followed by several weeks of immobilization; and a very gradual return to activity.

Ankle Sprain

A **sprained ankle** may be caused by stepping unevenly off a curb, into a hole, or any other sudden trauma involving imbalance. Running on uneven surfaces and repetitive hill running can also cause a sprain.

Basic Treatment for a Sprained Ankle is:

1. Stop bearing weight, and apply ice or cold water for 30 minutes.
2. Elevate the ankle, and continue cold wraps for the next 24 to 48 hours.
3. Once pain is absent, practice ankle movement in all directions with the foot elevated.
4. Wait 2 to 3 days before resuming training.

Tenosynovitis of the anterior tibial is an inflammation of tendon sheaths along the inner, larger bone of the calf, although pain may be largely present close to the ankle. This is usually caused by running too many miles too suddenly. Rest for two days, tape area from the base of the toes to the head of the fibular (top of ankle), and seek ultrasonics which may offer quick relief.

Calves

Most problems of a musculo-tendonous nature in the leg are attributable to either overuse or a mechanical deviation in the foot. Whereas immediate relief is obtainable through hydrotherapy, ultrasonics, or massage; if the cause is of a mechanical nature, there is a good chance for re-injury.

Heel lifts and other orthotic devices offer corrective therapy and keep a runner on the road.

Shin splints seem to offer an umbrella for several types of stress reactions. Too much mileage or too rapidly increased training reduces the muscles' protective relationship to the bones, and degrees of irritation commonly develop. With accumulated stress, stress fractures sometimes occur. Taping often helps to hold the muscles and tendons against the bone, and keep them from pulling loose which recludes friction and irritation. Ice applications and massage after training are usually beneficial.

Four-fifths of the muscles in the calf are for propulsion, the remainder are anti-gravity muscles in the front of the calf. Although these muscles receive less attention than the others, their responsibility is important because they affect the amount of shock that is transferred through the leg. Many runners have weak muscles in the fronts of their thighs and calves, increasing their potential for stress reactions. These muscles may be strengthened through weight training.

Knees

Knees seem to give triathletes the most problems! Yet, the knee troubles usually seem to lie in mechanical difficulties in the feet or in biking, from pedaling gears which are too high, especially on hills or too low a seat to improper toe clips. Analyze your foot mechanics . . . before you have a doctor analyze your knees.

The knee is a complicated joint which also involves the kneecap, or patella. The first symptoms of *"Runner's knee,"* a problem shared with cyclists, is tightness, followed by dull aches, and a gradual onset of pain, felt beneath and around the kneecap. Usually, these problems are mileage or stress related, and progress because the kneecap does not ride smoothly over the femur and above the tibia. There are several muscles and ligaments that work within this area . . . and if any of them are overworked, usually as a result of stress and/or imperfect form, injuries develop. Gradually, cartilage in the patella becomes softened, and can crack or fissure. When the kneecap has reached this advanced stage of degeneration, the condition is called *Chondromalacia* and can limit physical activity for the rest of one's life. Chondromalacia is first felt as a grinding beneath the kneecap.

At the top of the kneecap, or superior pole, are the quadricep muscles which control the extension of the leg. The most important of these muscles is the vastus medialis . . . which keeps the kneecap from rolling to the outside of the leg. When the kneecap does slip to the outside, it is called *lateral displacement.* A strong vastus medialis helps prevent lateral displacement and can be developed through weight training.

Patellar compression syndrome is another common knee problem with triathletes, in which the patellar tendon, at the bottom of the kneecap, is overused as a shock absorber for the knee and can be as painful as beinning chondromalacia. Usually, this can be remedied with some form of orthotic foot control, quadriceps exercises, and in some cases, taping of the knee to help lift the kneecap.

Lateral subluxation, where the kneecap moves to the outside of the knee in response to the inner roll of the leg during pronation, is another example of injuries which result from deviant foot pronation. Orthotic devices have been most successful in reducing this problem.

Quadricep exercises should be done by every triathlete. When the knee and its counterparts are strong, the risk of injury decreases significantly. Also, stay off hills . . . and if pain is present, pay attention to it. Take aspirin thirty minutes before a race or training, so that minor pains aren't so bothersome . . . if something does go wrong, your body is better prepared to deal with the resulting inflammation.

When encountering any knee problems, consult a specialist immediately. The consequences could be serious.

No bird soars too high, if he soars with his own wings. —William Blake

Illiotibial band syndrome occurs in runners who drastically increase their mileage. While it may feel like something serious in the hip or knee, it is commonly a strain of the illiotibial band, a muscle that runs the length of the thigh, ending in a narrow band within the fibular at the top of the outside of the knee. Reduce mileage, stay off hills, and avoid races until pain is gone!

Bursitis of the pes ansrinus is felt as deep knee pain and is sometimes confused with damaged cartilage. Three tendons meet inside the pes ansrinus, and they can tend to rub against one another, causing inflammation. While it may feel terrible, this deep knee pain is easily treated with rest, and orthotics to correct the deviations to cause the tendons to inflame one another.

Synovitis is inflammation of the coverings of the knee joint and also is easily treated with rest and orthotics.

Hip strains plague distance runners occasionally, and the only advice is to rest and use ice and massage, for it was caused by doing too much too soon. Gradually increase your mileage over time.

Microsurgery—Faster Recovery for Knee Problems

What's the difference between regular surgery on the knee and the new microsurgery I have heard about? Is microsurgery really surgery? What about recovery time?

Conventional or major surgery on the knee is done in an operating room in a hospital. It involves making at least one large incision and opening up the knee joint. It is usually followed by several days in the hospital to recuperate, with some form of immobilization such as a cast and one to four months of rehabilitation time. In "microsurgery," which is medically referred to as arthroscopy, an instrument slightly smaller than the size of a ball-point pen is placed inside the knee. The arthroscope has a light source, an optical system, and tools attached to it. The operation may be done in the hospital, but it may also be done as an out-patient in a surgery center.

Usually the patient, without a cast, walks away from arthroscopic knee surgery. Rehabilitation time is usually much shorter. Arthroscopic surgery cannot do all the things that conventional surgery can, but it is a very excellent tool for determining exactly what the problem is. It is also an excellent way of taking care of certain problems, such as torn cartilages, some types of arthritis, and softening of the kneecap, or chondromalacia patella. Arthroscopic procedures represent great progress in orthopedic surgery. If you are in need of knee surgery, consider this new method when possible!

Groin Injuries

Groin injuries may result from excessive squats in weight training or running too many hills. Treatment generally means that one must stop bearing weight, and see a physiotherapist who will prescribe specific therapy and exercises.

Prostatitis is an inflammation of the prostate gland . . . a gland located just below the bladder which secretes a fluid that empties into a man's seminal ducts during ejaculation. There is no doubt that people with chronic prostatitis may notice that their condition is aggravated by bicycle riding or any other activity that exposes them to vibration in the rectal area.

Treatment may include antibiotics, since sometimes prostatitis is caused by bacterial infection. Hot baths for 15 to 20 minutes at a time, two to three times a day, frequently relieve the inflammation causing the pain. Often, protate massage (get instructions from your physician) or frequent ejaculation can help resolve the problem. Zinc mineral supplement has been proven to relieve occurring prostate problems! Available in health stores.

Avoid caffeine, alcohol, and any other stimulants that act as diuretics. Cyclists with chronic prostatitis have discovered that changing saddles sometimes relieves the problem. For some people a wider seat brings relief, whereas for others it's a narrower seat. You'll need to experiment. Also, try tipping the nose of the saddle downward. Take every opportunity to get up off the saddle while riding—while climbing hills, while pedaling along a flat piece of road, etc.

Biking and Sexual Dysfunction

The continued abrasion and direct pressure on the area of the sexual organs in a man for a period of from 5 to 10 hours in a Century ride can have a debilitating effect on a man's sexual potency. Proper seat adjustment, adequate chamois lining in the riding pants, and occasional relief to the area by standing on the pedals and moving fore and aft and sideways can give some relief. Extreme cases result in lack of erection for 4 or 5 days after a long ride.

Hemorrhoids

There's a popular myth that bicycling can cause *hemorrhoids*. However, no medical research supports this idea. Hemorrhoids are enlargements of the blood veins in the rectal area that are like varicose veins. The actual cause is not well understood, but it probably relates to a combination of heredity and poor bowel habits. If you are a hemorrhoid sufferer, avoid sitting during flare-ups, and cut down on your cycling until you feel better.

The usual treatment for hemorrhoids is frequent warm baths. Avoid straining to evacuate bowels.

Prevention: The hemorrhoid sufferer will often benefit from a diet that is high in liquids and fibers . . . even supplemented by bran or other fibers . . . to increase the frequency and bulkiness of stools. Gently push them back up into place and then apply ointments to help relieve symptoms . . . but changes in diet and bowel habits address the cause.

Saddle sores are caused by pressure, combined with heat and perspiration. Rest and relaxation is the best prescription!

Preventative measures include using a leather saddle rather than a plastic one. Leather breathes, allowing heat and moisture to escape. Often a small adjustment to the saddle will solve a majority of the problem. While riding, get off the seat from time to time. Good quality shorts, with a chamois lined crotch, will reduce friction, which is a primary cause of the problem. Pay attention to your riding position, and make sure that your bike is adjusted properly, and try tilting the nose of the saddle down slightly. Always break in a good leather saddle slowly over the course of a few weeks, especially before a long ride.

Sciatic pain is often felt as pain along the back of the leg, although the trouble may be rooted either in the small of the back where the sciatic nerves are located, in the feet, or in the lengths of legs, which affect the balance of the spine. Heel lifts, abdominal exercises, and exercises that stretch the gluteal muscles (the buttocks) appear to offer the most relief for triathletes:

1. Lie on your back on the floor. Bring first you left, then your right, then both knees to your chest. Hug your knees to your chest. Put your feet back down on the floor and relax.

2. With your legs straight, lift them both three to six inches from the floor. Hold them off the floor for a count of three Do 10 or 15 such leg lifts, and then relax. Increase the number of lifts you do each day as your abdominal muscles increase in strength.

3. Support your weight at your shoulders and heels and raise your buttocks off the floor. This conditions your buttock and abdominal muscles to work along with your back muscles.

Reoccurring Bike Pains:

Neck Pains

New cyclists may experience some neck pain until their neck and shoulder muscles are conditioned to the riding position which requires you to twist your head back from time to time to check out the traffic.

Prevention: You can eliminate the main cause of this discomfort by wearing a small mirror (available in bike shops) that attaches to your glasses or helmet. This device lets you watch traffic behind you without twisting your head to look back.

Shoulder Pains

Most shoulder pains are caused by riding a bike with an improper seat or handlebar adjustment, which causes the rider to overuse the shoulder muscles. The treatment is rest and relaxation, massage by a friend, or hot baths.

Prevention: Make certain the bike is properly adjusted.

Numb or Tingling Hands

The continuous pressure of the handlebars against the ulnar nerve in the hand can produce numbness in the fourth and fifth fingers. Normal sensations will return if you give your hands a rest. Permanent damage to this nerve is rare and results only from ignoring early symptoms.

Prevention: 1. change hand positions frequently as you ride; 2. wear riding gloves or install padding on your handlebars; 3. adjust your handlebars higher and closer to your saddle for a more upright riding position which will take weight off your hands; 4. avoid rough road surfaces when you can; 5. reduce pressure in your front tire five to ten pounds to provide a cushier ride; 6. whenever you get a chance try out other bikes, investigate the possibility that your bike frame just isn't a comfortable one (there is great variation in bike frames where comfort is concerned).

Numb Penis

This condition is caused by the saddle pressing against the pubic bones and cutting off the circulation of blood to the penis. It is rarely serious, although it can make a person rather nervous. The treatment is rest and relaxation. Sensation will return by morning.

Prevention: Pay attention to your riding position, and make certain your bike is adjusted properly. Try tilting the nose of the saddle down slightly. Stand up frequently while riding to relieve pressure.

Bike Accidents Seldom Happen to Trained, Alert Bicyclists

People who have experienced falls and accidents know that there is a period of time immediately following a fall when you feel out of touch with your body . . . even if you are not seriously hurt. This is a normal response to trauma. Often the reflex is to get up and get back in the race before checking out your body or your bike. Adrenaline is pumping through your veins at a crazy rate. You're only vaguely aware of pain, and somehow the only message that gets through is "Get out of there as fast as you can."

To prevent further injury, sit down, and fully relax yourself. Do this consciously. Lean against a tree or a nearby building. Take a deep breath, hold it, let it out slowly! Do this two or three times! It will help you relax in a very real way! Then count your breaths until you reach 50 or 60. You'll feel the world come back into focus as you do these things. Then start evaluating any injuries. Starting with your feet and working up to the top of your head, ask yourself how each area of your body feels . . . just as though you were taking an inventory. Once everything checks out, get up and walk around slowly. If you have pains that you don't understand, or if you are particularly anxious, summon help. Get a friend to come and pick you up, or rally the aid of a passerby. If you need emergency help, request it!!! Best to play it safe and get help, etc!!!

If your body checks out all right, go on to check out your bike. Check the handlebars to see that they are straight. Check front and rear brakes to make certain they're in proper working order. Lift first the front of the bike and then the rear, spinning each wheel in turn to see that it isn't wobbling. Make certain that both ties are inflated. Check the seat and the derailleurs and the

All walking is discovery. On foot we take the time to see things whole. —Hal Borland pedals. When you are certain that everything is in safe working order, get back on and ride slowly for the first half mile or more. Ease yourself into the ride. Only when your confidence in your body begins to return—and you are certain the bike is mechanically safe—should you resume your normal riding pace.

Heat

Triathalons have been described by participants, spectators, sportswriters, and other, as being the "sports of the eighties." Over 200 triathalons take place in the United States every year.

Triathletes must compensate for environmental conditions that face them when traveling to an event, especially heat.

People are affected by increase in body temperature and excessive fluid loss when running distances over six or seven miles in extreme heat. This is especially true in Hawaii, at the Iron Man Triathalon, where many participants are not used to higher tropical temperatures. For cycling, the distance is about 25 miles. Triathletes become affected when the body temperature rises above 104° or fluid loss exceeds 6% of their body weight.

This means that warming up should be restricted to a few running and stretching exercises . . . keeping out of the sun, and finding a cool place to lie down for a short time before the race begins! If one has a raised body temperature when the starter's pistol sounds, the limits of endurance are already in sight. In cold climates, the opposite is true, and the triathlete should proceed from warm-up right to the race.

Clothing for distances should be white and give maximum exposure to the skin. The material should be cotton and hang loosely outside the shorts. Shorts should be worn high with vertical slits in the sides. A form of string vest, allowing extra exposure, is better than any type of tee-shirt.

The best way to handle hot weather is to train in it for 10 days (or more) prior to the event. Gauge your fluid loss, which ultimately should not exceed about 10 ounces for every 30-40 minutes. Douse the head and body liberally at each water stop, and drop ice down your back, if available. Fruit juices and orange slices are the best sources of fluid, for they contain essential minerals, such as potassium, which are absent in plain water.

Heat Exhaustion and Heat Stroke

There are two degrees of heat-related ailments that afflict triathletes. Heat exhaustion results from inadequate replacement of fluid and electrolytes, and is visible in symptoms of pale, clammy skin, and a normal or sub-normal temperature. Replacement of fluids is the best immediate treatment, while monitoring the victim's temperature: heat exhaustion may lead to heat stroke.

Heat stroke is extremely serious and can cause death. If the skin is red and very hot, take immediate action: reduce temperature! Other warning signs include dizziness, difficulty in breathing, accompanied by burning in the chest, headaches, and when you slow down, it hurts even more. Once someone has gone into heat stroke, cool him down immediately . . . hose him off, or pour anything on him that is available . . . whether it's water, beer, Gatorade, Coke, or anything else! Rub him vigorously, preferably with ice, to open up the surface blood vessels. Don't worry about fluid consumption until after the crisis is passed.

Training or Recovery—The Mature Triathlete

Patience is the primary ingredient in building endurance without injury while training! Too much—too quickly has hurt and hindered thousands of potentiates and veterans alike!

The same is true when treating injuries. Give the healing process time to take its course, or further injury is usually inevitable!

The adage of "haste makes waste" applies tenfold to the human body when conditioning for distances: the greater the haste, the greater the risk of permanent problems!

The Skinny Runner
Thin to Win—Or Dieting to Death?

The term "sudden death" has earned new meaning in the world of sports. In its familiar application, "sudden death" is slang for an extra time period that's added to a football, baseball, or basketball playoff game that has ended in a tie and allows one team to emerge as champion.

Recently, it's been coined for distance runners, to describe a frightening development called "sudden death syndrome." It seems that relatively young, well-conditioned distance runners are dropping dead, their hearts refusing to beat normally.

One running doctor, Pathologist Tom Bassler, believes he knows the reason why: nutritional arrhythmia. They starved their cardiac functions to death. Bassler has performed autopsies on over thirty distance runners who reported feeling fine hours before they suddenly died.

"When you look at the runners who've died from arrhytmias," said Bassler, in an interview with Eric Olsen **(Runners World)**, "**they did three things wrong: they had low body weight, they were running high mileage, and they were restricting their diets.** . . . The day you die (from dieting and distance running) is the day you run out of high quality fat! The fat molecule that keeps you alive is lineolic acid . . . which can be found in raw wheat germ, unsalted-raw nuts, and seeds, sunflower, sesame and pumpkin, whole grains, and milk and eggs (if the animals these foods come from were fed whole grains)."

When a runner goes for long distances, he burns off his lineolic acid, and sweats out a lot of zinc, copper, and potassium. A nutritional arrhythmia can occur if that person doesn't replace these required nutrients adequately, causing a deficiency that prevents the heart from beating normally.

Not everyone agrees with Bassler. One professional rival is another prominent (running) researcher, Nathan Pritikin, who claims that Bassler doesn't know the difference between an essential fatty acid and a nonessential fatty acid, doesn't know what lineolic acid is, and doesn't know what a lot fat diet is. Bassler is also on the board of directors at Pritikin's Longevity Center in Santa Monica. Bassler certainly must know something for Pritikin to keep him on.

Pritikin became involved with nutrition and running several years ago, when he was diagnosed as needing coronary bypass surgery. Through exercise and a diet he devised himself, he was able to avoid that surgery. Pritikin advocates strict dietary prudence whereas Bassler favors some dietary indulgence.

Diets designed for obese heart patients are great for a few months. "They suck the fat right out of you," says Bassler, "but they weren't designed for marathoners to follow for 18 months."

Anorexia Nervousa Men & Women

Looking at the physiques of many middle-aged distance runners, one wonders if these skinny guys have developed a form of anorexia nervousa, an obsessive self-starvation that's been occurring with increasing frequency among young female runners and non-runners.

Sherrye Henry, Jr., has a personal stake in understanding anorexia nervousa: She's been fighting it since her mother showed her an article about a young girl who had starved herself into a coma. Henry, a distance runner, at 5'4" and 90 pounds at the time, recognized some of the symptoms as her own.

After surveying over 100 young women runners, she contends that many of them develop anorexia as a defense against maturing into adults, wanting to avoid adult responsibilities, including the potential to bear children. Anorexics frequently stop menstruating when their protein reserves recede past a certain point. Perhaps they're trying to remain children for as long as possible, not only on a physical level . . . but on an emotional level as well, commanding excessive personal attention for their physical prowess as well as for their alarming thinness!

Perhaps middle-aged men are courting a similar obsession, through food restriction and exhausting exercise, trying to maintain a young man's virility well into old age. Nobody can blame them for wanting to be healthy and endure for as long as possible. And top competitors want to retain their status as long as possible, too. But is being extremely thin the same as being in perfect health?

At the end of a debate between Bassler and Pritikin at the American Medical Joggers Association Symposium in Houstin, Bassler made this parting remark: "I really enjoy mileage and marathoning, but I wish you guys would drop all the seriousness about your diets. It really bothers me to get all these letters about these neat diets you're on . . . and then I have to file them with your autopsies."

Irregular Heart Beat

As late as the 1970s, many medical authorities thought that it was impossible to have a heart attack if you were a conditioned marathon runner. Since then there have been many documented cases of fatal heart attacks or fatal cardiac arrests in experienced marathon runners, both at rest and while running. The current medical consensus is that regular long-distance running reduces the risk factors that are generally associated with heart disease and heart attacks. However, any individual can suffer a fatal heart problem, whether ot not he or she is a runner. It is just that a conditioned runner's chances are lower.

Treadmill Stress Test

You will get just about as many answers to this question as there are doctors and official organizations that make recommendations for health. Some doctors don't believe that anybody should have a treadmill stress test, and some believe in one every year for everybody. However, the following are guidelines, and if you fall into one of these categories, you should talk with your doctor about having a treadmill stress test:

• If you have been previously sedentary for many years, and are going to start a vigorous exercise program;
• If you are male and over 35 or a female past menopause, you should have a treadmill stress test at some time in your life;
• If you are past 50, you should have a yearly treadmill stress test;
• If you have one or especially two of the following problems, diseases or tendencies, you should have a treadmill stress test: high blood pressure, abnormal cholesterol or blood fat, cigarette smoking, abnormal electrocardiogram, high-stress lifestyle, family history of a parent or sibling have heart attack before age 60, diabetes, gout or overweight.

* * *

Q—Will a normal treadmill stress test guarantee that you can exercise safely without fear of death from a heart problem?

A—Not entirely. The treadmill stress test is only 70 to 80 percent reliable in making that type of prediction. Most deaths from heart problems in persons who exercise vigorously occur because of a blocked coronary artery (myocardial infarction or heart attack) or a cardiac arrhythmia (the heart beating so irregularly that it cannot pump blood). The treadmill stress test is about 70 to 80 percent reliable in predicting whether you have coronary artery problems or arrhythmia problems. Some critics of the treadmill stress test say that this means you have a 20 percent chance of having a heart problem go undetected by a treadmill stress test. Proponents say that 80 percent is fairly good reliability for most medical tests.

Caution

Editors Important Notice to
All Triathletes and Distance Athletes

You have just read the previous paragraphs on the Skinny runner. To a point . . . everything stated was true. There have been a number of unexplained deaths recently, nearing 40 in number, of athletes . . . primarily marathon runners and one was a 38 year old Triathlete, a participant in the February 1982 Ironman Worlds Triathlon. However, the previous material did not go far enough, at least to shed some light on the term *"Nutritional Arrhythmia"* and its full meaning. Of utmost importance are the preventative measures that can be taken to avoid serious delays in training and most of all of course, the unnecessary fatalities. Of athletes that from all outward appearances are in top condition as far as extensive Cardiograms and Treadmill stress tests can determine, is concerned.

To give an indication as to the perplexity experienced on the part of the non medical lay person as to the medical remedies and assistance that is available to the uninformed on the matter of Irregular heart rhythm. A gentleman recently inserted an ad in the Santa Barbara general circulation newspaper, asking for anyone that had any information on his heart condition to call him. From one classified ad, running only one day he received 18 replies from people with similar problems, all hoping that he could offer some enlightenment and help in curing this possibly fatal heart malfunction. Oh yes, nearly forgot, not one doctor or professional medical person responded to this call for help. The party that had inserted the ad had gone the rounds of specialists in the field. One doctor prescribed aspirin, one gave him a chemical medicine that gave no results, the rest said they had no solution for the problem. This seemed to be the treatment the callers had experienced with their problems. It was out of sheer frustration and panic that this man placed his classified ad. His symptoms were of the advanced state, meaning his heart would race in the middle of the night at sometimes twice his resting pulse. This is the period in which the majority of the runners deaths have occurred, not on the marathon run or the training road work.

Southeast Asian Unexplained Night Deaths

At the latest report over 80 South East Asian "Boat People" have died of a strange malady, for no apparent reason, normal healthy men for the most part . . . all in the same way, in the middle of the night with no indication of pain, in some cases only accompanied by a moaning.

The common denominator that ties these mysterious deaths together is that autopsies show no physiological reason for death . . . no sign of a heart attack, etc. In the case of the runners, autopsies showed above average heart development, no hardening of the arteries, and recent stress tests showed an excellent running heart vascular and lung condition.

Is There an Answer?

From the medical profession, no. Doctors can prescribe a chemical agent that is supposed to regulate irregular heart rate that does not always work . . . and sometimes causes side effects. There is an emergency remedy given to persons whose heart has stopped . . . by utilizing an electric shock. If the heart responds at all to this treatment . . . it could return to be a normal heart beat. In a recently published book, prepared especially for the heart doctor and compiled by three specialists in the field, little is said about heart rhythm problems and then only in the light of expensive surgery, chemical agents, drugs, pacemakers and the dangerous shock treatment, etc.

In the "Skinny Runner" paragraph we noticed where Dr. Bassler made reference to the problem as he sees it as . . . "nutritional arrhythmia," . . . in his reference meaning the loss of excessive weight and a certain weight quality that is essential to life maintenance! Dr. Bassler also made

First Aid for the Choking Victim
*The Heimlich Maneuver**

with the VICTIM STANDING or SITTING

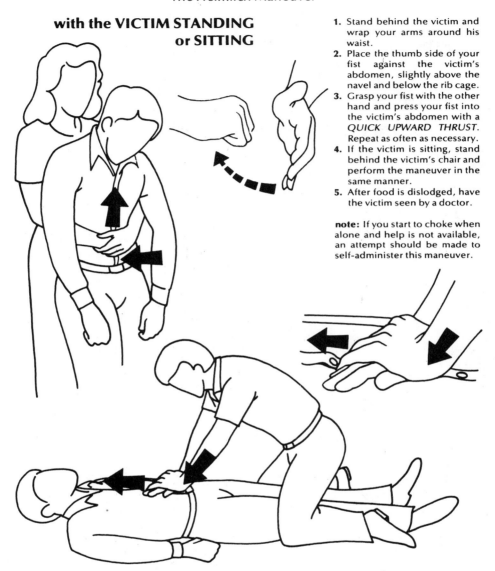

1. Stand behind the victim and wrap your arms around his waist.
2. Place the thumb side of your fist against the victim's abdomen, slightly above the navel and below the rib cage.
3. Grasp your fist with the other hand and press your fist into the victim's abdomen with a *QUICK UPWARD THRUST.* Repeat as often as necessary.
4. If the victim is sitting, stand behind the victim's chair and perform the maneuver in the same manner.
5. After food is dislodged, have the victim seen by a doctor.

note: If you start to choke when alone and help is not available, an attempt should be made to self-administer this maneuver.

when the VICTIM HAS COLLAPSED and CANNOT BE LIFTED

1. Lay the victim on his back.
2. Face the victim and kneel astride his hips.
3. With one hand on top of the other, place the heel of your bottom hand on the abdomen slightly above the navel and below the rib cage.
4. Press into the victim's abdomen with a *QUICK UPWARD THRUST.* Repeat as often as necessary.
5. Should the victim vomit, quickly place him on his side and wipe out his mouth to prevent aspiration (drawing of vomit into the throat).
6. After the food is dislodged, have the victim seen by a doctor.

This is an adaptation of a poster prepared by the New York City Department of Health for display in restaurants.
*Patent pending

CPR
IN BASIC LIFE SUPPORT

Place victim flat on his back on a hard surface.
If unconscious, open airway.

Neck lift, head tilt   or   Chin lift, head tilt

If not breathing, begin artificial breathing.

**4 quick full breaths.
If airway is blocked,
try back blows, abdominal or
chest thrusts and finger probe
until airway is open.**

Check carotid pulse.

If pulse absent, begin artificial circulation. Depress sternum 1½" to 2."

One Rescuer	Two Rescuers
15 compressions	5 compressions
rate 80 per min.	rate 60 per min.
2 quick breaths	1 breath

**CONTINUE UNINTERRUPTED UNTIL
ADVANCED LIFE SUPPORT IS AVAILABLE**

AMERICAN HEART ASSOCIATION
7320 GREENVILLE AVENUE, DALLAS, TEXAS 75231

77-006-A Rev
77-100-M
6-78-75M
© 1977 American Heart
Association

reference to the recent liquid protein diet fad that was held as responsible for the deaths of a number of persons, not because of the excessive weight loss . . . but the quality of fat lost.

My interest suddenly became sparked in this problem in an unusual and personal way! I had been training heavily for the Ironman Triathlon, with weekly distrances of 3 miles swimming, 250 miles biking and 60 miles running. After one particularly hard Century training ride into the mountains from Palm Springs, California, in which I made 3000 feet of elevation, I noticed a peculiar extra heart beat while taking my pulse. I had been training heavily for over 4 weeks, perspiring heavily . . . but getting adequate quantities of liquids so I thought, but that I could have possibly depleted my potassium reserve, thereby causing the heart beat irregularity. To be on the safe side I made an appointment for an EKG. The report showed a PVC . . . premature ventricular contraction running about 4 per minute. This did not satisfy me, so arranged for a stress tradmill test from one of the leading sports medicine doctors in the country. The report showed PVC's. The blood test showed no sign of heart damage, and all minerals were normal. The testing doctor gave no recommendation as to altered training schedule diet, liquid replacement, etc. In fact, I left his office with a $300 doctor bill and no offer of any kind, not even aspirin, for a solution to this problem!

I just happened to see an article in the Honolulu Newspaper indicating that an Australian research doctor had discovered the need for a certain type of calcium supplement as a cure for irregular heart beat. This opened many doors into the subject of proper nutrition and the need for various minerals in our diets to maintain the proper heart rhythm. I called Dr. Bassler and told him of this article and he did not seem to think it was of any great significance. He was still on the weight loss theory as the main cause.

To shorten a long story, Dr. Bassler was right, to a point but his theory did not go far enough. The loss of weight carried with it the loss of essential minerals, the minerals control the heart's function, fat does not. I called on my friendly health food stores vitamin-mineral supplement sections practitioner and shared some of the problems and questions I had come up with on this matter and sure enough I was filled in on all of the minerals required to maintain a healthy heart rhythm. Each case is different, no doubt but generally the cermino acid chelated, multiple mineral food supplement prescription of natural substances will cover everyone's deficiencies adequately.

First, we have to assume that we cannot get enough minerals out of the normal everyday diet . . . especially if you are training 3 to 4 hours daily. Next, the body's ability to assimilate these minerals has to be assured. For example, if your gall bladder is missing or malfunctioning, calcium will pass through your system with the fats in the diet unless the fats are broken down through the action of a healthy gall bladder. To insure an adequate digestion, enzyme with hydrochloric acid supplement should be taken with every meal. (Available at your local health store)

The supplement suggested for a person with heart irregularity are:

Calcium . . . . 1000 Mg
Vitamin D (fish liver oil) 400 Mg
Vitamin E . . . . 1000 IU
Magnesium . . . . 500 Mg
Iodine from Kelp . . . . . 250 Mg
Zinc . . . . 200 Mg
Potassium . . . . 100 Mg
Nutritional supplements
Cardiotrophin . . . . 500 Mg
Miniplex . . . . 200 Mg

For the athlete in training many doctors prescribe reducing your training schedule or even dropping out of sports completely. The latter advice is unfortunate as under normal circumstances the body will respond to this treatment within a week. The irregularity will reduce in severity until there will be no sign of abnormal heart rhythm within 2 to 3 weeks.

If you know anyone especially an athlete in heavy training or of extremely slight build from dieting, with the symptoms indicated in this article, please inform them of this supplement program as a preventive measure against a runaway heart beat that could prove fatal.

We are not in the business of selling vitamins and minerals . . . we just want to save the lives of runners or triathletes, in perfect physical condition, who might otherwise pass away in their sleep due to this strange malady.

Where Have All of the Doctors Been?

Certainly not in school, this is just one of the ever increasing examples of the lack of nutritional knowledge displayed by the medical profession. (See the Chapter on Vitamins as it explains the lack of training in this area of medicine). How many uninformed patients were sold a $6,000 to $12,000 heart pacer, or should the patient have an elevated blood pressure he could be convinced the only solution to his condition would be a Heart Bypass job costing from $15,000 to $50,000.

Too Many Surgeons—Too Much Surgery!

If you have a friend or relative that is running a dangerously high blood pressure, advise them to search out a Holistic Health Physician . . . who specializes in Chelation Therapy. This is a method of reducing the Plaque and calcified deposits in the blood vessels, by a purely natural way. They can be treated as an out patient 2 or 3 times a week for a prescribed series of treatments and will return to perfect health for the rest of a normal lifetime. No one has died as a result of this treatment out of over 1,000,000 patients. This is a natural medical substitute for the artery-by-pass surgery mentioned. Coincidentaly, over one-half of the patients of by-pass surgery die either on the operating table or within the first year of recovery, another 20% in the 4 years following. Within 5 years of heart by-pass surgery you are a candidate for another one. Whether your body can stand it or not. Did your doctor tell you this! This is caused by the fact that the habits of eating and living that brought on the problem still exists, requiring only a small area of artery to be blocked this time. Chelation therapy goes beyond this small artery transplant area and opens up the tiny blood vessels in the extremities that allow warm blood to flow freely through iving warmth to feet and hands in the winter months, and opening the blood vessels into the brain allowing oxygen to flow freely, giving back short term memory responses, thwarting senility and extending a useful active life to a normal life expectancy. Did your family doctor tell you of this alternative? If you will tell him you read of the alternate preventative treatment for high blood pressure I will tell you just exactly what he will say. "Why do you want to waste $50 on a treatment like that. While all the time he is planning on splitting the $15,000 to $50,000 by-pass surgery fee with the surgeon.

Prostatitus? Don't Operate

If you or a member of your family are bothered with a re-occurring prostate problem, and the doctor has recommended surgery—STOP! . . . do not do a thing until you have had at least 3 opinions and then STOP! . . . and do not do a thing until you have taken at least 200 mg's of Zinc mineral tablets, for not less than 3 weeks, stop the intake of all alcohol, coffee and strong liquids. Within 7 days the problem will be relieved and within 3 weeks you will be in good health again. NOW . . . if you still have a problem, then listen to your doctor. If you are well . . . keep up the zinc supplement, but then reduce it to 50 to 100 Mg for a healthy maintenance program. Did your family doctor tell you of this alternative. If you tell him you read of this alternative preventative treatment for prostatitus I will tell you just exactly what he will say. Why pay $50 a pound for that stuff, you might have cancer, while all the time he is splitting the $10,000 fee with the surgeon. If you have cancer 2 or 3 weeks will not make much difference. If you operate and lose your prostate gland, you are a vegetable the rest of your life. Ask someone that does not own one.

The Triathlete and Zinc

Due to the unnatural pressure of the horn of the bicycle seat on the base of the penis it is advisable to include in your vitamin supplement at least 100 mg's of Zinc. This supplement will help keep the prostate area healthy and active during long training rides Centurys and Triathlons. (See the Vitamin Chapter on Zinc for Zing)

The Prostate Gland and Zinc

Zinc is a bit of a newcomer to the nutritional scene; but it might be wise to consider the fact that the normal prostate gland contains more zinc than any other gland in the entire body. Also that a diseased prostate gland has a very low concentration of zinc. And that, for some reason, vitamin C seems to be more potent as an anti-infective in the presence of zinc. You can draw your own conclusions, but the presence of an adequate amount of zinc in the body certainly would seem to be prerequisite for prostate health.

An interesting sidelight that gives food for thought is the fact that of all the foods available to man, oysters outshine other foods in zinc content by a ratio of about four to one as compared to its nearest competitor which is wheat germ. And who hasn't heard of the rejuvenative, restorative, aphrodisiac properties of the oyster? Could it be the zinc content? Amazing how often what is considered folklore is proven by research to have sound basis in fact.

Bibliography—Swim, Bike and Run Injuries

Primer of Sports Injuries, by John P. Curran, M.D. by Charles C. Thomas, publisher, Springfield, Illinois, 1968.

The Encyclopedia of Athletic Medicine, by Dr. George Sheehan. Published by Anderson World, Inc. Mountain View, California, 1972.

Cures for Common Running Injuries, by Steven I. Subotnick, D.PM., M.S. Published by World Publications, Inc. Mountain View, California, 1979.

The Complete Middle Distance Runner, by Denis Watts, Frank Horwill, and Harry Wilson. Published by Anchor Press, London, England, 1972.

Pain Erasure the Bonnie Pruden Way, by Bonnie Pruden. M. Evans Co., 216 East 49th St., New York, N.Y., 10017, 1980.

Dr. George Sheehan's Medical Advice for Runners, The Foot Book, and *The Running Foot Doctor* are available through Anderson World, Inc. 1400 Stierlin Road, Mountain View, CA 94043.

Runners World Magazine, May 1982.

The Runner magazine, March 1982.

The world is moving so fast now-a-days that the man who says it can't be done is generally interrupted by someone doing it. —Elbert Hubbard

"I felt so good when I crossed the finish line. People who saw me on TV thought I was spaced out . . . all I did was go beyond my limit." —Julie Moss, 2nd Place Triathlon Finisher at Kona, Hawaii

Open air Bicycle Repair shops were set up by Kona Bay, by McCully Bikes of Honolulu and Daves Quality Bikes of Santa Barbara, California, to handle the many repairs required to keep 850 bicycles running for the 1982 Spring and fall Ironman Triathlon.

Fifteen bicycles one half of Daves Santa Barbara, California, shop lands in Hilo, Hawaii, in preparation for the 1982 spring Triathlon.

2

Stretching Exercises for the Swim-Bike-Run

by Bob Anderson, Stretching Specialist

Why Stretch

Stretching, because it relaxes your mind and tunes up your body, should be part of your daily life. You will find that regular stretching will do the following things:

- Reduce muscle tension and make the body feel more relaxed.
- Help coordination by allowing for freer and easier movement.
- Increase range of motion.
- Prevent injuries such as muscle strains. (A strong, pre-stretched muscle resists stress better than a strong, unstretched muscle.)
- Make strenuous activities like running, skiing, tennis, swimming, cycling easier because it prepares you for activity; it's a way of signaling the muscles that they are about to be used.
- Develop body awareness. As you stretch various parts of the body, you focus on them and get in touch with them. You get to know yourself.
- Help loosen the mind's control of the body so that the body moves for "its own sake" rather than for competition or ego.
- Promote circulation.
- It feels good.

Who Should Stretch

Everyone can learn to stretch, regardless of age or flexibility. You do not need to be in top physical condition or have specific athletic skills. Whether you sit at a desk all day, dig ditches, do housework, stand at an assembly line, drive a truck, or exercise regularly, the same techniques of stretching apply. The methods are gentle and easy, conforming to individual differences in muscle tension and flexibility. So, if you are healthy, without any specific physical problems, you can learn how to stretch safely and enjoyably.

When To Stretch

Stretching can be done any time you feel like it: at work, in a car, waiting for a bus, walking down the road, under a nice shady tree after a hike, or at the beach. Stretch before and after physical activity, but also stretch at various times of the day when you can. Here are some examples:

- In the morning before the start of the day.
- At work to release nervous tension.
- After sitting or standing for a long time.
- When you feel stiff.
- At odd times during the day, as for instance, when watching TV, listening to music, reading, or sitting and talking.

How To Stretch:

Stretching should be done slowly without bouncing. Stretch to where you feel a slight, easy stretch. Hold this feeling for 10-30 seconds. As you hold this stretch, the feeling of tension should diminish. If it doesn't just ease off slightly into a more comfortable stretch. The easy stretch reduces tension and readies the tissues for the developmental stretch.

After holding the easy stretch, move a fraction of an inch farther into the stretch until you feel mild tension again. This is the developmental stretch which should be held for 10-30 seconds. This feeling of stretch tension should also slightly diminish or stay the same. If the tension increases or becomes painful, you are overstretching. Ease off a bit to a comfortable stretch. The developmental stretch reduces tension and will safely increase flexibility.

Hold only stretch tensions that feel good to you. The key to stretching is to be relaxed while you concentrate on the area being stretched. Your breathing should be slow, deep and rhythmical. Don't worry about how far you stretch, stretch relaxed and limberness will become just one of the many by-products of regular stretching.

Bicycling Stretches:

I have heard the argument from some bicyclists that you do not need a great deal of flexibility for bicycling, and therefore you do not need to stretch. Of course, only a certain amount of flexibility is required in bicycling, but this does not mean that proper stretching is not beneficial to the bicyclist.

One problem is that many people think of 'stretching' and 'flexibility' as the same thing. They are not. Stretching is a method of safely elongating muscle tissues and reducing muscle tension. While flexibility is a term applied to the range of motion at any given joint. Stretching will increase flexibility, but more importantly for the bicyclist, it will relieve the unwanted muscle tension that can result from bicyling. Cycling in itself does little to maintain good muscle elasticity and unless relaxed stretching is used to offset this gradual accumulation of muscle and joint stiffness, then muscle and joint responsiveness is adversely affected. Stretching, when done regularly and correctly, is a perfect addition to any bicyclist's conditioning program.

I recommend stretching both before (8-10 minutes) and after (8-10 minutes) riding and also, on longer rides (2-4 hours), several 2-5 minute stretching/rest breaks along the way. In the following are 6 basic stretches for cycling.

I have two doctors, my left leg and my right. —G. M. Trevelyan

Swim, Bike, Run Anerobic vs. Interval Training

Interval Training as an Alternative

This chapter on interval training is included in this book with the understanding that it will give an alternative training method for the serious athlete to contemplate. I do not oppose the theory set forth because I believe that this is a highly clinical matter that requires a much higher technical knowledge than the average athlete possesses. This information is offered as a training option to the method in the chapters on biking and running. The method set forth in these two chapters is a tried and proven method practiced and taught by the great running trainer from New Zealand, Arthur Lydiard, and his protege, Max Telford, the world distance runner ... who now holds running and biking distance training classes in Honolulu.

In practice, the two systems differ only in application. The Lydiard-Telford Anerobic System consists of intervals of effort at and just a little into the anerobic barrier, constantly increasing effort into this condition ... careful not to create excessive lactic acid buildup, or taxing the cardiorespiratory system with excessive oxygen debt.

Interval training emphasizes breaking this anerobic barrier to create excessive oxygen debt for an extended period of time over a carefully measured distance. Each method stresses the need for the rest period, allowing the cardiovascular system to return to a lower steady rate before the next interval.

Throw Away the Schedules—Listen to Your Body

The Lydiard-Telford System leaves the physiology of the athlete as the guide, allowing him to stop when he is tired, thus relieving the athlete of the boredom of many round-the-track repetitions! There is no coach in the world who can say exactly what an athlete should do as far as the number of repetitions, distances and intervals are concerned ... not even a physiologist can tell an athlete that. The important point is that an athlete knows what he is trying to accomplish, and goes out and works until he does.

You can, therefore, make your judgement of the method you prefer or what system suits you best. Having trained with both, I much prefer the Lydiard-Telford System as it fits into the daily run and can be made an effort within the long slow distance workout during the hard day or easy day training period.

After the first marathon is under your belt, you will have a better feel for the heart rate in beats per minute, BPM and can push the maximum heart rate barrier without actually taking a count. You will also know when you are approaching the anerobic, oxygen debt area and can sense the lactic acid build-up in your muscle tissue. This then is the only timing system or distance measure you need. We are constantly reminded to listen to our bodies; be in tune with our bodies—I can think of no better or more natural method than this as a guide to advanced strength and speed training.

Interval Training

After the International Olympic Games were reinstituted in 1948, runners resumed serious training, and interval training became tremendously popular during the following decade. Furthermore, interval training has retained a dominant position in the training attitudes and schedules of middle distance runners ever since. Usually, interval training focuses on briskly run short distances with short or long recovery phases during which the athlete jogs, walks, or rests before running another quick interval. Favored distances range from 110 yards to one mile, but 220 and 440 yard intervals seem to be the most popular. Triathletes sometimes question the value of interval training when considering the 26.2 mile marathon gruel. What's the point, they ask, of running all those puny pseudo-sprints and slowing down between them?

Boost Stamina and Endurance

Interval training has proven to be one of the best methods available to build up stamina and endurance especially for the heart and lungs. In recent years, interval training has been used to train other metabolic systems to endure the rigors of long distance events for either swimming, biking or running.

Importance of the Cycle

More than anything else, the idea of interval training has proven to be valuable. It's the concept of putting into motion a cycle-causing oxygen, calcium, glycogen, electrolyte, and pH deficiencies through exercise and athletic stress . . . then slowing down or stopping to allow those elements to be replenished to a normal level . . . then exercising to cause another deficiency . . . then to perpetuate the cycle, which consistently improves physical capacities and performance!

Interval Training for the Distance Runner

For the distance runner, interval training is important in building stamina and flexibility of style. More important than speed in a distance event is the ability of the competitor to finish and to finish without undue stress. Only after a runner is able to finish a marathon should he become concerned with improving his time.

To prepare for longer distances, a runner should combine interval training with increasing mileage, fully aware that interval training will improve his ability to go longer distances with less fatigue.

Anaerobic and Aerobic Systems

Several systems supply the muscles with the energy needed for work or exercise. For the first three minutes of physical activity, anaerobic systems supply muscles with chemicals and nutrients that are already stored in and around the muscles, ready for immediate use. Beyond three minutes of activity, as the body continues to exercise, the need for oxygen arises and the aerobic, or oxygen system, beings to supply muscles with needed nutrients, minerals, and chemicals . . . as long as there is sufficient fuel. All endurance or continuous activity relies predominantly on this energy system. Yet the other systems, the anaerobic systems . . . which produce and utilize various acids and glucose compounds, also rely upon the aerobic system to replenish their resources. Hence, it follows that the more efficient the aerobic system is . . . the faster and more durable the athlete will be able to run! This principle applies to other sports as well, including swimming and cycling . . . to the triathlete in training.

What attracts my attention shall have it. —Emerson

Training Your Metabolism

To train these various systems is not difficult, and actually is essential to the long distance triathletic contender. Training your metabolism is no harder than training your muscles. It merely requires a little bit of knowledge and attention.

To condition any specific system, the energy expended and the duration of the expenditure should comply with that system. This is where interval training becomes important: what better way to train your metabolism than with intervals designed to tax certain systems, then allow them to regain normal levels?

Training Anaerobic Systems

Anaerobic systems react to short duration, high intensity, repetitive work, from a few seconds to two or three minutes. Recovery time varies but is comparable to the time used to exercise. By training anaerobic systems, energy production becomes more efficient, and muscle tolerance of lactic acid becomes greater which reduces muscle fatigue. Interval training is the best way to train these systems, using a few high quality intervals: 8-10 x 400, 4-6 x 600, 3-4 x 300, etc. Also, interval training forces a runner to run faster, thereby improving technique for those necessary spurts of speed.

Oxygen Debt

Oxygen debt occurs whenever one exercises beyond the immediate capability of the anaerobic systems, which require oxygen to produce and retain glucose, lactic acid, and other nutrients, minerals and chemicals so that the muscles can convert energy into motion. In other words, when you exercise for any extended period of time, the body requires an amount of time following exercise to absorb the adequate oxygen to allow the anaerobic systems to return to normal functioning levels.

Training Aerobic Systems

The oxygen system is the aerobic energy system. All continuous or endurance activity relies predominantly upon this system's use of fats and glucose (carbohydrates), which are converted into muscle energy by chemical interaction with oxygen. Oxygen is, of course, ingested through the lungs and circulatory system, and the more efficient the respiratory and cardiovascular systems, the better the aerobic energy system will work . . . and the better you will run!

The aerobic system responds to long, steady training. This training may take the form of an eight mile run (or more) or dozens of repeated intervals. This brings to mind the Fartlek Method, which emphasizes running various terrains . . . not only for the physical challenge, but to alleviate boredom, a common complaint among those who train predominantly with intervals. Yet, the interval method can be brought into play, even when training for distance: The most obvious reason, aside from training energy systems, is that it forces a runner to run faster for certain training periods . . . which improves his technique, and enables him to pour on the speed if he needs to during a race.

Interval Training
Bicycling and Swimming

The same concepts apply to bicycling and swimming. Not only do the same energy systems require training to endure distance events, but for the competitor, being able to break out of a steady pace to surge ahead . . . or catch up is as important as any other part of contention. Through interval training, the triathlete not only builds up his energy systems, making his muscles more efficient and his metabolism better able to supply muscular demands . . but he gives himself an edge over the non-interval-trained competitor, on the basis of available speed.

The Uses and Abuses of Interval Training

Many track and field athletes believe that all fast running interspersed with rest/recovery periods is interval training. It is not. Some of it is interval work, and there's a vast difference between them. What is that difference and how does it affect training for the various events? Perhaps we'd better start with definitions from a couple of experts:

Tony Nett, a top German coach who is editor of *Die Lehre der Leichtathletic (The Teaching of Track and Field)* published in Berlin, describes interval work as sprinting, and speed work as being primarily concerned with the training of the nerve/coordination of the muscles. The adaptation to the stress of exercise occurs during the period of work. The rest interval merely serves for recovery of the muscles and nerves after exertion.

Kenneth Doherty, one of the best known coaches in the United States, discusses interval training in his book, *Modern Training for Running.* He describes it as a system of repeated efforts in which a specific distance is run on the track at a timed pace, alternating with measured recovery periods of low activity. There are no actual recovery pauses, merely a slowing down of speed (jogging or walking) during the intervals. This system primarily trains the heart, and it is during the pauses or intervals that this takes place.

So, the basic difference in the two systems is that in one case the training effect occurs during the rest period, in the other, during the time when the athlete is exerting himself. This gives us a broad outline, but it still doesn't fully clarify how these systems work. Let's examine each in more detail, starting with interval training.

The identity of the man who originated interval training is obscure, but a pioneer in the field was Finnish coach, Lauri Pikhala, who in 1920 stressed the rhythm between work and rest and whose principles were applied by the great Paavo Nurmi.

The Gerscheler-Reindel Law of Interval Training

Then Drs. Herbert Reindel and Woldemar Gerschler of Germany examined the optimum amount of physical exertion necessary for a systematic improvement. After many experiments they established the Gerschler-Reindel law of interval training which states:

1. A warm-up should be used which brings the heart rate up to 120 beats per minute.
2. The runner then covers a given distance—100, 150, or 200 meters—in a given time which must bring the heart rate up to 170-180 beats per minute. He then takes a rest interval.
3. When the heart rate returns to 120-125, the runner starts again. The maximum time this recovery should take is a minute and a half, and it can be shorted by highly trained individuals.

Interval training is the ideal method for increasing the efficiency and size/strength of the heart. The two major factors which enable it to do this more efficiently than continuous training (running a given distance at a steady pace) are:

1. More work can be performed with less fatigue and in less time.
2. A greater stimulus to improvement of the aerobic capacity (oxygen transport system) is provided.

The explanation for the first factor is a bit complicated, involving the ATP-PC and lactic-acid systems of the body. ATP (adenosine triphosphate), which is simply the prime source of the energy for muscle work, while PC is phosphocreatine which is stored in the muscles and instantly manufactures ATP. ATP can provide enough energy to keep the muscles working at maximum intensity for 10 seconds.

In the lactic-acid system, glucose is chemically broken down to lactic acid when the oxygen supply is inadequate, and then ATP is manufactured.

More Energy . . . Less Pain

In their book *Interval Training,* Edward L. Fox and Donald K. Mathews state that less energy is supplied via the lactic-acid system in interval training than via the ATP-PC. This results in less fatigue, because during the rest periods the muscular stores of ATP-PC are replenished via the aerobic system, and part of the oxygen debt is repaid. This makes more ATP-PC energy available once more and "spares" energy from the lactic-acid system.

By contrast, they say, in a continuous run the stored ATP-PC is exhausted in a few minutes and cannot be replenished until the run is over. This means that energy from the lactic-acid system will be called upon and lactic acid will soon accumulate to exhausting levels, bringing the runner to a halt.

This is why one can perform more intensive work when running intermittently than when running continuously. It also has important considerations for training for specific events which will be dealt with later.

Drs. I. Astrand, P-O Astrand, E. H. Christensen, R. Hedman, and others have shown that in interval training as much as two and a half times the intensity of continuous running can be maintained before comparable blood lactic-acid levels (fatigue) are reached.

As to the second factor mentioned earlier—the improvement of aerobic capacity—Fox and Mathews point out that the stroke volume of the heart is higher during recovery than during exercise. Stroke volume refers to the amount of blood pumped by the heart with each beat. The more blood that is pumped, the more oxygen is transported to the working muscles.

Therefore, they say, interval running is more efficient than continuous running in developing aerobic capacity because of the many recovery periods which enable stroke volume of the heart to reach its highest levels as many times as there are intervals. In continuous running, there is only one rest interval: at the end.

Running Speed

Dr. Reindel suggests that the speed of the runs in interval training should not be too high because the heart reacts to high speeds not by pumping more blood but by increasing the number of beats. Stroke volume, therefore, is not trained and the stimulus for enlargement of the heart muscle is limited by the smaller number of repetitions (and consequently rest intervals) possible at higher speeds.

This implies that it is impossible to do interval work to improve the efficiency of the muscles and at the same time do interval training to improve the efficiency of the heart. There seems little doubt that interval training, while improving aerobic endurance, has little effect on anaerobic capacity (the ability to do work without oxygen—while in oxygen debt). Therefore, short and middle distance events require less interval training and more interval work, which does improve aerobic capacity.

Nett states that in the sprints and middle distances it is the skeletal muscles, rather than the heart, which should receive the "stress stimulus." This, he says, is brought about by fast—perhaps all-out—running speeds in which the stress stimulus affects the cross-section of the muscles, making them thicker, stronger, and faster while at the same time stimulating the muscle metabolism. Muscle metabolism is what gives muscles endurance while in oxygen debt.

Differences Between Tempo Work and Interval Work

Temp work, he says, also improves muscle metabolism while having less effect on muscle bulk and should form the basis of training for the middle distance runner. Tempo work differs from interval work only in that the distances covered are longer. Instead of sprinting all out for 100 or 150 yards, the tempo trainer might cover anywhere from 400 to 1,000 meters as fast as possible (at race pace), rest and then repeat.

Similar improvements cannot be achieved with interval training, Nett says, because of the slower pace required to allow for a number of repetitions to be run in order to train the heart. Although interval training should form the basis of training for distances above 1,500 meters, it should not be the only form of training for distance runners. They also require speed, strength, and muscle endurance. These are achieved not by interval training but by interval work, overload training such as hill running, and tempo running.

This is why the modern method of training for almost all distances is complex training. This utilizes all the different methods, emphasizing the particular one which brings about the desired results for the specific distance. The runner uses an optimum mixture to tone up all his different biological systems.

While interval training is a heart conditioner and hence useful for the endurance runner, we should keep in mind that more than a strong heart is required to win races. The ability to withstand pain is a vital asset, particularly the pain of competition associated with the demands of all-out, steady running. Interval training does not develop this, because the athlete stops before the pains of fatigue become a major factor. Only by subjecting himself in his training to the stresses of competition can the athlete learn to handle the mental aspects of competition. This can best be done through tempo running—running long distances at race pace.

Stability Through Gradually Developed Endurance

According to Nett, continuous running may not be quite as efficient as interval training in enlarging the heart and improving endurance in the shortest possible time. But, he says, it has a more stable effect. And Doherty warns that attempting too much-too fast, too soon in interval training can endanger muscles, tendons, and morale. Apparent success in interval training does not guarantee success in competition, he points out, and the athlete may be deluded into a sense of stamina which in actual fact is best achieved by a sound base of well-rounded, gradually developed endurance through continuous running.

Doherty believes that the systematic analysis of all aspects of the training situation possible in interval training can be considered a great asset if the athlete anticipates each separate run and enjoys overcoming its challenges. But, he warns, having to face the challenges of interval training day after day can become a drudgery and a stress factor.

Different methods of training, therefore, not only tone up the different biological systems but help to provide variety and prevent boredom and staleness.

Another weakness of interval training, according to Doherty, is that it can develop excellent interval trainers without developing excellent competitive runners. The athlete's performance in training becomes the primary concern, and he finds himself unprepared for the physical and mental aspects of competition. Specificity, both the physical and psychological preparation of the athlete is important.

Warning Regarding Interval Training

Although the problem with most athletes is doing too little work . . . Reindel also has some reservations about the unlimited use of interval training. He says that over-emphasized interval training—such as repeating 100-meter runs 50 or 100 times—has in recent times led to heart injuries. He advises that pulse rates be taken after a certain number of repetitions to ensure that injury does not take place.

This is not to overlook the positive aspects of interval training which can form the basis of conditioning for all sports. Interval Training permits the intensity of the workout to be adapted to the individual athlete and has great importance in sports medicine for prophylaxis and rehabilitation. The specific application of interval training is the improvement of blood circulation, the heart, and the cardio-pulmonary system. That's the purpose for which it should be used.

Warning Regarding Interval Training

Although the problem with most athletes is doing too little work . . . Reindel also has some reservations about the unlimited use of interval training. He says that over-emphasized interval training—such as repeating 100-meter runs 50 or 100 times—has in recent times led to heart injuries. He advises that pulse rates be taken after a certain number of repetitions to ensure that injury does not take place.

This is not to overlook the positive aspects of interval training which can form the basis of conditioning for all sports. Interval Training permits the intensity of the workout to be adapted to the individual athlete and has great importance in sports medicine for prophylaxis and rehabilitation. The specific application of interval training is the improvement of blood circulation, the heart, and the cardio-pulmonary system. That's the purpose for which it should be used.

Exercise Physiology Glossary

Most current training theories and programs used by the athlete and coach were developed from the sweat and toil of the athlete and coach, not from the laboratory experiments of the physiologists. To some degree this is changing, but still it is more a matter of the exercise physiologist confirming a coach's methods or of guiding the coach and the athlete to a better utilization of their methods. This is said not to belittle the contributions of and need for the exercise physiologist, but to give the coaches and athletes their due.

A knowledge of physiology can help the coach and athlete understand their training and responses to training programs. The difficulties the scientists will face in the future, they are facing now. Besides lack of research funding, the athlete, and quite naturally so, presents a formidable barrier to the researcher. Due to the necessity of his or her competitive development, the athlete cannot, and many times will not, submit to rigidly controlled tests designed to gain insight into exercise. The non-athlete, who lacks conditioning and the will to follow a rigorous exercise program, often does not respond in quite the same way to experiments. So, no doubt, many future training breakthroughs will still be made by the athlete and coach, though, hopefully, they will be made easier by the addition of scientific knowledge and experiment.

In applying physiological knowledge to the track and field events, the aim is not to develop one rigid system of training. Variability and experimentation are at the very heart of the scientific method. The aim is to supply knowledge about the physiological demands of the events, and the contributions to those demands of various training programs. The successful training programs in use today, involve physiologically sound methods and practices. The aim of exercise physiology should be to define, illustrate, and more successfully and carefully apply those methods and practices, as well as, to help refine old methods and develop new ones!

The following presents sections on the utilization of heart rate monitoring, to measure stresses, intensities, and durations of workouts; synopses of the major training programs; as well as, the physiological training concerns of each event area.

This glossary is provided to clarify the meaning of several terms used in this section. While many of these terms are in common use, their exact meanings can and do vary with the user. The generally accepted definitions are given to those terms more specific to science or technical works, while my definitions are given to those more specific to general coaching.

Aerobic Endurance: the ability, measure of the ability to do continuous work. Such work utilizes the O_2 energy system. Continuous running, ability is an example of a measure of aerobic endurance.

Anaerobic Endurance: the ability, or measure of the ability to do intense exercise or work, at maximum or near maximum levels; the ability to tolerate lactic acid fatigue. Anaerobic endurance is exemplified in the quarter-mile.

Anaerobic Threshold: the level of work or exercise at which lactic acid begins to accumulate, usually associated with a percentage of Max VO_2 or a heart rate in excess of 160-170 bpm. It marks the transition from the ability to use the O_2 energy system to the necessity of using the LA system, or the transition for aerobic work levels to anaerobic work levels.

Circuit Training: a type of training in which the exerciser advances from one exercise to another in some prescribed manner, usually in an "interval-type" format with timed rests and exercise periods. It usually involves the use of weights and calisthenics.

Competition-Specific Stress: an exercise that simulates or duplicates competition conditions and stresses the energy systems and muscles in the same manner and to the same degree as actual competition. Examples: for the shotputter—shotputting for distance; for the quarter miler—a 300m time trial, or, 3 X 200m at near maximum speed, etc.

Effort: effort, here, relates to the percentage of maximum effort, or the use of a percent of one's ability (power, speed, and endurance) in a particular exercise. Specifically, I use this term for sprinters in describing workouts that are not timed. 100% effort is an all-out maximum attempt. 99% effort is going as fast and as relaxed as possible, and is just minimally below an all-out attempt. 90% effort is fast, relaxed, and loose, and would involve, for example, running 200m 2-3 seconds slower than one's best time. 75% effort is a full stride run, with no attempt to run hard; it is the slowest one can run and still be at full stride.

Endurance Training: training that increases either anaerobic or aerobic endurance, or the ability to maintain a certain level of power output.

Hard-Easy Training Pattern: a method of training that alternates hard and easy days of training in order to prevent overtraining or staleness. Usually, a hard day is marked by high stress of the lactic acid energy system, or a very fast or very long continuous activity (e.g., 18-20+ miles). An easy day is marked by moderate to mild stress of the LA system, and/or moderate stressing of the aerobic system.

Intensity: a measurement of the degree of effort used in an exercise. A high intensity effort involves near maximum and maximum effort, and a fast build-up of fatigue (within a short distance or within a few repetitions). A low intensity effort is marked by a slow build-up of fatigue and less than 90% effort.

Isokinetic Exercise: Exercises, involving some type of "weight-machine" in which the resistance to muscle movement is constant throughout the range of movement, and adjusts to the force exerted by the muscles. Some models are also adjustable for speed of movement.

Isometric Exercise: exercises, in which resistance to muscle movement is fixed and immovable, and the muscle contracts against this fixed force at a certain percentage of contraction force (usually 70-100%) for a set period of time. In isometric exercise there is no movement and, thus, no physical work done.

Isotonic Exercise: exercises, typified by general weight training with non-isokinetic machines or free weights, in which the resistance to muscle activity changes throughout the range of exercise movement because the angles of pull or push of the athlete against the weight change. The weight doesn't change throughout the exercise, but the force needed to move or lift it is not constant, and is less at certain angles of movement than at others.

Jump Training (Pliometrics or Plyometrics also): a training for explosive power through the use of jumping, or a series of jumps, hops, or bounds. See the Plyometrics section for an elaboration.

Lactic Acid Fatigue: fatigue, loss of coordination, loss of muscle control, and the pain due to the accumulation of lactic acid in anaerobic exercise. A characteristic of the long sprints and middle distances. As lactic acid fatigue progresses, more and more effort is required to maintain a chosen pace.

Long Fast Distance: distance running, for training purposes, at near race paces. Usually, the pace is 90-99% of race pace for the distance. Generally, it is employed by most high caliber middle-distance and distance runners in some phase of their training.

Long Intervals: here, used to describe workouts in which the interval distance is between 200m and one mile, and the pace is at or slower than race pace. This "slower" pace allows a high number of repetitions and this tends to be a quantity instead of a quality workout method.

Long Slow Distance (LSD): distance running, for training purposes, at comfortable paces. Usually, the pace is 75-90% of race pace for the distance and more than likely at 85-90% of race pace. It should be noted that what is comfortable for some is not for others. (Speed is inversely proportional to time. To calculate 90% of a certain pace, for example, divide the race pace by .90. If one's marathon race pace is 5:00 per mile, a 90% pace is 5:00 divided by .90, or 5.56 minutes per mile or 5:34 pace.)

Overtraining: training too hard, as to exhaust the body's energy systems and create undue fatigue levels. These fatigue levels cannot, then, be recovered from by the next workout and the athlete's performance ability decreases. The athlete can then become more subject to sickness, injury, and further decreases in ability.

Peaking: generally, a process by which an athlete attempts to arrive at maximum performance levels for a particular meet. The general procedure involves an intensification in the workouts and a reduction of the volume in training in the 2 months prior to the big meet; and avoiding high stress, exhausting workouts in the 2 weeks prior to the big meet, while doing high quality, non-exhausting workouts.

Power: the production of strength within a time framework. Force times velocity, or work divided by time, where work equals force times distance. The ability to produce great strength in a short period of time equates with great power production. Having power is epitomized by the ability to move strongly and explosively, while strength is not limited by the time of movement. Strength is exerting force without regard to time.

Quality Work: a high intensity workout, generally at race paces or faster, that produces high levels of fatigue in a very short time. Because of its high intensity the duration and repetitions of the work are very limited.

Quantity Work: a lower intensity workout, generally at race paces or slower, that emphasizes volume, or high numbers of repetitions, and produces high levels of fatigue in a longer more drawn out fashion that quality work. Example (for the long sprinter): quality—3.4 x 300m fast; quantity—10 x 200m moderately.

Race-Specific Stress: see Competition-Specific Stress—a workout that through the manipulation of duration, intensity, and rest intervals simulates and stresses, efforts, and fatigue levels of a race.

Sharpening: A procedure of using speed work, high quality work and low to moderate fatigue levels, and ample rest to achieve a peak state of conditioning.

Speed Endurance: the quality of being able to maintain a high percentage of top sprinting speed over a given distance.

Speed Work: training aimed at increasing one's top speed potential. Generally, workouts consist of maximum speed and near maximum speed runs over 30-150m, with full recoveries between repetitions, and the maintenance of low fatigue levels.

Staleness: a condition brought on by overtraining in which the athlete's performance and/or workout ability decreases.

Strength: the ability or quality of being able to exert force, without regard to the time or duration of the exercise.

Strength Training: Generally, weight training, but any training that increases the athlete's strength or ability to exert force.

Stress Work (stress intervals): training designed to create a high level of stress or fatigue. High quality work with incomplete recoveries. Fast intervals with short recoveries and few repetitions.

Stretch Reflex: when a muscle is stretched there is a reflex action that causes contraction of this muscle to return it to an equilibrium position. In reference to exercise, when a muscle group is stretched under a load, the following contraction becomes much more forceful. This creates more powerful movements in many events.

Stretching: a warm-up procedure that involves stretching or the lengthening of various muscle groups. Ballistic stretching involves quick, bouncing movements. Static stretching involves holding a given muscle stretch position for several seconds.

Volume: the amount or quantity of work done.

Work: force times distance—the moving of an object (one's body or some other mass) by exerting force.

A Summary of Heart Rate Monitoring for Interval Workouts

General and Specific Workouts	HR and Time Recovery Between Intervals		Termination Indicators
Speed Work 30-150m 95-100% effort	120 bpm 1-4 minutes	100-120 bpm 2-5 minutes	Not achieving 120 bpm within 5 minutes.
Speed Endurance 60-200m 90-100% effort	120-140 bpm 1-3 minutes	120 bpm 2-5 minutes	Not achieving 120 bpm within 5 minutes
Stress Work 200-600m 90-100% effort	100-120 bpm 4-10 minutes+	100 bpm 4-15 minutes	Not achieving sub 120 bpm within 15 minutes.
Long Intervals 200-800m	120-140 bpm 1-3 minutes	120 bpm 3-5 minutes	Not achieving 120 bpm within 5 minutes.

General and Specific Workouts	HR and Time Recovery Between Intervals		Termination Indicators
Speed Work 4 x 100 90% 4 x 75 buildups 4 x 75 90% 4 x 50 100% 4 x 50 finish 50's	120 bpm 1-3 minutes	100bpm 2-5 minutes	As above.
Stress Work #1: 1 x 600 1 x 400 1 x 200	100-12- bpm 4-10 minutes	---------	Not achieving 120 bpm after 12 minutes
#2: 4 x 400m 4 x 200m	--------- 30-60 seconds	less than 100 bpm 5-15 minutes	Not achieving sub 120 bpm within minutes.
Long Intervals 10 x 200m Or 8 x 400m	120 bpm 1-3 minutes 120 bpm 1-3 minutes.	--------- ---------	As above. As above.

Rating Scale of Benefits to Multi-Sports

	RUN-NING	BICY-CLING	SWIM-MING	HAND-BALL/ SQUASH	TENNIS	WALK-ING	GOLF	BOWL-ING
Physical Fitness								
Cardio-respiratory endurance	21	19	21	19	16	13	8	5
Muscular endurance	20	18	20	18	16	14	8	5
Muscular strength	17	16	14	15	14	11	9	5
Flexibility	9	9	15	16	14	7	8	7
Balance	17	18	12	17	16	8	88	6
General Well-Being								
Weight control	21	20	15	19	16	13	6	5
Muscle definition	14	15	14	11	13	11	6	5
Digestion	13	12	13	13	12	11	7	7
Sleep	16	15	16	12	11	14	6	6
Total	148	142	140	140	128	102	66	51

Interval Training

Bibliography

Competitive Swimming Manual by Counsilman Co., Inc., 2606 East Second Street, Bloomington, Indiana 47401, 1977.

"Interval and Continuous Running." *Long Distances.* by Humphreys, John H. L. Tafnews Press, Los Altos, California, 1980, pp. 62-63.

Interval Training. by Nick Costes, World Publications, Mountain View, California, 1972-1978.

Running the Lydiard Way. by Lydiard, Arthur World Publications, Mountain View, California, 1978.

Running and Your Body. by Dare, Bernie Tafnews Press, Los Altos, California, 1979, pp. 55-58 Exercise Physiology: A Glossary.

Ironmen average 39 years of age

This is all well and good if our calendar years are few; but unfortunately, the majority of multi-sport contestants fall into a much older age group. The 1981, Original World Ironman Triathlon, held in Kona-Hawaii, boasted an average age of 39 years. This means that the biological years might far exceed the 39 calendar years. The resulting exposure to body polluting water and air, chemical fertilizers, preservatives, insecticides, and heavy metals in our food and water supply have compounded the actual years into a biologically older body. All of these elements which constantly creep into our bodies, voluntarily and involuntarily, are poisonous and the cause of many of our illnesses including cancer in various forms.

The multi-sport aspirant should be vitally interested in maintaining an internally sound, healthy body as a prerequisite to setting distance competition goals and "we feel confident that you will agree to this after reading about the Nine Doctors of Preventive Medicine, Body Purification and Fasting." The philosophy here, as old as time, is that you will acquire a new toxic poison-free, ageless body through a physical, mental, and spiritual rejuvenation maintaining a youthful body to carry you the total distance in winning time.

To start our training we must prepare this wonderful God given body, starting with an internal purification and followed by a diet which will maintain your body free from toxic poison build-up. Furthermore, a mental and spiritual outlook on life that will give joy and excitement to your training routines and also in your everyday life you will be more greatly blessed . . . physically, mentally and spiritually!

Can two walk together, except they be agreed? —Amos III:3

4

The Woman Triathlete

The Woman Triathlete

WITH THE HELP OF THE WOMEN'S MOVEMENT, new discoveries in sports medicine for both sexes, and the overwhelming appeal of athletics for women in the last decade . . . female athletes are finding their limitations are based only on individual effort, leaving goals open-ended and personal fulfillment attainable. To use fraility as an excuse is both unhealthy and self-defeating! Many women today are finding themselves in sports oriented situations they would not have considered ten years ago. But thanks to those courageous women athletes who never took no for an answer . . . women today are discovering they can shake off old, prevailing attitudes of sexual bias, extend their personal boundaries and eventually reshape cultural perception of women in sports.

Endurance for women has been, and is, two-sided. It applies to them through history and the shackles and ground rules laid there, and more obviously in their physical and spiritual will-power. Records to be set and broken are just the beginning for women today. There are two spotlights now . . . and women can now take their rightful place alongside men. A Babe Deidrickson is no longer an oddity, an anachronism. There is an endless succession of Babe Deidricksons and Wilma Rudoplphs now to take their place. Happily, we are finding that training programs should be geared to the individual specifically and not to the sex generally.

Women and the Triathlon Multisport Event

More specifically we should deal with the woman in triathletics. The multi-sport event of Swim, Bike and Run promises to be the great equalizer, not only man to man but woman to man. By the sheer nature of the three extended distance events combined, we have one event that appeals to the woman and her strengths in many ways. Upon witnessing the emergence of the woman triathlete since the inception of the event in Honolulu five years ago, I would like to predict the possibility and probability of a Woman Ironman at some time in the future.

In February of 1982, the International Olympic Committee approved the addition of a women's marathon to the 1984 Olympic Games. This decision, seen by many athletes as long overdue, shows clearly the legitimacy and viability of female participation in endurance athletic events. Long distance and multi-sport events offer unique opportunities to women, because as relatively new sporting fields . . . the chance for rapid improvement and advancement is high, and because psychologically and physiologically, women seem to be uniquely suited for those events requiring stamina over a long period of time. Thus the present time is an ideal one for women interested in these sports to undertake regular training programs, as the possible rewards are great. Whether you train for competition or solely for the personal satisfaction that can be gained . . . long distance running, swimming and biking are sports which are opening up to women at an amazingly fast rate.

Training for Women

For the most part, we are finding that training programs should be geared to the individual specifically and not to the sex generally; that is, women can successfully follow training procedures identical to those used by men, as long as they keep in mind the special considerations covered in this chapter.

New Strides. You are not frail, but a potentially strong and vibrant athlete who is also a woman. Sports science continues to show that many of the "genetic" differences are really fostered by culture, just as women's greater tendency toward shin splints is due to wearing high heels. We are learning that "innate weaknesses" often disappear with equal opportunity.

The triathlon is one event that will surely test your skills and endurance more than any other kind of sports contest. Your success is up to you as an individual, not as a woman, and hinges on whether your training program is the best you can do.

You should keep a log of your daily workouts!!! . . . even if you are a pro. You will begin to see your rate of progress increase, injuries that might occur . . . and most important of all, find out ways to improve yourself in future
training programs! You will also get the satisfaction of seeing your hard work come to fruition.

History of Women in Multi-Sport Events

Physiological Considerations. Physiologically, women have many characteristics which make them uniquely suited for long distance sports requiring endurance: the female's extra layer of fat cells acts as a buffer against extreme cold, which is extremely advantageous in ocean swims, and can serve as reserve fuel for longer efforts . . . the female tendency of perspiring less than men helps slow dehydration, which can be a critical problem during long distance events . . . wider hips provide stability and estrogen promotes flexibility. However, there are also physiological characteristics which can detract from female performance in long distance events, and these limitations and ways of minimizing them will be dealt with at length.

Knee Problems

Because of the width of their hips and the angle at which the bones and muscles of the leg are attached to the pelvis, females are more likely than males to be susceptible to runner's and biker's knee; a painful and often debilitating stress injury. The female's quadriceps (front thigh muscle) runs along the outside edge of the thigh, and attaches to the hip and the knee at the side. It may pull outward on the kneecap, which causes runner's knee. This danger can be minimized by careful preliminary stretching of the quads before training or competing (avoid knee-bends as exercises, however) . . . by running on yielding surfaces such as sand, grass or dirt, avoiding cement and pavement as much as possible . . . and by having your knees checked and treated by a trainer or doctor at the first sign of any discomfort. Don't put this off if you suspect there is a problem!

Menstruation

Problems associated with menstruation seem to vary greatly from individual to individual, with some women experiencing no discomfort and achieving record times when competing during their period . . . while other women have difficulty even completing an otherwise "easy" training schedule. Try to stick, as much as possible, to your regular training routine during menstruation because when training for the triathlon, daily workouts are crucial. Many women experience relief from discomfort when they exercise . . . and cramping may be reduced as the increased blood flow eases pelvic congestion thereby aiding cramps, and possibly because it relieves tension which can contribute to cramps as well. If you experience severe problems with menstruation, see a gynecologist who is sympathetic to your athletic needs as well as your medical ones. You may have to "shop around" before you find someone with whom you can have a good working relationship, but your health and your body are worth the time.

Another possibility is that your periods may become irregular or stop altogether during training (amenorrhea). Most doctors believe this is due to a low percentage of body fat (about 10%) . . . a healthy pregnancy could not be supported when these fuel reserves are depleted. Amenorrhea is not generally harmful, and menstruation usually resumes when weight is gained or when a period of time elapses for the body to adjust. In most cases, full fertility is restored when the level of training is lightened; if this is something that concerns you, seek the advice of a sports-minded gynecologist. A word of warning: amenorrhea is too inconsistent to be used as birth control . . . just because you aren't menstruating doesn't mean you aren't ovulating. Use another method to be safe.

Also connected with menstruation is the nutritional problem of anemia. Many women suffer from iron-deficiency, and with increased training, this possibility becomes even more likely. If you are even moderately progressing at an expected rate, have your blood checked. The minimum daily requirement for iron for women is 35 milligrams, and any health food store carries iron supplements. The best is the amino acid chelated iron because the absorption rate is 75%. If you suspect that you are iron deficient, you will need to take a therapeutic dose instead of a maintainence dose. Have a blood test to measure the severity of the problem and the amount of iron needed to resolve it.

Contraceptives

Some athletes who use an IUD or oral contraceptives for birth control find these methods can interfere with training and competition. The IUD can cause heavy bleeding and an increased risk of anemia, and the pill makes some women listless, draggy, bloated and nauseous. If you do suffer these side-effects, you might want to consider changing your birth control method, but this is ultimately a personal decision!

Pregnancy

Whether you should continue training or competing during pregnancy, and at what level, is a question for you to discuss with the doctor who is familiar with your individual case. Light exercise is actually beneficial during pregnancy, according to Dr. Evelyn Gendel, Director of the Kansas Division of Maternal and Child Health. Dr. Gendel feels there is no reason not to run if that is part of your normal routine. Potential benefits of continuing exercise during pregnancy include toning of muscles, relief of tension, and prevention of back problems . . . but if you have a history of miscarriages, incompetent cervix, or other problems your doctor may decide these benefits are outweighed by risk to you and your baby.

A test of aerobic fitness in expectant mothers, conducted by the Human Performance Research Laboratory and Division of Midwifery, indicated that women who swam regularly during their pregnancies have a greater level of fitness (as determined by oxygen uptake levels), fewer complications, and quicker deliveries than a control group of women who followed a "normal activity program" without regular swimming. Most doctors recommend that you wait to resume exercise until six weeks after delivery, but again, this can be more accurately determined by your own doctor. Generally, if you had no complications in birth and recovery, and you are feeling up to it, you can let commonsense be your guide!

Don't start a training program during pregnancy, and even if you are in shape, don't dramatically increase the difficulty level of your workouts! Don't work yourself to total exhaustion, as this will deprive the baby of needed oxygen! Though running and especially bike riding may become cumbersome as pregnancy progresses . . . swimming will probably remain relatively enjoyable even into the last months. Many doctors recommend that running be discontinued after the sixth month, but again, this depends more on individual cases rather than arbitrary schedules.

Safe Swimming

In pools it is best to always swim with a buddy, because cramps and head injuries during turns can endanger even the most experienced swimmers. In ocean swimming, the buddy system is absolutely imperative! . . . as rough waters, undertow, marine life and boats present added dangers! Anyone who spends time around water, would do well to take a lifesaving/CPR class . . . available through most Red Cross Chapters, YMCAs, and Colleges.

When ocean swimming, hypothermia is always a concern. It is best to always wear a bathing cap, because as much as 40% of the body's heat can escape through the top of the head. In the ocean, try to know the conditions of each location where you swim . . . ask locals about any problems, undertow, etc. If you do find yourself trapped in an undertow, don't fight against it. Swim parallel to the shore until you no longer feel the pull, then turn into the shore!

Dealing with Hassles

Dogs can be a problem, and in some cases even a danger. If you are on your bike, give a squirt in the face with your water bottle; this will usually discourage them. If you are running, slow down and try the friendly approach, talk to him . . . letting him smell your hand and run with you a while. There is also a dog repellent called "Halt" available in sports and bicycle shops.

Women runners, bikers, and to a lesser extent, swimmers, are often subjected to well-meaning advice from lookers on . . . and occasionaly obnoxious comments from those determined to impress or degrade them. For the most part it is best to ignore this abuse, as retorts and gestures are usually interpreted as encouragement. Just know in your own heart that these rude people are probably jealous of your determination and/or your physical condition . . . while they sit around getting fatter and flabbier and are more likely to die earlier deaths!

Safety Precautions While Training

It is sad, but in this society women have to be aware of the possibility of attack or assault during virtually all activities they undertake, and training is no exception. Though you don't want to be shackled with worry or excessive precautionary measures, there are some sensible and relatively painless steps to take to reduce the chance of your being victimized. Vary your routine. If you leave your front step at 5:30 every morning, rain or shine, to run the same route, it won't take much for anyone to plan to attack at some remote point along your path. Make variations in the times, places and speeds you run and bike and try to train with a partner! Always let someone know the approximate path you plan to take, give an estimate of when you will return, and instructions on what you want them to do if you don't make it back on time. Avoid training during dark hours, unless you are with another person; if you do train at night, wear reflective tape on your clothing and use a bike light! A good general rule of thumb is that if you wouldn't feel safe walking somewhere, don't run or bike there either!

If you feel you need to, you might consider taking a training course in self-defense or to be certified to carry Mace, which is available in small containers you could comfortably carry in your hand. Another weapon you can use is your keys or make a small, strong, pointed wood stick to hold lightly in your fist as you run, with the points sticking out between your fingers, and punch an attacker in the neck, face, or eyes if you have to . . . also kick or jam knee where it hurts most! Runners and bikers are not often attacked, partially because they do not usually carry much money, and partly because potential assailants do not want to choose someone who could outspeed them, but this doesn't guarantee your safety. Be aware, alert, and purposeful to reduce your vulnerability and to increase your ability to deal successfully with problems if they do arise. Studies indicate that women who scream, fight, and resist unarmed attackers are likely to escape unharmed, but if a weapon is evident, cooperation is probably your best bet for survival. If an attacker tries to drag or drive you to another location, it will probably be more remote than where you were first, so your best bet is to scream and fight there . . . rather than wait for a better opportunity, which may not arise. If you do decide to fight your assailant, give it all you have! Don't be afraid to go for the eyes or throat with keys, fingernails, pointed sticks, anything that's handy . . . remember, if you're being threatened, you are perfectly justified in this, and if you fight back half-heartedly . . . you may just anger your attacker rather than overcome him.

Once you have the chance, RUN!

If you are attacked despite your best efforts to prevent it, don't be too hard on yourself; most men are bigger and stronger than most women, and it is an unpleasant fact of the world that you may be overpowered. Try to get back to training as soon as you physically can, with a partner along the first few times out if you prefer, and don't hesitate to seek counseling if you are having trouble dealing with your feelings about your assault.

Some Specific Guidelines of What to Wear
for Each Triathlon Event

Athletic clothing for women is available in running and sporting goods stores with usually a large selection to choose from, . . . and larger general department or clothing stores. For many items, you may have to make do with small or extra small sizes in men's clothing; the best thing to do is try things on and do some stretches and reaches to make sure they are comfortable.

It is vitally important that you seek out those shops that specialize in competitive sportswear. Don't be afraid to ask their advice, and if you are not sure about what a salesperson tells you, ask to speak to the buyer or the manager of the store. Don't settle for second-best information.

For Swimming: Always wear a swim cap, as 40 percent of your body heat goes out through the scalp, and after leaving the water, keep your cap on for a while, as hypothermia can strike at any time until normal body heat returns.

Your swim suit should be one piece, designed specifically for speed swimming, and made of nylon or lycra. It should fit snugly for streamline movement and to help retain body heat. Goggles are necessary for training in chlorinated pools, and for ocean swims and competition.

For Biking: For training and competition of rides of 100 miles or more, you will need special biking shorts with either a polyester/cotton or chamois (chammy) lined crotch. Jerseys can be wool or a wool-nylon mix. Also popular are the new lycra-spandex one-piece skin suits (both shirt and shorts), which are comfortable and light weight. Helmets should be hard-shell plastic, which is durable and light-weight. Gloves should be pigskin or cowhide with a velcro closure to adjust the fit as your hands swell, and should have a cotton webbing for flexibility and ventilation. Gloves are necessary on long rides to cushion your hands, help absorb sweat, and help keep your grip firm! These gloves can also be used to brush off the tire surfaces while underway, if you notice a ticking sound of a tire having picked up a puncture, weed, seed, or a piece of glass. If caught soon enough you can avoid a puncture. In the days before hand brakes, for racing bikes with stiff sprockets (non-rachet), were stopped by applying the heavy palm surface of bike gloves to the front tire. However, I would not advise using this method, except in the case of dire emergency.

Bike shoes should be a top quality distance racing shoe, offering a strong stiff plastic or steel insert. This insures an even pedal pressure throughout the total foot area. Do not depend on a soft bike touring all purpose shoe for the 112 mile Ironman Triathlon in Hawaii. This event is an extreme test of bike shoe quality. Unfortunately, if the shoes you have trained in gives you trouble after you arrive in Hawaii you are out of luck. The bike shoe selection in Hawaii is minimal and you will have to suffer through. The rule for bike as well as running shoes is that you must have trained in them for a period of time! Do not buy a new pair of running shoes the day or the week before a marathon or triathlon. You must have put at least 200 miles on running shoes before an event . . . and 1,000 miles, including at least 3 century rides on your bike shoes. At the same time, do not go out in an old pair of running or biking shoes, just before they fall apart! Although they feel comfortable, they may disintegrate halfway through an event . . . and you want to go all the way!

Invest Properly in Run and Bike Footwear

The most important investment you will make in clothing for the triathlon will be your shoes! Do not skimp here. Take the advice of a running store proprietor, not a department store shoe salesclerk, or a street shoe store salesclerk. They no doubt mean well . . . but just don't understand the problems! Before you are through, you will end up having to make the big investment anyway.

In the case of bike shoes, you are obligated to find them only in a bike store whose proprietor, more than likely, is up to his elbows in bike bearing grease. Do not let this turn you off. If the proprietor is not a biker, find someone in the store who is. Look for stiff soles, adjustable pedal cleats, ventilation holes both in the uppers and in the soles, and leather uppers, as opposed to synthetic! Some synthetic mesh and leather uppers are acceptable.

Dr. Scholl's insoles offer an added degree of comfort on long rides. These should be lightly pasted in, and the shoe sole ventilating holes opened up in the insole to allow ventilation.

Leather Goods are the Best Insulator Against Bike Sores

Generally speaking, the biker should insulate himself from the bike at every contact point with leather or chamios. A new product out of New Zealand is chamois footwear, excellent for both biking and running. Chamois and leather breathe and absorb moisture, where synthetic does not. These foot formed chamois socks with wool knit ankle length uppers are called, "Champer," and are available at Runn shoe stores.

Wool socks are optional, but are still way ahead of the synthetics for wear under extended abrasion periods. Wet or dry, cold or hot, wool also breathes, while sythetic does not. In the case of synthetic bike socks, a century ride will cause the hard fibres to rub on the foot areas exposed to pressure, thus causing raw and red areas on the feet.

The Well-Dressed Woman Triathlete

Many exciting things are happening in the sports fashion world, as is evidenced by displays in Swimming, Biking, and Running Magazines. This, combined with a trip to the local sporting good store will certainly make you reach for your check book.

Running Gear: Running shops are displaying running shorts and tops in soft pastel shades of all the colors of the rainbow. Headware is getting much attention from sportsware manufacturers and designers. Colorful rope headbands, combination visor sweat bands of various designs and colors are especially designed for the woman competitor. Shoes now come especially designed for the woman, appealingly color coordinated.

Swimwear: Competition one piece swim suits offering the "French Leg" look are available in many hues and colors. The woman triathlete with the well endowed triathlete figure . . . strong shouldered swimmer's build combined with the powerful "quads" of a biker makes an outstanding appearance racing out of the water after a hard 2.4 mile swim.

Cycling Gear: At first glance, there seems to be little difference between men's and women's bike apparel. But as in the case of running gear, it has taken some time for the designers to differentiate between the two, and now women's colors and designer bike clothing is coming into its own. The one piece, chamois lined trunks with coordinated top is now available. There promises to be many innovations in women's biking gear in the near future!

Running Gear: Shorts should be light weight cotton/polyester or light-weight nylon for comfort. Many come with a built-in brief for absorption and comfort, though this is up to personal preference. Singlets (tank tops) of cotton/polyester are best for lightness and absorption. Sweats and T-shirts are fine for training but are not usually good for racing, due to their weight and bulk.

Bras designed especially for athletics are now available. Look for a cotton blend with seams and fasteners on the outside, with a smooth inside to avoid chafing!

You may also want to wear a visor or headband to keep the sweat and hair off your face. Look for a cotton blend.

Depending on the climate in which you live, you may want to invest in raingear for running and biking. You can't forego your daily training just because of unwelcome weather.

It is best to wash your clothing every time you use it. Though you may think clothes would last longer if they were not washed so often . . . sweat has a degenerative effect on fabric that is as damaging as frequent washings. Regular washing will also help prevent heat rashes.

Their Long Warmup Ended,
Women Finally Come Into Their Own

We are appreciative of the support given by Jim Fixx to this chapter, We highly recommend, The Complete Book of Running and the Second Book of Running for good reading on women participation in The Running Portion of the Tristhlone.

Bill Mongovan stood in a clover patch near the edge of the gray asphalt running track encircling the football field at Greenwhich High School, in southwestern Connecticut. A slight, weather-bronzed man with an angular face and an omnipresent stopwatch, he studied a half-dozen young women as they ran swiftly by, leaning hard into a curve. Mongovan (the accent, fittingly, is on the second syllable) purses his lips but says nothing. When the runners have passed, he remarked, "I try not to do too much coaching. If a girl isn't eager to run without my telling her to, I'm beating my head against a wall."

Mongovan has coached some five hundred women since he started specializing in women's track and field a dozen years ago. Intractable motivational problems have been rare. Just west of the field a wooded hillside slants toward the sky. Beyond a stand of ancient elms the sun has already set, yet Mongovan's charges push on as if they planned to run right through the dinner hour and into the night. He tells me, "Women are more highly motivated than men, especially when they're young. They improve so quickly they can't help being full of enthusiasm."

Mongovan has witnessed the burgeoning of women's running at close hand. Besides his coaching duties he is a member of the Amateur Athletic Union's women's athletics committee and of five of its women's subcommittees. He is the AAU's regional chairman for women's track and field, responsible for all athletic events in New England, New York and the northern half of New Jersey. He is the founder of the Gateway Track Club, which came into being a few years ago to allow more young women to enjoy track and field. He tells with mixed pride and dismay that in one recent year he participated in two hundred running-related activities, ranging from AAU meetings to track meets. In calculating the total he did not count phone calls, curbstone coaching sessions and impromptu pep talks.

Over the years Mongovan's attitudes toward women athletes have changed. When he started coaching he was wary of asking too much of them. In keeping with the prevailing prejudices about women's athletic potential, he let his athletes run far shorter and less tiring training sessions than were customary for men. Then, a few years ago, it struck him that since some of the women he coached were able to run faster and farther than many men, it was illogical to prescribe less rigorous workouts. Today, as a result, it is not unusual during certain phases of training for young women to run twelve miles at a time under Mongovan's tutelage. Nor are hard interval sessions foreign to them. "When they finish," he told me, "you can be sure they feel as if they've done a lot of work."

New Look at Women Athletes

The evolution of Mongovan's expectations parallels a widespread revision in the way knowledgeable observers view women athletes. Until a few years ago almost everyone assumed that arduous running, in ways both specified and unspecified, was almost certain to be harmful to women. Their breasts would surely droop, their reproductive systems dislodge or malfunction, their femininity dissolve in sweat. Even when these misfortunes did not materialize, a feeling prevailed that it was, well, unseemly for women to bestir themselves vigorously. The medieval view of woman as an ethereal, ineffably otherworldly species, too pure for the earthly concerns that trouble their brothers, was a long time in dying. In the past decade its throes have, however, been hastened by the discoveries of researchers who have reported that women are no more subject to athletic injury than men are, that their reproductive systems, even during pregnancy, are no less durable, and that the biomechanical aspects of their running, while different from those of men, are no less efficient.

Much of this had been known, at least in a general way, for decades. The earliest studies correlating athletic ability with the menstrual cycle, and revealing that menstruation had no discernible effect on athletic prowess, took place more than half a century ago. To most people, however, the available information had an unsatisfyingly theoretical cast. After all, if women were capable of outstanding athletic achievements, why did they perform so poorly compared with men? It was all very well for researchers to report, as five did at a medical conference in 1976, that women would one day cover a marathon course in two hours and thirty minutes or even less. But where were such women?

As it happened, they—or more precisely, she—was at that very moment busy training in Oslo, Norway, where she lived. She was twenty-two years old, her name was Grete Waitz, and two years later almost to the day, in the 1978 New York City Marathon, she was to cover the course in 2:32:30, more than two minutes faster than any woman had ever before run 26 miles, 385 yards and only seven minutes slower than the winning time for men in the 1956 Melbourne Olympics. Furthermore, the following year she covered the same course nearly five minutes faster. By so decisively breaking the existing record and then her own, Ms. Waitz, a schoolteacher, lifted women's running into orbit inconceivably remote from anything most people had thought possible. "Can you believe it?" one male runner said in astonishment. "I run a 2:30 marathon and get beaten by a *woman.*" Now that Grete Waitz had run that epochal marathon, anything could happen. Excellent as she was, after all, it was unlikely that she was athletically unique. Still more impressive performances were bound to be on the way.

Basic Differences Women Vs. Men

The only question was how long the extraordinary improvements in women's running would continue. When men break records these days, they typically do so by tenths of a second. In some events, records have not been broken for several years. It is only among women athletes that vast chunks of time are still being chopped off. Plainly the quantum jumps will not continue forever.

For one thing, unless we are hopelessly unregenerate wishful thinkers, we are bound to acknowledge that women have several well-documented handicaps.

They are not as strong as men. When Terrence Hoffman, Robert W. Stauffer and Andrew S. Jackson studied sixty West Point cadets, evenly divided by sex, they found that differences in body size were insufficient to account for men's superior strength, particularly in the upper body. "Male cadets," said the researchers, "are stronger than female cadets."

Women are, furthermore, less willing than men to endure discomfort in order to increase their strength. In a second experiment, also conducted at West Point, Colonel James L. Anderson, the academy's physical education director, enrolled twenty women, all of them former high school athletes, in a weight-lifting class. He reported that, compared with men, the women were hampered "by their inability to push past a perceived level of pain for a greater strength gain. . . . Society tells women they are frail and if an exercise hurts, they shouldn't do it."

In an experiment at Wellesley College, other researchers reported similar findings. Young women were asked to report how hard they felt they were exercising as they ran four times a week for progressively greater distances. These women, particularly if they had never previously engaged in heavy exercise, invariably underestimated their capacity for physical activity. Dennis Kowal, one of the researchers who conducted the experiment, commented, "Women can perform well above previous expectations, even their own." Women have proportionately smaller hearts than men. Their cardiovascular systems are therefore less efficient in transporting oxygen to muscles. Women have proportionately more body fat. By analogy with the metabolism of migrating birds, some medical authorities theorize that women's fat gives them an advantage in long-distance running. Not all researchers agree Dr. David L. Costill, director of the Human Performance Laboratory at Ball State University, said his experiments had yielded no evidence to support the fat-as-fuel view. It may turn out that excess fat, in women as in men, is little more than dead weight.

Women experience more injuries when they start running. Although these are thought to result from muscular weakness and athletic inexperience rather than inherent delicateness, such mishaps can nonetheless be discouraging. Women are more likely than men to be timid about taking up running. "For a woman who has not run a step since childhood," says Dr. Peter D. Wood of Stanford University, "initial embarrassment can be a problem. 'What will I look like?' 'What will the neighbors say?' The first step is the most difficult this woman will ever take as a runner, but once committed, slimmed down, toned up and confident—what a difference."

Positive Differences Women Vs. Men

Faced with the foregoing catalog of frailties, even a Gloria Steinem might conclude that, whatever their undoubted abilities in such sports as tennis and gymnastics, women simply are not meant for running. This is hardly the case. First of all, a similar list might readily be drawn up for men: excessive body weight, susceptibility to injury through over-training, and so forth. What do such lists prove? Only, perhaps, that a more benevolent deity could in his (or her) farsighted wisdom have designed us all like Bill Rodgers. Second, women runners do enjoy a number of advantages. They sweat more efficiently than men. In one hot-weather comparison of the sexes, only half the men were able to complete a four-hour work session. By contrast, 92 percent of the women were successful! The researchers concluded that women achieve proper thermoregulation with less sweat, perhaps because they are capable of a more precise sweating response.

Women, whatever injuries they suffer, seem to be no more subject to them than men, particularly when they are in shape. Not long ago Drs. Barry A. Franklin, Louis Lussier and Elsworth R. Buskirk reported on a study in which thirty-six sedentary women, aged twenty-nine to forty-seven, volunteered for a twelve-week conditioning program consisting of flexibility exercises, calisthenics, walking and running. The types and frequency of injury, according to the researchers, almost precisely paralleled those reported in earlier studies of male runners. A study at Annapolis, furthermore, showed a significant reduction in injuries as women's conditioning progressed. "Differences in performances between men and women," says Dr. Norbert Sander, "are far more the result of cultural sexual bias than physiological difference."

Other studies have shown that similarities between men and women runners are considerably more striking than the differences. When, for example, Edmund J. Burke and Florence C. Brush evaluated the aerobic power of thirteen women runners, all of them members of the Charger Track Club of Syracuse, New York, they found that it was virtually identical to that of young men of equal ability. Similarly, when Jack H. Wilmore and C. Harmon Brown compared top women distance runners with male runners of comparable achievement, they found that even differences in body fat were considerably less than had been expected. Well-trained women runners, it appears, do not carry nearly the fat handicap that had previously been reported. "The results suggest," said the researchers, "that the large differences observed between normal males and females in previous studies . . . are at least partially socially-culturally determined as opposed to being strictly of biological origin."

Finally, H. Harrison Clarke, editor of the *Physical Fitness Research Digest,* says psychological tests show that "male and female athletes are more alike than different in personality traits." Compared with nonathletic women, women who participate in athletics are more self-confident, better adjusted, and have greater self-control and psychological endurance.

Many writers on running, even otherwise enlightened ones, make a great to-do about the cosmetic benefits women derive from running, as if women as a sex were uniquely interested in how they look. It is true, of course, that vigorous exercise makes people, men as well as women, look better. It is, however, just as true that less visible benefits are equally important and equally valued. The typical woman, for example, finds unsuspected pleasures in athletic competition. At first she may hesitate to enter a race. "Women," writes Nancy Anderson in the newsletter of the New Orleans Track Club, "have been conditioned to be supportive and cooperative rather than self-seeking and competitive.

Many women equate competition with aggression and stressful battle for victory, qualities which they may feel are incompatible with the female personality and with the pleasure they find in non-competitive running." Eventually, however, they find that races are not the snarling, antagonistic enterprises they once seemed. Ms. Anderson continues: "Racing *is* aggressive, but we all, male and female, have aggressive impulses which can better be satisfied in honest, direct activities rather than more indirect, sometimes invidious ways. . . . So much in life seems inflexible and unchangeable, and part of the joy of running and especially racing is the realization that improvement and progress can be achieved."

Self-confidence and Control

Most women find, too, that running changes their attitudes toward themselves and even, for that matter, toward being women. Phoebe Jones, who in 1979 helped organize a conference on women's running, told the gathering, "Running is a statement to society. It is saying 'no' to always being on call, to sacrificing our daily runs for others' needs, and to the poverty and overwork so many of us face. When we run we are doing something for ourselves, and that is not in society's game plan. We regain control over our bodies and our lives through running." Should that seem an overpugnacious view of an essentially gentle sport, Dr. Gerald Besson's observation in *The Complete Woman Runner* is somewhat less so: "It is the female that bears an age-old burden of the subservient role in our culture. . . . Who does she see when she looks in the mirror but a reflection, not of self but of someone who is easily recognized by how well she plays the role she has accepted. She is someone's wife or sweetheart. Someone's mother. Someone's cook. Someone other than an individual in her own right. Running strips away all these sociocultural impositions and leaves the female runner quiet and alone with her true self." In a deft summary Janice Kaplan writes in *Women and Sports,* "The trouble so far in women's sports is that the athletes have been busy explaining, 'I do this *even though* I'm a woman,' while few have been wise enough to claim, 'This is *what it is* to be a woman.' "

Myths of Running for Women

Despite running's growing list of physical and psychological benefits, one old wives' tale persists with particular tenacity. It is that physical stress acts adversely on the female reproductive system, inflicting undesirable and even dangerous effects on both the menstrual cycle and pregnancy.

Current research, not to mention the experience of thousands of runners, suggests that this is simply untrue.

It is curious that exercise enjoys such a bad reputation in this respect, for there is plenty of contrary evidence. A half-dozen years ago, having reviewed much of the research on the gynecological ramifications of physical activity, Dr. Allan J. Ryan reported that sports participation usually produces no significant changes, either favorable or unfavorable, except that painful menstruation is less common among athletes than among nonathletes. More recently, Dr. Edwin Dale of the Emory University School of Medicine conducted a thorough inquiry into the effects of hard training on the menstrual cycle. In Dale's experiments volunteers, both athletes and nonathletes, were tested for the presence of a wide range of body chemicals during each phase of their cycles. Invariably, at some level of training intensity . . . the menstrual period became irregular or infrequent. Dale quotes one runner as saying, "My periods are absent now that I run more than four miles per day." Another said, "Since I have increased my mileage to 120 miles per week I have only three periods per year." Such changes might appear ominous for the childbearing futures of athletes if it were not for one fact: as soon as training is lessened, says Dale, normal hormone levels and physiological function can be expected to return.

Pregnancy and Running

So it is, too, with pregnancy. Running has nothing but excellent effects on healthy pregnant women. Coreen Nasenbeny of Fort Defiance, Arizona, told me how, despite neighborhood skepticism, she ran throughout her pregnancy: "Everyone in our community of well-educated professionals would ask in wide-eyed disbelief, 'Still running, Coreen?'—as though my activity were unnatural." The skepticism turned to awed admiration and even, she suspects, to a few conversions when, two weeks after her baby's birth, the same neighbors saw Mrs. Nasenbeny out running again. Medical authorities suggest that pregnancy is not the best time to start a running program, since it may impose unnecessary strain on a woman who has long been sedentary. If, on the other hand, a woman is already a runner when she becomes pregnant, most experts say there is no reason not to continue. They do, however, suggest running slowly and comfortably rather than trying to improve at that time.

Research suggests, incidentally, that hopes of giving one's offspring a head start on becoming an Olympic champion are not a good reason for running when you're pregnant. To see what might happen, researchers at the University of Iowa's Stress Physiology Laboratory required rats to exercise regularly during pregnancy. Their workouts did nothing, alas, to improve the aerobic capacity of their young.

As women more closely approach the running performances of men, the evidence grows that the training of women should probably not differ greatly from that of men. A few years ago Gail Campbell, having sent questionnaires to the fifty leading women marathon runners in the United States, compared the results with the findings in a similar survey of top men runners. The differences suggest one reason why until recently women ran more slowly than men:

Women Should Train More
To Run Faster

	WOMEN	MEN
Average miles for 8 weeks before fastest marathon	533	805
Minimum miles per week	46	74
Maximum miles per week	87	121
Average distance of lingest run	20	23.6
Number of runs greater than 20 miles	2.29	3.8

Today the signs are abundant that such differences in training are diminishing. Bill Mongovan, who was introduced at the beginning of this chapter, is convinced women should do more interval work and, after appropriate conditioning, should run greater distances than most of them currently do. Similarly, Dr. Joan Ullyot, an accomplished marathon runner and the author of *Women's Running,* wrote in *Runner's World,* "My feeling is that men and women can train along virtually identical lines . . . , since the psysiological principles that underlie training apply to both sexes." Bob Glover, co-author of *The Runner's Handbook,* agrees. "Women runners," he says, "do not need to be treated differently from their male counterparts. . . . It is not unusual to see a woman progress . . . faster than a man." Finally, a top runner named Patti Lyons, reflecting on the achievements of Grete Waitz, said, "She's making girls realize they can't work out like girls. They have to work out like athletes." Eventually, perhaps, even the International Olympic Committee will join the fold. Currently it permits women to compete at no distance greater than 1,500 meters, a little less than a mile. In the 1980s a more unnecessary restriction is scarcely imaginable. One respected researcher, Dr. E. C. Frederick of the University of Montana, recently predicted, on the basis of mathematical and physiological analysis, that by 1987 a woman will run a 2:17:17 marathon.

Don't Be Timid About Weight Training

In the past, you may have felt the need to include weight lifting as part of your training program, but may also have felt that it was "too masculine" or that a few muscles on your body might be contrary to being a woman. Nothing could be further from the truth.

During this training program, explore the possibility of including weight training. You may want to gain strength in a portion of your body you felt lacking more than the rest. It has been known for some time that women can increase their strength 50 to 75 percent. Some physiologists are even starting to think that, pound for pound, women are potentially *stronger* than men, since weight-lifting records show that lighter people tend to be more powerful in proportion to weight. A positive attitude about weight training can only enhance your position in the triathlon event . . . and at the same time, give a tone to your body you can be proud of.

Women's Triathlon Training

As stated on the opening page of this book . . . all situations pertaining to the masculine are also meant for the feminine, except in specific cases from time to time. Training schedules and methods work for the woman triathlete as well as the man. So therefore all of the training concepts are to be applied equally to both sexes. Distance formulas should hold true to both sexes without exception. Long slow distance followed by strength training and then speed training is the basic formula for the Swim-Bike-Run triathlon training. Due to the Equalizing effect the Multi Sport offers the participant, we know that a woman Ironman will emerge someday. We hope we will have contributed to this pleasurable happening.

WOMEN'S SECTION BIBLIOGRAPHY

Running for Health and Beauty: A Complete Guide for Women, Kathryn Lance. Bobb-Merrill Company, Inc. New York, New York, 1977.

The Complete Woman Runner, Total Woman's Fitness Guide, and *Women's Running* are available through Anderson World, Inc., 1400 Stierlin Road, Mountain View, Ca. 94043.

The Complete Book of Running Jim Fixx. Random House, New York 1977.

The Second Book of Running Jim Fixx. Random House, New York 1978.

Three things there are that ease the heart—water, green grass, and the beauty of woman.

—Frank Herbert, Dune

V

Triathlete Strength Training
for Swim, Bike and Run

Patricia Bragg believes in flexibility as per personal instructions of Bob Anderson, author of *The Complete Book of Stretching*.

Paul Bragg and Jack go through a workout in Jack LaLanne's personal gym in his home in the Hollywood Hills, California.

BOOK V

Total Body Strength Building on Nautilus Equipment

Most athlete's training should be a means of building strength for activities that are in no way related to lifting weights.

THE NAUTILUS CONCEPT OF HIGH-INTENSITY, brief and full-range exercise was originally developed through applications made with the barbell. The barbell, used properly, can be made to stimulate vast structural improvements throught the body. The barbell's correct application, however, remains a mystery to most laymen and bodybuilders alike.

Optimal barbell protocol was not thoroughly realized until the late 1960's. It was then that the Nautilus Training Principles emerged. But this new concept remained limited.

The Nautilus machine was introduced in early 1970. For each major muscular structure of the body, Nautilus provided a direct resistance source that was applied on a common rotary axis with the involved body joint. (The Nautilus cam was designed in order to vary the resistance in accordance with the muscle's positional resistance requirement (strength curve) throughout a full range of possible movement.) The barbell was not capable of rotary, direct, balanced and full-range resistance. Therefore, a correction of these faults was necessary.

There remains a great tendency to regard the Nautilus machines as a totally different exercise tool—they are not. A barbell can be a productive exercise tool when properly utilized and is a tool capable of providing work at a relatively high intensity (high force or great work quantity are not desirable). And such high intensity work is required for the stimulation of large-scale muscular growth. A Nautilus machine is a barbell from which many of the limitations have been removed. A Nautilus machine is merely a greatly-improved barbell, capable of providing harder, more intense work.

Many bodybuilders apply the principles inferred from their misconceived barbell training to a Nautilus machine. They incorrectly perform multiple sets and explosive single attempts. They totally disregard proper form. Bodybuilders commit these errors with any tool, with all equipment, exposing themselves to the risk of unnecessary injury and preventing a great measure of possible worthwhile results. Their training ideas are commonly erroneous.

Another common error is the incorporation of the split routine: train the upper body and the lower body on alternate days. This principle is analogous to alternately sleeping with one eye open and then the other, or trying to feed alternately different segments of the body with different meals. Bodybuilding posssesses the same requirements as any other physical training. A bodybuilder should train and then rest (at least forty-eight hours between successive workouts) the body as one entity, not in parts.

Be extremely careful when receiving advice from world-class bodybuilders. Listen to their comments, but remember that they are unique in genetic potential. They will achieve muscular size that others will find impossible regardless of the training program. A large part of their success may actually occur in spite of their training philosophy and methodology. Many "greats" could have attained muscular size and definition far beyond their lifetime best. This is often the case with any tool, especially when the trainee and the coach confuse quality with quantity in the program.

The barbell remains a productive, viable exercise tool. The innovation of manned flight did not replace the automobile. Flying is merely a more efficient mode of transportation. Likewise, the Nautilus machine is a more efficient exercise tool than the barbell ever can be. If we cannot adapt the body to an imperfect tool, we can adapt the tool to the body. Nautilus does that. But neither tool will ever approach its potential capability when its users fail to understand the mechanical and chemical requirements for muscular growth.

Nautilus machines are the only tool that provides all ten requirements for full-range exercise: positive work, negative work, rotary resistance, direct resistance, resistance in the fully contracted position, stretching, pre-stretching, automatically variable resistance, balanced resistance, and an unlimited speed of movement. The barbell offers six or seven of these requirements depending on the exercise.

The principles of high-intensity, low-force exercise apply with equal validity to all athletes, including bodybuilders. The difference in their muscular growth will be largely determined by their individual potential and best maximized by Nautilus equipment and training procedures.

The Present State of the Art

The Pullover Torso Machine was the first Nautilus machine, and the second and third . . . its development extended over a period of 22 years, and the first machine delivered to a customer was the 27th model. The exclusive features now incorporated in all Nautilus machines were outgrowths of the long, slow development of the Pullover machine. Certain basic features were required for the development of a practical airplane . . . lift, thrust and three-axis control . . . and until these requirements were understood and provided, the airplane remained a dream. Today all airplanes incorporate these same three basic features . . . as they must. The airplane is not the only means of transportation, but it certainly is the fastest.

A full-range exercise also has certain basic requirements . . . lacking any one of the required features, full-range exercise is simply impossible. Exercise can be provided in a number of ways . . . but full-range exercise can be provided in only one way. Nautilus machines provide the only source of full-range exercise, and the Pullover was the first Nautilus machine. Not the only source of exercise, but the only source of FULL-RANGE exercise, and certainly the fastest and most productive mode of exercise. Early attempts to build an airplane failed because the builders did not understand the basic requirements of flight . . . today, many forms of exercise fail for much the same reason; because the designers of the equipment do not understand the basic requirements for productive exercise. If an airplane fails to fly, its failure is immediately obvious . . . and the market for such an attempt at flight is zero, so our airports are not cluttered with thousands of unsuccessful airplanes, failures. And if the requirements for productive exercise are clearly understood, then it is just as easy to recognize an unsuccessful form of exercise . . . yet literally millions of worthless and near-worthless exercise devices are cluttering the homes and gyms in this country alone. Because many people do not understand the basic requirements.

Heavy Resistance

Actually, there is only one requirement for increasing strength . . . "heavy resistance through-out a full range of possible movement." Barbells provided the first practical source of heavy resistance for exercise . . . and the results of barbell exercises were (and are) far superior to any earlier form of exercise. But remember, HEAVY RESISTANCE alone is not enough . . . it must be provided throughout the FULL RANGE of possible movement. Barbell exercises do not meet that requirement, for several reasons . . . (1) because barbells provide "stright-line" resistance, while a rotary form of resistance is required . . . (2) because barbells provide an unchanging amount of resistance during the movement, while variable resistance is required . . . (3) because barbells cannot provide resistance directly against the body-parts that are moved by muscular contraction.

As a result of these failures, barbells provide exercise for only a small part of the involved muscles . . . full-range exercise is utterly impossible with a barbell. In some barbell exercises, resistance is provided at the start of a movement . . . OR, at the finish of a movement . . . but never at both ends of a movement. And in most barbell exercises, there is no resistance at either end of a movement.

If you can "lock-out" and hold the weight in the finishing position of an exercise, then it is obvious that no resistance is provided in that position. Such lock-outs occur in most barbell exercises . . . in squats, leg presses, bench presses, standing presses, curls and many other exercises. A lock-out occurs because the effective resistance has been removed from the muscles and is supported by the bones . . . a straight-bone support. When such a position is reached, the muscles can relax without dropping the weight. And since no resistance is available, no exercise is provided for the muscles. "Sticking points" are another sign of failure in an exercise . . . clear proof that the resistance is too heavy in some areas of movement, and too light in other areas of movement. Such sticking points are encountered in almost all barbell exercises. The result being that you are limited to an amount of resistance that you can handle at the sticking point . . . not enough resistance during the rest of the exercise. A small part of the muscle is worked heavily, but most of the muscle is exercised only lightly . . . and some of the muscle is not worked at all. Thus a barbell provides proper exercise for only part of the muscular structure . . . and yet barbell exercises are certainly capable of increasing strength and muscular development, eventually.

The Pulley & Lever

Thirty years ago we asked ourselves just what would happen if the entire mass of a muscle was exposed to heavy exercise. But the answer was a long time coming . . . because the necessary equipment did not exist. Redirecting the resistance by the use of pulleys was the first attempt in the direction of providing the proper mode of exercise . . . but this failed; primarily because the resistance was still "straight line" resistance. Although the direction of pull was changed, it still pulled in only one direction. Such pulley and lever machines did offer some advantages by comparison to barbells, but the advantages were limited to improvements in safety, convenience and appearance. Insofar as results were concerned, the exercises provided by such machines were little, if any, better than barbell movements . . . and, in many cases, the results were worse.

Nevertheless, the use of pulleys, levers and quick-change weight-stacks did lead to a far more widespread acceptance of heavy exercise. Conventional exercise machines were thus partially responsible for the growth of sports-connected strength training. But the problem with such machines was, and remains, the fact that they were simply copies of barbell exercises . . . attempts to improve the safety and convenience of a barbell.

Perspective

The entire approach to the situation was wrong . . . efforts were expended in the wrong direction . . . for many years, the people in the exercise equipment business continued to work within the limitations of a barbell. INSTEAD . . . they should have been working within the limitations of human muscles. They should have tried to determine the requirements of muscles. And, in far too many cases . . . "the MEANS became the END." Instead of lifting weights in order to become stronger, many people have tried to become stronger . . . IN ORDER TO LIFT MORE WEIGHT. Competitive weightlifting is a "means" . . . and an "end." The end result being an attempt to lift more weight than other men, in a contest . . . and the required means being the practice of exactly the same lifts that will be contested.

But most people who exercise with weights are not competitive weightlifters, are not concerned with just how much weight they can lift in a particular fashion . . . or, at least, SHOULD NOT be concerned. Instead, for most people, exercise should be the means of building strength for activities that are in no way related to lifting weights.

Lifting maximum weights, as in competitive weightlifting, certainly requires strength ... but also requires skill. A skill that can be developed in no other way. Which skill must be developed by the practice of lifting maximum weights. Skill that is of no slightest value for any other purpose except lifting weights. Apart from being a waste of time and effort, the development of a worthless skill is usually not bad in itself ... but in this instance, it is. Because it is dangerous, it exposes the trainee to great risk of injury FOR NO REASON. Every single one of the actually worthwhile results that can be produced by exercise can be, and SHOULD BE, produced with little or no risk of injury ... and the lifting of maximum weights is NOT THE WAY TO DO IT.

So the invention of the barbell was certainly a valuable contribution to the field of exercise ... until its value was perverted. The barbell taught us a great deal ... but should have taught us more. Used properly, the barbell is capable of safely producing very worthwhile results ... the problem arises from the fact that very few people use a barbell properly. But even when it is used properly, a barbell has certain definite limitations. So if the value of the barbell is clearly understood, and if the limitations of a barbell are also understood, it then becomes possible to take the next step ... an evolutionary step, a step up to a type of equipment that provides the actual value of a barbell without the limitations of a barbell.

And just what is the actual "value" of a barbell? It provides heavy resistance against the movement produced by muscular contraction. And what are the limitations of a barbell? Resistance is NOT provided against full-range movement. For several reasons. When those reasons are understood, it then becomes possible to build a type of equipment WITHOUT LIMITATIONS ... equipment that provides heavy resistance against the FULL-RANGE movement that is produced by full muscular contraction. The result being a form of exercise for the entire muscle, instead of merely part of a muscle.

Requirements of Full-Range Exercise

The Nautilus Pullover Torso Machine was the first successful tool designed to provide truly full-range exercise, total exercise. "Function dictates design" ... the use of round wheels is not an accident; round wheels are an absolute requirement for a smooth ride ... and, until that requirement was clearly understood, practical transportation remained an impossible dream. Full-range exercise requires a ROTARY form of resistance ... resistance that rotates on a common axis with the body-part that is directly moved by the muscle being exercised. Full-range exercise also requires resistance with a range-of-movement that actually exceeds the possible range-of-movement of the involved joint ... if this requirement is not provided, then the factors of "stretching" for increasing flexibility and "pre-stretching" for inducing high-intensity muscular contraction are not provided, since your available strength varies throughout the movement, full-range exercise requires a form of resistance that instantly and automatically varies in accord with your changing strength. Finally, the resistance must be DIRECTLY applied against the body-part that is actually moved by the muscle being exercised.

Chinning type exercises have been used for many years in an attempt to develop the large muscles of the torso ... but such exercises have severe limitations, for several reasons. ONE ... the large muscles of the torso are attached to and directly move the upper arms. DIRECT application of resistance thus requires a form of resistance opposed to the movement of the upper arms ... in practice, the resistance must be applied against the elbows. In chinning type exercises, the resistance is applied against the hands ... the result being that the muscles of the arms and hands become a limiting factor. A point of failure is reached in such exercises when the smaller, weaker muscles of the arms and hands become exhausted ... a point of failure that is reached long before the much larger and stronger muscles of the torso have been worked properly. So the development of the torso muscles is constantly limited by the weaker muscles of the arms and hands.

Before the invention of a squat rack, the development of the legs was limited by strength of the arms . . . a man was forced to shoulder the barbell before squatting. . . . The range-of-movement in chinning type exercises is limited to the mid-range of possible movement. Stretching is not provided in the starting position . . . and full muscular contraction is not provided in the finishing position. . . . The torso muscles directly move the upper arms, so we are concerned only with the movement of the upper arms themselves; what happens to the hands and forearms is of no slightest concern, so long as the hands and forearms do not limit the movement of the upper arms.

In chinning type exercises with a normal grip, the upper arms move through an arc of approximately 118 degrees. In "behind-the-neck" chinning, the range-of-movement of the upper arms is even less, approximately 60 degrees. . . . If a wide grip is used in behind-neck chinning, the range-of-movement may be as little as 45 degrees. Regardless of the style of chinning practiced, the movement is NOT a full-range movement.

Full-range exercise for these muscles (or for any muscle) requires movement against heavy resistance throughout a full range of possible movement . . . the movement must start with muscles in a fully stretched position and end with the muscles in a fully contracted position. Requirements that are utterly impossible to provide in chinning type exercises. When the resistance is applied directly against the upper arms (against the elbows), there is then no limitation in range-of-movement. Recently, a member of the Nautilus staff demonstrated a range-of-movement of 270 degrees. Truly full-range exercise for the muscles of the torso . . . a degree of flexibility that is a direct product of such full-range exercise, impossible to produce in any other way. . . . Chinning type exercises do provide variable resistance, but it is random variation produced by the constantly changing leverage factors that result from movement. As a consequence, the resistance is too light in some areas of movement and too heavy in other areas . . . "sticking points" are encountered where the resistance is too heavy, and you are thus forced to limit the resistance to an amount that you can handle at the sticking point.

This is clear proof that the resistance is too light in every other position . . . the muscles are being worked properly at the sticking point, but do not have enough resistance at any other point throughout the movement. The actual range-of-movement may thus be 118 degrees . . . but the effective range of exercise may be as little as 10 or 15 degrees of movement. When the above limiting factors that are encountered in chinning type exercises are clearly understood, then the solution is obvious . . . (1) the resistance must be DIRECTLY applied to the upper arms (the elbows) . . . (2) the resistance must rotate on a common axis with the shoulder joints . . . (3) the resistance must instantly and automatically vary in accord with your available strength in different positions throughout the movement.

The Nautilus Pullover Torso Machine

The Nautilus Pullover Torso Machine provides the above requirements, in the only possible manner . . . "fuction dictates design," and the functions of the torso muscles dictated design of the Pullover Torso Machine. The development of the Pullover Torso Machine was not a sudden "breakthrough" . . . instead, it was a slow, step-by-step process of evolutionary development. Solving one problem made us aware of other problems . . . the solution of which presented us with even more problems; until, finally, all of the requirements were provided . . . which happened, COULD ONLY HAPPEN, when all of the problems were understood and solved. Serious attempts in the direction of solving the problems involved in providing full-range exercise for the muscles of the torso were first undertaken in 1948 . . . and the first truly practical Pullover Torso Machine was built in 1967, nineteen years later. In the meantime, other people were working on similar problems . . . from another angle; which work led to the development of conventional type exercise machines. Resistance was provided in the form of self-contained, quick-change, pin-selector type weight stacks. It was no longer necessary to add or remove barbell plates; instead, the required amount of resistance could be provided by moving a pin from one hole to another . . . so the speed of use, and thus the convenience, was greatly increased.

Resistance was "redirected" from the vertical, "up and down" direction provided by a barbell ... this use of pulleys making it possible to perform exercises that were difficult or impossible to perform with a barbell. The resistance was "guided" by the use of guide-rods ... removing the requirement for balance that is involved in almost all barbell exercises. Which features, in general, were improvements ... but they were primarily improvements in convenience and safety; little or nothing was done in the way of improving the results of such exercise ... and equal degree of results could still be produced by a barbell. And, in some cases, a barbell would produce better results.

BECAUSE ... such exercises still had all of the same problems encountered in barbell exercises. The resistance was still "indirectly" applied to secondary body-parts, instead of being directly applied to the prime body-part ... the resistance was still straight-line in nature, instead of rotating on a common axis with the involved joints ... the resistance is still varied in a random manner as a result of changing leverage, instead of variation in proportion to available strength ... sticking points are still encountered ... areas of little or no resistance were still involved. In short ... FULL-RANGE EXERCISE WAS NOT PROVIDED.

The Leg Extension Machine

A few hesitant attempts at providing a rotary form of resistance were attempted ... the leg extension machine being one example, and the leg curl machine being another. But even a casual examination of these machines makes it immediately obvious that the designers simply did not understand the requirements. A conventional leg extension machine is a perfect example of this lack of understanding. In general appearance, at first glance ... the conventional leg extension machine seems to provide a rotary form of exercise; but look closer, appearances can be misleading ... and in this case, they are. The resistance is "directly" applied to the prime body-part, the lower legs, as it should be ... so far, so good, a start in the right direction. The axis of rotation of the machine is situated in line with the knee, as it should be ... another step in the right direction. ... At that point the designer went astray. Two sources of resistance are provided in a conventional leg extension machine: the primary source of resistance is a built-in stack of weights ... and this resistance is directed against the movement-arm of the machine by a series of pulleys. Directed in such a way that the "direction of pull" is approximately horizontal, parallel with the floor. The result being that DIRECT resistance is provided only at the start of the movement.

... As the direction of movement changes, as it must, the resulting change in the direction of pull of the resistance causes the amount of the resistance to rapidly drop off. In effect, the resistance is heavy at the start of the movement ... and then gets lighter at the end of the movement. ... The secondary source of resistance is provided in the form of a horn on the front of the movement-arm; a pin put there for the purpose of holding additional resistance in the form of barbell plates. And the geometry of this resistance source is exactly backward to the primary resistance source. Barbell plates added to the pin provide literally ZERO resistance in the starting position ... and provide direct resistance only in the finishing position. So the evolutionary development of this machine is obvious; the machine was first built with only one resistance source, the weight stack ... but, when it was seen that the weight stack did not provide enough resistance for this exercise, it was then decided to add more resistance in the form of barbell plates. And it is just as obvious that the designers of the machine remained unaware of the fact that one source of resistance was providing INCREASING resistance while the other source was providing DECREASING resistance.

Other Machines

Rotary MOVEMENT is not enough ... you must also have a rotary form of resistance against that movement. The conventional leg extension machine provides rotary movement of the lower legs, and it directly applies the resistance against the lower legs ... but it does not provide a rotary form of resistance.

A man named Bob Clark built a curling machine that did provide a rotary form of resistance, so it went a step more in the right direction . . . but again failed, because it was based on a round pulley; the resistance was direct and constant throughout the movement . . . all well and good, but it did not vary in proportion to your changing strength in various positions. The resistance was thus far too heavy at the start of the movement and too light at every other point in the movement. The so-called "butterfly" machine was another attempt in the direction of providing rotary form, full-range exercise . . . but it failed also, for the same reason that Clark's curling machine failed, and for another reason. It also failed because the location of the arm pads literally prevented a full-range movement. The pads prevented the user from reaching a position of full muscular contraction.

So we were certainly not the only people who were aware of the shortcomings of barbell exercises, and a long list of exercise machines and devices have been built by a number of people . . . but if the results of the developmental work on the part of other people is any clue to their knowledge, then it is obvious that their thinking is still being limited by the same problems encountered in barbell exercises. But a clear understanding of the requirements for truly full-range exercise did not come to us in a moment of flashing insight either . . . instead, it was a long, slow process.

The Pullover Torso Machine was the first result of our knowledge of the actual requirements for full-range exercise . . . and, once those requirements were understood, and the related problems were solved, it then became possible to apply the same principles to the development of almost any muscular structure. The mechanical problems were somewhat different in each individual case, but the basic principles remained the same . . . all muscles function in the same manner, producing movement of a related body-part by contraction, so the requirements for muscular development are the same regardless of which muscle is involved.

Isokinetics

. . . Along came "Isokinetics." The claims made on behalf of isokenetic exercises were many and varied . . . (1) it provided full-range exercise . . . (2) it provides a higher intensity of muscular contraction . . . (3) it provides a very safe form of exercise. None of the above three claims are true, for obvious reasons. Full-range exercise is utterly impossible without the "back pressure" of a force pulling against your muscles prior to the start of movement. Full-range exercise is also impossible without resistance in the fully-contracted position at the end of an exercise movement. Isokinetic exercises do not have "back pressure" . . . and thus stretching of the joints and pre-stretching of the involved muscles is not provided by such a form of exercise.

Secondly, without back pressure there is no resistance in the position of full-muscular contraction at the end of an exercise . . . again, isokinetic exercise fails to provide this requirement. Since there is no resistance at either end of a movement, isokinetic exercise obviously is not a full-range form of exercise. Next claim . . . that isokinetic exercise provides a higher level of intensity. Also invalid on the face of it, and for the same reason; there is no back pressure at the start of the movement . . . back pressure that is required for pre-stretching the involved muscles. It is a well-established fact that pre-stretching of a muscle is required for a maximum muscular contraction. So again the claim is false.

Final claim . . . that isokinetic resistance provides the safest form of exercise. When, in fact, it is probably the most dangerous form of exercise. Dangerous for two reasons . . . (1) because it results in greatly elevated blood pressure . . . and (2) because the involved forces are far higher than either necessary or desirable. Or, at least, the forces will be higher if the user performs the exercise in the manner suggested by the makers of isokinetic dces.

So all of the first three claims are patently false, obviously untrue . . . but some of the other claims being made in regard to isokinetic exercises are true. For example, it is claimed that such exercises produce little or nothing in the way of muscular soreness . . . and this lack of resulting soreness is attributed to the fact that isokinetic exercises involve no eccentric contraction (negative work). Both of these statements are true . . . but they certainly are not advantages. The total lack of negative work is the very root of most of the problems encountered in isokinetic exercises. It is negative work that provides stretching . . . negative work that provides pre-stretching . . . negative work that provides resistance in the position of full-muscular contraction. Without the back pressure that produces negative work, full-range exercise is simply IMPOSSIBLE. Obviously being clearly aware of this major shortcoming in their exercises, the makers of isokinetic devices engaged in a massive advertising program in an attempt to convince the public that negative work was somehow "bad" . . . of no value, to be avoided, dangerous.

After reading such statements for a year or so, and being clearly aware of the actual facts all the time . . . we decided to run some tests to determine the value of "negative only" exercise, as compared to normal exercise which provides both negative and positive work. When these tests were conducted, it was quickly obvious that negative work is actually the most important part of exercise . . . for the purpose of increasing muscular strength. So, in fact, the makers of isokinetic exercises had removed the most important part of exercise . . . and then pointed to the result as an improvement. Which is NOT meant to imply that positive work has no value as a part of exercise . . . it certainly does; but it is not as important as negative work for the purpose of increasing strength. And REMEMBER . . . full-range exercise is utterly IMPOSSIBLE without negative work. Not "difficult" . . . not "less productive" . . . utterly IMPOSSIBLE. Negative work does result in muscular soreness when used by a previously untrained individual . . . but this is apparently the unavoidable price of worthwhile results; and in any case, the soreness will be gone in two or three days . . . and will not return so long as you continue training on a fairly regular basis.

An isokinetic form of resistance could easily be incorporated into Nautilus Machines . . . and doing so would reduce the weight, the complexity and the cost of the machines, thus providing a much larger market. But this will never be done . . . BECAUSE, using an isokinetic form of resistance requires the total removal of negative work. The result being a mid-range, positive-only form of exercise with very little value. The only real advantage provided by isokinetic resistance is the fact that it does not require a heavy and expensive stack of weights . . . instead of weights, a simple and relatively inexpensive friction device is used. This "advantage" of course, is purchased at the price of almost total destruction of the function . . . so it is clearly no bargain, not even a compromise worthy of serious consideration.

Over a period of more than twenty years we gradually became clearly aware of all the requirements for a perfect form of exercise . . . these requirements are as follows:

Conventional exercises provide only one of those absolute requirements (negative-work potential) and thus conventional exercises are NOT full-range exercises, are NOT proper exercises, are nowhere near as productive as they should be in proportion to the amount of time and effort devoted to them.

Isokinetic exercises have NONE of these features and thus isokinetic resistance is the least productive form of exercise for any purpose.

Nautilus provides all of these requirements. Nautilus is the ONLY full-range exercise. Nautilus is the ONLY source of "total" exercise. For additional information please contact Nautilus Sports/ Medical Industries, P.O. Box 1783, DeLand, Florida 32720. Telephone (904) 228-2884. Outside of Florida call toll free: 1-800-874-8941.

Nautilus Routines the Same for All Athletes

At Nautilus Sports/Medical Industries, we receive many inquiries concerning the best training routines for football players, runners, basketball players, women, bodybuilders, Training Triathletes, losing weight, gaining weight, and so on. In designing a routine, you must first analyze the specific sport or activity you're involved in and determine the major muscle groups that are directly involved. The next step is to work those involved muscles throughout a full range of movement on Nautilus machines.

Almost all sports involve the contraction of every major muscle group in the human body. In other words, there is little difference between the Nautilus exercise routine that I would recommend for a 260-pound football player, a 190-pound bodybuilder, or a 120-pound housewife.

Meanwhile, it is important to understand that there is no single best routine. There are many best routines. Variety is not only the spice of life, but also the spice of exercise!

The following routines were designed for use in training centers or gymnasiums that have the basic Nautilus equipment. Within reason, substitutions can be made if certain Nautilus machines are not available.

Most beginning trainees should start with Basic Workout 1 and continue with it for at least a month. After the first month, they should start alternating 1 with 2, 3, 4, and 5. After two more months of training on the basic workouts, any of the other workouts can be used. Additional information about training on Nautilus equipment (including questions and answers) can be found in the first book in this series: *Strength-Training Principles.*

Nautilus Training Principles

General procedures to be followed on all machines where the regular (positive-negative) form of exercise is performed:

1. On any machine where seat adjustments or body positioning can be varied, make certain that the rotational axis of the cam is directly parallel to the rotational axis (joint) of the body part that is being moved.
2. Position your body in a straightly aligned manner. Avoid twisting or shifting your weight during the movement.
3. Never squeeze hand grips tightly, but maintain a loose, comfortable grip (a tight grip elevates blood pressure). Also practice relaxing the muscles that are not involved in an exercise, especially your facial muscles.
4. Lift the resistance (positive work) to the count of two . . . pause . . . lower the resistance (negative work) slowly and smoothly while counting to four.
5. For full-range strength and flexibility (and protection against injury) your range of movement on each machine should be as great as possible.
6. Breathe normally. Try not to hold your breath while straining.
7. Perform each exercise for 8 to 12 repetitions.

    a. Begin with a weight you can comfortably do 8 times.
    b. Stay with that weight until you can perform 12 strict repetitions. On the following workout, increase the weight (approximately 5%) and go back to 8 repetitions.
    c. Ideally, on every workout you should progress in repetitions and/or resistance.

8. For best cardiorespiratory (heart-lungs) conditioning, move quickly from machine to machine (this speed does not apply to the actual exercises). The longer the rest between machines, the less effective the cardiorespiratory conditioning.
9. When possible, follow your routine as the exercises are numbered on your workout sheet; however, any time the machine you are to do next is being used, go to another exercise and then return to the machine that was in use.
10. All compound and double machines were designed to make use of the pre-exhaustion principle (where a single-joint exercise is used to pre-exhaust a given muscle and a multiple-joint exercise is used to force the exhausted muscle to work even harder); therefore, it is important to move very quickly (in less than 3 seconds) from the primary exercise to the secondary exercise.

11. Your training session should include a maximum of 12 exercises, 4 to 6 for the lower body and 6 to 8 for the upper body (a compound machine counts as two exercises).
12. Exercise the larger muscle groups first and proceed down to the smaller muscle groups (hips, thighs, back, shoulders, chest, arms, abdominals, and neck).
13. Your entire workout should take from 20 to 30 minutes.
14. The time lapse between exercise sessions should be at least 48 hours and not more than 96 hours.

Hip and Back Machine Duosymmetric/Polycontractile

BUTTOCKS AND LOWER BACK

1. Enter machine from front by separating movement arms.
2. Lay on back with both legs over roller pads.
3. Align hip joints with axes of cams.
4. Fasten seat belt and grasp handles lightly.
5. Seat belt should be snug, but not too tight, as back must be arched at completion of movement.
6. From bent-legged position, extend both legs and at same time push back with arms.
7. Holding one leg at full extension, allow other leg to bend and come back as far as possible.
8. Stretch.
9. Push out until it joins other leg at extension.
10. Pause, arch lower back, and contract buttocks.
11. Repeat with other leg.

Important: In contracted position, keep legs straight, knees together, and toes pointed.

Hip and Back Machine Super Geared

BUTTOCKS AND LOWER BACK

1. Lay on back with both legs over roller pads.
2. Fasten seat belt (snug but not tight).
3. Crank hips into starting position by pulling vertical handle.
4. Align hip joints with axes of cams.
5. Grasp handles beside hips.
6. From bent-legged position, extend both legs and at same time push back with arms.
7. Knees should be together, legs straight, and toes pointed.
8. Pause, arch lower back, and contract buttocks.
9. Slowly return to stretched position and repeat.
10. Eject from machine by pressing forward on horizontal handle below cranking handle.

Compound Leg Machine

FRONTAL THIGHS OR QUADRICEPS

Leg Extension

1. In a seated position, place feet behind roller pads with knees snug against seat.
2. Adjust seat back to comfortable position.
3. Keep head and shoulders against seat back.
4. Straighten both legs smoothly.
5. Pause.
6. Slowly lower resistance and repeat.
7. After final repetition, immediately do leg press.

Compound Leg Machine

QUADRICEPS, HAMSTRINGS, AND BUTTOCKS

Leg Press

1. Sit erect and pull seat back forward.
2. Flip down foot pads.
3. Place both feet on pads with toes pointed slightly inward.
4. Straighten both legs in a controlled manner.
5. Return to stretched position and repeat.

Important: Avoid tightly gripping handles and do not grit teeth or tense neck or face muscles during either movement.

Leg Curl Machine

HAMSTRINGS

1. Lay face down on machine.
2. Place feet under roller pads.
3. Lightly grasp handles to keep body from moving.
4. Curl legs and try to touch heels to buttocks.
5. When lower legs are perpendicular to bench, lift buttocks to increase movement.
6. Pause at point of full muscular contraction.
7. Slowly lower resistance and repeat.

Important: Top of foot should be flexed toward knee throughout movement.

Pullover/Torso Arm Machine

LATISSIMUS DORSI MUSCLES OF THE BACK AND
OTHER TORSO MUSCLES, INCLUDING ABDOMINALS

Pullover

1. Adjust seat so shoulder joints are in line with axes of cams.
2. Assume erect position and fasten seat belt tightly.
3. Leg press foot pedal until elbow pads are about chin level.
4. Place elbows on pads.
5. Hands should be open and resting on curved portion of bar.
6. Remove legs from pedal and slowly rotate elbows as far back as possible.
7. Stretch.
8. Rotate elbows down until bar touches stomach.
9. Pause.
10. Slowly return to stretched position and repeat.
11. After final repetition, immediately do pulldown.

Important: Look straight ahead during movement. Do not move head or torso. Do not grip tightly with hands.

Who walks with beauty has no need of fear;
The sun and moon and stars keep pace with him;
Invisible hands restore the ruined year,
And time, itself, grows beautifully dim.
—David Morton

Pullover/Torso Arm Machine

LATISSIMUS DORSI OF BACK
AND BICEPS OF UPPER ARMS

Torso Arm Pulldown

1. Lower seat to bottom for maximum stretch.
2. Grasp overhead bar with palms-up grip.
3. Keep head and shoulders against seat back.
4. Pull bar to chest.
5. Pause.
6. Slowly return to stretched position and repeat.

Pullover Machine Duosymmetric/Polycontractile

LATISSIMUS DORSI MUSCLES OF THE BACK AND
OTHER TORSO MUSCLES, INCLUDING ABDOMINALS

1. Adjust seat so shoulder joints are in line with axes of cams.
2. Assume erect position and fasten seat belt tightly.
3. Move both movement arms to mid-range position and place elbows on pads.
4. Hands should be open and resting on curved portion of bars.
5. From mid-range position, rotate both elbows down until fully-contracted position of back is reached.
6. Holding one arm ("lat" muscle) at full contraction, allow other arm to rotate as far back as possible.
7. Stretch.
8. Rotate stretched arm down until it reaches contracted position.
9. Pause and contract "lat" muscles by pushing back with elbows.
10. Repeat with other arm.

Important: Look straight ahead during movement. Do not move head or torso. Do not grip tightly with hands.

Behind Neck/Torso Arm Machine

LATISSIMUS DORSI OF BACK
AND BICEPS OF UPPER ARMS

Behind Neck

1. Adjust seat so shoulder joints are in line with axes of cams.
2. Fasten seat belt.
3. Place back of upper arms (triceps area) between padded movement arms.
4. Cross forearms behind neck.
5. Move both arms downward until perpendicular to floor.
6. Pause.
7. Slowly return to crossed-arm position behind neck and repeat.
8. After final repetition, immediately do behind neck and repeat.

Important: Be careful not to bring arms or hands to front of body.

BEHIND NECK PULLDOWN

1. Lean forward and grasp overhead bar with parallel grip.
2. Keeping elbows back, pull bar behind neck.
3. Pause.
4. Slowly return to starting position and repeat.

Rowing Torso Machine

DELTOIDS AND TRAPEZIUS

1. Sit with back toward weight stack.
2. Place arms between pads and cross arms.
3. Bend arms in rowing fashion as far back as possible.
4. Pause.
5. Slowly return to starting position and repeat.

Important: Keep arms parallel to floor at all times.

Double Chest Machine

PECTORALIS MAJORS OF THE CHEST
AND DELTOIDS OF SHOULDERS

Arm Cross

1. Adjust seat until shoulders (when elbows are together) are directly under axes of overhead cams.
2. Fasten seat belt.
3. Place forearms behind and firmly against movement arm pads.
4. Lightly grasp handles (thumb should be around handle) and keep head against seat back.
5. Push with forearms and try to touch elbows together in front of chest.
6. Pause.
7. Slowly lower resistance and repeat.
8. After final repetition, immediately do decline press.

Double Chest Machine

CHEST, SHOULDERS, AND
TRICEPS OF ARMS

Decline Press

1. Use foot pedal to raise handles into starting position.
2. Grasp handles with parallel grip.
3. Keep head back and torso erect.
4. Press bars forward in controlled fashion.
5. Slowly lower resistance keeping elbows wide.
6. Stretch in bottom position and repeat pressing movement.

Double Shoulder Machine

DELTOIDS AND TRICEPS

Lateral Raise

1. Adjust seat so shoulder joints are in line with axes of cams.
2. Fasten seat belt.
3. Pull handles back until knuckles touch pads.
4. Lead with elbows and raise both arms until parallel with floor.
5. Pause.
6. Slowly lower resistance and repeat.
7. After final repetition, immediately do overhead press.

Important: Keep knuckles against pads and elbows high at all times.

Overhead Press

1. Grasp handles above shoulders.
2. Press handles overhead.
3. Slowly lower resistance keeping elbows wide and repeat.

Important: Do not arch back. Thighs should be resting on seat throughout both exercises.

Biceps/Triceps Machine (plate loading)

BICEPS OF UPPER ARMS,
TRICEPS OF UPPER ARMS

Biceps Curl

1. Enter machine from left side.
2. Place elbows on pad and in line with axis of cam.
3. Grasp bar with hands together and palms up.
4. Smoothly curl bar until it reaches neck.
5. Pause.
6. Slowly return to stretched position and repeat.

Important: Lean back at full extension to insure stretching.

Triceps Extension

1. Adjust seated position (with pads if necessary) until shoulders are on same level as elbows.
2. Place elbows in line with axis of cam and hands (with thumbs up) on pads.
3. Straighten arms smoothly.
4. Pause.
5. Slowly return to stretched position and repeat.

Compound Position Biceps Machine

BICEPS OF UPPER ARMS

1. Adjust seat so both elbows are in line with axes of cams.
2. Place thighs on seat.
3. Arms should be fully extended as hand grips are lightly grasped.
4. Curl one arm behind neck.
5. Pause.
6. Slowly lower resistance.
7. Repeat with other arm.
8. Movement arms can also be curled together.

Compound Position Triceps Machine

TRICEPS OF UPPER ARMS

1. Adjust seat so elbows are in line with axis of cam.
2. Keep elbows against pads, head and shoulders against seat back, and thighs on seat.
3. Lightly grasp handles with sides of hands on pads.
4. Smoothly extend arms.
5. Pause.
6. Slowly return to stretched position and repeat.

Important: For proper performance, elbows must be held against pads at all times.

Omni Biceps Machine

BICEPS OF UPPER ARM

1. Place elbows on pad and in line with axis of cam.
2. Adjust seat so shoulders are slightly below elbows.
3. Wrists should be under pads and palms open.
4. Twist (supinate) hands as resistance is curled.
5. Keep torso and head back.
6. Pause in contracted position.
7. Slowly lower resistance and repeat.

Important: Exercise may be performed in negative-only fashion by lifting resistance with legs and lowering with arms. Exercise may be performed in negative-accentuated fashion by lifting resistance with both arms and lowering with only one arm.

Omni Triceps Machine

TRICEPS OF UPPER ARM

1. Adjust seat bottom so shoulders are slightly below elbows.
2. Adjust seat back so elbows are in line with axis of cam.
3. Pads of movement arm should be on wrists.
4. Keep thumbs up and head back.
5. Straighten arms smoothly.
6. Pause.
7. Slowly lower resistance and repeat.

Important: Exercise may be performed in negative-only fashion by lifting resistance with legs and lowering with arms. Exercise may be performed in negative-accentuated fashion by lifting resistance with both arms and lowering with only one arm.

4-Way Neck Machine

Anterior Flexion

FRONT, BACK, AND SIDES OF NECK

1. Face machine.
2. Adjust seat so nose is in center of pads.
3. Stabilize torso by lightly gripping handles.
4. Smoothly move head toward chest.
5. Pause.
6. Slowly return to stretched position and repeat.

Posterior Extension

1. Back of head should contact middle of pads.
2. Stabilize torso by lightly grasping handles.
3. Extend head as far back as possible.
4. Pause.
5. Slowly return to stretched position and repeat.

Lateral Contraction

1. Left ear should be in center of pads.
2. Stabilize torso by lightly grasping handles.
3. Smoothly move head toward left shoulder.
4. Pause.
5. Keep shoulders square.
6. Slowly return to stretched position and repeat.
7. Reverse procedure for right side.

Rotary Neck Machine

ROTATION OF THE NECK AND HEAD TO THE RIGHT AND LEFT

1. In a seated position (facing away from machine) move head between pads.
2. Adjust head pads to a snug position by pulling overhead lever from right to left.
3. The resistance in this machine is provided by the user through the use of hand levers. Negative-only exercise can be provided by pressure on either hand lever, which will force the head to turn. This turning pressure is resisted by the neck muscles.
4. Pushing with the right-hand lever (or pulling with the left-hand lever) forces the neck and head to rotate to the left . . . and vice versa.
5. Perform 6 negatives-only repetitions to the right, and 6 negative-only repetitions to the left in an alternate fashion.
6. Release head pads by pulling overhead lever from left to right.

Important: Avoid twisting shoulders during movement.

Neck and Shoulder Machine

TRAPEZIUS AND BACK OF NECK

1. In a seated position, place forearms between pads.
2. Keep palms open and back of hands pressed against bottom pads.
3. Straighten torso until weight stack is lifted (seat may be raised with elevation pads).
4. Smoothly shrug shoulders as high as possible.
5. Pause.
6. Slowly return to stretched position and repeat.

Important: Keep elbows by sides when shrugging. Do not lean back or try to stand while doing the movement. Do not rest weights on stack during movement.

Multi-Exercise Machine

Calf Raise

1. Adjust belt comfortably around hips.
2. Place balls of feet on first step and hands on third step. Back should be parallel to floor.
3. Lock knees and keep locked throughout movement.
4. Elevate heels as high as possible and try to stand on big toes.
5. Pause.
6. Slowly lower your heels.
7. Stretch at bottom by lifting toes.
8. Repeat.

Triceps Extension

1. Loop a lightweight towel through weight belt.
2. Grasp one end of towel in each hand. Stand and face away from machine.
3. Arms should now be bent with elbows by ears.
4. Adjust grip on towel until weight stack is separated.
5. Straighten arms in a very smooth fashion.
6. Pause.
7. Slowly lower resistance and repeat.

Parallel Dip (Negative only with or without weight belt)

1. Adjust carriage to proper level (allow ample stretch in bottom position).
2. Climb steps.
3. Lock elbows and bend legs.
4. Slowly lower body by bending arms (8-10 seconds).
5. Stretch at bottom position.
6. Climb up and repeat.

Chin-up (Negative only with or without weighted belt)

1. Place cross-bar in forward position.
2. Adjust carriage to proper height (when standing on top step, chin should be barely over bar).
3. Grasp cross-bar with plams up.
4. Climb steps.
5. Chin over bar, elbows by sides, and legs bent.
6. Slowly lower body (8-10 seconds).
7. Stretch at bottom position.
8. Climb up and repeat.

Important: Movements can also be done in a behind-neck fashion by using parallel grip.

Wrist Curl

1. Sit in front of machine (use small bench or chair) with toes under first step.
2. Attach handles directly to movement arm.
3. Grasp handles in a palms-up fashion. (Palms-down grip should also be used.)
4. Place forearms firmly against thighs.
5. Curl handles upward.
6. Pause.
7. Slowly lower resistance and repeat.

Important: Do not move forearms. Only hands should move. Keep knees close together. Avoid jerky movements.

Other Movements

Biceps curl, shoulder shrug, bent-over row, hanging leg raise, side bend, deadlift.

Triathlete Strength Training Bibliography

How your Muscles Work, Ellington Darden Ph.D. Director of Research Nautilus Sports, Anna Publishing, Winter Park, Florida 32792

Strength Training Principles, Same as above.

Strength Training The Present State of the Art Arthur Jones, Director, Nautilus Sports/Medical Industries, P.O. Box 1783, DeLand, Florida 32720

Astrand, Per-Olaf, and Rodahl, Kaare. *Textbook of Work Physiology.* New York: McGraw-Hill, 1970.

Kendall, H. O.; Kendall, F. P.; and Wadsworth, G. E. *Muscles: Testing and Function.* Baltimore: The Williams and Wilkins Company, 1971.

Lamb, Lawrence E. *Metabolics: Putting Your Food Energy to Work.* New York: Harper and Row, Publishers, 1974.

Langley, L. L.; Telford, I. R.; and Christensen, J. B. *Dynamic Anatomy and Physiology.* New York: McGraw-Hill, 1974.

Lewis, Paul, and Rubenstein, David. *The Human Body.* New York: Bantam Books, 1971.

Mathews, Donald K., and Fox, Edward L. *The Physiological Basis of Physical Education and Athletics.* Philadelphia: W. B. Saunders Company, 1976.

Radcliff, J. D. *Your Body and How It Works.* Pleasantville, N.Y.: Reader's Digest Press, 1975.

MUSCLE MAN, FRONT VIEW

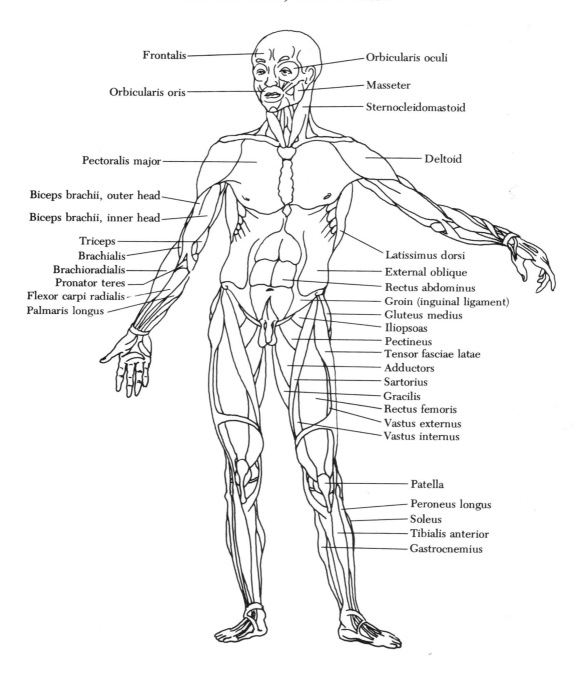

Frontalis

Orbicularis oculi

Orbicularis oris

Masseter

Sternocleidomastoid

Pectoralis major

Deltoid

Biceps brachii, outer head

Biceps brachii, inner head

Triceps

Brachialis

Brachioradialis

Pronator teres

Flexor carpi radialis

Palmaris longus

Latissimus dorsi

External oblique

Rectus abdominus

Groin (inguinal ligament)

Gluteus medius

Iliopsoas

Pectineus

Tensor fasciae latae

Adductors

Sartorius

Gracilis

Rectus femoris

Vastus externus

Vastus internus

Patella

Peroneus longus

Soleus

Tibialis anterior

Gastrocnemius

MUSCLE MAN, BACK VIEW

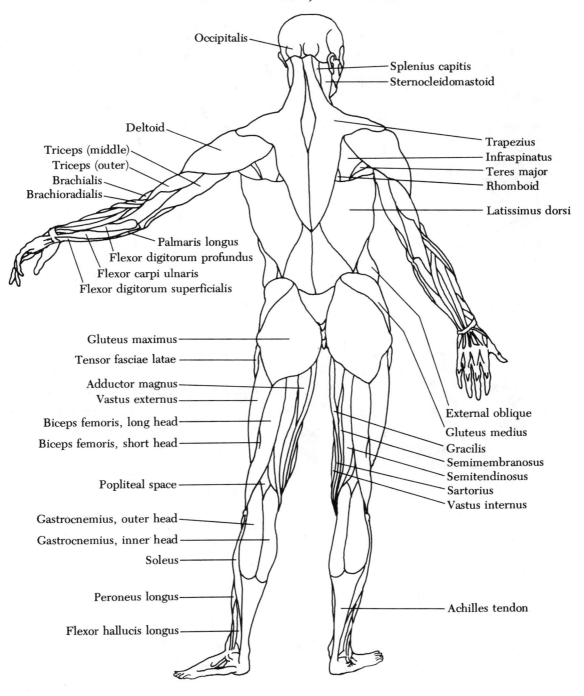

Occipitalis

Splenius capitis

Sternocleidomastoid

Deltoid

Trapezius

Triceps (middle)

Infraspinatus

Triceps (outer)

Teres major

Brachialis

Rhomboid

Brachioradialis

Latissimus dorsi

Palmaris longus

Flexor digitorum profundus

Flexor carpi ulnaris

Flexor digitorum superficialis

Gluteus maximus

Tensor fasciae latae

Adductor magnus

Vastus externus

External oblique

Biceps femoris, long head

Gluteus medius

Biceps femoris, short head

Gracilis

Semimembranosus

Semitendinosus

Sartorius

Popliteal space

Vastus internus

Gastrocnemius, outer head

Gastrocnemius, inner head

Soleus

Peroneus longus

Achilles tendon

Flexor hallucis longus

273

Ian Emberson in the 1979 Nautilus Ironman biking up the long grade from Wainai through the sugar cane and pineapple fields.

The sight of over 1,000 swimmers, packed tightly and flailing away near Kona's Kailua Pier, is truly one of the most exciting spectacles of the October 1984 Ironman Triathlon.

Photo by Mike Plant

VI

Swim Training
for the Triathlon

Introduction to Books VI, VII, and VIII

The following three books are specifically training books for the Swim-Bike-Run. These three books are then followed by Book IX which deals with the triathlon as a combination of the three. It is important that we consider a point in our training for each one of these three sports individually where we begin to combine our training habits to include a second sport training routine in consecutive order. For example, an early morning swim training routine may be followed by a bike ride or possibly a late afternoon bike ride followed by a run. Times and distances will depend on the level of training you have achieved at any given point. If the swim, bike and run training is on schedule, I feel that the 4th month of running would be an appropriate time, skill and strength-wise, to start the combination training routine. This formula is assuming, of course, that there are no extremely strong or weak sports. If this is the case, it is important to devote less time or extra time to that sport, whichever the case may be.

The schedules for swim and bike for the 4 month period has taken the training triathlete into an area of effort that will make it possible, strength-wise, to adjust to the combination training and start to build an early base of physiological muscle interaction. The building together of all three sports is the ideal way to train into the triathlon.

Daily routines, as we have stated in the following chapters, are entirely a personal matter dealing mostly with family life, work and personal duties.

Lengthy schedules, except for the monthly achievement goals set forth at the end of each chapter, are avoided. This formula for training, be it swim, bike or run, involves maintaining a maximum aerobic effort, and an optimum heart rate, meaning that we advance our pace to a comfortable breathing rate, pushing but never entering the breathless, lactic acid pain build-up state that signals the anaerobic effort.

Australia-New Zealand Training Concepts

The above training formula is not a new creation. This concept is responsible for the training of many Olympic Games. Gold Medal 1sts. Percy Cerutty of Australia, Arthur Lydiard, and the World Class Scottish running instructor Max Telford, both of New Zealand, have used this tried and proven formula for years with great success! Combining the aerobic principal of training with Long Slow Distance . . . followed by strength training . . . and then speed training. This order is the secret of their own personal running achievements and success in training some of the world's greatest runners.

The Anaerobic Interval Training Alternative

For the training triathlete who wishes to venture into and beyond the anaerobic, lactic acid pain threshhold or barrier, we have offered the alternative. In each one of the chapters as well as the special chapter on interval training, there is warning that the minimal results gained by this method might not be worth the psychological burden created.

1

Swim 2.4 Miles in 12 Months Training

Hawaii the Swimming Place

Planned distance swimming of from 2.5 to 4 or 5 miles takes place weekly off of Waikiki. Many 2.5 rough water competitive distance swims occur in Hawaii throughout the year. The most outstanding swim (as to the total number of contestants) is the annual Labor Day Routh Water 2.5 Mile Swim. This is the Boston Marathon of the swimming community strictly by the number of participants that join in the event. The starting points on the beach between the Memorial Nautorium and the Kaimana Beach Hotel is completely filled with more than 3,000 swimmers from many countries. The end of the swim is the Rainbow Tower of the Hilton Hawaiian Village Hotel. All of this and 70 to 80 degree crystal clear water is hard to beat! Hawaii is taking the lead in triathlon training and you can easily see why — with 365 days of perfect training weather! The community boasts one runner out of every seven island residents and is very supportive to the training athlete.

With the emergence of the triathlon as a professional sport, Hawaii promises to be the focal point for pre-season training for the serious triathlete. The annual triathlon season ends up in Kona on the Island of Hawaii in early October. The plan of many competing triathletes is to make the Maui Channel Relay from the Island of Lanai to the harbor at Lahaina, Maui 2 days prior to the Waikiki Swim. These events are well attended by swimmers and triathletes starting their climate adjustment and their on the spot training for the Ironman World Triathlon. The channel swim takes place on the Saturday before Labor Day Monday each year. Then on to Oahu for the fun event of the distance swimmers' lives; the Waikiki Rough Water, 2.5 mile swim on Labor Day. These events can then be followed by 5 weeks of intensive training for the Ironman World Triathlon both on Oahu and the big island of Hawaii.

Introduction to Swimming

As practiced by man, swimming is an art. Fish, amphibia, water-fowl, and practically all quadrupeds are either born with the ability to swim, have instincts which enable them to acquire swimming ability very rapidly, or employ a form of locomotion on land which with little adaptation is suitable for making progress through the water. If man possessed any one of these characteristics or, even if he had six inches more of neck and six inches less of thigh, there would be no art to swimming. No swimming methods would have had to be devised; no one would have to be taught how to swim; nothing would have to be written or said about it. Everyone could, as the need or desire arose, simply enter the water and swim away just as most animals can and do. But in so doing man would have foregone an experience which has enriched him not only physically but mentally as well. Furthermore, he would have missed completely the opportunity to become that which he is, one of the most amazingly versatile of all creatures in the water.

It is true that man is very badly handicapped by structure and habit when he enters the water. His normal position for locomotion on land is upright and he walks or runs by thrusting against the ground with a relatively small area of the foot. An erect position in the water is a poor one for making progress not only because of the resistance offered but, more important, because of the narrow margin of buoyancy possessed by the average man. The specific gravity of a human being is so nearly that of water itself that the average man, when suspended motionless in the water, finds that he submerges to approximately the level of the eyes. Since in this position his mouth and nose are below the surface, he is quite unable to breathe without making some move to lift himself a little above his normal flotation level. If, in this position, he attempts to employ the same movements he uses in walking on land, the thrust of the small area of the foot against such an elastic medium as water can barely hold him in a position in which he can breathe, and any sustained progress is out of the question. Even such natural and instinctive movements of the arms as pawing and pressing downward against the water, produce little result either in keeping a person's head above water or in moving through it. So, since man's natural position and locomotive movements cannot serve him in the water with any degree of success, other positions must be assumed and different types of movements employed. Such positions and movements have been discovered and developed, many of them in use to this day being as old as man's experience in the water. Born of reason, nurtured by constant experiment and practice, and passed along from generation to generation, through the ages as a singularly simple, but important and fundamental physical art. It is doubtful if anyone has ever learned how to swim in any manner other than with the crudest of animal movements, without some foreknowledge of this art.

It is literally true that with his acquired art of swimming, man is one of the most, if not the most, versatile of all living creatures in the water. He is limited, of course, in the distance he can swim, the depths to which he can descend, the speed he can make, and even the length of time he can be immersed. In these things, fish, amphibia, even some mammals exceed.

Man's Versatility

Man excels in the water rather in the great variety of positions, swimming movements, maneuvers and directions he can assume, employ, or take. Man can swim on the front, on the side, on the back, at the surface or beneath it. He can swim forward, backward, even sidewise with ease. He has the ability to somersault either forward or backward, or to rotate on his long axis like a rolling log. But above all, he has and can use many varied and different movements of his limbs to sustain and propel himself in the water.

Aside from his capacity to reason things out and his singular, imitative ability by which he learns from others, man has one physical asset which accounts in large part for his versatility in the water. This is a set of swivel or ball and socket joints in his shoulders and hips which permit a wide range of movement in the arms and legs. Swimming animals are limited by their mechanical structure to far fewer patterns of swimming action.

Because man differs so markedly in structure and mechanical movement from other forms of animal life, there is little or nothing that he has been able to copy from them in developing his art of swimming. While he has evolved many swimming stunts and given them animal names, such as seal-diving, alligator-roll, muskrat-swimming, porpoising, and many others, they are only simulations of effects. The physical action employed to accomplish them is usually radically different from that of the animals he seeks to emulate. The dog and the frog have often been cited as examples among animals, the swimming movements of which may be copied by man for certain styles of swimming.

One crude style of elementary stroke is called the dog-paddle almost universally, yet only in the pawing action of the arms and hands does it in any way resemble the swimming action of the dog, and even that is modified. If the legs were employed as the dog uses his hind legs, practically no progress would be made for any distance. Another classic example from nature of erroneous pattern is found in the development of the breast stroke where all through history learners have been told to imitate the frog in using the legs. Indeed, the breast stroke kick is commonly termed the frog-kick. Yet only in the negative or recovering portion of that stroke does the human swimmer even remotely resemble the frog. By thrusting backward against the water as the frog does with his widespreading webbed foot, man would get little result for his efforts.

So there is really little or nothing that man has been able to borrow from the rest of the animal kingdom in the development of his own peculiar art of swimming. Slowly and patiently over the centuries he has had to discover his own principles and methods. To swim, man has had to learn from other men, and such variations and improvements in styles of swimming as have been evolved through the years have of necessity had to be based on what had gone before.

Through the years there has been developed a literature on swimming and, more recently, photographic reproductions, both still and motion, of the elements of the art. Teaching methods have been devised for people to acquire the art more readily. It is not necessary for anyone to go through the whole painful "trial and error" method of learning how to swim so long as there are now swimmers to imitate, books on swimming to read, pictures to look at, and instructors available to teach.

Pre-history of Swimming

What prompted man to take to the water is a matter of pure conjecture, yet from what is known of the pre-history of man and from our present day knowledge of primitive peoples, it can be said that the three fundamental motivating forces were economic necessity, comfort and preservation of life in the face of danger. Of these three, economic necessity was, undoubtedly, the dominating force. The myriad forms of marine life must have been from the very first a great source of sustenance for man. In tropical and sub-tropical regions, seeking to escape the discomfort engendered by extreme heat, man must have discovered early in his experience that immersion allayed that discomfort; and over all the inhabited earth man has used the water from earliest times as a refuge from fire, animals or men. It can be said also, that man may have learned to swim as a result of accidental immersion in deep water but it is doubtful if his experience in his struggle to regain the land ever prompted him to repeat it, or others to follow his example. Other motivations may be cited such as that of cleanliness, bathing as a religious rite and even sport, but as unique developments, they must have come much later.

When it comes, however, to the actual development of swimming strokes, it is not necessary to guess what the process was. Every self-taught swimmer in the matter of learning to swim demonstrates clearly the evolution of it. His motivations are the same as those of the first beginners; namely, to keep from drowning, to make progress through the water and to sustain the effort to limits consistent with need and comfort.

To swim, man learned that another position had to be assumed, that artificial movements had to be made and that all negative movements had to be made gently in order that they should not impede his progress. Swimming developed on these bases. The long process of development was on a "trial and error" basis and through the ages it must have been painfully slow. Little structural change was possible but possibilities of mechanical adaptation were almost unlimited. And so, by constant experiment and by simulation, man learned which movements would propel him and which would retard his progress; which would bear him up and which sink him and how these movements could be coordinated for the best effect. When coordinations were established which were somewhat efficient and suitable for others to imitate, swimming as an art, was born.

Learning How to Swim

It is possible for one to learn how to swim by his own effort. This can be done by imitating swimmers, by following the simple directions of any number of published methods from the printed page, or under the crude instruction of self appointed untrained teachers. It is a fact, however, that fundamentals are more easily learned and that progress is made more rapidly under skilled instruction. Over and above all that, however, the beginning swimmer is *safer* under the watchful eye of a trained instructor, a factor of considerable importance in the first stages of learning how to swim when the beginner is venturing into a new and, to him, often unknown element.

With or without a trained instructor, however, the non-swimmer should have a thorough understanding of what plan he will follow to learn how to swim. Furthermore, he should be sure that he is going to be safe while he is learning. At organized bathing places and in tanks his efforts should be confined to those areas reserved for non-swimmers. In all other waters an area of shallow water should be sought in which there are no holes or sudden "step-offs." Likewise, the non-swimmer should avoid waters where there are strong currents and hidden menaces such as snags, rocks, or channels. The bottom should shelve gradually and if the area is protected by natural or artificial boundaries, which limit range and provide for reasonably calm water, this is even better. The learning process should not be undertaken alone or merely in the company of another non-swimmer. The presence of a swimmer or a person trained in life saving is fundamental to the safety of the beginning swimmer. A safe place in which to learn and someone to aid if something goes wrong are vitally essential because of a near-drowning experience in the early stages of learning either greatly inhibits the learner's progression or discourages him from continuing.

Swimming Fundamentals

Thousands of self-taught swimmers, through lack of understanding of the underlying principles which govern swimming development, go through the whole painful "trial and error" process in learning to swim. Some swimmers eventually learn how to swim quite well, by close observation and imitation of skilled swimmers and constant practice, but the vast majority fumble their way along with crude methods of compensating for their lack of fundamental knowledge. Because of this they must always be limited to short distances or very slow progress through the water and may never know the joy and satisfaction that comes with skilled performance.

The whole evolution of the art of swimming has produced a number of broad fundamental principles that are common to all swimming. If properly understood and incorporated in swimming practice, they make progression easier, but if ignored or imperfectly understood, they make swimming development uncertain and difficult.

Strokes are the movements of the rms and legs made in swimming to propel or in some positions to support the body in water. They are made by pressing backward against the water with the largest possible arm or leg surface to limits consistent with strength, maintenance of equilibrium and recovery in the easiest and least resistant manner possible.

Leg Strokes — Leg strokes are more variant in action since there are four distinct types employed in swimming. Beating back against the water, as exemplified in the "human stroke" or dog paddle, with the shin and instep is the least effective of the methods used. The application of power is crude and not productive of anything but the poorest of result for the effort expended. Pressing the legs against the water from widely angled positions is stronger than any other form of leg drive despite the handicap of negative action in the recovery portion of the stroke. The scissors and the breast stroke kicks are examples of this. In these strokes a considerable amount of leg and foot surface is driven against the water with corresponding results. The third form of using the legs in swimming is quite unlike any other type of kick. This is the flutter, an alternate undulating action of the legs which when properly done causes the feet to deliver a continuous series of driving thrusts on both the up and down beat with practically no negative action. This stroke, used in the crawl, will be discussed more fully later.

Body Position and Balance — As everyone knows, the best position for swimming is at or near the horizontal. In this position a minimum of resistance is offered to progress and the weight is more evenly distributed to take advantage of the buoyant effect of the water; that is, in this position there is less likelihood of carrying too much weight above the surface. At the same time legs and arms are low enough in the water to obtain the best possible leverage in stroking.

Observation of swimmers from a point of vantage below the surface, however, indicates that even speed swimmers are much lower in the water than previously had been supposed.

Relaxation — Relaxation must be discussed and linked up to body position and balance, since obviously relaxation is hardly possible if the swimmer's position or balance is faulty.

Muscles held in a state of tension, whether they are making visible effort or not, are at work and if the tension is sustained, they quickly become fatigued. It is a common fault among swimmers to assume this state of general tension when they enter the water with the result that they will soon tire. It may be stated broadly that all groups of voluntary muscles not directly involved in stroking should be relaxed and that muscles employed in a stroking movement should, as soon as the effort is completed, relax at once so that they may rest. An example or two may be cited to illustrate the point. Contact with cool water causes exhilaration which manifests itself by an almost involuntary contraction of the muscles. In the first plunge and brief swimming dash, it is the usual thing for many swimmers to arch the ribs high and pull in the muscular wall of the abdomen. In so doing they greatly inhibit breathing and since they are getting an insufficient supply of oxygen they tire quickly. Or a swimmer attempting a burst of speed over a relatively short distance performs his stroking movements so hurriedly he does not relax even in the recovery portion of his stroke. As a result he soon "dies off" and either quits entirely or finishes with a much slower and less fatiguing stroke.

Breathing — Faulty breathing is a handicap under which far too many persons in all classifications of swimming perform. As stated before, an inadequate supply of oxygen is one of the chief causes of fatigue and it is more often apt to be breathlessness which causes a swimmer's difficulty and inability to continue than it is muscular fatigue. Furthermore, incorrect breathing all too frequently affects the health of swimmers, affecting as it does the upper part of the respiratory tract, particularly the sinuses of the head. Swimming, especially in the newer strokes, requires an exactness and rhythm in breathing not encountered in any other form of physical activity, yet it is rarely dealt with adequately until a swimmer has become expert enough to enter competition. It is so important, however, both from the standpoint of health as well as efficiency that correct application of its principles should start as soon as a person begins to learn how to swim.

In many styles of swimming on the front or the side, the face is carried beneath the surface a good part of the time, owing to the necessity for holding the head in line with the spine to get better body position and balance in the stroke. In the cycle of the stroke there is only a brief interval in which the face lifts or turns to come above the surface for air and it is then that the inhalation is taken. Since the interval is so short, air must be taken at a gulp through the mouth as the nostrils are far too small to take in an adequate supply of air before the face is again buried beneath the surface. This fact is well understood and practiced by most swimmers; what is done after the face goes under water is where the major difficulty lies. Usually novices hold their breath while their face is under water and attempt to exhale when the face comes above the surface again before taking the next breath. If accomplished at all, this has to be done so explosively that an entirely inadequate supply of air is inhaled and after only a few strokes breathlessness develops to such an extent that the swimmer must stop or change his stroke. Furthermore, the very act of holding the breath contributes to breathlessness. Exhalation must take place beneath the surface in the cycle of the stroke unless the swimmer is employing a stroke which permits him to keep the head above water at all times.

This fact has been recognized for years and for a generation at least, learning swimmers have been told "to inhale through the mouth above the water and exhale through the *nose* below the surface." One serious omission and one grievous error are present in this admonition. First, rarely has the swimmer been instructed to begin the exhalation as soon as the inhalation is completed so that breath holding would be eliminated, and second, and much more important, the breath should *not* be exhaled solely through the nose.

Man drinks through his mouth and breathes through his nose, although he can and often does use the mouth for breathing. The mouth being used to water, can take in air readily and not be irritated if some water gets in at the same time. The nose, however, is sensitive to water and if some is taken in with a breath of air the effect is extremely uncomfortable, causing gasping, choking, and sneezing which effectually disrupt the normal process of breathing. Since the face is so close to the water in swimming, even when rolled or lifted to clear the surface for air, and since the water is agitated by the action of the swimmer, some water in the form of spray is almost bound to be taken in when the breath is taken. Because of this it is quite understandable why the mouth and not the nose should be used to take in air while swimming. The reason why a swimmer should exhale through the mouth is a bit obscure and requires further explanation.

To exhale through the nostrils alone in the comparatively brief interval in the cycle of a stroke when the face is buried beneath the surface, requires a distinct effort; the air must be pushed out quite forcibly. If there is any water in the throat and there generally is, the act of forcibly exhaling the air through the nose would carry this water in droplets or finely divided spray along with it. If this water was merely pushed out through the nasal passages no ill effect other than irritation would be manifest, but, unfortunately, there are other places within the head into which this moisture may be blown. There is no single guiding tube which will insure that loose water will be discharged through the nostrils. Forcibly pressure is quite likely to distribute it, driving it from the nasopharynx into the tubes leading to the ears and even into the sinuses of the head. Aside from the irritation caused by water entering where water has no place unless it is absolutely sterile, infectious organisms or germs may be carried with it. Even sterile water will no longer be sterile after it has washed the mucous membranes of the mouth and throat.

If the exhalation is made with the mouth open, less pressure will be needed to force the air out and it will take less time. While most of the air will escape through the mouth, some will inevitably trickle out through the nostrils but the pressure will not be great enough to force droplets into places where they may cause trouble.

It is most distressing to those who know what the consequences may be, to note how commonly accepted as inevitable a "head full" of water is among swimmers. The beginning swimmer emerging from an involuntary plunge beneath the surface spouting a stream of water from the nostrils, is not only uncomfortable but in danger of developing serious infection. The swimmer hopping on one foot and vainly thumping the side of his head in an effort to get water out of his ear, water which may have been driven into the middle ear from the inside, offers another example of what faulty breathing may do. And finally, the accomplished swimmer bending over in the locker room to tie a shoe an hour after he has emerged from the water, observes without distress a thin stream of water dripping from his nose. He may not be distressed but he might be if he knew that it was draining from his sinuses.

These things have too often branded swimming, especially in pools, as dangerous to health, when it has been the bad practice and not the water that was at fault. No water need penetrate to the sinuses or to the middle ear, if the bather knows how to hold the breath when submerged or to breathe properly in swimming.

Coordination — When strokes are made at random by the arms and legs, no matter how accurately they are pulled and recovered, they cannot be effective for any length of time. When, however, they are so combined that one or both of the legs or arms are resting or recovering while the others are propelling, and when one part is in position ready to take up the stroke as another part completes its portion, the stroke becomes a continuous propulsive movement. The uncoordinated stroke is characterized by jerky, uneven progress which soon tires the swimmer because legs and arms are not getting proper resting intervals.

Likewise, breathing is coordinated with the strokes employed. In a stroke it is almost invariably the rule that the swimmer inhales at the point in the stroke where the head is highest, generally as the forward arm (or arms) starts to pull. In some strokes the head is lifted and in others rotated on the neck to bring the mouth above the surface. The face settles or rolls beneath the surface again with the recovery of the arm, or arms, and there the exhalation takes place through the remainder of the stroke and glide.

Glide — The glide is the distance between strokes which a swimmer rides, drifts, or slides without visible effort, which may be done with one or both arms extended forward of the head. The most notable examples of maximumglide are found in the breast and side strokes where the long gliding interval between strokes is very definite. At the other extreme, the stroke in which there seems to be little if any glide is the sprinting crawl stroke. The slower the stroke, the longer the glide. Its value is undoubted as it is progress with little effort, and fewer strokes have to be taken to cover a specified distance. It is frequently said of a swimmer in training that he is losing speed because he is "shortening his stroke" when, as a matter of fact, he is losing speed because he is not riding the forward arm or arms.

There are other factors which may be said to be fundamental in swimming such as strength, flexibility, and vital capacity, but they are really secondary and are important not in the initial development of swimming ability but rather in developing stamina and speed. Strength is developed through swimming, as are flexibility and lung capacity. This development may be hastened, however, by special exercises on land designed for the purpose.

Sculling — First, it should be stated that correct sculling is entirely a hand movement and that the arm is not used except as it rotates in its socket at the shoulder to change the position of the hand and thus facilitate its use, and secondly, that there are no negative recovery movements. Apropos of this Ralph Thomas writes of sculling, "The marvel of proper sculling is that there is no unprofitable action, no slip" and, facetiously, it is suspected, " . . . it must therefore be with this stroke nature intended human beings to swim."

To describe correctly the sculling movement of the hand is not easy. If everyone knew how to scull a boat with an oar would be stated simply that the arm is used in much the same manner as the oar, but since so few persons know how to use an oar for sculling it must be otherwise described. With a flexing wrist the hand is made to describe a figure of eight in the water, first pressing outward with the little finger angled toward the surface and then with a rotation of the arm inward toward the body with the thumb inclined upward. In its greatest scope it should not exceed twelve inches.

Leg Strokes — It is generally known that progress in the water is most efficiently made by using both arms and both legs, but observation of self-taught swimmers would lead one to believe that most of them had never heard that the legs are of equal importance with the arms. As a matter of fact, it is very easy for the average person to learn to stay afloat and propel himself crudely for a short distance with arm strokes largely and leg movements only incidentally. This may be because arm strokes are more easily and naturally mastered than those of the legs due to greater flexibility and range of movement of the arms and closer proximity to the eyes. In other words, a beginner can see what the arms are doing in swimming but can only sense the action of the legs. Whatever the cause may be, however, it is known that novices who concentrate on arm strokes learn to propel themselves quickly enough but thereafter are always limited in endurance and comfort until the legs are brought under control and made to do their real share. It would seem, therefore, in an orderly learning process that the more difficult portion of the various styles of swimming should be mastered primarily. Therefore, in this progression the use of the legs is placed before the arms.

The Flutter Kick — If ever a stroking movement was misnamed it was this one. The word flutter is defined by Webster as "moving with quick vibrations" or "to move agitatedly with little result." This is precisely what hundreds and thousands of learning swimmers do when they attempt to swim the crawl; they vibrate the legs with little result. Understanding of this method seems to have begun and ended with most learning swimmers with the idea that if the legs are alternately shaken up and down in the water that is all there is to it. There seems to be no general understanding among swimmers of the principles involved in the stroke and of its correct execution.

The alternate up-and-down vertical thrash of the legs as exemplified in the "human stroke" has been known apparently for thousands of years. Some primitive peoples in various sections of the world have used it in combination with the hand-over-hand stroke of the arms for unnumbered generations. In comparatively modern times, the stroke was borrowed from the natives of Ceylon and taken to Australia. There it was adopted by the leading competitive swimmers of the time and refined into what has become known as the Australian crawl, the refinement consisting of the development of a synchronized rather than a haphazard method of stroking. This synchronization or timing consisted of using a pull of an arm on one side and a vertical downward thrust of the shin and instep of the leg on the other side. This was followed by a pull of the other arm and a kick of the other leg to complete the cycle of the stroke. In this form it was brought to England and the United States by the Cavill brothers, noted swimmers of that time, who used it with remarkable success in racing at sprint distances. It was quickly adopted by speed swimmers in both Europe and America, but from this point on, the record of its further development is obscured.

The Cavills themselves, Sundstrom and Daniels, both American swimmers, and others are variously credited with taking the next step in the evolution of what is now described as the American crawl. Actually, it is probable that all of these contributed something to its development. Essentially, the next step in the progression was merely a speeding up of the leg action until they were beating four, six, and even eight times in each cycle of the arms. For a time, apparently, no one knew exactly why the speeded up "kick" made swimmers go faster. The fact that for sprint distances at least swimmers could improve their times by this means was enough to cause them to adopt it eagerly. The water was thrashed violently in a hundred pools and confusion reigned. Swimmers learning the new stroke were advised variously to "hold the legs rigid from hip to toe" or to "loosen the knee and smash the shin and instep downward against the water." They were told to "narrow the stroke" until it was merely a vibration of the legs; one swimmer of note developed a twelve beat crawl. The angle of the legs from the hips was changed again and again. Sprint swimmers swam faster and faster even if they were "all out" at the end of fifty or a hundred yards. Then out of the welter of churning waters began to appear swimmers who could use the stroke more slowly and with surpassing grace and ease over ever increasing distances, and reason began to emerge. Perhaps there was something in this manner of using the legs that could do something in swimming other than merely support the feet at the surface while the arms tore through the water in the hand-over-hand stroke. Legs were dropped somewhat lower in the water; emphasis began to be placed on the upward lift of the foot as well as on its downward drive and gradually flexible undulation of hip, knee and ankle began to supplant the vigorous smashing beat of the legs. The number of kicks began to drop back and became stabilized at six and for some conditions at four. Crawl swimming became more and more effective over ever increasing distances and training methods were evolved to help meet the new demands for more strength, flexibility and increased efficiency.

Description of the Stroke

It has been said of the flutter kick that the swimmers who use it most successfully have "rubber" legs. This may be interpreted as meaning that they have a controlled flexibility of the ankle, knee and hip joints which permits an undulating movement to start at the hip and move progressively to the thigh, to the lower leg and to the foot, where it is finished by a straightening of the leg and a backward and upward lash of the foot. The legs alternately whip up and down in the vertical plane, the upward movement finishing as the heel breaks the surface and the downward stroke pressing to a depth of anywhere from twelve to eighteen inches. These limits are placed on the stroke for greater effectiveness, since any stroking above the surface is wasted effort and any below a depth of eighteen inches increases resistance by throwing the body too far out of the horizontal plane.

Learning Method

Although there is nothing natural about the flutter kick, its essentials are rather easily mastered if a progressive learning method is followed.

It is doubtful if land drill in the reclining position is of much value in the learning process since in the strained position necessarily assumed the movements of the legs are stiff and awkward. It is better to start the learning process in shallow water either with the hands on the bottom or bracketed against the side of a pool or dock. In the horizontal position the legs are extended to the rear and close together just below the surface. The back is flattened and the feet are slightly lower than the hips. When an easy and comfortable position is assumed, the legs are lifted and dropped alternately. At first the movements are made slowly as they are brought under control. The emphasis is placed on the upward lift of the leg. In the early stages of this process the movements of the feet may be likened to those used in pedalling a bicycle of very low gear, the backward and upward extensionof the foot being almost identical in both cases. After the movements are brought under control they are performed in rhythmic sequence until the actions become semi-automatic. To establish a rhythm that can be incorporated easily into the whole stroke, it is recommended that the beats or strokes be made in a continuous series of cycles of six with the first and fourth beat of each cycle deliberately accented. Thus the governing count would be ONE, two, three, FOUR, five, six, or better, LEFT, right, left, RIGHT, left, right, in which a beginning, a mid-point, and an end of each cycle is indicated.

In the second step in the development of this stroke a free floating support is used for hands and arms while strength, endurance and "finish" are developed by continuous rhythmic practice. Over a defined course the learner slowly "kicks" his way back and forth until the stroke is done smoothly and easily and he is capable of continuing it for a period of several minutes. If the learner is unable to sustain the effort it may be due to one of two things: either he is holding the legs too stiffly or he is stroking too rapidly. If he makes no perceptible progress the stroke is being done incorrectly. Success in the use of this stroke is dependent upon controlled flexibility and relaxation.

Editor's note:

It is with great honor that we were able with permission of the author, to include a portion of Dr. Counsilman's *Competitive Swimming Manual* in this chapter. Basically, we are only concerned with the crawl stroke and its refinements as it pertains to distance swimming. We would encourage the triathlete to obtain for him or herself the complete book for a much greater depth of information on this stroke, the three additional principle strokes now used in competitive swimming, plus much more pertinent material that a training triathlete will find indispensable. For this book, a complete coverage on the subject of competitive swimming, a text used by swimming instructors worldwide, write to: The Counsilman Co. Inc., 2606 E. 2nd Street, Bloomington, Indiana 47401.

Biography of Dr. Counsilman

Here are a few of the firsts that can be attributed to Dr. Counsilman in his research into the most successful training methods:

• The first person to publish an article on the use of interval training in swimming (1948).

• The first person to manufacture pace clocks for use with an interval training program (1948).

• The first to describe and clearly define the two-beat crawl stroke (1957).

Dr. James E. Counsilman Biography (cont.)

- The first to apply the Bernoulli principle to stroke mechanics (1970). This particular research project, which revolutionized the concepts of stroke mechanics, is described and illustrated in this manual.
- The first to apply the principle of isokinetic exercise to the strengthening exercises for swimmers. He was instrumental in the design and development of the present equipment used by most world-class swimmers in the United States and now being used by the East German and Russian swimmers.
- The first to publish on the use of hypoxic training in swimming (ASCA Annual Convention Proceedings, 1974).

Dr. Counsilman's Stroke Analysis Clinic for Swimmers, conducted in June and July, is the most successful swim clinic in the United States. For information about this clinic write: Counsilman Co., Inc., 2606 East Second Street, Bloomington, Indiana 47401.

James E. Counsilman, PhD is a former national swimming champion and American record holder. He still competes in the Masters Swimming Program and has held a number of national masters records.

Dr. Counsilman has been coaching at Indiana University for the past twenty years, during which time IU teams have won seventeen consecutive Big Ten Swimming titles, six consecutive NCAA titles and 190 dual meets while losing only six. His teams have also won seven Outdoor and four Indoor National AAU championships.

A list of swimmers who have swum for Doc would read like a who's who of swimming — Mark Spitz, Jim Montgomery, Gary Hall, John Kinsella, Mike Troy, Charles Kickcox, Don McKenzie, Chet Jastremski, Tom Stock, George Breen, Mike Stamm, Alan Somers, Ted Stickles, Larry Schulhof, John Murphy, and many others.

His consistency in coaching is demonstrated by the amazing fact that he has had swimmers whom he was coaching at the time of the Olympic Trials — not just swimmers with whom he worked at one time or another — make the last eight United States Olympic teams. No other coach comes close to this record. Doc also was head coach of the two most successful United States Mens Olympic Swimming Teams, 1964 and 1976. In 1976 the United States men swimmers won 12 of 13 possible gold medals. His swimmers at one time or another have set world records in every single swimming event, an accomplishment no other coach has approached.

Dr. Counsilman's research in swimming has contributed immensely to the development of the present techniques in training and stroke mechanics as practiced by most swimmers throughout the world.

Methods and Principles of Training

Nearly everyone understands some of the basic concepts of training. For instance, when you train (or work out), you get into "condition." The exercise that you do in your training program places a stress on your body, which adapts to this stress by changing itself in order to be better able to handle this *particular* stress.

These changes are physiological changes that permit the body to function more efficiently. If you swim long distances, your heart will improve its efficiency and be able to pump more blood to the muscles. This blood will bring oxygen and glycogen to the muscles, remove the fatigue products, and, in the process, improve endurance.

In this instance the stress factor is the training program of *long-distance or overdistance swimming;* the change or adaptation that is made as a result of this stress is increased cardiac (heart) efficiency, and the final effect on your performance is that endurance is improved. Many other changes occur in the body as a result of overdistance swimming, but to illustrate this point, only the improvement in heart or cardiac efficiency will be mentioned at this time. Overdistance swimming will bring about changes that will enable a person to swim long distances better, but it won't result in the necessary changes that will permit him to spring short distances at top speed. To bring about these changes some *spring training* must be introduced into the program. Sprint training imposes a stress factor that is of shorter duration but that is more intense than slower and prolonged distance swimming and that causes the muscles to adapt by improving their ability to contract quickly against a greater force — in other words, the muscles become more powerful. If a swimmer wants to be conditioned for both speed and endurance races, he must introduce both overdistance and spring training into his training program.

Theoretically, it is possible for a swimmer to be conditioned to perform well in a long-distance race such as a 4-mile swim, to also be conditioned to perform well in a sprint race (50 yards) and at the same time not to be conditioned to swim a good middle-distance race (200 meters).

Swimming a middle-distance race well depends on the ability to work at a fast pace for a moderate length of time. During an all-out middle-distance race the swimmer is not able to take in as much oxygen as he is burning. To be in condition for the middle-distances his body must change to be able to take in more oxygen and to be able to operate more efficiently when in oxygen debt. This type of change is brought about only by swimming middle distances at fast speed.

Specificity of Training

The fact that the body makes specific adaptations or changes to specific types of training is called *specificity of training* and is one of the most important principles to be aware of in designing a training program.

If you want to swim a good spring (50-meter race), a good middle-distance race (200- to 400-meter race), and a good distance race (400 meters and over), all three types of training methods that have been discussed must be used. While there is some transfer of training effect from one type of training to another, the amount of this transfer is dependent upon the similarity in the types of training. For example, a swimmer who is using only overdistance training will probably sprint faster than he would if he were doing no training at all, but he will not sprint as fast as he would if he were doing sprint training, nor will he sprint as fast as he would if he were doing some middle-distance training.

The Use of Intermittent Work and Its Application

Most of the physical activity in which humans engage is of an intermittent nature — very little can be characterized as continuous. We engage in short bouts of activity interrupted by periods of light work or rest. This is true of most of our sports activities — football, baseball, tennis, etc. It is also true of vigorous work, such as digging ditches, working on an air hammer, and so on. Children and animals play their games in this manner. This type of intermittent physical activity is so common that it could be characterized as an inherent pattern of behavior.

Man and animals can work at very intense levels of maximal effort for only short periods of time. They must, therefore, if they are to work continuously, pace themselves and work at lower levels of intensity, or if they do work at high levels of intensity, must alternate these work periods with rest or diminished work. Fatigue during intense activity results from the build-up of fatigue products in the muscle — primarily lactic acid — plus depletion of muscle glycogen and the inability of the body to supply enough oxygen to the muscle. When periods of rest are permitted between the bouts of exercise, the body is able to recover from some of the effects of fatigue by decreasing the level of lactic acid and raising the level of glycogen and oxygen in the muscle. This type of intermittent exercise permits the athlete to work at a more intense level of stress without suffering as much from the cumulative effects of fatigue.

As we will see when we examine the training schedule of champions, most of their training is done with some form of intermittent work.

For many years swimmers trained almost exclusively on continuous types of training, thirty years ago the workout schedule of a champion might have consisted of the following:

Swim 1 mile   Kick ½ mile   Pull ½ mile

This workout would be an application of the one training method we mentioned earlier — overdistance training. As he got near the bigger swimming meets at the end of the season, a swimmer would probably add some springs, such as 4 x 50-yard all-out efforts, to his training program.

Training the Distance Swimmer

The swimmer who trains for the 1000-yard to the 1650-yard swims must do a great deal of aerobic work progressively nearer the rate at which he will wish to compete. He should train at least on a six day per week basis at first with some elements of distance training and Fartlek training, but then predominantly with the slow interval training. Distances from 8,000 to 15,000 yards per day are desirable and probably necessary for peak adaptation. Across his training season the amount of fast interval training he does should be increased, but the bulk of his program should be slow interval training, at first with rest periods long enough to permit him to do the work at the required rate but gradually lowering the rest period below 30 seconds, thus forcing him to do aerobic work. In some kinds of training schemes, his rest period may be as short as 5 to 10 seconds. he must adjust the rate at which he swims to allow himself to swim aerobically, as the rest period does not allow adequate time for resynthesis of the anaerobic systems. If he swims hard enough to utilize the anaerobic metabolic systems, an accumulation of lactic acid in the muscles will soon force him to stop.

Interval Training and Related Methods

After World War II — in the late 1940s — champion swimmers started using an intermittent form of training that runners had been using since 1939 — a method known as interval training.

Interval Training. Interval training is a method of training in which the body is subjected to regularly repeated submaximal bouts of exercise interspersed with controlled periods of rest. The rest periods are relatively short, and while they do permit partial recovery, they do not permit complete or even nearly complete recovery of the body from the fatigue of the previous bouts of exercise. An example of an interval training routine would be to swim 15 x 100 yards with a rest interval of 10 seconds between each 100-yard swim.

The term *interval training* is often erroneously used to describe any training method in which a series of bouts of exercise is interspersed with a series of rest intervals. The term *interval training* has its origin from the use of fixed distances and rest intervals, but to qualify as interval training the method must meet the following criteria:

1. There must be a series of bouts of exercise at submaximal effort.
2. The interval of rest must be short enough to permit only partial recovery from the previous bouts of exercise.

If the swimmer were to swim 5 x 100 with 3 to 5 minutes rest between each effort, and if each effort was at maximal effort, this would not qualify as interval training but would be categorized as *repetition training*.

Repetition Training. Repetition training is a method of training in which the body is subjected to a series of bouts of exercise at maximum or near-maximum speed interspersed with controlled long periods of rest in which there is relatively complete recovery of the body from the fatigue of the previous bouts of exercise.

The average speed at which the swimmer swims the 15 x 100 with 10 seconds rest interval would be slower than when he swims 5 x 100 with 5 minutes rest. For example, Mark Spitz swam 15 x 100 with 10 seconds rest with an average time of 55.2 seconds, whereas when he swam 5 x 100 with 5 minutes rest his average time was 47.8 seconds.

Repetition training is the ultimate method in terms of intense training stress and should be used sparingly. A small amount of it can be used each day, but if large doses of it are used in each training session, the body will fail to adapt to this level of stress and the swimmer will become overstressed and will be pushed into the stage of failing adaptation.

Repetition Training

The proper use of repetition training conditions the body to swim for a moderate length of time at an intense speed, whereas the use of interval training adapts the body to swim at a moderate rate of speed for longer periods of time.

It is desirable to use both methods of training, but the total amount of interval training used in a mixed program of training will be 5 to 10 times greater in total distance than the amount of repetition training. Table 1.2 lists the differences between the two types of training, using sets of repeat swims as done by Olympic champion Jim Montgomery as examples.

When using either method of training, the swimmer or coach has to make decisions concerning four factors before setting up the workout routine. These factors can be easily remembered by remembering the cue word DIRT:

D—distance to be swum
I—interval of rest between each repeat swim
R—repetitions or how many bouts of exercise or repeat swims
T—average time the distance is to be swum in

The difference between the two methods may be summarized under each of these headings as follows:

1. *Distance.* Both methods can use the same distances (50, 100, 150, 200, 300, etc.).
2. *Interval of Rest.* Interval training uses short rest intervals (5, 10, 15, 30 sec.) while repetition training uses long rest intervals (1, 2, 3 min.).
3. *Repetitions.* Interval training involves the use of many repeats, such as 30 x 50, 20 x 100, 10 x 200, etc., while repetition training uses considerably fewer repeats, i.e., 10 x 50, 5 x 100, 4 x 200, etc.
4. *Time.* In interval training, the times used are much slower than those used in repetition training. Repetition training times should be 5 to 15 percent faster than interval training times for the same distance.

In a training program, a swimmer might also want to swim some of his repeat swims with a moderate amount of rest. For instance, he might swim 10 x 100 with a 45-second rest interval. Would this be interval training or repetition training? It actually is not important what we call it. In distinguishing between the two methods of training I was trying primarily to develop a concept, and it is really not important what the methods are called as long as the reader remembers the following concepts:

Important Concepts

1. The shorter the period of the rest interval between repeat swims, the greater the effect on building endurance and the less the effect on speed.
2. The longer the period of the rest interval, the higher the quality of the repeat swim.
3. A swimmer can tolerate large volumes of low or moderate-quality work such as over-distance or interval training, but large quantities of high-quality work such as repetition training or all-out time trials can cause overstress.

The use of pulse rate helps the swimmer and coach to evaluate:

1. How much effort the swimmer used in swimming a given effort. The higher the pulse rate, the harder the effort has been, with most swimmers reaching maximum pulse rates of 180 to 200 beats per minute.

2. The condition of the swimmer. When the swimmer is in poor condition, a given effort (for example, 60 seconds for 100 yards freestyle) will cause a higher pulse rate than when he is in good condition.

3. His state of fatigue. It may even show when he is ill or becoming ill. Under any of these conditions (fatigue, illness, or incipient illness), the swimmer will have a higher pulse rate than his average. This is particularly true after a moderate swimming effort.

The advantage of the use of the intermittent work training methods discussed is obvious:

1. It permits the athlete to use a more intense training stimulus than continuous training methods.

2. It permits the athlete to be exposed to the stress he will encounter in race conditions not just once but many times in a single workout.

3. It permits unlimited opportunities for changing routines and consequently avoids the boredom associated with continuous training methods.

4. Intermittent type of physical activity is probably more basic to man's nature than is prolonged continuous work.

Five Types of Training

1. **Fartlek Training** (speed play). Fartlek training consists of swimming relatively long distances of one-half mile and over continuously, using a variety of speeds.

2. **Overdistance Training** — Overdistance training consists of training at distances greater than the distance of the event for which the swimmer is training and, naturally, at a speed slower than that he will use in the actual race.

3. **Interval Training** — Interval training consists of swimming a series of repeat efforts at a given distance with a controlled amount of rest between efforts. The rest interval is long enough to permit partial, but not complete, recovery of the heart rate to normal.

4. **Repetition Training** — Repetition training consists of swimming a series of repeats of a shorter distance than and at a greater speed than that swum in a race. The rest interval is long enough to permit almost complete recovery of the heart and respiratory rate.

5. **Sprint Training** — Sprint training consists of swimming all-out efforts at top speed, either in a series (6x50 all-out efforts with a long rest) or as isolated efforts (1x75, 1x50, 1x25).

A Mixed Program of Training

Nearly all world-class competitive swimmers use a combination of at least three or four methods of training. When a combination of methods is integrated into a single program of training, it is called a *mixed program*.

Hypoxic Training — Hypoxic training is a method in which a swimmer practices controlled breathing and breathes fewer times than he ordinarily would.

For instance, if he breathes once every arm cycle when swimming a 200-meter repeat swim, he might breathe only half as often by breathing every second arm cycle, or he might even try breathing only one third as often by breathing every third arm cycle. It is really not so much a method of training as it is a type of breathing that can be used with the different methods. This type of breathing can be used when doing any of the five methods of training mentioned earlier in this chapter. When the swimmer takes in less air, the level of oxygen debt in the body is increased and becomes a stress factor that brings about certain desirable physiological changes. Several research studies show that this type of training has desirable effects and improves the athlete's ability to extract more oxygen from the inhaled air.

Hypoxic Training and Other Methods of Training Evaluated

When discussing methods of training, it seems logical to first talk about the physiological changes or adaptations that result from the various methods. But, in fact, such an approach is often limited to something like the following statement: "When you sprint, you develop speed; when you swim over-distance, you develop endurance." While this statement is true, it is certainly simplistic, and to allow our intellectual curiosity to proceed no further is to limit our understanding and possibly the advancement of training methods.

For years the exercise physiology books discussed the gross physiological changes that occur as a result of training; i.e., when overdistance work is done, the cardiovascular ability is improved, the athlete's heart can pump more blood and consequently can carry more oxygen to the muscles and take away more carbon dioxide, and so on. Such changes as these have been studied and restudied and are old hat to all of us.

More recently — just in the past few years actually — researchers have begun to examine the physiological changes at the cellular level and are making some important and interesting discoveries. These discoveries and their implications in evaluating our training methods are subjects that intrigue me both as a coach and as a physiologist. It is this area I want to explore with the reader.

First, let us examine the muscle and see what makes it contract. A good comparison can be made between the internal combustion engine and the human engine. The pistons compare to the muscles, and both of them must have fuel to do their work. In the automobile's engine the fuel, of course, is gasoline; in the muscle the fuel is ATP (adenosine triphosphate). When the fuel tank is empty the car's engine can no longer operate. The same is true of the muscles: without ATP they cannot contract or relax. The gasoline needs to be oxidized (or burnt) before it can release its energy. This type of energy-release is referred to as aerobic because it involves the use of air. Oxygen comprises 21 percent of the air we breath, and it is this oxygen that is needed to oxidize the gasoline. The engine can also be turned over by stepping on the starter and allowing the battery to do the work anaerobically (without air). The muscles can also contract both aerobically and anaerobically. In the absence of oxygen the car's engine can turn over for only short periods of time until the battery runs out of charge. This is also true of the muscle; the total energy it can release without oxygen is very limited compared with what it can do with aerobic work.

ATP—CP System of Energy (Anaerobic) — The ATP immediately available in the muscle can only supply the energy demands of all-out sprinting for a short period of time (approximately 5 to 10 seconds). Since the swimmer can swim only a 25-yard all-out effort using this system, if he continues to swim hard for the next 25, 50, or 75 yards his muscles must receive their source of ATP from another system.

Lactic-Acid-ATP System Anaerobic — The next source of ATP is the lactic-acid-ATP system. This system is also anaerobic and is also limited insofar as the length of time it can operate, (i.e., 10 seconds to 2 minutes, as in swimming 50, 100, even up to 200 yards). The ATP during this period comes from the breakdown of muscle glycogen or glucose in the presence of certain catalysts in the cytoplasm of the muscle, resulting in an accumulation of lactic acid. This accumulation of lactic acid along with exhaustion of the supply of glycogen becomes the main limiting factor in muscular activity and causes fatigue. The muscle also builds up an oxygen debt that must eventually be repaid. In other words, when the swimmer receives ATP from this source there is a build-up in both oxygen debt and lactic-acid concentration.

ATP is the first-hand energy provider for the muscle. As it breaks down to adenosine diphosphate, it loses one phosphate molecule. Creatine phosphate is available to resynthesize adenosine triphosphate from adenosine diphosphate ($CP + ADD$ = Creatine + ATP). This activity can go on theoretically until the supply of creatine phosphate is exhausted. It is likely that the level of CP in the muscle can be increased by sprint training, i.e., 10 X 25 with 20-second rest interval.

Glycogen breaks down into pyruvic acid to provide high-energy phosphates which are available to change ADP (adenosine diphosphate) back into ATP. Pyruvic acid is then changed to lactic acid by picking up a hydrogen ion.

Aerobic or Stead-State System

The third source of ATP for the muscle comes from aerobic activity. In this type of exercise the effort is less intense, and if it is completely aerobic can be continued almost indefinitely, as in swimming a very long race, such as across the English Channel. The oxygen supply to the muscles is sufficient to oxidize and resynthesize the lactic acid into glycogen with the release of carbon dioxide, water, and energy. The availability of oxygen to the muscle cells in the final analysis is what determines endurance in prolonged physical work. There is no lactic-acid accumulation during aerobic work and also no oxygen debt. When the body works at a level at which there is no oxygen debt build-up, it is said to be in the *steady state*.

In events under two minute's duration (approximately 200 yards) the work is predominantly anaerobic. After this period the aerobic ability of the swimmer becomes more important. In the 1500-meter swim approximately 90 percent of the energy used is developed via the oxygen system. Obviously a person training for this event should stress training that improves his ability to transport oxygen and to use the oxygen at the cellular level, such as overdistance training and short-rest interval training.

Type of Overload Determines the Type of Change at the Cellular Level

It becomes very important to understand that there are two entirely different types of adaptations made to endurance training versus speed training. When using speed training, you overload the muscle in terms of intensity — this is somewhat similar to weight lifting. To test this premise, in the summer of 1974 our sprinters were trained with over-distance training, interval training, and repetition training they did no spring training. In lieu of sprint training, strength-building exercises done at a fast speed with near maximum resistance using isokinetic exercisers were substituted. The swimmers were highly successful, placing first, second, and seventh in the National AAU Championships Long Course.

The swimmer must devise a plan of training, using a combination of the four methods of training shown in the following paragraphs.

1. Overdistance Training

Definition: Continuous swimming of long distance, such as 400, 1500 yards or meters or even longer distances

Percentage aerobic/anaerobic:

70% to 95% aerobic

30 to 5% anaerobic

Physiological changes: The advantage of this type of training is that it places a great demand on the oxygen-transportation system, resulting in the following adaptations: increased cardiac output and greater stroke volume of the heart; a slower resting pulse rate; improved ability of the lungs to extract oxygen from the air; improved quality of the blood, enabling it to carry more oxygen; storage of more glycogen in the liver and muscles; increase in the number of functional capillaries in the muscle; increase in the number and composition of the mitochondria in the muscle fibers.

2. Short-Rest-Interval Training

Definition: Swimming various repeat efforts at a moderate speed with a short rest interval between each — 5 to 20 sec. For example: 15 x 100 with 10-sec. rest interval

Percentage aerobic/anaerobic:

55 to 85% aerobic

45 to 15% anaerobic

Physiological changes: The changes manifested here are similar to those mentioned above under over-distance training plus, to a lesser extent, those mentioned below under repetition training. The advantages of this method over over-distance are (1) during the short rest period some of the ATP-CP resources are partially replenished and available for use in the next repeat swim, thus delaying the accumulation of lactic acid somewhat, with the result that even though the work is more intense than in overdistance training, extremely high levels of lactic acid are not accumulated; (2) even during a short rest interval some of the lactic acid is resynthesized to glycogen (in the liver and kidneys) enabling the swimmer to work at a more intense level than he can in overdistance training; (3) during the rest interval the swimmer can restore some of the oxygen debt he has created. Oxygen debt is the main stimulus for many of the physiological changes that improve both aerobic and anaerobic capacity; thus it is not advantageous to eliminate it completely.

3. Repetition Training

Definition: Hard efforts at near top speed with long rest intervals. For example: 4 x 150 near top speed with 5 to 10 min. rest interval.

Percentage aerobic/anaerobic:
   30 to 50% aerobic
   70% to 50% anaerobic

Physiological changes: During this type of training most of the ATP comes from anaerobic breakdown of glycogen in the cytoplasm. The catalysts required for this activity are also found in the cytoplasm of the muscle cell. There is apparently an increase in both the glycogen and catalyst stored in the muscles, and this is perhaps the main adaptation that results from repetition training.

The high level of oxygen debt and lactic acid incurred during this type of training probably is the stimulus that brings about changes that cause more efficient absorption and transportation of oxygen — that is, increased number of functional capillaries, increased number and quality of mitochondria, advantageous changes in blood chemistry, and so on. This type of training adapts the muscle tissues to high lactate concentrations.

4. Sprint Training

Definition: All-out sprinting for short distances. for example, 10 x 25 yd. with 20 to 30 sec. rest.

Percentage aerobic/anaerobic:
   85% anaerobic
   15% aerobic

Physiological changes: This type of training improves the muscle's ability to contract fast (due to improved neuromuscular coordination) plus increased strength (due to increased levels of actomyosin). There is also probably an increase in the ATP-CP level in the muscle, resulting in the increased ability of the swimmer to sustain sprinting tempo for a longer period of time.

The four methods listed above do not preclude their use in combinations and variations such as interval training with moderate rest (i.e., 15x100 with 30 seconds rest interval). This type of interval training is more anaerobic than the type mentioned above under Short-Rest-Interval Training, but is not so anaerobic as that mentioned under Repetition Training.

These four methods and their variations and combinations are all based on the concept that the body has the ability to adapt itself to maintain a high level of the ATP in the muscle. Insofar as endurance is concerned, the more ATP that can be produced aerobically the better, since glucose can provide 19 times as much energy per gram mole aerobically as it can anaerobically. It appears that any adaptations that bring about better transportion and absorption of oxygen and tolerance to lack of oxygen would benefit the athlete. It is reasonabe to assume that these changes could be facilitated by running high levels of oxygen debt in the muscle. Ordinarily the swimmer does this by working at such an intense level that he has to create the ATP for the muscle's contraction anaerobically (either via the ATP-CP system or the lactic-acid system).

Hypoxic Training

A high level of oxygen debt may be created at even lower intensities of work is to inhale less air by breathing less often, thus making less oxygen available to the cellular level — in other words, through the use of controlled breathing, also termed hypoxic training. In training for track, the Czechs, East Germans, and even some American athletes have tried this type of training using such patterns as the following: inhale for six steps, hold the breath for six steps, exhale for six steps, and so on. Some have even practiced breath-holding when not exercising. I'm not convinced this latter practice is of much value.

Some research on hypoxic training has shown desirable effects. Kenneth Sparks, in a research project at Indiana University in 1973-74, trained two groups four days a week, using interval training. One group used normal breathing, while the other trained in the same manner with the addition of hypoxic breathing. Sparks concluded that the hypoxic group showed a greater efficiency in the extraction of oxygen. "it can be concluded that training using controlled breathing can benefit the athlete in his extracting more oxygen per unit volume ventilated."

Under hypoxic conditions, at a given rate of swimming or exercising, the oxygen debt and the blood lactate (also the lactic-acid concentration in the muscles) are higher than those attained under the same training program, but using a normal breathing pattern.

Hollman and Liesen tested the effect of hypoxia training on 36 subjects. The subjects breathed a mixture of air with only 12 percent oxygen content, rather than the normal 21 percent, while training on a stationary bicycle or on a treadmill. This type of breathing is not the same as the controlled breathing used in swimming or track training, but there is so little research on the subject of hypoxic training that I refer to this study for lack of other available research material. The result was that a lower amount of oxygen was available to the muscles, the same finding as under controlled breating conditions. Reference to this study at this point might therefore have some relevance.

The maximum oxygen intake per minute rose with the hypoxia-trained group by 16.6 percent, while the control group improved only 5.5 percent. This difference of increase is significant and favors the hypoxia group. There was no detectable increase in the number of erythrocytes (red blood cells) or in the amount of hemoglobin. The heart volume also remained unchanged. The acid-base equilibrium showed a slight reduction of the negative acid excess value and a slight rise of standard bicarbonates.

The following three points can be considered as an explanation for the increased cardiopulmonal capacity under hypoxia conditions:

1. The intramuscular blood distribution can be additionally economized and hence the efficiency of the blood supply increased . . .

2. An improved vascularization could be the result of hypoxi training. But the possibility of improved capillarization is undecided . . .

3. An enlargement of the intracellular metabolic capacity with an increase of the energy supplying process per unit of time.[5]

For workouts consisting of swimming 5 x 200-yard repeat efforts with an average time of 2:05.1, leaving every 3 minutes (approximately 55 seconds rest interval), the Indiana swimmers recorded the following pulse-rate increases:

1. Normal breathing — pulse rate after last 200 — 150.4
2. Hypoxic breathing every second arm cycle — 153.4;
3. Hypoxic breathing every third arm cycle — 167.3

An interesting aspect of the above data is that there is very little increase in the pulse rate when the breathing rate is changed from a normal to a controlled breathing pattern of once every second arm cycle. In swimming 100 efforts the increase was only 2.9 beats, while in changing from a normal breathing pattern to one of every third arm cycle the increase was 13.8 beats per minute. The same pattern can be observed in the 200-yard swims. Later in the season (eight weeks) the difference in the pulse-rate increases between the three breathing patterns narrowed considerably: for 5 x 200-yard swims with times of 2:03.4, they were as follows:

1. Normal breathing — 150.8
2. Breathing every second arm cycle — 152.9
3. Breathing every third arm cycle — 161.4

This represents a difference between 1 and 3 after eight weeks of hypoxic training of 10.6 seconds, compared to 16.9 seconds when the experiment first started.

Unfortunately, no control group was used in this experiment, but it is reasonable to think that the decrease in heart rate after eight weeks of hypoxic training was due to some physiological adaptations. The main stimulus for this adaptation is probably a decreased level of oxygen and an increased level of carbon dioxide and lactic-acid concentration in the muscles and the blood.

Obviously the additional stress imposed on the swimmers by breathing only every second arm cycle is not so great that it causes much of an increase in the swimmers' heart rates. A high level of carbon dioxide in the blood acts on chemoceptors in the carotid artery and in the respiratory center, causing an increase in the pulse rate. Assuming that thorough hypoxic training we are trying to increase the oxygen debt and lactic-acid level in the body generally and in the muscle fibers specifically, it would seem that a higher pulse rate would be desirable. For this reason, once the swimmers (in this case free-stylers) become accustomed to breathing every second arm cycle, I encourage them to proceed immediately to breathing every third arm cycle. For short distance repeats, such as 50s, they may try breathing only every four arm cycles.

Guidelines for Use of Hypoxic Training

Here are set down a few principles of hypoxic training that can serve as a guide for the swimmer and coach:

1. Caution: hypoxic training is potentially dangerous. If the breath is held too long, unconsciousness will result. Remember — drowning is permanent!

2. If headaches develop with the use of hypoxic training, they should disappear within a half hour. If they persist, the amount of hypoxic training used in practice should be decreased and only slowly reinstated. Adaptation may be an individual matter; thus progression should take place with this in mind.

3. Approximately a quarter to a half of the total workout should be done hypoxically.

4. All of the pulling in a workout should be done hypoxically — breathing every second or, even better, every third arm cycle.

5. Most of the hypoxic training in a workout should be done at controlled speeds. Very little of sprinting at top speed should be done hypoxically.

6. Competitive races should not be attempted using hypoxic breathing. The breathing pattern that best suits the individual swimmer should be used.

7. The shorter the repeat swim, the more strokes the swimmer should take per breath. When swimming 10 x 50, he might breathe every third or fourth arm cycle; while swimming 4 x 500, he might breathe every second or third arm cycle.

8. When using hypoxic breathing for strokes other than freestyle, the following patterns should be used:

Butterfly — Breathe every second or third stroke on 100 and 220 swims; breathe every third, fourth, or fifth stroke on 25, 50, and 75 swims.

Backstroke — The same as for freestyle.

Breaststroke — Breathe every second or third stroke, never failing to lift the head as if for breathing in order not to disturb stroke mechanics. Also try taking two long strokes off the wall at the turn.

9. A conscious effort should be made *not to change stroke mechanics* when breathing hypoxically. There is a tendency to shorten the pull in order to take more strokes per breath.

The swimmer should concentrate on retaining good stroke mechanics.

10. The swimmer should practice race breathing patterns when using hypoxic training. For example, if he swims a 50 taking one breath on the first and two breaths on the second 25, he can use the same pattern when swimming 5 x 50 with a 30-second rest interval. This technique would also apply to the breathing pattern for the 100-yard race, and so on.

11. Each week the swimmer should swim some overdistance training at slow to moderate speed, concentrating on stroke mechanics, but using hypoxic breathing (i.e., 1000 yards within 30 seconds of best time).

12. At the risk of being repetitious, remember the hazard involved in breath-holding drills. The swimmer should *never* attempt to see how far he can swim without breathing. When using hypoxic training for any distance over 100 yards, the swimmer should take at least two breaths per 25 yards.

Pulse Rate Related to Anaerobic Work

Most of the literature on the topic states that up to a pulse rate of 150 beats per minute the source of energy is aerobic. Above this rate the shift is toward an anaerobic source of ATP. Many factors, however, enter into determining the pulse rate. Such factors as state of emotion, age and individual differences, elapsed time since eating, elapsed time since intake of coffee, and so on, must be considered. If the swimmer and coach want to use the pulse rate as an indicator in determining roughly whether the swimmer is performing aerobically or anaerobically in practice, they should use the pulse-rate table.

Respiratory Rate and Distress Used in Evaluating Aerobic and Anaerobic Work

Along with the pulse rate, the breathing rate after an effort and the desire to breathe plus the respiratory distress felt during the actual swim are all indicators as to whether the swimmer is performing aerobic or anaerobic work or a combination of the two. In the course of the swim, if he (1) has no desire to breathe any more than he is breathing and feels no respiratory distress, he is performing aerobic work; (2) wants to breathe more but is not feeling extremely distressed, he is performing a combination of aerobic and anaerobic work; (3) feels a strong desire to breathe more frequently and his breathing is extremely distressed, he is working most anaerobically.

After the effort is completed, the same indicators mentioned above apply, but the rate of breathing and the recovery of the breathing rate toward normal also can serve as additional measures to evaluate the type of work done.

Adaptation of the Nervous System and Development of Resistance to the Feeling of Fatigue — For years it was believed that neuro-muscular block in voluntary effort was an important factor in the onset of fatigue. That is, the syraptic resistance at the point where the nerve and muscle meet become so great that it is difficult for the nerve impulse to get to the muscle. Transmission fatigue at the neuromuscular junction is no longer considered a plausible weak point.

Fatigue developing in the central nervous system (C.N.S.) is now considered to be one of the main limiting factors in voluntary muscular effort. Training no doubt improves the ability of the C.N.S. to adapt to moderate exercise prolonged over a period of time or to the stress of extremely intense effort over a short period of time. Each type of training must also bring about specific adaptations in the C.N.S., as well as in the muscles and organs of the body. We are conditioning the C.N.S. and the heart, the blood, the muscles, etc., simultaneously.

It is important that swimmers at some time use all methods of anaerobic and aerobic training to aid in these adaptations. It appears not only that the swimmer's body in general and the tissues of his muscles specifically must become accustomed to high levels of oxygen debt, but that the swimmer must also learn to tolerate the uncomfortable feelings associated with this condition. When he has done so, he may truly be said to have learned to tolerate pain. Hypoxic training appears to be a good supplement to a regular training program to accomplish this goal, as well as to facilitate the gross physiological changes and those at the cellular level.

Principles Common to All Four Competitive Strokes

There are slight and sometimes not-so-slight differences among the stroke mechanics of champion swimmers. These may be relatively unimportant idiosyncracies, such as a peculiar flip of the hand during the recovery phase of the arm pull, or major differences, such as one crawl swimmer's using a two-beat kick while another uses a six-beat kick. Such major differences need not lead the reader to think that these swimmers are applying different principles of fluid mechanics. All great swimmers obey certain principles of fluid mechanics, or they would not be great swimmers. For the same reason there are certain of these principles that are common to all four competitive strokes.

1. The hands are not pulled through the water in a straight line, but in some form of elliptical pattern. For many years crawl swimmers were told — and sometimes still are told — to pull their hands in a straight path down the center line of their bodies. In the butterfly, swimmers were told to put their arms in the water in front of their shoulders and to pull straight back. Fortunately, most swimmers, at least the better ones, did not follow these instructions, but pulled in elliptical patterns.

Why isn't a straight-line pull effective? Or put it this way: why is the elliptical (zigzag) pull pattern better than the straight-line pull? It seems reasonable to believe that if you push the water directly backward, you will be obeying Newton's third law of motion ("For every action there is an equal and opposite reaction") and will be pushing yourself directly forward. If the athlete were on a solid surface, such as the ground, this would be true, but the swimmer is pushing his hand against water, and when he does so, the water naturally moves in the direction the hand pushes it. If the hand continues to maintain a straight path, it can get little propulsion from pushing against water that is already moving in the same direction. This the hand must alter its path in order to contact still water. The best way for the hand to accomplish this is for it to move in some form of elliptical pattern.

Another reason for the hand to pull in this manner is that it is able to combine its elliptical pull pattern with a pitch in the position of the hand that will contribute a lift force generated by the hand.

Careful study of underwater movies of champion swimmers has shown that none of them pull in a straight line, no matter what competitive stroke they are swimming. Each champion swimmer may have a pull pattern slightly different from that of any other swimmer. In fact some backstrokers and crawl swimmers have a slightly different pull pattern from one arm to the other. The only swimmers I have photographed who pulled their hands through the water in a straight line were beginning swimmers or those who were poor swimmers and had had difficulty learning to swim.

Huh, your feet must be stronger than your head! —Stranger, to Colin Fletcher, during 1000 mile walk.

Grow up as soon as you can. It pays. The only time you really live fully is from thirty to sixty. . . . The young are slaves to dreams; the old servants of regrets. Only the middle-aged have all their five senses in the keeping of their wits. —H Allen

When swimming any of the four strokes, the swimmer starts his pull with the elbows straight (or, in a few cases, with just a slight degree of bend). As he pulls his arms through the water, the elbow (or elbows) starts to bend and continues to bend until it is in a vertical position (90 to 105 degrees) at which point the maximum degree of elbow bend should occur. From this point on backward, the degree of elbow bend begins to decrease until, at the very end of the pull, the elbow reaches almost complete extension (except in the breaststroke), at which time the arm recovery begins.

The elbow is carried in a high position during the pull. As the pull begins and the elbows bend, the upper arm should rotate medially (inwardly). This keeps the elbow in a high position during the first half of the pull. This action, plus the end in the elbow, places the hand in a good position to push the water backward.

The best way to illustrate this medial arm rotation is to hold your arms out directly in front of your chest at shoulder height, palms together. By rotating your arms inwardly, turn the hands around until the knuckles of each hand are touching one another and the palms are facing outward. During the actual swimming stroke, you will not medially rotate your arms this far, but you can begin to understand the action through the use of this drill. To get a better idea of how this action feels when swimming, do the same drill as mentioned above but begin with the elbows bent slightly. Keep the elbow bend constant and rotate the arm only half way so the palms are facing downward instead of out. In performing this action in the manner described you have imitated the high elbow position that is desirable in the first part of the pull in the butterfly, crawl, and breaststroke. In the backstroke, medial arm rotation is also desirable, but with the difference that the swimmer is inverted and his arms are pulling laterally instead of beneath him.

The hands should be pitched properly upon entry into and exit from the water. Upon entry into the water the hands should be pitched in such a manner as to knife the water cleanly and prevent dragging air bubbles after them. The entrapment or dragging of air bubbles after the hand decreases the amount of lift that the hand can create and thus decreases the effectiveness of the pull. In swimming the backstroke, the hands should enter in a vertical position directly over the shoulder with the little finger entering first and the palms facing outward. The entry of the hands should not be made with a relaxed hand that slaps the water. The fingers should be closed and in good alignment in order that the hand may knife into the water cleanly. The hand should not be tense, but should be controlled.

In swimming the butterfly and the crawl strokes, the hands enter the water pitched at a 35 to 45-degree angle, palms facing outward. If they enter the water flat, they will entrap air bubbles.

The pitch of the hands as they leave the water is also important. They should be lifted out of the water in a streamlined position in order that they may not pull the swimmer down or create a water turbulence against the swimmer's body. The swimmer should not intentionally push the water upward at the end of his pull on any of the strokes.

The hands should be pitched properly during the pull in order to obtain maximum lift. The pitch of the hands during the pull is also important. They should not be at right angles to the direction of the pull. They rather should be pitched at an angle of approximately 37 degrees with relation to their path through the water. The pitch of the hands during the pull of each stroke will be discussed in detail in the section for that stroke. The reader should understand exactly what pitch is and why it is important. The hands can be used to push the body forward in the water without ever moving backward themselves through the use of sculling action. To prove this the swimmer need only lie on his back, and, keeping his hands at his sides at hip level, use a figure-eight sculling action to push himself forward. In this case the swimmer is using hydro-dynamic lift (the Bernoulli principle) to propel himself forward.

When swimming the four competitive strokes, a swimmer also uses a sculling action of his hands as they are pulled through the water in an elliptical pull pattern. He is actually using his hands in the same manner as a propeller that is pushing a boat or an airplane forward.

298

Applications of Bernoulli's Principle

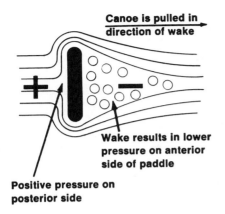

Canoe is pulled in direction of wake

Wake results in lower pressure on anterior side of paddle

Positive pressure on posterior side

Wake formation from a paddle. The canoe is pulled in the direction of the wake.

The propeller of a boat also uses Bernoulli's principle in the same manner, except that the blade moves in a vertical plane and the lift effect is used to push the boat in a horizontal plane.

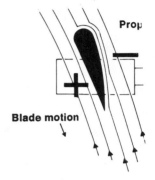

Prop

Blade motion

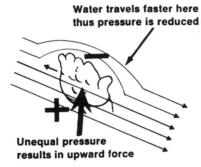

Water travels faster here thus pressure is reduced

Unequal pressure results in upward force

The hand of a swimmer can use lift to propel the swimmer forward by using Bernoulli's principle

The pitch of the right hand as it appears from underneath the surface

Counsilman's Crawl-Stroke, Arm-Pull Pattern
Dr. James E. Counsilman
World Famous U.S. Olympic Swimming Team Coach . . . Maker of Olympic Champions

1. *Zigzag pull*: On all competitive strokes some form of elliptical pull is used.

2. *Elbow bend*: Straight-bent-straight elbow action is used. Maximum elbow is 110 to 90 degrees.

3. *High elbow*: During first part of pull elbow is carried in an elbow-up position.

4. *Pitch of hands*: Hands are pitched 45 degrees as they enter water, so they create fewer air bubbles. They are also pitched as they leave so they create less resistance.

5. *Three types of kick* are used: (1) six-beat kick, (2) two-beat kick, and (3) two-beat crossover kick.

1. As one arm begins the pull with the elbow straight, the other arm begins its recovery by bending and lifting the elbow upward. The legs kick up and down in a flutter kick.

2. The pulling arm bends at the elbow. As it is pulled under the body the elbow is held high.

3. The pulling arm reaches maximum elbow bend as it passes under the shoulder and chest. Recovering arm enters the water directly in front of the shoulder.

4. As the arm pull nears completion, the head is rotated to the side for breathing.

5. Breath is taken as arm leaves water. Inhalation is through the month.

Theory and Research of Stroke Mechanics

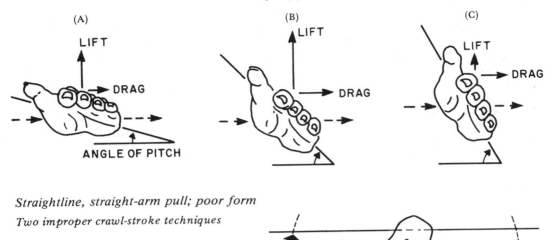

Swimmer's hand-edge view:
Lift-drag force interaction for
three angles of pitch

Straightline, straight-arm pull; poor form

Two improper crawl-stroke techniques

The straight-elbow, straight-line pull. This type of pull has been advocated by many people for many years and is inefficient.

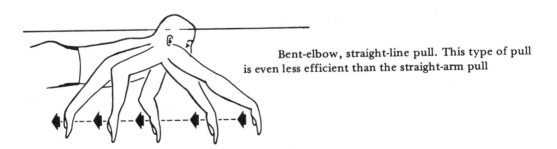

Bent-elbow, straight-line pull. This type of pull is even less efficient than the straight-arm pull

The swimmer does not pull with a straight arm, but uses a straight-bent-straight elbow action. If the swimmer were to pull with a straight arm, the hand would not be in a good position to exert force backward except during the middle of the pull.

For this reason he must pitch his hands in a manner that will provide maximum lift. This angle is approximately 37 degrees, as measured in relation to the path of the hand through the water.

The principle of streamlining has application in swimming, as in other methods of propulsion. A careful study of underwater movies of good swimmers as compared with those of poor swimmers shows that good swimmers are streamlined and create less resistance or drag than do poor swimmers.

Resistance or drag is composed of three types: (a) head-on or frontal residence, (b) eddy resistance, and (c) skin friction or resistance.

a. Head-on or frontal resistance is the resistance offered by any part of the body that faces forward in the direction in which the swimmer is progressing.

b. Tail suction or eddy resistance is the result of inability of the water to flow around the body in a liminar pattern and to fill in all of the curves, indentations, and parts of the body facing backwards. Water in these areas is therefore pulled forward and forms eddies.

c. Skin friction is the resistance resulting from the thin layer of water that encounters the skin as this water flows over the body.

Good swimmers create less frontal and eddy resistance than do poor swimmers and literally trade it for skin friction. Poor swimmers frequently swim slowly because they are inclined in the water at an angle and drag a lot of water along with them.

To create as little drag as possible, a swimmer should try to keep his body in a horizontal position and to develop as little sideward movement of his body as possible. Lateral or sideward movement of the body also increases frontal and eddy resistance. Sometimes a swimmer must sacrifice decreased resistance somewhat toachieve a more effective stroke. In the backstroke the swimmer will not swim in a completely flat horizontal position or his kick will be ineffective because it will be too high out of the water. He must therefore drop his hips a few inchs to keep his feet underwater where they can be effective.

The reader will also see that the swimmer has to sacrifice streamlining in the breast-stroke kick in order to achieve a more powerful kick.

The swimmer should not throw water against his body. If the swimmer is not aware of the consequences, he may unknowingly increase the amount of water resistance he must overcome by throwing water against his body or legs with his hands and/or arms. To move forward the swimmer must push water backward. As we have seen earlier in this section, the water moves backward at an angle and not directly backward. If this backward-moving water is pushed against any part of the swimmer's body, it will increase his drag and slow him down. The swimmer should never be able to feel any turbulence created by his arms against his body or legs.

The swimmer's forearm and hand may be so close to his body that some of the water turbulence is bound to be directed against his body. This may happen when the hands get too close to the body in the crawl or butterfly stroke, particularly during the middle part of the arm pull. It also tends to happen during the last part of the long arm pull after the turn in the breaststroke. At the end of the backstroke pull there is a tendency for some swimmers to push the palms of their hands directly toward the upper legs instead of toward the bottom of the pool. This technique creates a turbulence against the legs and results in increased resistance.

The Crawl Stroke

There are slight variations in the stroke mechanics of champion swimmers. For instance, some world record holders use a six-beat kick with the crawl stroke, while others use a two-beat crossover kick, and still others a straight two-beat kick. The same is true of slight variations in the pull pattern. Some crawl swimmers use an inverted-question-mark pull pattern, while some use an S-shaped pull pattern. The fact that such variations exist does not mean that each swimmer should be left alone to devise his own stroke mechanics. The swimmer must obey certain mechanical principles to swim efficiently.

The Great Hawaiian surfer and swimmer, and Olympic swimming Gold Medalist of the 1908 and the 1912 Olympic Games, Duke Kahanamoku (center) with some of the younger beach boys of this era. From the left, Paul Strauch, Jr., Joe Cabel, Duke, Fred Hemmings, and Butch Van Artsdaden. Duke popularized the "Flutter" leg stroke. He is also called the "Father of the Surfboard." It was said that due to the size of his feet, #17, that by kicking the flutter kick only, he could plane through the water with his head high out of the water. Duke was a very good friend of Dr. Bragg, being Olympic teammates in the 1912 games.

Arm Recovery

There is a lot of confusion about where the pull finishes and where the recovery begins in the arm stroke. The arm recovery begins when the hand and forearm are still in the water. Many coaches and swimmers believe the hand is pushing backward during the entire time it is underwater; as a result, they also believe the hand should finish the underwater pull with a vigorous thrust backward and upward with a flip of the hand. Careful study of underwater films of champion crawl swimmers reveals that none of them does this, even though some have stated that they do. All, however, finish the pull and begin the recovery when the hand position changes. The momentum of the arm and hand, developed during the pull phase of the stroke, continues without interruption into the recovery phase, but at the end of the arm pull, the palm of the hand is positioned facing directly backward. During the transition from pull to recovery the palm of the hand starts to be turned inward, so that it faces the thigh. As the hand lifts upward, the little finger leaves the water first and the hand, knifes out of the water, creating very little resistance.

A good way to describe this action is to liken it to sliding the hand out of a pants pocket.

The out of water arm recovery is made as the elbow lifts upward and is swung forward. Too little attention is paid to the out of water recovery phase of the total stroke. The often repeated statement "The only part of the stroke that counts is what happens under water" is an oversimplification of the complexities of stroke mechanics. A particular stroke defect prevalent among women swimmers is the use of the straight-arm recovery. In this type of recovery the elbow is not bent much, and the arm is carried over the water in a wide swinging movement. This type of recovery results in excessive lateral movement of the body; the hips and legs wiggle back and forth sideways in an application of Newton's third law of motion: "For every action there is an equal and opposite reaction." This movement causes an increase in frontal and eddy resistance and slows the swimmer's progress.

When the arm is recovered properly, the elbow is bent and carried in a high position, with the hand being held close to the body. This action keeps the radius of rotation close to the body and results in less lateral displacement of the hips and legs.

Common Mistakes in Arm Recovery

1. The most common mistake in arm recovery technique is the one already mentioned: too wide an arm recovery.

2. Swinging the hand too high — allowing the hand to swing so high that it is carried higher than the elbow — is another common stroke defect. It tends to cause body displacement, uses more energy, and may break the rhythm of the stroke.

3. Breaking rhythm — this can be done either by excessive acceleration or deceleration of the arm during the recovery. It cannot be shown in a picture, but it can be noticed by observing the swimmer's arm recovery and watching for any jerky movements or any sudden changes in velocity during the recovery phase of the stroke. The most common cause of this break in rhythm is late breathing. The swimmer breathes so late in the stroke that he must rush his arm forward. More about this later.

Arm Pull

Hand Entry into the Water

This occurs when the hand enters the water immediately before the elbow becomes fully extended.

Pitch of the Hand upon Entry

The hand is pitched so the palm is facing diagonally outward. If the hand is held flat in a horizontal position as it enters the water, it will drag air bubbles underwater with it. Such air entrapment decreases the efficiency of the pull and should be avoided. By positioning the hand's entrance into the water with the palm held at approximately a 45-degree angle to the surface — the thumb entering first — the hand can become submerged underwater without dragging a lot of air with it.

The Underwater Pull!

The underwater pull is a complex movement which is first described in a very general manner, analyzing each aspect of it later.

In the process of discussing the pull, it dispels a common misconception that the hands and arms should be pulled in a straight line directly underneath the body. Photographs show that swimmers, while they use a variety of elliptical pull patterns, never pull in a perfect straight-line pattern. Some swimmers may use a variation of this pattern in which the pattern may assume more of an S shape. The width of the pattern may also vary slightly from one swimmer to the next, due perhaps to variations in strength, flexibility, or other factors of which we are not cognizant.

Another common misconception is that the elbows should be kept straight during the pull. The pull begins with the elbow straight or almost straight, but during the pulling phase, it bends.

The Beginning of the Arm Pull

Once the hand and arm become completely submerged, the palm of the hand is turned from the diagonal position by rotation of the forearm, the action occurring between the radius and ulna bones. As soon as the swimmer starts his pull he should concentrate on bending the elbow immediately.

Wrist Flexion during the Beginning of the Pull

During the very beginning of the pull in movies of such great swimmers as Mark Spitz, Jim Montgomery, and John Murphy, there is a noticed marked flexion of the wrist. This places the palm of the hand in a favorable position to push the water backward at a better angle than if the wrist were to remain in straight alignment.

Elbow Bend during the Pull

As the arm is pulled down and back, the bend in the elbow increases until it reaches maximum bend when the hand is directly under the body and the upper arm is at a 90-degree angle with the body (Figs. 4.24C and 4.25). From this point backward the hand is pushed backward by extension of the elbow until, at the end of the pull, the elbow reaches almost complete extension.

Hand Pitch

The swimmer's "feel for the water" is determined by his ability to pitch his hand and forearm. Contrary to popular opinion, "feel for the water," or the ability to maintain purchase on the water does not imply that the hand is held at 90° to the direction of motion of the pull. In order to produce lift forces the hand must be pitched or angled.

Either less or more pitch will result in a decrease in lift force. In the case of too much pitch an airfoil is said to be stalled, and in swimming this indicates that the hand is being used as a paddle instead of a propeller blade. With too little pitch both lift and drag forces diminish and the hand is in effect sliding. Thus we see that in order to produce maximum lift forces a swimmer must strike a delicate balance in hand pitch based on his sensitivity or feel for the water.

The horizontal, or drag force, components increase continuously with the angle of pitch. It is through the use of the interaction of both lift and drag forces that the swimmer achieves straight forward progress from his widely fluctuating pulling patterns and hand velocities.

Note that the size of the lift and drag force components entirely determines the orientation of the resultant propulsive force. Too steep an angle of pitch will produce a force angled to the side, and possibly introduce lateral hip motion in the swimmer.

Thus, efficient propulsion is dependent on lift-drag force interaction. For the swimmer this means that the pitch of the hand must be continuously adjusted to ever changing directions of pull. Even the forearm can be pitched to increase propeller-like pulling surfaces. High elbow position is common among talented swimmers.

It is interesting to note that the hand and forearm may not always be oriented to produce a force directly backwards. At times, extraneous inertial and kicking forces must be canceled by the pull in order to produce straight forward propulsion upon the swimmer's free body diagram.

That the arm pull adjusts lift-drag force interaction in response to the kick sheds light upon the variation in style between six-beat and two-beat freestyle. Carlile observed that at the Munich Olympics the six-beaters had a low stroke frequency (as low as 39 strokes per lap in a 400-meter race) and the two-beat kickers had a high stroke frequency (as high as 54 strokes per lap). That the two groups swam equally well appears mysterious at first, especially when one considers Counsilman's conclusion that the kick does not directly provide propulsion in freestyle. An understanding of lift-drag force interaction does provide an explanation, however.

It seems that a six-beat kicker could achieve higher sideways and up-and-down hand speeds at midstroke because of the availability of lateral and vertical kicking forces. The drag component of the hand could neutralize eccentric kicking forces and the lift component could approach its maximum value.

Pull Pattern

The hand is pulled through the water in some form of elliptical pattern. This pull may appear to be almost straight-line, but the reader must remember that the pull is three- not two-dimensional.

High Elbow Position

The elbow should be carried in a high position during the first half of the pull. This permits the hand to be in a good position to push the water backward at an efficient angle. This action is accomplished through two separate movements of the upper arm and the elbow. The upper arm is rotated inwardly (medially) and the elbow is simultaneously bent.

The mistake most commonly seen in poor swimmers is the dropped elbow during the pull. This type of pull does not permit a good application of force. Due to poor positioning of the hand, the direction of the force is downward and not backward, resulting in little forward thrust.

Head Position

A great deal of misunderstanding prevails concerning the position in which the head should be carried. The head should not be carried in a high position with the water line striking the swimmer at the forehead, but should be lower so as to achieve a more streamlined position.

Summary

This study examines the possibility that the propulsive force exerted by the water on the hand is one of lift rather than drag. Through the study of champion swimmers' underwater arm-pull patterns, as determined by sequence photography and time-exposure photography with flashing lights attached to the swimmers' hands, various elliptical pull patterns were observed.

A swimmer swims more efficiently by moving a larger amount of water back more slowly than by moving a smaller amount of water back more rapidly. The champion swimmers observed in this study accomplished this by applying Bernoulli's principle. They moved their hands in elliptical patterns and changed the pitch of their hands so the flow of the water over the knuckle side of their hands was at a faster speed than that of the water on the palm side of the hand.

The propeller is the most efficient means of propulsion in water currently known. The propeller blades do not push any water directly backwards, but, instead, they actually move forward in the water continuously, always encountering still water. The sideways rotation of the propeller produces a force backwards in accordance with Bernoulli's principle of fluid mechanics. Bernoulli's principle, or the lift principle, explains how Newton's third law of action-reaction can be met without pulling on a straight line. The lift force results from pressure differences and is directed at right angles to the line of motion of the wing or propeller blade.

Lift Force

Thus, in order to produce a forward lift force a swimmer must move his hand in a sculling motion from side to side or up and down. These sculling motions can achieve the pressure difference illustrated above provided the hand is pitched so that the flow of water over the knuckle side of the hand is faster than the under the palm side of the hand.

Proper placement of the head permits the swimmer to breathe at the bottom of the bow wave. Carrying the head too high causes a slight drop of the hips and increases drag or resistance. In addition it places the head in a position such that when the swimmer turns his head to breathe, his mouth will be in the bow wave. He will then have to turn his head farther to the side than he would have to do if his head were lower.

Breathing

The air is inhaled in the very short period of time that the mouth is out of the water. Ideally, the air is exhaled almost continuously during the time the face is underwater. The air is forced gently out of the mouth during the first part of the exhalation. During the last part of the underwater exhalation, exhalation becomes more vigorous as air bubbles can be seen leaving the nose as well as the mouth. The final exhalation is a sudden push of air out of the mouth as the mouth breaks the surface. This action forces the drops of water away from the lips so the swimmer can inhale without sucking in water.

One formerly held opinion about breathing that has recently been revived is that of "explosive breathing." This method of breathing was first advocated forty years ago and has been rejuvenated by coaches who want to develop a "new" technique. It provides poor ventilation and causes too much tension in the breathing muscles. The rhythmical breathing method used by Mark Spitz and described above is the preferred type of inhaling and exhaling.

A common defect in breathing concerns the timing of the head movement with relation to the arm stroke. The breath (inhalation) should be taken when the body is at its maximum roll to the side. This point occurs when the hand on the breathing side is beginning its recovery.

Body Roll

The body rolls 35 to 45 degrees on each side as the swimmer makes a complete arm cycle. The swimmer rolls more on the side on which he breathes than on the nonbreathing side. He should not roll intentionally, but he should allow the roll to come as a natural reaction to other parts of his stroke. He also should not try to swim flat and inhibit the roll.

The Kick

Swimmers use various types of kick with the crawl stroke. In 1976 the United States World Games Trials finals in the men's 100-meter freestyle seven of the eight swimmers used a six-beat kick with their strokes, and the eighth used a two-beat crossover kick. This was also true in the case of the women's 100-meter freestyle; seven of the finalists used a six-beat kick, but the winner, Shirley Babashof, used a straight two-beat kick. In the finals of the men's 1500-meter freestyle, the winner, Tim Shaw, as well as six of the eight finalists, used the two-beat crossover kick, while only one swimmer, Mike Bruner, used a six-beat kick. In the women's 800-meter freestyle event, seven of the finalists used the straight two-beat kick, and only one of the finalists used a six-beat kick.

It would appear from these data that the six-beat kick is better adapted for sprinting, and the two-beat kick for distance swimming. Indeed, this seems to be true. This may be due to the fact that in a distance race the heart cannot continue to supply enough blood to the arms and legs. The swimmer may therefore automatically modify his kick to make blood readily available to the main source of propulsion — the arms — or it may be that the swimmer who adopts this style of kicking tends to be more successful in distance events due at least partially to the fact that he has made more blood available to his arms.

Some swimmers have the ability to switch back and forth from a two-beat to a six-beat kick. Ken Knox and Tom Hickcox are two swimmers on the Indiana Team who do so. Others can swim only with the two-beat kick (Tim Shaw, Jenny Turrall, Steve Holland, and Shirley Babashof), and still others use only the six-beat kick (Mark Spitz, Kornelia Ender, Jim Montgomery).

The Two-Beat Crossover Kick

This kick is used primarily by men swimmers; the straight two-beat kick predominates among women. In this stroke, one kick is given by each leg during each arm pull. This gives a total of two kicks per complete arm cycle. During part of the kicking phase, one leg crosses on top of the other, and during the next kick the position of the two legs is reversed.

The timing of the kick is probably tied in with the arm recovery although this is a source of controversy. The timing ends up the same for all swimmers, and the swimmers using it need not worry about the timing since they will automatically fall into the correct pattern.

The Straight Two-Beat Kick

Swimmers using the straight two-beat kick also use only two beats of the kick per arm cycle (one stroke per arm). In this case the legs do not cross on top of each other, but kick almost straight up and down.

Which of the two kicks is the better for a swimmer to use? I don't know if this question can be answered or if it has a definite answer. Some coaches have speculated that the straight two-beat kick is superior to the two-beat crossover kick because the crossover action is wasted motion, though the crossover action of the legs may serve some purpose such as cancelling out the reaction of the arm recovery and in this way preserving body alignment. The fact that few men use the straight two-beat kick and few women use the two-beat crossover kick implies the responsibility of some anatomical difference or the role of some variation in buoyancy, flexibility, or strength.

Both of these kicks contain a definite pause when there is no movement of the legs. In the two-beat crossover kick the pause occurs when the feet are crossed one on top of the other and are in a streamlined position. In the straight two-beat kick the pause occurs when the feet are at their farthest spread. The pause at this point would seem to cause an increase in drag and therefore be detrimental, though the pause of the legs in this drag position serve the purpose of ruddering or holding the body in position possibly to maintain good alignment and to prevent wiggling. Research and good conceptual thinking of fluid mechanics of these two types of kick are needed to answer these questions.

Eyes — Open or Shut?

A careful examination of both the out of water and underwater pictures of crawl swimmers in this section will show the reader that champion swimmers keep their eyes open, both under and out of water. This is the desirable technique and should be followed by all swimmers. There is a brief period in which the eyes close as the swimmer's eyes enter or leave the water. This is due to the "blinking" reflex. Today's competitive swimmers do most of their training while wearing goggles to prevent eye irritation. It is a good policy for swimmers to practice without goggles some of the time in order to learn to keep their eyes open without goggles, as described above.

Acceleration of Arms During the Stroke

The hands do not move at a constant rate during the pulling phase of the stroke. When the catch or the beginning of the pull is made, the speed of the hands is relatively slow. As the pull begins to overcome the inertia of the body, the hands accelerate.

Poor swimmers will often either lunge into the pull too fast and get too much acceleration at the beginning of the pull and two little acceleration later in the stroke or, in some cases, will make the entire pull with no acceleration, maintaining the same speed throughout.

THEORY AND RESEARCH OF STROKE MECHANICS

The Role of Sculling Movements in the Arm Pull

Swimming movements in the water, particularly of the arms and hands, which seemed so very simple to swimmers, coaches, and writers of the past, now appear more complex and involve principles and concepts never before considered or published. Although some rather complex descriptions of these movements have been published, when compared with the underwater sequence photographs of champion swimmers performing, they usually have been shown to be erroneous. What, then, is the proper stroke?

In 1950, Louis Alley conducted an experiment in which he compared the effectiveness of what he called the normal crawl arm stroke, which was a straight-arm pull although the elbow was bent slightly at the end of the pull to facilitate recovery, with that of the bent-elbow pull. In this study, the bent-elbow pull was described as one in which the swimmer pulled his arm under the body, once again in a straight line, and bent his elbow up to 90 degrees as it was pulled directly under him. Alley figured if the swimmer pushed the water directly backward and not in an arc as was done in the straight-arm pull, he would have a more efficient pull and it would push him more directly forward.

Since, according to Newton's third law of motion, every action has an equal and opposite reaction, it would appear that this latter method would be superior. However, Alley concluded his study in this way: "The mean (force) for the normal-arm (straight) stroke was greater than the mean (force) for the bent-arm stroke." In other words the straight-arm stroke was superior to the bent-arm stroke as Alley was directing his subject to use it.

One important principle was not considered in this study, and it is perhaps one of the most important we can consider in all propulsive movements of humans, other animals, fish, and even boats in water:

To use an example that would be comparable to the study cited, we can cite an experiment conducted by an inventor almost 100 years ago. He reasoned that the paddle wheelers plying the rivers were inefficient because the force created by the large paddle wheel was improperly applied since each of its blades did not push directly backward at all times.

So he devised a caterpillar (tractor) arrangement of a series of paddles. He believed that every paddle would be pushing directly backward and the resultant reaction would be for the boat to be pushed directly forward more economically than in the paddle-wheel method. Unfortunately for him and his financial backers, the boat practically stood still when it tried this method of propulsion. It was reported that the inventor left town in a hurry and never published his findings in a scholarly journal. Perhaps we coaches are lucky that we don't have to leave town when advocating the same technique for swimmers.

Our inventor was violating the principle briefly stated above: in his conveyor belt each paddle was pushing a small amount of water a long distance. Once the water was started backward by a paddle, the paddle could no longer find any traction (propulsive force) from that moving water. Paddles, to get traction and create propulsion, must push against still water or water going in the opposite direction; they cannot effectively push against water that is already going backward. A good analogy would be that of a swimmer swimming upstream.

What then is the answer? For boats the answer was to go to a type of arrangement that would push a lot of water a short distance. This problem was solved by use of a screw propeller. The propeller of a boat or airplane never pushes the water or air directly backward, and it is *always moving forward into still water or air.* Every time it turns it contacts new water or air that is stationary, not moving backward.

It is my contention that swimmers also should not try to push the water directly backward but should use sculling motions of their hands and feet to propel them forward.

Assuming that all of the foregoing is valid and that we cannot gain much propulsion from water already headed backward, the swimmer must solve the problems of (1) how to evolve a stroke pattern that, once he has started the water moving backward, will allow him to get away from that water and work with still water and (2) how to pitch his hands so they will serve as propellers and not as paddles.

Pitch of the Hands

If the hands are being used as propellers and not paddles, the palms of hands must be pitched or tilted in a manner much like that of a propeller of an airplane or boat, or a more common object with which we are all familiar, the blades of a fan.

When the hand is traveling in one direction it must be pitched at a certain angle; when it changes its direction of pull, the pitch of the hand must also be changed so that it can be used effectively as a propeller.

Summary

There is evidence to substantiate the theory that good swimmers use their hands and legs as propellers or foils to push against the water in much the same way as the propeller of a boat or the fins of a fish.

The concept that we should push the water directly backward so that we can be pushed directly forward is negated by the fact that once water is started backward, a paddle can get very little traction from this water. For this reason good swimmers invariably evolve a zigzag pattern in their pull.

Flexibility for Swimmers:
See Chapter on Stretching

Every athlete needs flexibility in a specific joint or joints. The hurdler in track needs above-average flexibility in forward flexions of his upper leg in order to be able to go over the hurdles and still keep his center of gravity low. The swimmer can get by with only average flexibility in the hip joint, but he must have well-above-average flexibility in his andles to have an exceptionally good kick. Butterfly, freestyle, and backstroke swimmers need flexibility in the shoulder joints and in extension (plantar flexion) of the ankle. The freestyler and butterflyer need shoulder flexibility in order to be able to recover their arms over the water easily. A tight-shouldered freestyler will have to roll more to recover his arms and/or use a wide, flat arm recovery, both of which stroke defects will be harmful to body position and will increase drag. A flyer lacking shoulder flexibility will either have to climb too high in the water to recover his arms over the water or will skip them along the surface of the water, creating more drag. The breaststroker needs only average shoulder flexibility since his arms always work within the normal range of movement.

During the leg kick of the freestyle, back stroke, and fly the ankles should extend as far backward as possible in order to thrust the water backward and downward in the case of the flyer and freestyler, and backward and upward in the case of the backstroker. The ankle stretcher exerciser is used to improve this plantar flexion of the swimmers' ankles. The breaststroker needs to flex his feet in the opposite direction, that is, dorsiflexion. This permits him to apply the force of his kick in a more backward direction and is best improved by the Achilles-tendon-stretcher exercise.

Swimmers' Flexibility Tests

Shoulder Flexibility—Horizontal

Sit with back erect, legs extended, and knees straight. Raise arms to sides at should height, palms facing forward. Keeping arms at should height and without bending forward or turning palms downward, pull arms backward as far as possible. Do not lower arms as you pull them backward, but keep them at shoulder height. Keep elbows straight.

Tester: Measure the distance in inches or centimeters between the fingertips of two hands.

Shoulder Flexibility—Vertical

Lying on chest with face in a vertical position and chin touching the ground, grasp a broom handle or some other small wooden stick at shoulder width. Without bending the elbows or the wrists, lift the stick as high as you can.

Tester: Measure the height that the stick is lifted from the ground.

Forward Trunk Flexion

Sitting down, with legs extended, spread feet 1 foot apart. Interlace fingers behind neck, and bend trunk forward as far as possible. Do not bend knees.

Tester: Measure distance from forehead to ground.

Ankle Flexibility—Plantar Flexion

Sit down with legs together and extended and with trunk in an erect position. Without bending knees try to touch big toe to ground. Do not rotate leg or ankle inward (medially).

Tester: Measure closest distance from the bottom of big toe of least flexible foot to the ground.

Dorsiflexion

Assume same position as in previous exercise, but place sole of foot firmly against a wall, Keeping the heel against the wall, dorsiflex ankle so that all but the heel of the foot is pulled away from the wall as far as possible.

Tester: Measure distance from bottom of least flexible big toe to the wall.

Breaststrokers Sit-down (Pass or Fail)

Stand erect with hands behind neck and fingers interlaced. Keeping toes, heels, and knees together, do a full squat without letting the heels leave the ground. This must be done barefooted. If you lose your balance and fall backwards or if you feet leave the ground, you fail the test. Be sure that you reach a full squat position and that you do not remove your hands from behind your neck.

Tester: Score on a pass/fail basis.

Flexibility Exercises for the Ankles

Ankle Stretcher—Plantar Flexion

Sitting on the ankles, lift the knees up and shift weight so as to place stretch on the ankles. Repeat 10 to 20 times, holding for 3 to 5 seconds each repeat.

Achilles-Tendon Stretcher—Dorsiflexion

This exercise should be used by all breaststroke swimmers and individual-medley swimmers. It can be done in several ways: (A) on an inclined plane, (B) on alligator shoes, (C) standing on a curbing of some type, and (D) with no equipment. When doing any of these four exercises, the swimmer should keep the knees bent slightly. This causes a greater stretch in the calf muscle/and in the Archilles tendon than in the hamstrings. The swimmer bends forward as far as possible and bounces 4 or 5 times, then straightens. He bends forward and repeats the bouncing action again. He does this for a total of 5 to 10 efforts.

Archilles-Tendon Exercise As Performed on Inclined Plane

Lean forward as if to touch the toes, bend knees slightly and shift weight of body forward so calf muscle and Achilles tendon are stretched. Hold position for 3 to 5 seconds. Repeat 10 to 20 times. The angles of the inclined plane can be made 35° or 50°—the lower angle for swimmers with normal or subnormal flexibility, the higher angle for those with above-average flexibility.

Achilles-Tendon Exercise As Performed with No Equipment

A form of this exercise that swimmers use before competition to stretch out the Achilles tendons is used with no equipment except a wall to push against. Lean forward and place one foot half way between the wall and the back foot, and the hands against the wall. Bend the knee of the back leg just slightly so that the heel of the back leg is elevated. Push against the wall and press the heel of the back leg to the ground, feeling the stretch on the Achilles tendon and the calf muscle. Repeat several times and gradually increase the stretching action, bouncing each leg 10 to 15 times. Reverse legs and stretch the opposite leg. Repeat with each leg 3 to 5 times.

Summary of Swimming Schedule

As stated earlier in this chapter, it is absolutely essential that a novice swimmer avail him or herself of competent swimming instruction. This is for the beginner novice and progressing through all of the swimming skills, including rough water distance swimming.

The Y.M.C.A. system throughout the country has an excellent swimming program for all ages and certainly should be checked out first. Next are the school systems. Most schools, especially universities, have excellent 50 meter or 50 yard pools and are geared to take non-faculty and students into various swimming instruction classes. Now we have an elite swimming club program becoming popular as swimming emerges as an attractive participation sport. These clubs, in the main, are dedicated not only to raising up promising young swimmers to national and international competition level, but are also open to beginners and masters program swimmers.

Swimming and Biking Differ from Running

In swimming and biking, style and form equate to speed. Running does have certain established criteria for perfecting speed and distance but on a more individual style basis. For this reason it is important for the novice swimmer to start right, avoiding incorrect habits and practices that could easily be more difficult to correct than to start over. This holds true of intermediate and advanced swimmers; to perfect finely tuned style and swimming mechanics by oneself is virtually impossible. You cannot pick up mistakes in stroke, kick, body position, breathing, etc alone, someone with training skill has to detect these errors from the poolside, underwater photos of a personal view.

In this chapter, we have attempted to alert and expose the swimmer, at whatever level he or she might be swimming, to certain concepts that should go a long way towards convincing a serious student of swimming of the necessity for skilled, professional instruction.

Dr. Counsilman has set forth certain training concepts that will improve the intermediate swimmer's style and swimming rate. It is well to study this material as you participate in a recognized swimming program. This system, as given by Dr. Counsilman, was responsible for swimmer Mark Spitz's phenomonal success in Olympic competition. The material in this chapter is but a brief portion of the Competitive/Swimming Manual distributed by Dr. Counsilman. We are primarily concerned in this chapter with the crawl stroke and distance swimming. A serious student of swimming desiring to learn all that there is to know on the subject and the additional swimming strokes should acquire this manual by writing, The Counsilman Co. Inc., 2606 East Second Street, Bloomington, Indiana 47401.

Why 12 Months to be Able to Swim 2.4 Miles?

Let's assume that you have acquired a reasonable ability to swim the length of a pool through your own devices or a novice swimming program. You are equipped to deal with the fear of water, but extended swimming is just not your best sport. In other words, I am giving you the benefit of the doubt by giving you a 3 to 6 month head start in our year schedule. I will state that it will take you at least a year of reasonable effort, says 3 swimming periods a week, to be able to swim 2.4 miles in rought water conditions in a reasonable time period, say 1:30 minutes. Some will never make it, others will survive after 2 plus hours, a few will surpass the 1:30 minutes. For the most part, it will take a good 12 months to achieve this enviable goal. For a person starting with the ability to swim with reasonably good style ¼ mile, and willing to put in 4 to 5 swimming sessions of not less than one hour per day with supervision, they could accomplish this 1:30, 2.4 mile rought water swim in 6 months.

Swimming Schedules

Swimming schedules are a very personal thing. If you have followed our advice and are enlisted in a training program with a professional teacher, you will not need a schedule because your schedule is pretty well set out for you by our instructor. Any formula set out here would only be confusing to you and should not be followed. For those that are bound and determined to ''go it alone,'' we will give a set of schedules from which to build toward the 2.4 mile sub 1 hour and thirty minute goal.

We have to assume that you can start with the ability to swim a 10 to 12 minute non-stop ¼ mile.

Training the Distance Swimmer

Earlier in this chapter the difference between the type of workouts used for distance swimmers and those for the rest of the team was discussed. The difference is probably obvious to the reader, but he will gain more insight into the necessity for different types of workouts if he reads ''Hypoxic Training and Other Methods of Training Evaluated'' and ''Power: What Is It, How Do You Measure It, and What Does It Mean to the Coach and the Swimmer?''

The main differences for the distance swimmer are as follows:
1. More aerobic work
   a. Overdistance swimming
   b. Short-rest interval training
2. More work: The swimmer should go 20 to 40% more total distance in each workout (providing the time is available).
3. Longer repeat swims than the rest of the team is doing. If the rest of the team is doing a set of repeats such as 8 X 150, the distance swimmer should double this distance and go 6 or even 8 X 300.

Some of the typical sets of repeats for senior-level distance swims, as used in separate workouts, are listed here:

20 to 40 X 100	8 to 12 X 400
10 to 20 X 200	4 to 8 X 800
8 to 14 X 300	1,2, or 3 X 1500

In ''How Champions Train'' the reader may examine some workouts of distance swimmers. It will be noted that even the better distance swimmers do not eliminate all speed work, such as sprinting, or high-quality work, such as repetition training, from their training programs. All swimmers need a mixed program of training — the distance man, however, must put more emphasis on those types of training that develop endurance.

Everything has been thought of before, but the difficulty is to think of it again. —Goethe

Types of Sets of Repeat Swims

While much of the discussion of repeat swims has mentioned the use of rest intervals of 10, 15, 30 seconds, etc., swimmers very seldom use exact rest intervals in their training. Rather than use exact intervals of rest it is much easier to use departure times. That is, a swimmer is swimming 10 X 100 yards with 20-second intervals of rest and he swims each 100 yards in 60 seconds, he can leave every 1 minute 10 seconds, but if he swims each 100 in 58.5 seconds he must start the second one 68.5 seconds after he started the first one. The third one he must then start 2:17.0 after the first one, etc. The bookkeeping becomes staggering. it is much simpler for him to start a 100-repeat swim every 1 minute 10 seconds. For this reason the rest intervals as they are given in this book are only approximations, and each swimmer must work out his departure time so that it gives him approximately the desired rest interval. All of the sets mentioned can be done in an interval or repetition training method.

Straight Sets. A straight set of repeat swims is a set in which the swimmer holds the distance, the rest interval, and the time of each repeat swim constant. Example: 30 X 50 meters, departure time 45 seconds, average time to swim distance 28 seconds, average rest interval 17 seconds.

Typical Straight Sets

10 X 50 or	10 x 100 or	8 X 200 or	5 X 400 or	3 X 800 or
20 X 50 or	15 X 100 or	10 X 200 or	8 X 400 or	5 X 800 or
30 X 50	20 X 100	14 X 200	10 X 400	5 X 800

75s, 150s, 300s — in fact any distance can be used.

Descending-Time Set. In a descending-time set of repeat swims the swimmer tries to swim each successive repeat faster than the previous one.

Example: 6 X 400 meters, departure time 6 minutes.

	1	2	3	4	5	6
Time	4:40	4:38	4:34	4:30	4:28	4:22

This type of set is particularly popular with most world-class swimmers at this time and is used by such world record holders as Mark Spitz, Tim Shaw, Jim Montgomery, Shirley Babashoff, and others. It enables the swimmer to impose various intensities of stress on his body and is physiologically sound. Typical descending-time sets are the same as above in straight sets.

Out-Slow—Back—Hard Set. In this type of set the swimmer swims the first half of each repeat swim slower than the second half; i.e., swim 8 X 200, departure time 3 minutes on each 200. Swim first 100 in 1:08 and second 100 in 1:06 or better for a total time of 2:14 or better. This type of swimming gives the swimmer confidence that he can come back hard in the second half of his race, and it teaches him to pace himself.

Typical Out-Slow—Back-Hard Sets

4 X 200	3 X 400	3 X 800	3 X 1500
8 X 200	5 X 400	6 X 800	
	8 X 400		

Decreasing-Rest-Interval Set. The most popular variation of the standard set of repeats that has been developed recently is the set of repeats in which the interval of rest is decreased as the set progresses, i.e., swim 20 X 100 meters.

1. The first 10 X 100 meters is swum with a departure time of 1:20 (this must be adapted to each swimmer — 1:20 would be used for at world-class man freestyler) average time 1:10 or better, average rest interval 10 seconds.

2. The next 5 X 100 would be swum with a departure time of 1:15 (average time 1:08 or better).

The devil never yet asked his victims to take a walk with him. —John Burroughs

3. The last 5 X 100 would be swum with a departure time of 1:10 (average time 1:05 or better).

The world-class freestyler could do the same type of set using 200 meters as the distance swum with the following departure times:

5 X 200	departure time 2:35
5 X 200	departure time 2:30
5 X 200	departure time 2:25

This type of set varies the stress on the individual and is very challenging. As the season progresses and the swimmer gets into shape, the departure time is gradually decreased. This type of set is particularly good early in the workout because it gives the swimmer a chance to warm up before he really has to exert himself. The swimmer can also measure the improvement in his conditioning by being able to use a shorter departure time.

Typical Decreasing-Rest-Interval Sets

20 X 50 meters on 45	4 X 150 on 2:00	4 X 400 on 5:00	3 X 800 on 10:00
10 X 50 on 40	4 X 150 on 1:50	4 X 400 on 4:50	3 X 800 on 9:30
10 X 50 on 35	4 X 150 on 1:40	4 X 400 on 4:40	

Increasing-Rest-Interval Set. If the rest interval between sets is changed enough, it is possible to combine training methods into one set of repeats. For example, if a swimmer is assigned to do a set of 20 X 100-yard repeat swims, the first 5 X 100 can be done with a 10-second rest interval between each 100, the second 5 X 100 with a 20-second rest interval, the third 5 X 100 with a 30-second rest interval, and the last 5 X 100 with a 1-minute rest interval. As the rest interval is increased, the swimmer is expected to swim at a fast speed, and the method changes from the first set, which is strictly interval training, to the last set of 100s, which has a 1-minute rest and which qualifies as repetition training (in reality the swimmers will not use exact rest-interval times but will use departure times as described in the previous set of repeats).

Typical Increasing-Rest-Interval Sets
(Using departure times for good male freestyler)

10 X 50 m. on 40	4 X 200 on 2:30	3 X 400 on 5:00
10 X 50 on 50	4 X 200 on 2:45	3 X 400 on 5:30
10 X 50 on 60	4 X 200 on 3:00	3 X 400 on 6:00

It is important to restate here that the different stroke swimmers on your team will all have different take-off intervals. Even swimmers using the same stroke will have to use different take-off intervals, depending on their ability.

Varying-Distance Sets. A set of repeat swims that many swimmers find challenging is one in which the distance of each repeat swim is changed.

Example A.
1. Swim 400, look at 300.
2. Swim 300 faster than you were at the 300 on the way to the 400 — look at your 200.
3. Swim 200 faster than the 200 above in 2, look at 100.
4. Swim 100 faster than above in 3.

Example B. Typical Varying-Distance Sets
1. Swim 4 X 400, 30-sec. rest interval.
2. Swim 4 X 200, 20-sec. rest interval.
3. Swim 4 X 100, 10-sec. rest interval.
4. Swim 4 X 50, 10-sec. rest interval.

Example C.
1. Swim 100   Allow 30 sec. to 1 min. between each swim.
2. Swim 200
3. Swim 300
4. Swim 400
5. Swim 300
6. Swim 200
7. Swim 100

Example D.
1. Swim 10 X 50, 10-sec. RI.
2. Swim 4 X 100, 15-sec. RI.
3. Swim 4X 200, 30-sec. RI.

This type of set of repeats offers limitless opportunities for variety. The swimmer and coach must be careful not to use these sets exclusively, because they do offer a smorgasbord of bits and pieces and cannot be substituted for the use of straight sets or broken sets. We use them in our program two or three times a week (when doing one workout a day). They can be done either in interval-training or in repetition-training methods.

Broken Swims. A method of training that we use at least twice a week during the hard-training phase of our program is referred to as broken swims. If the swimmer is training for a 200-meter race he might want to work on his 200 pace of perhaps 2 minutes by 200 meters. He can do this by swimming 4 X 50 repeat swims, and swimming each 50 meters in 30 seconds and allowing 10 seconds rest interval between each 50 swim. This permits him to swim his broken 200 at the same tempo he will want to use in the 200-meter race. The 10 seconds rest between each 50 permits enough recovery to maintain a fast tempo for the entire 200 meters.

Broken 300s. Broken 300s usually consist of 3 X 100 repeats, with 10 seconds rest interval between each 100. This gives the swimmer a total of two rest periods of 10 seconds each, or a total elapsed rest-interval time of 20 seconds. If the swimer is using a pace clock he can start when the second hand hits 20, and then his actual swimming time will show up on the pace clock.

Broken 400s. Broken 400s can be swum as 4 X 100 with a 10-second rest interval between each 100 for a total elapsed time of 20 seconds, and once again a swimmer can cancel out this rest-time interval by starting his broken swim when the second hand hits 30.

They can also be done as 8 X 50. If the swimmer is doing 400 with a 10-second rest interval between each 50, he will have a total of 7 rest intervals or a total rest time of 70 seconds. He must therefore start his broken swim on 50.

Broken 800s. Broken 800s are usually done as 8 X 100 with a rest interval of 10 seconds between each 100. The swimmer should start when the second hand hits 50.

Broken swims can be of any distance the swimmer or coach wants to make them, i.e., broken 100—4 X 25, broken 1500 — 15 X 100. The rest interval can be 5, 10, 15, 20 seconds, etc. If the set of repeats is short, such as 4 X 50 (broken 200), and the rest interval is short (such as 10 seconds), the type of training would qualify as a cross between interval training (because of the short rest interval) and repetition training (because it will probably be swum at a very fast speed).

Typical Sets of Broken Swims
Swim 8 X broken 200s (4 X 50)
Swim 5 X broken 400s (4 X 100)
Swim 3 X broken 800s (8 X 100)
Swim 2 X broken 1500s (15 X 100)

These can be swum with the swimmer trying to keep them at the same time or trying to go each succeeding one faster as in decreasing time sets.

The swimmer can also do his kicking or pulling in the same manner such as 2 X broken 400 kicks (4 X 100 — 10 second RI).

Mixing Broken Swims and Straight Swims

A combination of two methods is the use of alternating broken sets and straight swims as follows:

Example A.
1. Swim a broken 200 (4 X 50 — 10 sec. RI).
2. Swim a straight 200.
   Repeat the above 3, 4 or 5 times so a total of 6, 8 or 10 X 200 has been swum.
   Allow approximately 1 min. between each 200.

Example B.
1. Swim a broken 400 — 4 X 100 (or 8 X 50).
2. Swim a straight 400.
   Repeat the above 2, 3, or 4 times until a total of 4, 6 or 8 X 400 has been swum.

Example C.
1. Swim a broken 400—4 X 100—10-sec. RI.
2. Swim a straight 400.
3. Swim a broken 300—3 X 100—10 sec. RI.
4. Swim a straight 300.
5. Swim a broken 200—4 X 50—10-sec. RI.
6. Swim a straight 200.
   Allow 1 to 2 min. between each swim.

Planning a Year's Training Program

Careful planning of a season's program consists of establishing a general outline of a program for the entire season that is based on a sound physiological concept. This outline does not have to be followed rigidly, and the fact that the swimmer or coach has set the plan down in writing does not commit him to staying with the plan if he decides it is not "doing the job." A preseason planning session with the coach and the team is a necessity in my opinion, and should consider all of the training concepts and principles discussed in this section.

Each program varies one from another. The program I have outlined for the swimmers I coach can serve as a guide, but each coach must make adaptations that will suit his team and its particular circumstances.

Summary of Swim Schedules

The schedules listed above are just a sample of many potential combinations. Each person can devise his or her own training routine based on the above chart to improve on the schedule's attempt to decrease the resting time between laps when possible. For the distance swimmer, strength and speed training are combined with distance, with an emphasis placed on Pull Bouy, kick board and short turnaround sprints. Ocean distance swimming should be mixed about 50-50 with pool training. Pool training is qualitative side of distance training.

Again, it is important to stress the need for competent instruction not only for instruction's sake but for the discipline that is entailed. If you know that the instructor is waiting at 6:00 A.M. for your presence, you will be there eager, and on time to proceed with the day's routine. You will say when it's over as Jack Lalanne does, "I did it again, and I'm glad."

350 Triathletes sprint for the Sea, in a Le Mans start of the 1981 Santa Barbara 1/2 Triathlon. Proceeds went to the Special Olympics Fund. This Triathlon is set on the distances of: 2000 meters cold rough water swim, 56 miles of steep mountain biking and a hilly 1/2 marathon of 13.1 miles. 1968 Olympic Team member Diane Giebel, in the black suit in the foreground, was the first person out of the water!

Diane Giebel, 1968 Olympic Team Member

Diane's swimming career began in New Jersey where she learned to swim at the age of two. She began to swim competitively in AAU clubs when she was five. After moving to Southern California, she swam on the Woodland Hills Swim Club under Vic Cook for 3 years. Cook perceived that she had Olympic potential and sent her to Peter Deland, coach of the Los Angeles Swim Club at that time and also coach at the University of Southern California (USC), with whom she trained for 2 years. Training under Deland was a vigorous full-time commitment, 2½ hours a day during the winter and 5 hours a day during the summer. Her dedication was well rewarded however, when she qualified for the 1968 Olympic team. Diane was fifteen when she swam the 200 meter fly in the Olympics and placed 6th.

During high school Diane only swam one year, trying to capture the life of the "normal" teenager which she had never known. Returning to New Jersey she went 2 years to a junior college and graduated from Glassboro State with a degree in Teacher of the Handicapped (Special Education). Although only swimming 1 year for Glassboro State, Diane distinguished herself in aquatics by being the first woman to win and make the Sea Isle City ocean swim lifeguard try-outs. Even to this day, women ocean lifeguards are discouraged on the East Coast.

Diane didn't start swimming seriously again until she got pregnant. Then her goal this time around was weight control and not speed, she swam 1 mile, 3 or 4 times weekly. Some might say her dedication bordered on extremism, in view of the fact that she swam 50 laps unknowingly in labor on the day she gave birth.

After she had her son Cale, she began swimming in Master Swim Meets around Southern California. Although Diane has spent most of her life in the pool, ocean swimming is her new passion. This area of swimming cannot be enjoyed all year long...but when the weather and water temperature is right, this sport offers a new challenge. Diane's new fascination with the ocean lies in its unpredictability and the swimmer's responsibility to read it accurately in order to reach his or her destination safely and efficiently.

Diane is Excited by the Triathlon

Soon after Diane began ocean swimming...the Triathlon peaked her interest. She swam in 2 Triathlons as a team member, her team placing 3rd and 2nd. Because of her extensive experience with both pool and ocean swimming, she recommends a unique combination of the two for your triathlon training.

While you are training you should spend at least 3 to 4 days a week in the water. One of these swims should be a long ocean swim (1½ to 2 miles approximately).

When swimming in the ocean Diane recommends mostly freestyle. She finds it best to use a number of strokes in order to work out all your muscles. (Especially if you are already biking and running I have found, for example doing backstroke kick after I have been on the Bike seems to use similar muscles.) It is probably best to avoid breaststroke, though this alleviates the risk of new stress. Spend sometime working on pulls and kicks by themselves. If you can do the butterfly, this stroke is by far the best conditioning stroke! Work on bilateral breathing on freestyle...either breathe every three strokes or five strokes, to build the lungs and also direction. Pool workouts should be spent doing intervals for speed and stroke work.

One last thing before we move to specific workout schedules: whether in the pool or the ocean, practice finding a focus point and keeping yourself centered on that point! This will be essential in order for you to maintain direction in an ocean swim. Diane remembers being very poor at that when she first started ocean swimming, usually swimming extra distance unnecessarily and one time, swimming right into a surf board, causing a broken nose. She learned real fast about focus points then!

As far as interval training, people need to remember to keep their times consistant and pace. Don't kill yourself on the first and second one if you have 5-100 freestyle to do. Build up, try to get faster on each one, even if it's only a tenth of a second improvement. For example, if you have a 5-100 of freestyle to do, leaving on 1:30 and your best time is 1:10 . . . see if you can do the 5-100 at 1:15 to 1:16-1:17, etc. . . . varying a tenth here or there, but don't start giving up! Make sure you leave on 1:30 for each one. At first it will be difficult to judge your pace, but through practice and listening to your body you will be able to know if you are on target.

For those who haven't been swimming at all, where do you begin? First, take a few lessons and have someone look at your stroke. Work mostly on perfecting your freestyle; if time permits conquer the other strokes later. I wouldn't worry about interval training at this time, but just on being able to swim consistently for periods at a time. If you are having trouble doing laps of freestyle, try doing a lap of backstroke or elementary backstroke to relax you and then go back into freestyle again. The main thing to be concerned with is being able to swim without stopping for extended periods at a time!

Olympic Swimmer Diane Giebel's Recomended Triathletes Workouts

1. 1000 swim breathing every 3 or 5 strokes
    1000 kick (alternate strokes if you can)
    1000 pull (alternate strokes if you can)
    300 cool down

2. Warm up 500 swim
    10 - 50's of kick leaving on 1:30 or 2:00
         keeping times consistent
    500 swim every 3rd lap all out or butterfly
    10 - 50's of pull leaving on min or 1:15 keeping times consistent
    500   free all out
    200   cool down

3. Warm up 300 swim
    5-75's   free on 2:00:00
    200'   easy swim
    5-75's   free on 2:00:00
    500   swim mixing strokes or doing 100 swim, 100 pull, 100 swim, 100 kick, 100 swim all out
    300   cool down

4. 1000 free - breathing every 3 or 5 strokes
    5 x 100 SM Leaving on 1:30 or 2:00 mins. depending on your speed if you can't do fly do free, back, breast and free. Keeping times consistent.
    200   kick free   200   pull free   300   cool down

    Work out schedule if you have 4 days of pool time.
    3 days ocean - lake or river   2 days pool
    1 day pool with intervals (and stroke work) or 2 days ocean

Anyone planning to compete in a Triathlon must become as comfortable as possible with swimming in the ocean. Because of its unpredictability, the ocean offers challenges and difficulties not encountered in a pool. Wave rhythms, water temperature, lack of lanes for direction, problems measuring distance and floating objects . . . all contribute to make the ocean swim unique and an ever-changing challenge! Don't fool yourself into thinking it will be an easy transition from pool training times to fast ocean times. There is only one way to become an accomplished ocean swimmer . . . swim and practice in the ocean!

Outfit yourself with a tight comfortable fitting suit, a good pair of goggles and a bright swim cap. For safety and support in training . . . swim with a friend—the buddy system is not only safer, but much more enjoyable!

2

Jack LaLanne on Cold Water Swimming for the Triathlon

Jack LaLanne has been a continuing inspiration in my life since 1939 while in Oakland, California, where I was studying navigation in preparation for a merchant Marine Navigating Deck Officer's License. Evenings after studies, it was enjoyable to go down to Jack's gym and "blow off steam," pump some iron, take a swim and a steam bath, and consume one of Jack's cocktails . . . health cocktails.

In the longest continuous show on television, Jack appeared nationwide with his admonition to get you off of your duff and do something, eat right, exercise! Unfortunately we do not always find time in a busy life to follow his advice. After 30 years of doing my own thing, I finally began to reap the harvest of unhealthful living, improper eating, and lack of regular exercise. I found myself overweight and in poor health at the age of 52.

I lived in Hawaii, and chanced to stroll upon a group of people exercising at Waikiki beach,(Fort DeRussy Grass Area) one day. The leader of this group of dedicated, tanned, healthy looking people was a young man of 92. I was impressed and joined in . . . When the time came to jog, I was unable to go 50 passes without pain. In an ensuing counseling session with the exercise director, I realized that I had been a health "sinner" and was paying the price for straying from the words of counsel I had heard years earlier from Jack LaLanne: "To rest is to rust."

The name of this doctor of good health was none other than the same person Jack credits with turning his life around at the early age of 15, Dr. Paul Bragg, nutritionist, life extension specialist, health advisor to Hollywood stars and the greats in business and industry.

Upon the advice of this new found health counselor, I cut out of my diet salt, white sugar, white flour, coffee, tea, alcohol, and devitalized, devitaminized, processed foods. Within a few weeks, I was ready for an extended fast to rid the body of the impurities I had stored up during my life. Needless to say, my aches and pains went away as did excess weight and back came the desire to be physically active in tennis, handball, running, and swimming. Incidentally, this same exercise class is still going strong. From 9:00 a.m. to 10:30 a.m., 50 to 150 people still meet on the lawn between the Military Museum and the Sea at Ft. De Russy, Monday through Saturday, rain or shine. Now in its 12th year, this exercise class stands as a living, health and fitness memorial to its founder, the late Dr. Paul Bragg. All health minded visitors are invited to attend the daily workouts followed by a swim.

Invited to Attend Jack's Birthday Swimming Feat

I had been invited to attend Jack LaLanne's great feat of physical endurance to commemorate his 60th birthday. With both his hands and feet closely shackled together, Jack towed a 1,000 pound boat across the cold, 54° San Francisco bay from Alcatraz to the Dolphin Club, over 1.5 miles. This was merely one of his many outstanding performances of

The start of the Maui Channel Relay.
Ian Emberson in the foreground.

The start of the 1980 Ironman. The swim was
moved to the Ala Moana channel due to extremely rough seas off Waikiki Beach.

stamina and endurance. Every year on his birthday, Jack astonishes the world with feats of physical prowess not equaled by a man half his age. Impressed? I was revitalized with enthusiasm and began to set goals of physical activity, with emphasis on endurance events.

Jack sets an example for everyone to follow, especially people who are over the age of 50. The legacy of health and natural living left by Dr. Paul Bragg, after his untimely death at the age of 96, is perpetuated by the enthusiastic Jack LaLanne; a continuing inspiration to live by nature's laws and to take care of this beautiful God-given gift, the human body.

Jack and Elaine LaLanne and I have been good friends for many years. I recently mentioned to Jack that many triathletes were experiencing cold water swimming problems and asked if the greatest cold water swimming advocate of the decade would offer some advice . . .

Spreading Gospel of Health

Jack LaLanne tells how Paul C. Bragg
Started Him on Road to Health over 50 Years Ago!

This Associated Press interview with Jack LaLanne appeared nationally.

Over fifty years ago, Jack LaLanne's mother dragged her 15-year-old to a lecture by nutritionist Paul Bragg. They arrived late and had to sit on stage close to Bragg in front of some 3,000 people.

"My mother forced me to go," LaLanne recalls. "I had dropped out of school for six months. I was a shut-in. I wouldn't go out and see people. I had pimples and boils and I was wearing glasses and I was thin and I couldn't participate in sports. I didn't want anyone to see me.

"Here my mother and I sat in front of 3,000 people. It just had to be the most embarrassing, most humiliating, exasperating time of my life. I didn't want anyone to see me, and I thought they were all looking at me. Little did I know that they had problems too."

Bragg told his audience they could reverse their physical problems by eating right — words that struck a chord in LaLanne.

"I was weak and sick. I used to have blinding headaches every day," he said. "I wanted to commit suicide. I used to pound my head against the wall because I couldn't stand the pain. I wanted to get out of this body I had, and this man told me I could be born again."

After the lecture, LaLanne went to Bragg's dressing room and the two talked for hours.

"He asked me, 'What do you have for breakfast, for lunch, for dinner?' and I told him, 'cakes, pies, ice cream.' He said, 'Jack, you're a walking garbage can.' That night I went home and I got on my knees by the side of my bed and I prayed. I didn't say 'God, make me a Mr. America. I said God, please give me the intestinal fortitude and the willpower to refrain from eating these foods when the urge comes over me. God, please give me the strength to exercise when I don't feel like it."

There hasn't been a jelly donut in LaLanne's life since. In the 44 years since he opened his first gym in downtown Oakland, LaLanne has spread his gospel of happiness through nutrition and exercise in lectures, a 25-year television show and with a variety of extraordinary physical feats — 1,033 pushups in 23 minutes, swimming from Alcatraz to San Francisco while handcuffed and shackled and a recent mile-long swim in which he towed 13 rowboats filled with 76 people. La Lanne owns scores of health spas and has a number of nutritional and exercise products on the market — all of which has made him a wealthy man. But the muscle mogul with the 47-inch chest and 28-inch waist says he cares nothing for material rewards.

"I never thought about making money in my life," he said. "You know, this is a capitalistic country, you do a good job and you're to be compensated. I want to help people.

The start of the swim segment and of the 1981 Ironman, Kailua Kona bay.

I want to open a chain of health food restaurants. I want to open more health spas. I've got two books I'm writing. I'm back on television with a brand new show. I want to get more involved than I ever have. See, I haven't started. Col. Sanders never made a dime until he was 68. I'm only 66, I figure everything is ahead of me.''

LaLanne is gratified by the billion dollar industry that physical fitness and nutrition has become and believes the emphasis on exercise and proper diet portend better, healthier days for the nation.

"I used to talk about (the dangers of) white flour and sugar 25 years ago and people thought I was some kind of a fool. Now, it's every doctor — white flour, sugar, salt — killers, killers, killers,'' he said, punching his couch for emphasis. "It's exciting what's happening. This is going to be the salvation of America, you watch and see. The incidence of dope and alcoholism is going to decrease significantly in the next five years.''

Young People Turn to Drugs, LaLanne Says, Because Of Eating Too Much Sugar

"How do you think kids get on this damn dope thing?'' he says. "It all starts with excessive use of white sugar. There's no doubt about it. When you use too much sugar it destroys the B-complex vitamin. You destroy the B-complex vitamin and you can't make decisions, your energy's down, you're apprehensive about life. These are facts. You get off that white sugar, you feel better immediately.''

LaLanne's personal regimen includes vitamin tablets and a big 2½-hour workout each day. He starts exercising at 4 a.m. because it's tougher that way.

"You know, everybody thinks Jack LaLanne's a superman — he loves to work out,'' he said. "I hate to go down to my gym in the morning. Getting out of a warm bed at 4 in the morning — I'd rather take a beating. But, boy, when I'm through . . . I think, Jack, you did it again. And if I've got the willpower to do that, everything else is easy by comparison.''

LaLanne, married 22 years to his second wife, Elaine, and the father of two, says he still has "enthusiasm and I won't get fat in my profession.''

Jack LaLanne on Cold Water Swim Conditioning

Hello there, triathletes! My hat goes off to you for what you are doing, each one of you, as you train and participate in the sport of the 80's — the triathlon. Since my early indoctrination to good health and fitness, I have been dedicated to just such conditioning as you are experiencing. You are acquiring a truly totally fit body through the diversity of the events for which you are training.

First, everyone is capable of swimming for extended periods of time in cold water. Often we hear, "Oh, but I'm different.'' No one is different in this respect, so let's put that foolishness behind us. It all starts in the shower. It's easy to top off a nice hot shower with a hot rinse, but that will never get you through a triathlon or a long, cold, rough water swim. Turn off the hot and turn on the cold . . . start with the scalp and let it run over the body. If this seems too severe at first . . . start with a quick splash and the next day for a longer period, until you can stand a full cold shower for an extended period!

Water has been a part of my life for nearly as long as I can remember. My mother was a strict Seventh-day Adventist, and one of their teachings was hot and cold fomantations, or the application of hot towels and cold towels to a specific part of the body. The principle of the hot and cold fomantations is quite valid as it increases circulation.

Your Body's Heat Regulator

The body has a thermostat, so to speak, just like an automobile, although your body's heat metabolism is not an interchangeable part. If its ability to adapt to temperature changes is exercised, a wider range of temperatures are comfortable for distance rough water swims.

Paul and Patricia Bragg shown with Jack and Elaine LaLanne in front of the LaLanne, Hollywood Hills home.

To quote my dear friend, Dr. Paul Bragg, with a couple of his favorite cliches: "You use it, or you lose it," . . . and "He (or she) has become a hot-house plant." What this means is that unless you purposely expose your body to changes of temperature, your body will lose its capacity to regulate these changes; you will become like a hot-house plant, requiring an evenly regulated climate or suffer severely through radical climate changes.

Europeans are well aware of this need for radical temperature changes. Their saunas include a cold plunge tub if it's not practical to run and roll in the snow. The use of the Knipe System of Hydro conditioning is also popular in all of the European health resorts and fitness spas. This treatment involves blasting alternately cold and hot water on the standing body front and back on all muscle tissues from a hose directed by an attendant.

The combined hot and cold water works with the massaging effect of the water's pressure, stimulating your system's thermostat to work, thereby better equipping the individual to cope with cold winters.

We've just heard of an exclusive club, the 300 Club, that exists at the North Pole. To become a member, you must sit in a 200° sauna for a period of time, run a half-mile, dressed only in boots, to the north pole marker in a temperature of minus 100°, take a picture of yourself, and run back. Only "minor" areas of frostbite were recorded. This goes on record as being the ultimate combination of hot and cold exposure.

My Cold-Water-Conditioning Started Young

I started my formal fitness program at the age of 15, having been inspired by Dr. Paul Bragg. I attended one of his health lectures, and he told me I could trade my body in for a new one if I obeyed nature's laws. At this time, I was eating cakes, pies, cookies, and the like: I wore arch supports, shoulder braces, glasses and had boils and pimples. Well, I did obey nature's laws; I refrained from eating anything with white flour or white sugar, replacing these poisons with natural, fresh fruits, vegetables, seeds and grains. I started exercising at the local YMCA and saw a miraculous change in my body, and wanted to tell the world.

My life, right then and there was dedicated to helping people feel and look better. I started studying the body, and I haven't stopped since . . . having studied everything that I can about the body, it is my belief that the body has to be stressed in order to respond and become healthier. I would always take cold baths and showers even in the winter time. At the age of 15, I started swimming in the San Francisco Bay and the ocean. What little physical condition and health I have achieved, I attribute largely to the rigors of cold water. This puts many demands on the entire body, especially the mind. When the body is subjected to anything it is not used to, it rebels. However, if this subjection continues, the body gets stronger, tougher and has more endurance and we adjust mentally to these changes.

I am of the belief that most Americans are much softer and weaker than they should be, but if they would use cold water as a method to get stronger and healthier, it would pay big dividends. If cold water therapy was preceded with extra hot water, it would be much more effective. Remember, hot water dilates the blood vessels, and cold constricts . . . so the combination of the two improves the cardiovascular system and increases the will-power it takes to subject the body to cold water. Your 70 trillion cells will dance with delight, and you will really understand the joy of vibrant good health . . . Brrrrrrr!!!

As part of my training, I lie in a bathtub for one hour with 100 pounds of ice. Please note that I gradually work up to the one hour period, as the body must be able to handle the extended temperature change.

I am a great believer of hot and cold showers and vigorous amounts of exercise as this was my training for my swims. I advocate complete physicals before any vigorous training programs and recommend everyone to see his or her doctor for personal advice before starting any training program.

Cold Water Distance Swimming

There is not a newspaper in the country which will pass up the opportunity to give credit, sometimes tongue-in-cheek, to the antics of a few hardy types who insist upon diving into the nearest body of water early New Year's morn.

Such exploits become mundane, though, when compared to hundreds of triathletes and distance swimmers plunging into a cold lake or an ocean for distance swims of one mile, two miles, three miles, even more, for extended exposure over periods of time . . . swimming constantly. These exhibitions of mind over matter and cold water body conditioning are achieved through personal fortitude, knowledge of the problems involved and intelligent training concepts.

Cold Water Swimming Knowledge is Vital to a Successful Triathlon Finish

Beyond doubt, this is the most important chapter in your Triathlon Training Manual. For unless you can go the distance in the first event, usually the swim, you will not finish and receive a final official time! Many first or second year triathlons are incorporating relays which give the strong swimmer, cyclist, or runner a chance to go for it in his own particular event. Many of the cycling and running relay contestants readily admit they shy away from solo participation in a triathlon because they can't stand cold water for extended periods of time.

Diversity is the great equalizer in a multi-sport event. The mediocre biker or runner who will train to overcome cold water for extended periods of time suddenly becomes a contender for the entire event. A novice biker can survive a 112-mile bike ride, and a middle of the pack marathoner can survive a 26 miler by making compromises, such as taking brief rest-recharging period when you can't run by lying down, sitting on a curb, or walking! Cold water distance swimming gives no quarter: the nearest piece of land to lean against or rest on is 30 to 100 feet away, straight down.

The Most Important Swim Safety Item

The importance of the swim cap can not be overemphasized. Most triathlons and biathlons issue swim caps at the time of registration, stressing the mandatory rule that all contestants are required to wear one. First, for life-saving visibility, the cap should be a bright color, preferably dayglow, and red, orange, or chrome yellow, all colors that are easily seen in rough water. White is not acceptable because it doesn't show up in choppy, windswept water. Next, tests have proven that 40% or more of the body's heat escapes through the scalp. The reason for this is that the two main arteries supplying blood to the brain deliver a substantial percentage of the heart's total output to that area. This blood is exposed directly to the elements through the thin skin of the scalp. When too much vital heat is lost, the body's core temperature may lower to an unhealthy level, a condition known as hypothermia. In hypothermia, the metabolic processes are slowed considerably, and in extreme cases can cause death. Usually, though, one experiences "the shakes" and a chilled sensation easily identified before becoming dangerous.

Guard Against Hypothermia

During long exposure to cold water, a great deal of heat may be lost through the scalp, hence the swim cap requirement. While training for the World Ironman Triathlon in Kona, it was evident that many of the triathletes were unaware of this simple fact as a number of them were experiencing hypothermia symptoms during daily swims out and back to the Kona Hilton. Upon being informed of the need for a swim cap, they were no longer subjected to the bone-chilling coldness that one feels when hypothermia sets in. Remember that the Kona Coast sea water temperature ranges from around 68° to 85°. If swimmers can't handle this temperature, how can they compete in 55° to 65° Pacific Ocean water or freshwater lakes even colder without special training for this extreme exposure?

In the event a triathlete or distance swimmer still experiences a degree of coldness, it would be advisable to use two swim caps. In placing either one or two caps on your head, attempt to trap some air between the scalp and cap. Never pull the cap down tight on the head. This bubble of air acts as an insulation cell separating the scalp area from the water. Of course, two cells of air supplies twice the insulation.

Upon coming out of the water after an extended exposure to colder water than you are normally used to, it is a good time to take stock of your condition . . . are you at the point of chilling, shivering or uncontrolled shaking? In either case, do not remove the swim cap for as long a period as necessary to normalize the body temperature (determined either by a clinical thermometer or the feeling of general well-being). Enter a hot shower or put on a workout suit and blankets with the swim cap still on or a towel wrapped around your head to normalize rapidly your body's temperature. Maintain this condition until the shaking stops and your body returns to a normal temperature.

To repeat this important word of caution . . . it is possible for a cold water conditioned swimmer to experience hypothermia to a degree after leaving the water because he removed his cap too soon. Let this be a warning to all cold water swimmers . . . it's a good idea to keep the swim cap on for a period of time after leaving the water!

To Grease or Not to Grease

This question will never be fully settled. Many years of English Channel swims and distance swims around the world have shown the participant covered with a thick layer of grease. This is necessary for these marathon swim distances. Various studies have given various opinions as to the insulating effect of this practice, for shorter distances.

Multi-sport events fall into another category, in which the entire event . . . the swim with its cold water; the biking with its heat and headwinds; the run with its hills, etc. . . . are a combination of debilitating factors. Because nobody can be the best at all three . . . at least, nobody has been yet . . . every contestant competes with his peers on an equal basis.

Mainland triathlons consider greasing up prior to an event as optional. Short of a full "English Channel Grease Job," there is a strong opinion among experienced cold water swimmers that greasing is a waste of time. There is always the clean-up after the swim and before the bike ride . . . which is time consuming and distasteful to many serious competitors. Some swimmers have said that they are more comfortable spreading Vaseline around the neck and shoulders, although this could be a placebo.

As a lubricant, Vaseline is effective, especially in the areas of the latissamus where they contact the arm triceps and of course between the upper legs. Women's one-piece suits often bind at the shoulder straps; another place for lubrication during a long swim.

Training for extended periods of cold water immersion is as much a part of total triathlon training as swimming, biking, and running and should be approached accordingly. So grit your teeth, and turn on the cold shower!

For Women Only

Speed swimmers and short and middle distance swimmers make a practice of wearing two, one-piece suits while training. The effect is an additional drag on the body without the restriction to leg movement that a tow bouy offers, thereby giving an improved arm stroke workout. The extra layer of suit offers an additional warming effect to the mid-body. At this writing triathlon rules have not dealt with this consideration, and until they do, ladies, be our guest.

For Men Only

To shave or not to shave; beards that is. For those of you who are especially endowed with a strong beard, for better or worse, it is advisable to shave before a distance swim. The proper chin position while breathing is tucked against the collar bone. In a distance swim of one to 2.4 miles or longer, a few thousand abrasions of chin stubble against the tender skin over your protruding collar bone will render the area extremely raw!

The Squeeky Clean Body
Men and Women

Serious cyclists can be distinguished in a crowd by their hairless legs and arms. Believe it or not, excessive body hair, when exposed to the wind, is a drag. While bucking the strong Hawaiian Trade Winds that blow off the Kona Coast during the World Ironman Triathlon, you would wish that all wind resistance of every kind had been removed.

Competitive swimmers also remove all body hair. There is no doubt about the negative effect excessive body hair has on a swimmer's speed through the water. Drag, whether in wind or water, should be dealt with accordingly.

The all-purpose body suits coming into vogue require a body shave to be effective.

My Hat is Off to You, Triathletes

Again, I salute you for your desire to maintain your body in top physical condition. But remember, physical conditioning is not always the way you look. That is cosmetic. Physical well-being has to do with the way you live, the food you eat, your attitude towards life, the sport, and the people with whom you mingle.

The computer age has coined a phrase which pretty well says it all, from the food we eat to the thoughts we think, to the friends we keep: "Gigo," which is short for "garbage in, garbage out." This body's marvelous God-given bundle of bones, muscles, arteries and nerves . . . and 65% water, when cooked down, is less than a cup full of minerals worth less than a dollar. Therefore, in its vibrant, alive and active state, the triathlete must care for it well to keep it in the highest possible trained condition mentally and physically to be able to swim 2.4 miles in rough water, bike 112 miles in all terrains and climates, and then run 26.2 miles, sometimes far into the night, with a body which has long been depleted of its valuable store of glycogen. To this end this book was conceived. Read it cover-to-cover, practice fasting for body purification, and abide by the nutritional concepts offered.

May God go with you on the Triathlon. — Jack LaLanne

. . . the brisk exercise imparts elasticity to the muscles, fresh and healthy blood circulates through the brain, the mind works well, the eye is clear, the step is firm, and the day's exertion always makes the evening's repose thoroughly enjoyable.

DR. DAVID LIVINGSTONE

Man is an animal, and his happiness depends on his physiology more than he likes to think. . . . Unhappy businessmen, I am convinced, would increase their happiness more by walking six miles every day than by any conceivable change of philosophy.

BERTRAND RUSSELL

"Everything in excess is opposed by Nature." — *Hippocrates*

Training for the Individual Medley

Workout Pattern for All Swimmers—Minimum of 11 workouts per week: 6 afternoon practices (2¼ hrs—6000 to 9000 yds.) and 5 morning or evening practices (1 hr. 10 min.—3000 to 5000 yds.)

Monday	Tuesday	Wednesday
Warm up 400 Swim 12 × 100 on 1:15 Kick 400 Pull 400 Swim 2 × 500 Entire workout done free-style	Warm up 400 Swim 6 × 150 Kick 4 × 150 Pull 4 × 150 Swim 18 × 50 Entire workout swum back-stroke	Warm up 400 Swim 6 × 100 Kick 200, then 3 × 100 Pull 200, then 3 × 100 Swim 400, 300, 200, 100 Entire workout swum breast-stroke
Warm up 800 (200-s, 200-k, 200-p, 200-s) Kick 100, pull 100, swim 100—repeat 10 times alternating strokes Swim 800 free Swim 8 × 200 on 3 min.-1st 200 fly, 2nd IM, 3rd back, 4th IM, 5th breast, 6th IM, 7th free, 8th IM	Warm up 1200 Swim 20 × 50 fly 10 × 50 free Kick 500, then 5 × 100, free and fly alternating Swim 30 × 25 sprints, free and fly alternating Swim 16 × 100 on 2 min. in 4 sets of 4 × 100—1st set fly, 2nd free, 3rd fly, 4th free	*Switching workout** Warm up IM Swim 3 broken 400 IMs-4 × 100, 10 sec. rest Sprint 30 × 25—1 kick, 1 pull, 1 swim, alternating Kick 600 IM, then 12 × 50, alternating strokes Pull same as kick Swim 4 × 200 from dive—1st 2 IM, 2nd 2 fly
TOTAL: 7000 yd.	TOTAL: 7000 yd.	TOTAL: 6000 yd.

*Switching Workouts: In this type of workout, emphasis is placed on working on switching from one stroke to another. For example, if the swimmer swims a 400 IM, he might switch strokes every 25 instead of every 100.

Late-Season Workout
(Right Before the Taper Begins, Using Five Methods of Training)

Procedure	Type of Training	Pulse-rate Range (Low-High)	Quality Developed (Approx. Percentage)
1. Warm up 800	Overdistance	120	Endurance 95%, speed 5%
2. Swim 8 × 200, 15 sec. rest; 8 × 100, 10 sec. rest; 8 × 50, 5 sec. rest	Interval training	130-180	Endurance 80%, speed 20%
3. Swim 20 × 25 variable sprints, 20 sec. rest	Sprint training	95-170	Endurance 20%, speed 80%
4. Kick 10 × 100, 20 sec. rest	Interval training	130-180	Endurance 75%, speed 25%
5. Pull 1000 yards, 2 lengths slow then 1 length fast, etc.	Speed play (hypoxic breathing)	120-170	Endurance 85%, speed 15%
6. Swim at a very fast speed, 2 to 3 rest intervals: 200, 150, 100, 75, 50	Repetition training	95-180	Endurance 50%, speed 50%
7. Loosen down 500	Overdistance		

Total Distance: 7125 yd. Here a greater emphasis is placed on speed than in previous two workouts.

7 Day Triathlon Swim Training Schedule

	Monday	Tuesday	Wednesday
MORNING	1. W.U.800 2. Swim 16 × 75 Hyp. 　on :55 (Fly on :60, 　　　Back on :60, 　　　Br. on 1:10) 3. Kick 500 continuously 4. Pull 5 × 100 on 1:15 　Free to 1:45 Br.Hyp 5. Swim 1000 for time 　split negative Dis. Men—W.U.800, then 　Swim 4 × 1000 　　*Total Distance* 　　Others—4000 　　Dis.—　4800	1. W.U. 500 2. S.10 × 125 Hyp. 3. K.5 × 100 4. P.500 continously 　Hyp. 5. S.5 × 300 　Dis.—4 × 500 　　*Total Distance* 　　Others—4250 　　Dis.—　4750	1. W.U.800 2. S.3 × 200 　3 × 150 　3 × 100 3. K.500 continuously 4. P.10 × 50 Hyp. 5. S.12 × 25 　Dis.—S.1650 　　*Total Distance* 　　Others—3450 　　Dis.—　4700
AFTERNOON	1. W.U.1200 　S.Hyp. 　10 × 100 on 1:10 Free 　　　　　1:15 Back 　　　　　Fly 　　　　　1:25 Br. 　5 × 100 on 1:05 Free 　　　　　1:10 Back 　　　　　Fly 　　　　　1:20 Br. 　5 × 100 on 1:00 Free 　　　　　1:05 Back 　　　　　Fly 　　　　　1:15 Br. 3. S.12 × 25 Every other one 　fast from a push-off 4. K.400-then 3 × 200 5. P.400-then 4 × 150 Hyp. 6. S.4 × 500 on 7 min. 　Dis. 2 × 1000 　　*Total Distance* 　　Others—7500 　　Dis.—　8500 　　Spr.—　6000	1. W.U. 800 2. S.5 × 200 on 2:20 　3 × 200 on 2:15 　2 × 200 on 2:10 　Dis.—8 × 400 　Spr.—Go 100s 3. S.800—negative split 4. K.800—then 8 × 25 5. P.1000 Hyp. 6. A. S. broken 400, 4 × 　100—10 sec. R.I. be- 　tween 100s B. S. straight 400 C. Repeat A and B for a 　total of 6 × 400 Spr. 300s 　　*Total Distance* 　　Others—8000 　　Dis.—　8600 　　Spr.—　6400	1. W.U.1200 2. S. 　6 × 150 on 1:45 Free 　　　　　1:55 Back 　　　　　Fly 　　　　　2:15 Br. 　4 ×150 on 1:40 Free 　　　　　1:50 Back 　　　　　Fly 　　　　　2:10 Br. 　4 × 150 on 1:35 Free 　　　　　1:45 Back 　　　　　Fly 　　　　　2:05 Br. 3. S.16 × 50 variable sprints 4. K.600 continuously, then 　8 × 50 5. P.600 continuously, then 　2 × 200 6. S.1000 continuously, con- 　centrating on working 　turns hard and swimming 　easy 7. S.5 × 200 Repetition 　Training (with long R.I. of 　3 min.) 　Spr.-150s 　Dis.-4 × 500 　　*Total Distance* 　　Others—7700 　　Dis.—　8900 　　Spr.—　6450

Note:　Most workouts outlined for "Others" are for middle-distance freestylers, breast, back, and butterfly swimmers. In repeat swims the sprinters do either half or three-fourths of the distance assigned the "Others," and unless noted otherwise, the distance men double the distance, (i.e., if the "Others" are doing 10 × 100, the sprinters would do either 10 × 50 or 10 × 75, and the distance men 10 × 200)

7 Day Triathlon Swim Training Schedule

Thursday	Friday	Saturday	Sunday

1. W.U.500
2. S.10 × 100
3. K.500 continuously
4. P.500 continuously
5. Complete the workout with anything you want to do to a total of 1500
 	
Total Distance
Others—4000
Dis.— 5000
Sp.— 3000
	1. W.U. as you would before prelims. of NCAAs
	For example:
	  A. S.K. or P. a total of 800 yd.
	  B. S.4 to 6 × 50
	  C. K.300
	  D. K.2 × 50
	  E. Sprint 2 × 25
	  F. Loosen down 200
	2. S. any of the following:
	  A. 1 × 400 B. a pace
	    1 × 300 1650
	    1 × 200 C. 20 × 50
	    1 × 100 on :60
	
	Total Distance
	2450 to 3000
		Dual Meet at 2:00 P.M.
		
		All swimmers must work out before the meet.
			Morning off unless you want to be videotaped for underwater stroke analysis, in which case be at the pool between 10:30 and 1:30.

1. W.U.1200   :40
2. S.20 × 50 on :45
            :50
            :35
   10 × 50 on :40
            :45
            :30
   10 × 50 on :35
            :40
   Dis. 30 × 100
3. S.1000 split negative
4. K.1000 continuously
5. P.1000 continuously Hyp.
6. S. 1 Broken 400-10 R.I.
    1 Straight 400
    1 Broken 300-10 R.I.
    1 Straight 300
    1 Broken 200-10 R.I.
    1 Straight 200
   Dis.1 Broken 1500
    1 Straight 1500
   Spr. 200-20-0-200-150-
   150-100-100
	1. W.U.800
	2. S. 8 × 100
	     8 × 75
	     8 × 50
	   Dis.—Double
	   Spr.—Half
	3. K.10 × 100
	4. P.10 × 100 Hyp.
	5. S. Others 3 × 500
	   Dis. 3 × 100
	   Spr. 3 × 300
	6. Work on Starts and Relay Take-offs
		Dual Meet at 2:00 P.M.
		
		Swimmers come in at 12:30 P.M. and do the following warm-up:
		
		1. W.U.800
		2. S.20 × 50 (Dis.12 × 100)
		3. K.400
		4. P.400 Hyp.
		5. S. Sprints, such as 2 × 25
		After the meet, team members who go 20 × 100 will receive credit for one workout
			4:30—6:30 P.M.
			
			There will be a make-up workout for those who have not done 11 workouts this week
			
			1. W.U.500
			2. S.8 × 50
			3. K.400
			4. P.400 Hyp.
			5. S.3 × 800

	Total Distance Others—6100 Dis.— 7600 Spr.— 5500	*Total Distance* Others—4650 Dis.— 4850 (Not including distance swum in races)	*Total Distance*-4100 All swimmers do same workout
Total Distance Others—7000 Dis.— 9200 Spr.— 6100			

Code: W.U.—Warm up, S.—Swim, K.—Kick, P.—Pull, Hyp.—Hypoxic, Dis.—Distance Swimmers, Others—Middle Distance Swimmers, Spr.—Sprinters, Fly—Butterfly, Br.—Breaststrokers, Back—Backstrokers, on 60 sec. refers to departure time, R.I.—Rest Interval. Distance is measured in yards.

The civilized man has built a coach, but he has lost the use of his feet. —Emerson

12 Month Triathlon Swim Training Schedule

		September	October	November
Number of Workouts per Week		Workouts are optional.	5	6
Total Time and Distance per Week	A.M.			
	P.M.		1 hr.—3000 yd.	2 hr.—6000 to 7000 yd.
Dry-Land Exercises How Often and How Long		Administer strength, flexibility, and power tests.	1 hr.—4 days a week—mostly isokinetic exercise	45 min.—5 days a week—isokinetic exercise
Type of Training Type of Sets		Either stay out of water or play water polo or Swim easy—no formal training.	Overdistance and short-rest-interval training Do sets of 150s, 200s, 300s, 400s, 800s—stay away from short-distance and sprint training	Overdistance, short-rest-interval training, repetition training, and some sprinting Add 50, 75, 100 repeats plus some 25 yd. sprints
GENERAL PLAN		This is the best month to take it easy, to get away from the pool—play some tennis or paddle ball. The body needs to rest—use this time for a change of pace.	Practice begins this month. Concentrate on building strength and doing some swimming. This is a good time to work on stroke mechanics, for team members to look at movies and work on weaker strokes.	The tempo of practice picks up and more high-quality work is introduced into practice. Still keep up the isokinetic exercise, but reduce time by 15 min. Continue stroke work and talks on training.

		March	April	May
Number of Workouts per Week		8 to 10	6 to 10	5 to 10
Total Time and Distance per Week	A.M.	45 min. to 1 hr.—2000 to 3500 yd.	Short loosen-up workout	1 hr.—3000 to 4000 yd.
	P.M.	1 hr. to 2¼ hr.—3000 to 7000 yd.	1 hr. to 1½ hr.—3000 to 4000 yd.	2 hr.—6000 to 8000 yd.
Dry-Land Exercises How Often and How Long		20 min.—3 days a week	15 min.—3 days a week	30 min.—4 days a week
Type of Training Type of Sets		Mixed training—avoid too much high-quality work. Do lots of easy swimming, some slow interval training, some sprinting and pace work.	Mixed training—just enough to stay in shape to swim in National AAUs in mid-April.	Mixed training—as in Jan. and Feb., but concentrate on endurance work.
GENERAL PLAN		This is the time for tapering. Start taper 2 to 2½ weeks before big meet. Gradually reduce yardage until 3 days before meet when it should be 2000 to 3000 yd. Prepare mentally for big meet.	Swim for first 2 weeks until National AAUs, then lay off for 2 weeks before beginning training for summer season.	Swimmers work once or twice a day, depending on academic schedule. (At Indiana University classes end the first week of May and swimmers begin twice a day in 50-meter pool as soon as exams are over.)

December	January	February
11	11	11
1¼ hr.—3000 to 4500 yd. 2¼ hr.—6000 to 8000 yd.	1¼ hr.—3000 to 4500 yd. 2¼ hr.—6000 to 9000 yd.	1¼ hr.—3000 to 4500 yd. 2¼ hr.—6000 to 9000 yd.
30 min.—4 days a week—isokinetic exercise	30 min.—4 days a week—isokinetic exercise	30 min.—4 days a week—isokinetic exercise
Mixed training—a combination of all methods. Break team into 3 groups: sprinters, others, and distance. Do all types of sets.	Mixed training—introduce broken swimming into workouts; start doing more sprints. The swimmers should start feeling tired.	Mixed training—have swimmers try to do best repeat times. Watch for good performances in repetition sets of repeats.
For next 3 months the swimmers work out twice a day. Exercises continue. Swimmers should improve times in repeats and begin reducing take-off times on short-rest-interval training repeats.	Continue hard work, keep interest high by varying workouts. Don't break training for dual meets. Get a few swimmers ready to make cut-off times in their events. Continue stroke work.	This is the month in which swimmers are most likely to get sick. Watch for colds and other respiratory infections. Tell swimmers to dress warmly, get plenty of sleep, and eat properly.

June	July	August
12	12	8 to 11
2½ hr.—7000 to 9000 yd. 2 hr.—5000 to 6000 yd.	2½ hr.—5000 to 9000 yd. 2 hr.—3000 to 6000 yd.	1-1½ hr.—3000 to 5000 yd. 1-1½ hr.—2000 to 3000 yd.
30 min.—4 days a week	30 min.—3 days a week	Eliminate all dry-land exercise
Mixed training—emphasize improving times and decreasing departure times for the various sets of repeats.	Mixed training—more time spent on pace work and sprinting. Avoid too much high-quality work.	Mixed training—decrease number of repeat swims. Increase pace work and sprinting.
This will be the hardest month of the year. Swimmers must get plenty of sleep and rest and must watch diet. Coach must plan workouts carefully and watch for signs of failing adaptation.	This is the last full month of training because Nationals occur in mid-August. This should be a month of moderately hard work in which swimmers are not pushed so hard they can't recover by the National Meet.	Tapering begins around first of August (assuming Nationals, discontinue training for two weeks).

to swim from one point to another. Have a friend stand on the beach and follow you to see if you are going straight, or use a paddler. Remember, keep arms wide, shoulder width pull, and head high. I realize some people aren't fortunate enough to live near the ocean...but a lake, river, or bay will do as well.

Tips for Timing
- Be courteous to other swimmers. Always walk behind the clock so you won't interfere with the view of others.
- If the pace clock is a plug in type, watch out for the electrical cord.
- If you are working out in a pool in which lanes are designated for speed, stroke or equipment, choose the appropriate lane.
- Don't overestimate your abilities. If you are participating in a workout with other swimmers, choose a lane in which you can maintain the appropriate speeds and intervals.
- If you are sharing a lane with other swimmers be sure to move out of their way at the end of each repeat swim so they can touch the wall and easily read their correct time. Better yet, if you can get times for a fellow swimmer during a set of repeat swims be sure to do it.

HOW FAT HELPS YOU FLOAT

Fat floats. If you throw a pound of butter into a swimming pool, it will float just like a cork. The fat in your body is no different. The more fat you've got, the better you'll be able to float in a swimming pool. In contrast to fat, lean body mass does not float.

There are many ways to estimate the amount of body fat you're carrying, but the best way is based on how well you float. Precise measurement takes sophisticated equipment, but here is a way to approximate your proportion of fat. All you need is access to a swimming pool.

Float on your back after filling your lungs with air. Then blow your air out.
- Above 25 percent fat, people float easily.
- At 22 to 23 percent fat (healthy for a woman), one can usually float while breathing shallowly.
- At 15 percent fat (low for a woman, healthy for a man), one will usually sink slowly, even with a chest full of air.
- At 13 percent fat, one sinks readily, even with a chest full of air in salty ocean water.

This brings up another training hurdle for the slim Triathlete. The energy demand on his fuel-fat supply will be increased substantially over that of a contestant carrying a larger percentage of body fat. The extra energy required to maintain body heat and to cover extra distances in the water will be an endurance factor in the bike and run segments of the event. For this reason it is difficult to establish aerobic points in swimming. The aerobic effort exerted by a heavier person is much less than that of a slim person, due to the extra energy required on the part of the slim person just to stay afloat.

Swimming Bibliography
Competitive Swimming Manual, Councilman Co. Inc., 1977, 2606 East Second Street, Bloomington, IN 47401.
Swimming Magazines
Journal of Masters Swimming, Dept. of P.E., Western Illinois University, Macomb, IL 61455.
Swim-Master, 2308 N.E. 19th Avenue, Fort Lauderdale, FL 33305.
Swim Swim and *Swim, Bike and Run*, Box 5901, Santa Monica, CA 90405.
Swimmers Magazine, P.O. Box 15906, Nashville, TN 37215.
Swimming Technique, Swimming World Pub., Box 45497, Los Angeles, CA 90045.
Swimming World and Junior Swimmer, Box 45497, Los Angeles, CA 90045.

VII

Bike Training
for the Triathlon

Paul Bragg was an avid bicycle racer throughout the years. He participated in early day board track racing that was popular at the time.

1

Bike 112 Miles Competitively in 12 Months Training

Introduction to Triathlon Bike Racing

Bicycle road racing, in all its forms and styles, has finally come of age in America. For many years bike racing was considered one of Europe's major spectator sports, although the U.S. participant and spectator have never been greatly impressed with the spectacle of bike racing.

The advent of the health and physical fitness craze which started the running boom in the early 70's brought millions of Americans to their feet, away from the TV set and out onto the highways, byways, and footpaths, early and late, walking, and jogging for health. This same motivation carried American's into competition in first the 10-kilometer run (6.2 miles), the half-marathon, and finally the big one; the full 26.2 mile marathon. From the 26.2 mile full marathon, a few ventured into the ultramarathon, the 24-hour distance run, the 100 miles, etc. Only the dedicated running fanatic ventured forth into these ultra distance endeavors.

It was only a natural progression, probably sparked by the pounding boredom of distance running, the resulting injuries, the desire to achieve a more rounded physical conditioning and technical expertise not available in the running mode, that brought about the need for a new vehicle, a new training goal, a new competitive game, a test of stamina and endurance — the bicycle road race.

Let's take an inventory of bike and run attributes. Bicycling is an endurance sport, a natural combination with running. Some of the muscle structures required for each of the two events are diametrically opposed to each other requiring body building and distance training of new and relatively unused muscle fibers. When brought into unison, the result is improved running and biking ability.

From out of the water came the swimmer, a whole other breed, 10% feet 90% upper body. We wondered how long he could stay away from the fun. We looked with awe at those pectorals, deltoids, latissimus and trapesus. Even so, we knew we had him down on two counts — legs. Even so, we certainly were not going to tell him bikers and runners were afraid of the water. We knew he had lung power and was a proven, style-conscious training nut. Style translates into speed in the water and on a bike. Given a little time and training help, this, swimmer might be difficult to beat, but first he will have to shake out those flutter kick fins called feet, stand vertically and learn how to put one foot ahead of the other in rapid order.

Not to worry swimmers, we bikers and runners have our work cut out for us acquiring the style and stamina to successfully train ourselves to swim beyond the length of our backyard pool to 2.4 miles in all kinds of conditions: cold lakes, cold rough water oceans, etc. We now add swimming to our inventory of physical attributes of Swim, Bike, and Run.

Aerobically there is a strong cross benefit from running to biking and to swimming. Interval training in each discipline improves the performance in the other two.

Technically the runner has to meet his mark. True, there are many runners and swimmers who are mechanically gifted which is a prerequisite to being a bicyclist. This leaves the rest of the-all-thumb's runners and swimmers with an extra learning requirement before they venture more than a block from the bike repair shop.

Some material in this chapter has been reprinted from The Custom Bicycle, copyright 1979, by Michael J. Kolin and Denise M. de la Rosa.

Beyond the mechanical techniques required in taking up the sport of bike road racing, we enter into a whole new world of riding style, dress, shoes, and rules of the road. Time and distance arithmetic, crank revolutions per minute, miles per hour, inches covered in revolutions per minute for each of the 10-12-14-18-21 speed gearing combinations available now in quality bike equipment, are all important. For the purist, a computer has been devised that will give a L.E.D. read out of all factors involved, including heart rate through which he can better record his training progress and Omega Triathlon testing procedures.

Diet and liquid intake take on a whole new meaning contrary to running concepts. A biker must maintain a steady calorie and carbohydrate intake during an extended ride, adequate liquid replenishment because perspiration evaporates and dissipates the body's liquids unnoticed at bike speeds through a still air day, and gives the runner and swimmer a false reading until it is too late and they are dehydrated. The marathon runner getting off a bike must reprogram his marathon mind to an ultramarathon concept. He has already completed the equivalent of two full marathons in glycogen expenditures; first in a 2.4 mile swim where a quarter-swimming mile equals 2.5 running miles and in half-mile bike ride where five bike miles equals one running mile.

The ultramarathon concept, more fully explained in another chapter, is a "laid-back" form of marathon running that we will have to emulate if we expect to go the distance or finish. A runner and swimmer should plan on at least two years of continuous bike training to maintain both good form and endurance at a respectable speed.

Again, as with swimming, "style is speed." No quarter, no sloppy positioning of knees, elbows, ankle flexing, no lazy gear changing when pedal RPM's slow down — or knee injuries begin to be noticed. An absolute "nose glued to the top of the headset" semi-fetal position against a headwind is necessary.

The runner has his running crowd, the 8-9-10 minute mile gaggle of guys and gals that he is comfortable with when out on training runs. The swimmer has his rough water swim group, an elite enjoyable group of bronzed men and women who never seem to tire in the water regardless of the temperature. Swimmers and runners are reluctant to cut the umbilical cord and venture out into that bicycle world of "different people."

Long, tight-fitting, Chamois crotch padded shorts, shoes in which you can't even walk much less run, and that outer space-type crash helmet or "hair net," the form fitting multi-colored jersey, advertising tires, bikes, hardware, races from 3 continents, are all strange. The most notable change is the nomenclature of terms and words in the pre - or post-ride bull session. No mention of endless "injuries" or how long it will be before we can build up some running miles as it is with the running crowd. Biking offers a exciting new positive conversational world of gear clusters, sew-ups versus clinchers, trade names for accessories, and mixing Japan, Italy, France, and England on one bike.

A real explosion is happening with new things, faces, concepts, disciplines, styles, hardware, conversations, people and most of all, places. A runner's scenic training world is five miles, give or take a few, out and back. A biker's scenic training world is 50 miles out and back, or 100 miles in a two-day weekend. Wonderful new vista experiences, plans for extended summer touring, foreign country bike touring, the only limit is your imagination and your personal renewable source of energy. Competition is plentiful; join a local bike club, and you will be drafting with the best in training runs. Go for it solo in time trials, occasional centuries and half-centuries, sprints, etc.

Having come out of the swim or run disciplines, it is only natural that you look for the dual or multiple sport events to enable you to capitalize competively on your inherent strengths, combining cycling with one or both of the two additional sports.

The triathlon is the ultimate in participating multi-sports . . . if you are mentally and physically read for it, sign up and have the thrill of a lifetime!!!

Cycling is Faster than Jogging,
Cheaper than Driving, and Fun for a Lifetime

POOR MARK TWAIN. He learned to ride a bicycle in about 1880, and the bike he learned on was an "ordinary" or "Penny Farthing" bicycle. Invented by Englishman James Starley in the early 1870s, this precursor of the modern bike consisted of a large front wheel anywhere from 39 to 59 inches across, and a much smaller rear wheel.

In spite of being taught by an "expert," Twain had trouble learning to ride the Penny Farthing. Even something as basic as getting off the machine was a problem.

In his "Taming of the Bicycle," he explains:

"It is quite easy to tell one how to do the voluntary dismount; the words are few, the requirements simple, and apparently undifficult . . . but it isn't. I don't know why it isn't, it just isn't. Try as you may, you don't get down as you do from a horse, you get down as you would from a house afire. You make a spectacle of yourself every time."

Despite his difficulties, Twain advises in the end, "Get a bicycle. You will not regret it if you live."

In 1980, there are some people who are equally confounded by the sleek and complex 10-speed bicycle that dominates today's market. Such uncertainty has not, however, interfered with a steady growth in cycling's popularity: The number of "bicycle people" in America today has tripled in the last two decades to 105 million.

The reasons for this growth are obvious: Cycling is a fuel-free means of transportation; it's nonpoluting (the only thing it burns is calories—between 12 and 20 per *minute*); and, above all, it's great exercise and fun.

Those who have taken up cycling in recent years are predominantly recreational riders and commuters. (The number of racers has leveled off at about 8,000, most of whom belong to the 400 clubs in the U.S. Cycling Federation.)

It's the commuters who are getting increased attention these days—from local, state and federal governments. According to the U.S. Department of Transportation, 470,000 people biked to and from their jobs in 1975. By 1985, the use of the bicycle as an alternate means of transportation may be saving between 16 and 23 million barrels of oil a year.

"Bicycle Transportation for Energy Conservation," a recent study by the Department of Transportation suggests that, if the federal government wishes to encourage more people to commute by bike, it must not only make Americans aware that the bicycle has commuting potential, but also provide more hospitable biking environments such as bike paths and augment support facilities—bike racks, lockers, etc.—at various places of business.

All these statistics should not obscure what cycling really means to most bicycle people. For commuter, recreational rider and triathlon participant alike, it's a chance to get reacquainted with the scents and sounds of the countryside; to slow down and measure the world in feet, not miles, per hour; and, finally, to escape from everyday life for at least a little while.

To a person uninstructed in natural history, his country or sea-side stroll is a walk through a gallery filled with wonderful works of art, nine-tenths of which have their faces turned to the wall.

THOMAS HUXLEY

Walk while ye have the light, lest darkness come upon you. —St. John, XII:35

Editor's Note

I was greatly impressed with the introduction to John Marino's bicycling book telling the story of John the athlete, who, after a serious injury, gave up all hope of recovery. Upon meeting a doctor who practiced preventive medicine and a holistic approach to body rejuvination and good health, John started on the long road back to the complete recovery of his injured and neglected body.

I can relate to John's story through my own experience in meeting a preventive medical man. Through a life natural diet of fresh fruit, vegetables, seeds, nuts and grains, avoiding all processed, refined white sugar, flour, rice and overly processed, de-vitaminized foods, I regained my health. John's dedication and accomplishments in his cross-country bicycle races is absolute proof that proper, natural nutrition works. Let us not forget that the bicycle was also his exercise vehicle on his road to recovery. This is a good example for many to follow.

With permission of the author, we offer excerpts from his book on bicycling for the training triathlete. As it is in swimming, so it also is in bicycling; style is speed, distance and endurance. Contrary to running, biking is a very complex sport when it involves competitive riding. Unlike swimming, style is easy to acquire and to perfect with the right instruction. We have briefly utilized some of the basic concepts of biking in this chapter starting from the bicycle's beginning history and progressing through riding. There is a world of material available in John Marino's book that warrants the serious triathlete's investigation, much more than space would permit in this chapter.

Again, as in swimming, our statistics prove that the accomplished bicyclist accounts for less than 10% of the number of aspiring triathletes. We probably cannot tell bicyclists much about their sport so we will be concerned with the remaining 90% of training triathletes who wish to start this enjoyable sport. We would seriously advise you to acquire the book, *Bicycling,* by John Marion (Dr. Lawrence May, a preventive medicine specialist, and Hal Bennet, an avid cyclist and author of health oriented books are co-authors). It is available through J.P. Tarcher Inc., 9110 Sunset Blvd., Los Angeles, Ca. 90069.

The John Marino Story

In a very real way I owe the quality of my life today to a bike. Let me tell you how that came about.

When I was a 19-year-old college sophomore, I was drafted by the Los Angeles Dodgers. Having played baseball all my life, this seemed like a dream come true. Then, toward the end of my first baseball season, my life took a sudden tragic turn.

As part of my regular training program, I was lifting weights to build strength. I attempted to lift 525 pounds, which was too much for my physical condition at that time. Suddenly there was a loud crack that sounded as though a gun had gone off in the weightroom. My back exploded with pain, an electric shock raced down my spine. My toes curled, my legs shook uncontrollably, and I collapsed to the floor.

I had suffered a severe compression fracture of the lower lumbar vertebrae. My doctors informed me I had a permanent disability and from that day on for the rest of my life, my activities would have to be severely restricted.

The implications of this were almost unbearable. I was an athlete by nature. The accident had robbed me of my most important form of self-expression, and a central source of pride and self-esteem.

I visited one medical specialist after another, searching for that magic remedy that would give me back a normal life. But this search proved futile. Time and again I was told that nothing could be done.

For the next five years my physical and mental state declined. I gave up all forms of exercise and consoled myself with food. I gained weight and grew lazier by the day.

I am proud of John Marino who is the epitome of health and fitness and lives the basic Bragg health life with natural foods, fasting, deep breathing and exercise. –Patricia Bragg

Then in 1973, another dramatic change took place in my life. I met a doctor with a holistic approach to health who urged me to stop looking for miracle cures and start taking care of myself. He told me that the human body has regenerating powers greater than anything the medical world can offer. His prescription for getting my body back to health started with diet—low fats, no sugar, no alcohol, no tobacco, no refined food products of any kind, and no red meat. It seemed to me like a severe sacrifice, but I was desperate enough to try anything.

I followed the doctor's recommendations to the letter, and though I was skeptical in the beginning my body definitely began to respond. By simply purifying my diet, my back began to show the first signs of improvement. For the first time in years I allowed myself to daydream about being active in sports again.

Running was out of the question, and that eliminated most types of sports. I needed something gentle, an activity that wouldn't put any stress on my back. When a friend suggested a bicycle, I knew that was it!

I started riding one or two miles a day. The more I rode the better I felt. And the better I felt the more I wanted to ride. Soon I was riding 10 and 20 miles at a stretch. My back relaxed and the painful muscle spasms that had once kept me a slave to my injuries began to subside. And along with my physical improvements I noticed that my attitude was picking up as well. Until that time I'd never realized how much the two were intertwined.

As I started losing weight, my self-esteem soared. My body, that miraculous self-regenerating machine, was again becoming a source of pleasure to me. Though the pain persisted—and persists even to this day—I found I could deal with it because I felt good about my life.

As the months passed, bicycling became a way of life for me. And eventually my love for the sport motivated me to do something special. I set the biggest goal I'd ever set in my life—to pedal from Los Angeles to New York City, a distance of nearly 3,000 miles. This challenge has been compared to running 43 consecutive marathons or swimming the English Channel 18 times in a row. This would be my tribute to the bike, to which I owed so much.

Looking through the *Guinness Book of World Records* one day I discovered that the official record for the transcontinental ride was 13 days 5 hours and 20 minutes. That was an average of well over 200 miles a day. I really didn't know how I was going to pull this off, but I was determined to break that record. I trained for 2½ years, one step at a time. During that time I learned that I could become an increasingly better and more efficient rider, and still have fun in the process. There was always something to keep me interested: constantly changing terrain, developing different riding techniques, making small changes on the bicycle itself that improved it and even made it more personal to me.

Finally, I was ready for the challenge. I set my date of departure: August 13, 1978.

At 4:50 *A.M.* on the morning of the big day, I left Santa Monica City Hall on my bike, and began the most challenging experience I'd ever confronted.

The miles rolled by. My performance was proving to be even better than I had expected. My body and mind worked together in perfect harmony—my mind nudging me on when my body grew tired, my body nudging me on when my mind grew tired.

I have to confess, the journey was much tougher than I had ever imagined. But on August 28, I arrived at City Hall in New York City with a new world's record to my credit. My riding time: 13 days 1 hour and 20 minutes.

The next year I tried to break my own record. I was in for a whole new set of experiences. Mother Nature beat me up. It rained—not just a gentle shower but a downpour!—for the last six days of the ride. I sloshed through flash floods, suffered through pelting hail and fought wind storms that under other circumstances would have sent me indoors. Sixty miles short of New York I stopped the ride when I ran out of time. Finishing the ride would have been an empty formality.

My failure to break my own record was a disappointment but also a challenge to try again the following year.

On June 16, 1980, I again left Santa Monica City Hall on my third challenge of the record. Twelve days 3 hours and 41 minutes later, I arrived in New York, having broken my record by nearly a full day.

Sometime during this third ride I got the idea for writing a book. I wanted to share my enthusiasm with others, encourage them to discover in bicycling some of the rewards and pleasures this sport has given me. At first I thought of writing about my own experiences. But then I realized that wasn't enough. Instead, I decided to do a complete, step-by-step guidebook to help every rider or potential rider get off to the right start or improve his or her performance. This book is no longer a dream. Like my cross-country challenge, it is a reality. These pages contain a broad program for improving every aspect of your physical and mental well-being as you embark on the exciting adventure of bicycling.

I'm neither a professional writer nor a trained professional in the field of health. I'm a bicyclist who knows what cycling has done for my body and mind. In other words, my accomplishments were within everyone's reach. Anyone could do what I have done if they only applied themselves.

A Brief History of the Bicycle

The Velocipede

In 1860, a Scotsman by the name of Kirkpatrick Macmillan constructed a beautiful and functional machine that was a prophecy of things to come. Built of wood and iron, it was "pedaled" by an ingenious leverage system attached to cranks on the rear wheel. This velocipede had a front wheel that could be steered, a brake system operated from the handlebars, a sprung seat to absorb road shock, and even a fender to protect the rider from dirt thrown up by the rear wheel. Thereafter, bicycle technology progressed by leaps and bounds.

By about 1865, bicycling had become a craze that affected France, the United States, and England. The railroads had replaced stagecoach travel between most large cities, and its influence undoubtedly spurred an active interest in developing other mechanical means of travel.

The average person living in Europe at that time couldn't afford a horse. Getting out of town for a weekend jaunt in the country, or just getting away for the afternoon, was expensive. The bicycle changed all that. People who couldn't afford to buy and maintain horses could afford bikes. The purchase of a bike offered the adventure and romance of travel to whole classes of people who had never previously ventured past the city limits.

Diaries of this period tell of people traveling distances of 50 or more miles on their bikes. Bikes were not just playthings for the wealthy classes any more. They were the world's first personal vehicles, carrying single riders at distances and speeds that would compete with the horse.

The Ordinary

One problem faced by early bicyclists was the condition of the roads, which were rough and full of potholes and ruts that made passage on small-wheeled bikes difficult because the smaller wheel would drop down into the holes. The most important technical advance, therefore, was the large, high-wheeled bicycle, then called the "Ordinary." The large front wheel made high speeds over rough roads possible for the first time, since it simply rode over the potholes.

Although the high-wheeled ordinary carried the sport of bicycling a giant step forward, it was not without its drawbacks. With the rider seated near the top of the wheel, his head seven feet above the ground, the machine was not very stable. If the rider ran into an immovable object, or his wheel dropped into an especially large pothole in the road, he was instantly launched over the handlebars into the ditch.

From the Safety Bicycle to the Ten-Speed

As the 1890s approached, inventors put their efforts into developing what came to be called the "safety bicycle." Bike design as we know it today—that is, with two wheels of equal size, pedals driving the rear wheel through a system of chain and sprockets—made its appearance in 1884. The "Rover" produced in England in 1886, looked very much like today's bikes. And with the advent of these bikes, recreational rides of 50 miles and more became commonplace.

Early bicycle wheels were equipped with hard rubber tires, which transferred road vibration directly to the rider's poor derriere. In 1888, a Scotsman by the name of John Boyd Dunlop invented and patented a pneumatic tire that absorbed road vibration and bumps like magic. By 1892 every bicycle produced was equipped with this new invention.

Although dominated by men, the sport of bicycling had many female enthusiasts, which made an impact on bicycle design. Drawings of cyclists depict women riding bikes as far back as the 1830s. Illustrated history books show pictures of bicycles designed specifically to accommodate women's long skirts.

Around the turn of the century, Sturmey-Archer of England developed the multiple-speed rear hub. Whereas the high-wheeled Ordinary and other bike designs of the period limited the rider to a single gear ratio and pedaling speed, the first multiple-speed hub enabled the cyclist to select three different ratios with a flick of the tiny lever on the handlebars. The bicycle's capacity for touring long distances over hilly terrain was greatly extended, and higher speeds on a bicycle were made possible.

Soon after Sturmey-Archer's invention became popular in the 30s, the derailleur system of shifting gears appeared on bicycles in France and Italy. This was an adaptation of a ratio-varying technique utilized for decades in mill machinery and other devices driven by chains and cogs. Whereas the early Sturmey-Archer hubs were limited to three speeds, the first derailleurs provided five and eventually ten speeds. Because the early derailleurs were expensive and extremely difficult to operate, they were originally used only by racers. It wasn't until the late 50s that the mechanism had been refined to the point where it began to appear on European touring bikes. It was left to Japanese manufacturers in the 60s to bring the cost down and make the ten-speed available to the general user.

Although bicycles were kept amazingly light in weight (from 30 to 50 pounds) after the appearance of the safety bike, the frames tended to be soft—that is, springy and flexible. Soft, flexible frames provided riding comfort, but they also wasted the rider's energy. In bearing down on the pedals, the cyclist's efforts were absorbed by the frame instead of being transferred cleanly to the rear wheel. The science of metallurgy, with the development of lightweight, extremely strong alloys, made it possible to produce highly efficient frames that were also comfortable for riding long distances. The new, high-quality metals, used only in the frame, increased the efficiency of the average bike as much as 15 percent.

Cycling as a Physical and Mental Rejuvenator

For getting in shape and keeping fit, bicycling has the unique advantage of providing a thorough physical workout while still being gentle to your body. For this reason, bicycling is often the preferred sport for people with spine or joint problems. Moreover, with a bicycle you can get in your exercise without having to recruit a partner, assemble a team, reserve a court, or join a club.

Like other vigorous activities, a regular cycling program can bring about dramatic changes in your physical and mental well-being. Sharon Weber, a schoolteacher in Michigan, spends her summers bicycle touring. When the weather permits, she commutes five miles each way from home to her classroom. In spite of being a self-confessed foodaholic, she now manages to stay trim and fit. "Diets," she said, "never worked for me. I enjoy eating good food, and dieting was always a major deprivation. After a couple of days of counting calories, I would begin to get depressed and then give up." Bicycling allows Sharon to have her cake and eat it too, burning away the traces of her gourmet delights at the average rate of 16 calories per minute—or nearly a thousand per hour—while feasting on the pleasures of the great out-of-doors.

Benefits for the Heart and Lungs

Shedding extra pounds and firming up flabby tissue are only part of the story of why bicycling can be so beneficial to your health. The internal changes are no less significant than the external, cosmetic ones. Over a period of time, a regular cycling program can increase the capacity of your lungs by as much as 20 percent. At the same time, your heart can become healthier and stronger because you'll grow vast new networks of capillaries to carry nutrients to the heart muscle itself. As your heart muscle improves in this way, the rate at which it will need to pump in order to perform a particular task will decrease.

Commenting about the training of competitive cyclists in *Bicycling* magazine, William Sanders observes that the healthier heart "can thump along in the 50s and 60s [beats per minute] at rest, and this means it doesn't wear out as fast as a heart that runs 80 or 90 all the time." In a report to the American Heart Association, Ralph S. Paffenburger, M.D., of the Stanford University School of Medicine, states that if people can burn up to 2,000 calories per week (about two hours of bike riding, depending on speed and terrain) they can reduce their risk of heart attack by 64 percent.

Many doctors today regard bicycling not only as a valuable means of building health and preventing disease, but also as an excellent means of rehabilitation. Bicycling is recommended for insomnia, hypertension, indigestion, anxiety, and even for recuperation from major heart attacks. Writing in the prestigious *L.A.W. Bulletin* about techniques doctors might apply to help survivors of myocardial infarction, Dr. Robert E. Bond relates his medical knowledge to his own personal experience: "Five years have elapsed since I suffered a heart attack. . . . Since that time I have ridden many miles in many states and several countries over widely varied terrain. I enjoy every mile and I look forward to every weekend."

Similarly, a cardiac patient by the name of Lee Walton, after two years of training at the Cardiac Rehabilitation Unit of Rancho Los Amigos Hospital in Downey, California, rode a "triple century" (300 miles) in 22 hours. His average speed was just under 14 miles per hour. Like others who have become extraordinary cyclists after suffering severe heart attacks, Lee is a member of the Specialized Coronary Outpatient Rehabilitation (SCOR) Cardiac Cyclists Club of Los Angeles.

Biking Toward Longevity

Staying physically active greatly enhances your enjoyment of health in your later years. That bicycle riding—or anything else—increases longevity is impossible to prove scientifically. But looking at the number of cyclists who are still going strong, touring and even racing after passing their seventh decade, it seems quite likely that this may be the case.

Writing in *Bicycling* Magazine, Dr. David L. Smith states: "Active exercising people are granted the benefit of an active old age. For most, active exercise like cycling will lead to a longer life span, and the extra years will be vigorous ones. There are many cyclists in their 70s, still vigorous and capable of long miles every day. Ed Delano and Clifford Graves (who are both in their 70s) are still riding centuries [100 miles in a day]."

Competitive Cycling

The mushrooming popularity of the bicycle has had a stimulating effect on cycle racing in the United States and Canada. This includes road and track racing, and the multi-sport events of the Triathlon and Biathlons.

In Europe, bicycle racing causes as much public excitement as baseball in the United States. Each year France hosts the famous Tour de France, a race that lasts 22 days and follows a grueling course up sheer elevations through the Alps and Pyrenees, as well as through scenic rural villages and city streets. The most famous of all bicycle races, it draws athletes from all over the world.

Every country in Europe has its own version of the Tour de France. In recent years Canada and the United States not only have sent athletes to these events, but also have begun sponsoring races that are drawing world-class cyclists to our shores.

Whereas Europe continues to dominate the world in organized bicycle competition, cyclists in the United States excel in advancing the technology of the bicycle. Most of this activity is centered on breaking world speed records.

Although most bicyclists ride at an average speed of 10 to 12 miles per hour, the world record is .138.7. This record, held by Allen Abbott, was accomplished on the Bonneville Salt Flats, using a race car to break the wind. The speed record for bikes not assisted by another vehicle is 62.93 miles per hour, accomplished with an aerodynamic bike designed by Al Voight, a California aerospace scientist. In a race on conventional bikes, a well-conditioned athlete will average from 20 to 34 miles per hour, depending on the distance and time of the race.

Many athletes active in other sports consider bicycling an essential part of their training. Ray Cortez, the supervisor of a Richmond (California) chemical plant, took up cycling so that during the summer he could stay in shape for downhill skiing. Bicycling is particularly useful for skiers, nd helpful to runners and swimmers as well. In the case of multi-sport enthusiasts, it is the claim)f certain triathletes that bicycling is the event which determines, more than any other, the)utcome of a given competition.

Buying Your First Bike

Shopping for a new bike sparks the excitement of even the most seasoned cyclist. Each year, subtle new technological and stylistic refinements attract the discerning cyclist's attention.

Because of all that's available today, shopping for a bike can be as bewildering as it is exciting. This chapter is intended to guide you through the maze of choices so that you come out the other side with the bike that best suits your needs.

Making the Right Choice

Weigh your needs carefully before you set out to buy your first bike. Don't buy more bike than you need, and don't buy less.

Look for names associated with the bicycle world: Raleigh, Peugeot, Gitane, Motobecane, Schwinn, Fuji, Dawes, Windsor, Univega, C.C.M., and Nishiki, to name a few. Most bicycles will need minor repairs from time to time. If you get a *name* bike, you can be assured of service at a reputable bike shop.

Before buying a bike, make absolutely certain that the vendor has a full-time service department devoted *only* to bicycle adjustments and repairs. The shop mechanic will, after all, be setting up and adjusting your bike. His or her skill can mean the difference between annoyance and delight with your first bike. Bike adjustments can be very subtle, and rider comfort, ease of operation, and reliability all depend on the assembly and adjustment being done properly.

The Triathlon Bicycle

At this point we are primarily concerned with the bike as a vehicle for competition in Distance Road Racing, more specifically the Multi-sport Events: Biathlons and Triathlons.

The selection of a proper bicycle for these events requires a more specific set of accessories than the normal road racer, otherwise the bicycle is the same as the road racing bike normally selected. Lightweight and dependability are prime factors in any bike purchased for distance road racing.

Gearing is the next most important consideration for the Triathlete's bike. With the advent of the 6 and 7 rear cluster and the three sprocket front chain rings, we can achieve a greater, "spinning," gear selection for the novice rider. As his power builds he can gradually reduce the number and size of the gears on his rear cluster and do away with the number three chain ring, at the same time reducing the bicycle's weight by a few grams.

It is absolutely essential that an 80 to 90 R.P.M. pedal count be maintained by the novice biker.

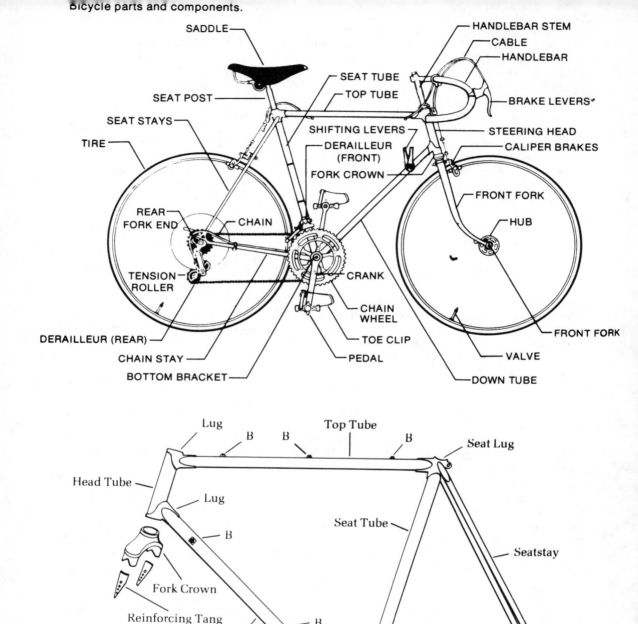

SADDLE
HANDLEBAR STEM
CABLE
HANDLEBAR
SEAT TUBE
SEAT POST
TOP TUBE
BRAKE LEVERS
SEAT STAYS
SHIFTING LEVERS
STEERING HEAD
TIRE
DERAILLEUR (FRONT)
CALIPER BRAKES
FORK CROWN
FRONT FORK
REAR FORK END
CHAIN
HUB
TENSION ROLLER
CRANK
DERAILLEUR (REAR)
CHAIN WHEEL
FRONT FORK
CHAIN STAY
TOE CLIP
VALVE
BOTTOM BRACKET
PEDAL
DOWN TUBE

Lug
Top Tube
B
B
B
Seat Lug
Head Tube
Lug
B
Seat Tube
Seatstay
Fork Crown
B
Reinforcing Tang
Down Tube
B
Chainstay
B
B—Brazed-on Fittings
Bottom Bracket
Rear Fork Ends (Dropouts)

The main triangle.

Key to Bicycle Parts

Pedals: The first part of the leverage system that transfers your energy to the rear wheel of the bike.

Cranks or crankarms: The steel or alloy levers that transfer your energy from the pedals to the chain.

Bottom bracket: The bearing assembly by which the crankarms are connected to the frame. Contains a ball-bearing system that minimizes friction as the crankarms are turned.

Chainwheels or chainrings: The two large sprockets fastened to the crankarm assembly and turned by the pedals.

These parts together make up the crankset.

Chain: The average chain has over a hundred links, each with its own bearing surfaces to deliver energy from your feet to the back wheel of the bike. Different gear ratios are attained by shifting the chain from one size sprocket to another.

Freewheel: A cluster of five small gears attached to the rear wheel hub. The chain turns the freewheel, which in turn rotates the rear wheel. The freewheel includes a ratchet system to allow the bike to coast forward.

Front derailleur: The mechanism that moves the chain from one chainwheel to another. It is controlled by the shift lever (9) on the left side of the bike.

Rear derailleur: The mechanism that moves the chain from one gear to another on the freewheel. It is controlled by the shift lever (9) on the right side of the bike.

Gear-shift levers (usually referred to as *shifters*): Two levers, one on the right, one on the left, by which the rider moves the derailleurs to select different gear ratios.

Tension roller (an integral mechanism in the rear derailleur): A system of two small chain sprockets providing spring tension to keep the chain taut as it shifts from one set of gears to another.

Hubs: This assembly contains the bearings for the wheels. The hub flanges have 36 holes for the spokes.

Quick-release levers: A lever system that replaces nuts for fastening the wheel to the frame. These levers are so named because they allow the cyclist to remove a wheel instantly without the use of tools, for repairing flat tires or making other minor repairs on the road.

Spokes: Each wire spoke has a wire nipple which connects it to the rim. This nipple is threaded, providing a way to tighten or loosen the spoke, adjust the wheel for stiffness, and remove wheel wobble.

Rims: Steel or alloy bands which hold the tires and which connect to the axle and hub assembly through the spokes.

Tires: Two basic types are available — clinchers for touring and recreation and sewups for racing and high-performance cycling. Sewup and clincher tires require different kinds of rims.

Tire valves: Devices for inflating the tires.

Saddle: The purpose of the saddle, in addition to supporting you, is to place your body in its most efficient position in relation to the pedals and handlebars.

Seat post: A steel or alloy tube that connects the saddle to the bike frame and allows it to be adjusted for height.

Seat tube: The frame member that runs from the seat to the bottom bracket.

Top tube: The frame component that runs from the seat to the head tube.

Seat stays: Frame tubes that run from behind the seat to the rear axle of the bike.

Seat lug: A pressed-steel reinforcement that connects the top tube, seat tube, and seat stays to the frame. The seat lug also has a clamping device which provides a way to tighten seat post into the frame.

Chain stays: The frame tubes that run from the bottom bracket to the rear wheel of the bike.

Rear dropout: A lug brazed to the ends of the chain stays, providing a junction for the chain stays and seat stays and a surface for attaching the rear wheel to the frame. The dropout on the right side often has a built-in bracket for fastening the rear derailleur to the frame.

Head tube: A frame member that joins with the top tube and down tube of the bike. A bearing insert called a headset allows the fork to be attached to the head tube.

Front fork: The assembly that holds the front wheel, connecting it with the frame through a system of bearings mounted in the head tube. The handlebars connect to the fork at the top of the head tube.

Fork crown: The metal assembly that joins the two fork tubes to the steering tube.

Front dropouts (also called fork tips): Lugs brazed to the front fork tubes that provide a solid metal surface for attaching the front wheel axle to the frame.

Headset: A ball-bearing assembly, including one bearing at the top and one at the bottom of the head tube/fork assembly. This bearing system allows the front wheel to be turned while holding the fork in the frame. Good-quality headsets are important because they must absorb road shock transmitted from the road through the front wheel while also allowing the bike to be smoothly steered.

Lugs: These metal reinforcements are used wherever one or more frame tubes come together. The shaping and finishing of the lugs is often the trademark of custom frame-builders, distinguishing their product from others.

Down tube: The frame member that runs from the head tube to the bottom bracket.

Handlebars: In addition to steering the bike, the handlebars are an integral part of the leverage system by which the bike is powered forward; pulling up on the handlebars increases the force exerted on the pedals.

Handlebar stem: The metal clamp assembly fastening the handlebars to the front fork. These come in different sizes, making the distance between the handlebars and the seat longer or shorter to accommodate individual rider differences.

Caliper brake: Either side-pull or center-pull brakes, shaped like calipers, that press the brake pads against the wheel rim, allowing the rider to stop the bike.

Brake lever: The hand lever—mounted to the handlebars—that allows the rider to control the brakes.

Brake cable: A thin wire cable that runs from the brake lever to the calipers, controlling the brakes.

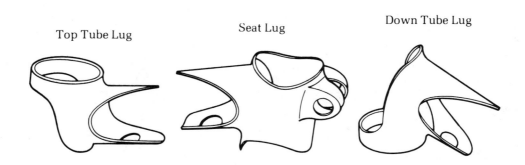

Top Tube Lug   Seat Lug   Down Tube Lug

Lugs manufactured by the Italian firm, Cinelli Cino & C.

This will be covered later in this chapter but it cannot be over emphasized. The only real workout injury acquired in biking is knee tendon stress caused by using too low gears and not enough pedal revolutions.

You can pretty well tell the ability of a bike racer by the size and tooth count of his rear cluster gearing. The Macho pride an accomplished bike racer has in his biking ability is centered around his rear chain cluster. The sprocket size is a tribute to his years of bike training and the many cross country road races under his belt. He has earned the 12 or 13 point small end gear and is proud of it.

Price should not be a factor, only quality of the frame and mechanical accessories should control the purchase investment of a Triathlete's bicycle.

Ten-Speed Bicycles

The ten-speed bicycle comes closer than any other human-powered vehicle to fulfilling the age-old dream of a perfect relationship between the human body and a machine. With its wide range of gear ratios, the ten-speed guarantees you the maximum speed and distance for the energy you expend in cranking the pedals.

In buying a ten-speed it is especially important to remember that bicycles come from the manufacturer only partly assembled and that it is up to the retail dealer to do the final setup and adjustments. Because of the relative complexity of the ten-speed, it is crucial for this work to be performed properly. Check out the action in the repair shop before selecting a dealer. A good mechanic always has a lot of business, and that's what you're looking for.

The Bicycle Frame—Tube Construction

Before you look at anything else on the bike, look at the frame. The tubes in a quality bike frame will be made of high-carbon steel called chrome molybdenum. Bikers shorten this to "chrome moly" (pronounced "molly"). This steel, developed for the European racing circuit, provides extraordinary qualities: strength, lightness, and a lively feel. Chrome-moly tubing absorbs road shock while preventing or minimizing frame "flex" or "whip."

Whip—twisting that happens when you stress the tubes by pedaling—is the mark of a low-quality frame. Even a biker of medium strength can twist the frame of an inexpensive bike enough to make the chain rub against the derailleurs, causing the latter to malfunction. Not only is this whipping action annoying, but it also means that the metal is flexing, causing fatigue in joints and in the tubing itself.

A high-quality frame requires significantly less human energy to pedal than does a low-quality frame, mainly because the rider's efforts are going directly into turning the rear wheel rather than bending the metal. The high-quality frame feels good to ride—lively, comfortable, and efficient. What's more, everything stays adjusted on a good frame derailleurs, brakes, and wheel alignment. On a low-quality frame, tube alignment is in a constant state of flux, and consequently nothing stays adjusted for long.

TYPES OF TUBING

The finest quality bicycle tubing is "double-butted." Look for a seal with names like Reynolds 531, Vitus, Tange, Columbus, and Ishiwata on the frame. Double-butted frame tubes are thick at the points where they join together and thinner between the joints. The extra thickness provides strength and surface for joining the tubes, while the thinness reduces the overall weight. Because each tube must be individually manufactured, double-butting adds considerably to the cost of the tubing. A good-quality straight-gauge tubing, which is thick through its length, adds a few pounds—usually between three and five—to the total weight of the bike while reducing the cost of the bike between 15 and 20 percent over a double-butted frame.

FRAME ASSEMBLY

The manner in which the tubes are jointed together also affects the bicycle's performance. On the best frames, the ends of each tube are filed or mitered until they form a tight, perfect joint where they are to be connected.

On a finely crafted frame, tubes are jointed with a reinforcement device known as a lug. All the frame parts are clamped into a jig and then skillfully brazed—or, in the case of the best frames, silver-soldered—together. Well-crafted joints, whether executed by brazing or silver-soldering, can make the difference between a long-lasting, responsive bicycle frame and a whippy one that might even break when you really pour on the power.

The fork tips and dropouts of a good frame will usually be forged—that is, cast of high-quality metals—and have a smooth, sculptured look about them. Here again you'll find highly skilled soldering or brazing.

FINISH WORK — AESTHETIC APPEAL

Quality framebuilders take a great deal of pride in their paint. A good paint job is unmistakable: smooth and evenly colored. Most of the classic bicycle frames have a clean, uncluttered appearance. Sometimes you'll find tasteful, reserved striping around the lugs, but most paint jobs will be understated, as if to say that the frame speaks for itself and needs no embellishment. Good frames have few if any decals or stickers, the exception being a discreet seal identifying the tubing that went into the frame's construction.

Sometimes frame and fork tips are chrome-plated. Chrome stands up a little better than paint where the wheels are being removed and replaced frequently to change tires, put the bike into a car, etc. But there are frame builders who refuse to chrome-plate any part of a frame because they say it changes the temper of the tubes.

After a couple of hours looking at good frames, you'll begin to appreciate the handcrafting that goes into them and justifies their cost. Albert Eisentraut, a California framebuilder, was a sculptor before he started building frames, and his products continue to reflect his fine-arts background. Hence, you will find art collectors with no intention of ever riding them purchasing bicycles to hang on their walls.

WHEELS — WEIGHT AND SPOKING

The first thing to note about a wheel is weight. The rim—that is, the circular strip of metal to which the tire attaches—can be made of either steel or aluminum. Steel rims can add as much as ten pounds to the total weight of the bike. However, ten extra pounds of weight in the wheels is equivalent to twenty additional pounds in the frame. This is dictated by the laws of physics. The only reason to use steel rims is that they cost less than aluminum ones. Steel rims are not stronger.

Next look at the spoke pattern of the wheel. Bicyclists use terms like "three-cross" and "radial spoking" to describe the way a wheel is spoked. Radial spoking means simply that the spokes radiate straight out from the hub to the rim, in the fashion of a wagon wheel.

Three cross spoking is a bit harder to explain. In 1876 James Starley showed that a strong yet resilient wheel could be built with wire instead of wooden spokes if the spokes came from the hub at an angle rather than radiating directly out from it. By crossing the spokes, Starley created a wheel that made excellent use of the muscular force exerted by the rider and absorbed road shock and vibration better than any other wheel design. Starley's innovation quickly caught on and has been used ever since.

Three- and four-cross spoking patterns are the most popular designs used in wheel building today. Because the distance the spoke must span is greater in four-cross than in three-cross, a longer spoke is required. The longer spoke is more elastic than a short one, so a four-cross wheel will be softer—that is, more resilient—than a three-cross, two-cross, or radially spoked wheel.

———————————

For my part, I travel not to go anywhere, but to go. —Stevenson, *Travels with a Donkey*

THE HUB

The third element of the wheel to consider is the hub. Except in the least expensive bikes, these are cast of aluminum. The axles fasten to the frame with either nuts or quick-release levers.

Look for smooth-running bearings in the hubs. A good bearing will turn easily as you spin the wheel and will be as smooth as those you'd expect to find in the most precise industrial machine.

There are both high- and low-flange hubs. This refers to the size of the side flanges from which the spokes radiate. Because the spokes must be longer to span the distance between the low-flange hub and the rim, a low flange produces a softer, more resilient wheel. For that reason, some tourers prefer it to the high-flange design.

TIRES – CLINCHER VERSUS SEWUP

Finally look at the tires. The best tires will carry from 85 to 130 pounds of pressure per square inch (psi). The higher pressure reduces rolling resistance significantly. There are two styles of tire construction: clincher tires, which hold onto the rim in much the same way an automobile wheel does, and sewup tires, which are glued to the rim.

Sewup tires are preferred by racers. With tire and tube constructed as a single unit, the racer can carry a spare in a neat package under the seat. In the event of a puncture, an experienced rider can strip off the old tire and put on the spare in a matter of three or four minutes. Patching the sewup is another matter altogether. For an inexperienced person, sewup tires take as much as an hour to patch. For this reason, many cyclists end up throwing punctured sewup tires away, even though there may still be hundreds of miles of tread left on the casings. At a cost of $18 to $50 apiece, sewup tires can become an expensive proposition. If you are a competitive cyclist for whom winning the race is the ultimate turn-on, sewups will probably be worth the price, since they'll allow you to change tires quickly and get on with the race.

In contrast to the sewup tire, clincher tires can be patched in a matter of minutes. But because the tube and tire are two separate units they take a little longer to change on the road. Most clinchers will require the use of lightweight tire irons to remove them from the rims, whereas sewup tires can be removed without the use of tools. Recreational riders and tourists prefer clinchers because they can be easily patched on the road and are relatively inexpensive to maintain. A high-quality clincher tire will sell for $20, on the average. A tube for the clincher will sell for around $4. Both can be used over and over again, and they require very little skill to patch.

Today's tire technology has provided us with clincher tires that perform as well as sewups. They are as narrow (1 inch) as a sewup and can carry as much pressure (up to 110 psi), so they have about the same rolling resistance (friction or resistance at the point where the tread meets the pavement) as the sewup. With these recent technological developments, even racers are turning to clincher tires for their training rides.

CRANKSETS

The crankset is the assembly that includes the crankarms, to which the pedals are attached; the two large chain sprockets, called chainwheels or chainrings, which are turned by the crankarms; and the bearings which hold the whole unit in the frame. A high-quality crankset will be made of aluminum alloy except for the bearings, which are steel. It will be cast and finished smoothly and precisely. Each tooth of the chainwheel will be carefully shaped and machined to minimize friction as it turns the chain. Similarly, the bolts that hold the various parts together will be precision cast.

On the best cranksets, the hardness of the metal has been carefully formulated to minimize distortion (or bending) of the crankarms and chainrings.

Chainrings on good-quality cranksets can be easily changed. There are two advantages to this: First, worn chainrings can be replaced without replacing the entire crankset; second, larger or smaller chainrings can be bolted on to provide another set of gear ratios. Selecting larger or smaller chainrings can be important if you ride in hilly terrain.

HANDLEBARS

Handlebars serve several important functions. First, the handlebars carry a fair amount of your body weight. Second, when you are pedaling hard uphill, or pedaling fast, you can pull against the bars for extra leverage and power.

DERAILLEURS

The word "derailleur" comes from the French, meaning literally "to derail." When you move the shift lever on a ten-speed bike, a cable activates the derailleur cage, moving it to the left or right, depending on which way you moved the lever. As the derailleur cage moves, it pushes the chain off one gear sprocket (derails it) and lines it up with another gear sprocket. In the front there are two gear sprockets, technically known as chainwheels; in the rear you will find a freewheel with five gear sprockets which transmit the power you exert on the pedals to the rear wheel.

What is the reason for all these gears? With the choice of a wide range of gear ratios, you can select the way you will use your energy. A low gear lets you repeat the pedaling action more times per mile than with a higher gear. The principle of repetition is the same in pedaling a bike as in lifting a given amount of weight. A very strong person might easily lift a 200-pound weight in a single motion. A weaker person can lift the same 200 pounds, but must do it by repetition—that is, by lifting 50 pounds four separate times.

Excellent derailleurs come from Japan as well as Europe, but the Italian-made Campagnolo still maintains first position with bicycle aficionados.

BRAKES

Ten-speed bikes come equipped with one of two kinds of brakes: center-pulls or side-pulls. When constructed of high-quality alloys, the side-pull design gives more exacting control and better braking power than center-pulls and is preferred by professional racers. Because of its engineering peculiarities, the manufacturer must use extremely high-quality, costly alloys in its construction. A good set of side-pull brakes (front and rear complete) will cost from $70 to $175.

Center-pull brakes can provide excellent service even though constructed of only medium quality alloys. This design is the choice of cyclists wanting good performance at a reasonable price ($30 to $45). The center-pull, therefore, is standard equipment on bicycles ranging in price from $150 to $500.

Some three-speeds and low-quality ten-speeds come equipped with low-quality side-pull brakes. These are suitable only for light duty. Since they are made of low-quality alloys, the metal parts tend to flex, and even bend permanently, making for a brake that can be trusted only at lower speeds on relatively flat terrain, carrying light loads.

The Best Bike for Your Money: A Comparison

Bottom-of-the-line ten-speeds, costing (at this writing) between $250 and $350, come equipped with heavy frames made with straight-gauge tubing. The wheels have heavy steel rims and low-pressure tires. Derailleurs, handlebars, and cranks are of steel rather than alloy. Weight is from 35 to 39 pounds.

Bikes in this group, from any of the major bike manufacturers, are fine for commuting short distances (under ten miles each way) and for light recreation, but because of their weight they are not recommended for cycle training, commuting long distances, racing, or touring.

Middle-of-the-line bikes—$350 to $750—come equipped with frames that are reasonably light, efficient, and comfortable. Often the three main tubes are double-butted, while all the other tubing is straight-gauge. Wheels have alloy rims and are equipped with high-pressure clincher tires of medium quality. Derailleurs, cranksets, and handlebars are made of alloy and are of good quality, though not necessarily beautiful in their finish. Weight is from 25 to 32 pounds. Bikes in this group are excellent for commuting, recreation, cycle training, and touring. Frames are, as a general rule, on the soft side compared to top-of-the-line racing bikes, so they are not recommended for serious competition.

Top-of-the-line production bikes start at $750 and can run as high as $3,000. They come with all-double-butted frames. Wheels have alloy rims with a choice of sewup tires or narrow, high-performance clinchers for competition or wider clinchers for touring. Components such as cranksets, derailleurs, and handlebars are either top-of-the-line Japanese products or a combination of Japanese and European. Weight is from 21 to 26 pounds. With these better bikes, one should be specific about how it is to be used; racing bikes have short, stiff frames, and tourers have longer, softer frames with brackets for attaching touring racks.

Custom-Built Bicycles

Custom bikes are built up by bike shops according to your own specifications. You choose the frame and components yourself. You can even have special wheels built with your choice of hubs, spokes, rims, and tires. Before having a bike built, you should know exactly how you want to use it. If you are not an experienced rider and aren't certain about the kind of riding you'll be doing, buy a production bike, ride it for several months, become fully acquainted with your biking needs, and then consider ordering a custom-made bike. Otherwise, the choice of components will all be guesswork.

The custom bike begins with a good frame, as described in the previous section, and that's where you start when money is no object and you want the best bicycle available. After purchasing a frame you pick out your own components, from Weinmann center pull brakes at $30 a set to Campagnolo side-pulls at $150 a set; from SR handlebars at $7.00 to Cinnelli bars at $30; from a molded plastic saddle for $10 to an Ideal 90, with titanium frame, at $75; from a Suntour derailleur set at $30 to a Campagnolo at $150; and, finally, wheels from $75 a set to more than $300. Beginning with a high-quality, bare frame at $300, your finished bike can have a final price tag of anything between $600 and $1,500. What do you get for your money? You get efficiency, speed, excellent handling characteristics, components that operate like clockwork, aesthetic appeal, and the opportunity to hand-pick every piece of equipment that goes on the frame.

Getting the Proper Fit

Proper bicycle adjustment includes the obvious matters of choosing the right size for the frame and adjusting the seat and handlebars. But it doesn't stop there. It also includes making those refinements in your equipment (adding toe clips and handlebar padding, exchanging your saddle for a better one, etc.) that will give you the lasting pleasure that comes from knowing your bicycle is perfectly tailored to suit your individual needs.

Basic Adjustments

Bicycle Frames come in many sizes, usually 19, 21, 22, 23, 24, and 25 inches. Frame size always refers to the distance between the seat lug and the center of the bottom bracket.

Don't make the mistake of thinking that if your frame is a little too small for you, you can adjust it simply by raising the seat. Standard seatposts can safely be raised only about 3½ to 4 inches above the frame.

A frame that is too large for you can pose a real danger in mounting and dismounting from the bike. This is the main source of groin injuries to bike riders.

DETERMINING FRAME FIT

There is a rule of thumb among bikers that the bike frame should be nine to ten inches less than your inseam measurement—the distance between your crotch and the floor while you are standing in your bare feet. As a general rule, this works out pretty well. But because of certain other variables—notably, bottom-bracket and tire-size variations—it may prove less than a perfect formula. The top tube of the frame should be from ¾ inch to 1 inch below your crotch.

SEAT HEIGHT

To adjust the saddle height, sit on your bike in a normal riding position with your hands on the handlebars and your bare feet flat on the pedals. Have a friend adjust the saddle up or down to accommodate you. The crank arms should be in such a position that your right leg is fully extended, and your heel is centered on the pedal. Your pelvis should be level on the seat—that is, not tipped either to the left or to the right.

After establishing the correct height of the seat, adjust it so it's approximately level across the top from front to back. Some people will find that the saddle is more comfortable with the front tipped slightly down, while others will prefer it slightly up. Experimentation after a number of miles of riding will reveal what's best for you.

The saddle may also be adjusted forward or back. The rule here is that the nose of the saddle should be 2 to 2½ inches behind a centerline drawn perpendicular to the bottom bracket.

The Bike Saddle

Most bicycles in the low-to-medium price ranges come with molded plastic saddles which are inadequate for anything but short rides. Sometimes these saddles are padded and have a vinyl cover. Some bikes may even come equipped with inexpensive cushioned saddles with coil springs that are supposed to make the ride more comfortable.

Cushioned saddles usually feel more comfortable than narrow leather racing saddles when you sit on them in the store, but that comfort may not extend to a ride beyond three miles. The narrow racing saddle may look uncomfortable and may even feel that way when you first try it out, but this design has evolved through several decades of bicycling history, and it does work better than anything else in the long run.

The narrow traditional bicycle saddle prevents chafing around your buttocks and upper thighs by supporting your pelvis while allowing your legs to move freely. With the seat and handlebars properly adjusted, your body weight rests on both the handlebars and the seat—not just the seat. In addition, much of your weight is distributed to the pedals when you are pedaling, so your comfort will come not merely from the *softness* of the saddle but also from the way in which the complete bike accommodates your body while you're cycling.

The so-called hard leather saddles conform to the rider's body after a hundred miles or so, and, as in breaking in a pair of new boots, one must endure a certain amount of discomfort in the process. The leather does soften in time, and it does become compatible with your rear end. The crucial feature of leather is that it breathes, preventing sores caused by perspiration that wouldn't be able to escape with a plastic saddle. Also, plastic saddles—even those equipped with leather coverings—radiate heat much more than traditional all-leather models.

ADJUST THE SADDLE FOR PROPER HORIZONTAL ANGLE

Use a yardstick and adjust the *saddle angle* so that the front of the seat is slightly higher than the rear of the seat. Although it seems that the adjustment would be uncomfortable, this position will tend to keep the rider from sliding forward on the saddle. A saddle that is tilted downward in front will cause increased wrist, arm, and shoulder fatigue due to the need for constant pressure to maintain the position in the saddle. In some situations, a female rider may find this position uncomfortable. If the discomfort persists after 200 to 300 miles of riding, the tip of the saddle should be lowered until it is level or tilted slightly downward. After 500 to 1,000 miles of additional riding, muscles will develop which should enable her to tilt the saddle upward to its correct position.

HORIZONTAL SADDLE ADJUSTMENT (FRONT AND REAR)

This adjustment is one of the least understood in cycling. It is not used to correct for differences in top tube length or to make up for a handlebar stem that is too long or too short. The horizontal saddle adjustment is designed to accommodate varying styles of riding and differences in individual variance in *thigh length*. The height of the saddle corresponds to the overall length of the rider's leg—the horizontal saddle adjustment corresponds to the size of the rider's thigh. Some people have very long thighs and correspondingly short shins while others have very long shins and short thighs. In other words, the horizontal saddle adjustment is used to insure the proper angle of thrust of the leg.

To set up the horizontal saddle position, sit on the bicycle with both feet in the toe clips. Rotate the cranks until they are parallel to the ground. Have a helper drop a plumb line from the center of your knee of the forward leg. The plumb line should extend through the pedal axle.

MAINTENANCE AND BREAKING IN

Leather saddles require simple maintenance and a breaking-in period. Before installing the saddle on your bike, lay it upside down in the sun and swab the underside with neatsfoot oil for several days in a row. Insofar as possible, avoid getting oil on the face of the saddle—that is, the part you'll be sitting on. After several days of the sun-and-neatsfoot-oil treatment, take the saddle inside and work the outer surface with saddle soap. A few evenings spent squeezing the leather with your fingers, kneading the edges, and working in saddle soap, will be that many hours you won't have to work the leather with your posterior.

Handlebar Adjustments — Height and Reach

Handlebars can be adjusted to suit not only the size of your body, but your riding style as well. Accordingly, the type of adjustments made for a recreational rider will be different than those for a competitive cyclist.

There are two adjustments to consider here: height and reach. Height is established by raising or lowering the stem. But bear in mind when you're doing this that you must keep about 2½ inches of stem in the frame. If you have less than that, a number of problems may occur, from a wobbling, squeaking stem to a broken one. Start out with the bars an inch below the saddle. Ride the bike a mile or more and see how it feels. Then, if you feel that the bars should be higher or lower, make your adjustments accordingly. Don't be afraid to experiment.

Most bicycles come equipped with a stem that provides the average rider with a comfortable reach. If this stem-reach average doesn't suit you, it can be changed. To measure for this adjustment, place your elbow against the nose of the saddle and reach out toward the handlebars. The tips of your fingers should be somewhere between just brushing the edge of the bars and ending about an inch away.

ADJUSTING THE BRAKE LEVERS

The hoods of the brake levers are used by most riders as extensions of the handlebars. Indeed, *riding on the levers* is one of the more common riding positions among experienced bikers. With your hands on the brake hoods, your fingers actually touch the brake levers—a feature you'll fully appreciate if you have to make a sudden stop. When the brake levers are properly adjusted you will find this position comfortable, easy, and efficient.

To adjust the brake hoods, sit on your bike and place your hands on the hoods. You should now be able to wrap your fingers around the levers. If you can't, you'll want to adjust the position of the hoods on the handlebars.

After removing the tape you'll be able to see that the brake hood is clamped to the handlebar by a thin metal band. The band must be loosened to move the brake. This is accomplished by means of a screw inside the hood.

When you've loosened the adjustment screw for the metal band that holds the lever to the bar, you'll be able to slip the lever up or down the bar until you find the right position. Then tighten the adjustment screw and see how it feels. If it feels comfortable and you can reach the brake lever with your fingers, your adjustment is complete. Rewrap your handlebars with the tape and you're ready to go.

Why Quality Pedals?

The reason for upgrading the pedals on your bike is this: In normal riding you turn the pedals at an average of 60 to 90 revolutions per minute. This translates to 3,600 to 5,400 revolutions for every hour you ride. Thus even a small amount of friction, multiplied by the above factors, can make a tremendous difference in the amount of energy you must exert to ride for an hour or more.

A good-quality pedal can last a lifetime and will waste only a minute amount of energy. An inexpensive pedal may last only a few hundred miles before its bearings begin to break down and eat up energy that should be going to the back wheel. Good-quality pedals priced from $12 to $35 are made by Lyotard, Atom, and KKT.

Toe Clips — Efficiency Boosters

Toe clips add both safety and efficiency to your ride. As a safety factor, they prevent your feet from slipping off the pedals and causing you to lose control of the bike. And, they allow you to exert pressure on the pedals on both the downstroke and the upstroke, increasing your efficiency by 30 to 50 percent, depending on your strength and riding skill.

Toe clips come in small, medium, and large sizes. Just as with all other bicycle adjustments, getting the right toe-clip size is important. Clips of the wrong size, especially if they are on the short side, can cause a variety of leg and back complaints. To get the right fit for you, wear the shoes you intend to wear when you ride. At the bike shop, place your foot on the pedal with the ball of your foot directly over the pedal axle. Then hold the toe clip in place against the pedal. (You'll need someone to assist you.) The toe clip should not rub against your toe, as this could cause chafing—either ruining your shoes or irritating your toes. If you must make a choice between clips that are slightly too small and clips that are slightly too large, go with the slightly larger size.

Rear Gear Cluster Ratios

The freewheel is the five-geared assembly attached to the rear wheel hub. The main reason to replace the freewheel is to change the gear ratios available on your bike. The most common freewheel setups on production bikes have gears with 14, 17, 19, 22, and 26 teeth. But freewheels are available with as many as 34 teeth in the largest gear—called an "Alpine" gear for extremely hilly terrain. Racers prefer what is called a "close-ratio cluster," a freewheel with only a small difference between gears: 13, 15, 17, 19, and 21 teeth.

Freewheel gears, or sprockets, can be changed individually rather than replacing the whole unit. Consult your local bicycle shop for exact details on how to do this, since each manufacturer has a slightly different design. A good bicycle shop will be set up to change sprocket sizes for you at a nominal fee.

Wheels

When properly maintained—spokes tightened and "trued," bearings repacked and adjusted yearly—wheels will last for many years. Occasionally rims get dented as a result of hitting a curb or riding over a deep pothole, requiring that the rim be straightened out or replaced. Spokes sometimes break, but this usually necessitates only replacement of the broken spokes, plus a "trueing" of the wheel if it wobbles as a result.

If your bike is presently equipped with steel rims, you might consider upgrading it by having a wheelbuilder replace the steel rims with alloy. This can be done usually at a cost of around $65 per wheel. The alloy rim, equipped with top-quality tire, will vastly improve your bike's performance, making it faster, more comfortable, more responsive, and easier to pedal.

Professional wheelbuilders have their own theories about wheel construction, so you'll want to discuss the new wheels in detail with your wheelbuilder.

The Rewards of Detailed Adjustments

Many changes, whether in adjustments or in the installation of higher-quality components, make only subtle differences in your comfort or riding efficiency. You may not notice the differences in the first couple of miles, although they are important, but after several miles your body will begin to signal its response to the changes by manifesting comfort and ease. Keep this in mind whenever you work on your bike. Unless the change you make definitely feels wrong the first time you try it, give your body a chance to feel the effects of the change and respond to them. Your patience and attention to detail will reward you many times over with riding pleasure you might otherwise find difficult to imagine.

Fitting the Shorter Rider

The setup relationships described in this chapter will hold true for almost everyone. Although a person over 6'5" is limited to a 25-inch or 26-inch frame (because most builders will not build a larger size), a suitable handlebar stem and seatpost can be obtained that will allow an efficient cycling position. Even basketball star Bill Walton, has been properly fitted for a bicycle. For several reasons, proper sizing of the bicycle becomes a serious problem when the rider is shorter than 5'2".

The first and most important obstacle in accommodating the short person is faced in the physical limitations of designing a frame that is small enough. Stock frames rarely are found in less than the 19½-inch size because the top tube and down tube practically touch at the point where they join on the head tube. It is obvious, therefore, that the builder can only marginally reduce the frame size under 19½ inches. Some custom builders have gone to great lengths to join the top tube and down tube in an attempt to accommodate the small rider. Many times, however, it is impossible to design, or build, a "standard" frame that will allow proper cycling position for the short rider. A secondary problem in fitting small persons is the lack of components designed for the short person. This is because most bicycles and components are designed for the "average" male physique. Until recently, cycling has been a predominantly male sport and the cycling accessories have been designed accordingly. It is not entirely uncommon, however, to see a woman riding an all-Campagnolo lightweight bicycle in this country.

Let's take a look at the specific problems encountered by the short rider and review possible solutions to these problems.

FRAME

The short rider finds it much more difficult to find a standard frame that will be comfortable (or even ridable in some cases) if the rider has disproportionately long or short legs. If the rider has very long legs, the reach to the handlebars will be too great. On the other hand, if the rider has a disproportionately long torso, the lowest saddle position may still be too high. A change in handlebars or saddle will have no effect since the frame tubes cannot be built any shorter. What next? We suggest talking to some of the custom builders who can design a frame that uses 24-inch wheels.

Most people react negatively when first presented with the idea because they feel that no quality equipment is available for the 24-inch-wheel bicycle and that they are forced to ride a "child's" bicycle. If you are too short for a 19-inch frame and you are interested in a quality 10-speed, you owe it to yourself to examine some of the equipment that is available. We will concede that the equipment isn't readily available, but it does exist. For starters, try Paris Sport Cycle in Ridgefield Park, New Jersey. Their resident frame builder, Francisco Cuevas, builds top-quality lightweight frames in both standard and small sizes and the store carries 24-inch rims and tubular tires. They also carry most of the components necessary to complete a quality 24-inch-wheel 10-speed. Don't eliminate the 24-inch-wheel bicycle until you have looked at the "good" equipment. If you are a short rider that can "get by" on a 19-inch frame with a short handlebar stem and the saddle resting on the top tube, optimum cycling position may be improved with careful selection of the frame components.

HANDLEBARS

A handlebar is considered to be the correct size if it is as wide as the rider's shoulders. If the bars are too narrow, breathing is restricted; if the bars are too wide (normally the situation for the small rider), the arms are inefficiently supporting the rider and causing increased wind resistance. The drop and reach of the handlebars may be too great for the small rider. Many riders are unaware that some handlebars come in various widths and bends. Measure the width of the handlebars before you purchase them; Cinelli handlebars, for instance, are available in 38-cm., 40-cm., and 42-cm. widths. If you are very small, you may want to investigate the good-quality alloy handlebars that have been designed for a bicycle with 24-inch wheels. With the correct width handlebars combined with a small stem, the short rider should be able to set up the bicycle for comfortable and efficient cycling.

BRAKE LEVERS

Similar to most quality cycling accessories, the brake levers are designed for the average male hand. This is an area that causes even more problems than oversize handlebars, since the potential for an accident is increased if the rider cannot easily manipulate the brake levers. There is a small amount of variation between the reach of most standard brake levers, so the search for a "small" reach lever may be unnecessary. There are two ways to attack this problem. The first is to increase the strength of your hands so that the brake lever can be used with only two or three fingers. Even riders with very small hands (women's glove size 5-6) can operate most levers after practice and exercise. The best and least expensive method to increase hand and finger strength is to regularly practice squeezing a tennis ball. If you are a rider whose hands are too small for brake retention with two or three fingers, you should contact a builder who carries 24-inch wheels and tires since he should be able to supply small brake levers that will fit the junior-size handlebars.

In most cases, going to the smaller, scaled-down equipment may not be entirely necessary. For instance, it may be necessary to use a 24-inch-wheel frame because of height and leg measurement, but narrow handlebars may not be necessary if the individual is broad shouldered. Equally true, smaller brake levers may not be necessary for someone who may need a 24-inch-wheel bicycle but who has large hands. Obviously, the equipment should match the rider's physical needs.

SADDLE

Proper selection of a saddle *may* permit use of a 19-inch frame in the situation where the rider has very short legs, but adequate torso length to fit the standard-size frame. Generally, the plastic saddles (Cinelli Unica Nitor, for instance) have less height than the traditional leather saddle. Before you purchase the saddle, check the distance from the saddle's frame support

rails to the top of the saddle itself. Often the plastic saddles are much shallower than their leather counterparts. The shallow saddle can effectively reduce the distance from the top of the saddle to the pedal by as much as an inch.

Careful selection of handlebars, stem, and saddle can increase comfort and efficiency, but one problem remains—how do we compensate for the rider's shorter legs and smaller foot size and their effect on pedaling efficiency?

CRANKS

A very short person should consider cranks which are shorter than the standard 170 mm. How short? Unfortunately, we cannot provide a rule of thumb. In fact, in our discussion with Eddie Borysewicz, national cycling coach, he indicated that no one can unequivocally provide an answer. Because so little is known about optimum crank length, Eddie has considered devoting two or three years and his doctoral dissertation to the relationship between crank length and leg length! Small cranksets are available to those with very short legs, but only use the short cranks if you feel they are absolutely necessary since the accompanying chainwheels are usually too small to provide adequate *gear ratios* for the adult. We recommend that you do not vary crank length without the advice of a competent coach. Presuming that standard-size cranks will be used, let's turn our attention to one last item that must be utilized to assist in efficiently transmitting your energy into motion—pedals.

PEDALS

Just like all other cycling components, pedals have been designed to fit the average male foot. Unfortunately, the adverse
effect of an oversize pedal is much greater than a pair of handlebars that are too large. If the handlebars are too big, the rider will endure some discomfort; if the pedals are too big, the rider's pedaling motion will be very seriously affected. An analysis of one of the fine points of coaching should help clarify this point.

There are two basic extremes in pedaling style—the pusher (the rider that uses relatively high gears at low rpm's) and the pedaler (the rider who uses relatively low gears at relatively high rpm's). *Generally,* the pusher is a heavily muscled individual who utilizes brute strength instead of finesse. The inverse is true of the pedaler, who is usually of slight build and uses high pedal rpm's to maintain overall cycling speed. To maximize the effects of either of the two pedal styles, the toe clips and shoe cleats should be carefully adjusted. As a general rule, the pusher should have his foot deeper into the toe clip than the pedaler. That is, the ball of the foot of the pusher may be as much as 1/4 to 3/8 inch *ahead* of the pedal axle. The pedaler should have his foot as much as 1/4 to 3/8 inch *behind* the pedal axle.

Unfortunately, it logically follows that if the rider's foot is very small, the ball of the foot will always be ahead of the pedal axle even with a short toe clip! Use of the short Christophe toe clip on a standard-size pedal will not allow proper placement of a shoe smaller than a ladies' size 7. Therefore, without choice, the rider with small feet is forced to pedal like a pusher, regardless of his or her appropriate style. You should remember this analysis when buying pedals for your bicycle; most people are amazed at the amount of increased pedaling efficiency resulting from proper foot placement.

We have attempted to briefly cover the major obstacles encountered by the short person—the list is not all inclusive. We hope that these guidelines will help encourage the short rider to spend a little extra time in search of components that will provide optimal use of his or her individual physique.

Cycle Clothing

IN RECENT YEARS the design of cycle clothing, especially jerseys, has been heavily influenced by the world of high fashion. Bold colors, dramatic stripes, and high-quality knit fabrics have brought a new dimension to cycling clothes.

A number of practical considerations have dictated designs in cycle clothing: low wind resistance, ability to adjust clothes to regulate the body temperature as exercise raises it, and freedom from binding or chafing as the cyclist pedals.

Cycling gloves, shoes, and helmet—each has its own set of design problems. Gloves should be well ventilated while providing padding against road vibration and a sure grip on the handlebars. Helmets must be protective, light in weight, and cool. Shoes must be light, cool, and strong enough to protect the cyclist's feet from injury by the steel pedals after miles and miles of pedaling.

The clothing that has evolved for cycling competition is useful for racer and tourist alike. If you're a tourist, you'll want to add to your wardrobe certain garments that protect you from the weather or make you more visible in traffic.

Cycle clothing is comparable in price to similar garments for everyday use. A jersey is about the same price as a knit sweater, for example, and, like sweaters, jerseys come in a variety of fibers, from polyesters to lamb's wool. Naturally the price varies accordingly. Cycling shorts may be a few dollars more than a good pair of casual pants.

Basic Clothing

HELMETS

Helmets designed specifically for bicyclists are manufactured by Bell, MSR, Pro-tec, and Skid-Lid. A few bike shops still stock the kind designed for racers 50 years ago, featuring strips of padded leather that line the top of your head. In a fall these can protect you, to some degree, from abrasions, but they're of little more use than a baseball cap for protection from concussion or a fractured skull.

THE JERSEY

The upper part of your body is the largest area visible to motorists as you ride on the street. Take advantage of that fact by wearing the brightest, most attractive jersey you can find. They come in a variety of colors, from grey to shocking pink, and in recent years there has been a move toward colorful stripes similar to those used in ski sweaters. The combination of bright colors and an aesthetically arresting appearance will go a long way toward making motorists aware of your presence.

As for function, the design which has evolved for bicycle jerseys is perfection itself. Tight-fitting, the jersey has low wind resistance. A zipper at the neck is easily adjusted while you're riding, providing more or less ventilation as you go.

The jersey is long in the waist so it doesn't ride up as you bear down. A wide pocket across the back gives you a safe place to store your wallet, a piece of fruit for your lunch, and even a tire patch kit. Located in the rear, the pocket is out of the way, and, even when it's bulging with a spare sewup tire, it won't interfere with your performance. A few jerseys are made with small breast pockets in addition to the one in the back.

CYCLING SHORTS

Cycling shorts are made of stretchy fabric which fits skintight, eliminating chafing in the thighs. And smooth seams prevent irritation of the sensitive skin of the crotch.

Cycling shorts are usually longer than conventional shorts, with legs extending to the middle or lower middle of the thigh. The greater length prevents the fabric from riding up on your legs and bunching in the crotch as you ride. And cycling shorts are lined with soft chamois, which minimizes abrasion in the sensitive genital areas.

Cycling shorts are designed to be worn without underwear, but some people prefer to have fabric next to their skin. Men's underwear is usually constructed with seams in the crotch, which can become quite uncomfortable after 20 miles of riding. However, women's cotton underwear is all but seamless and can be worn beneath riding shorts for extra comfort.

LEG AND ARM WARMERS

On an early morning ride the air may be cold enough so that your bare arms and legs need some extra protection. For this there are arm and leg warmers—simple sleeves of fabric that fit snugly and can be slipped on and off in seconds.

CYCLING SHOES

Traditional cycling shoes are made of leather, often perforated for ventilation. They are very light in weight but sturdy. There's no heel, and the soles are of leather. The bottom of the shoe is reinforced with an inner metal shank that protects your foot from the metal of the rat-trap pedal.

A pair of good cycling shoes weighs in the range of 1½ to 2 pounds—the lighter the better.

A good shoe is designed to fit snugly into a pedal equipped with a toe clip. For maximum efficiency, a metal or plastic cleat can be fastened to the bottom of the shoe. This holds your shoe firmly in the pedal, minimizing twisting movements that might otherwise waste energy, maintaining your foot on the pedal in the most effective position, and allowing you to pull up on the backstroke without having your foot slip from the pedal.

Whatever you do, don't try to cycle distances of more than five miles in tennis shoes. Most "sneakers" are much too soft on the bottom, and without this necessary support you can injure your feet.

GLOVES

Gloves seem like a luxury until you've gotten into the habit of riding with them. Cycling gloves, which look like regular gloves with the fingers cut off, usually have backs made of a coarse weave and palms of leather.

The best cycling gloves are padded to absorb road shock transmitted to the handlebars. In addition, they give you a good grip and prevent your hands from slipping when they're sweaty.

Weathering the Wind and Rain

Cyclists who are in top physical condition often ride in the rain with no more than a jersey and shorts.

Gore-tex togs are the best there is. Several companies make rain jackets suitable for biking. Early Winters, a company that makes many different kinds of sports clothes, makes a jacket designed specifically for cyclists.

A hood on the jacket keeps your head dry and prevents the rain from trickling down the back of your neck. But check out the hood before you buy. When you turn your head, the hood should turn with you, or you'll find yourself staring at the inside of the hood instead of the road.

Gore-tex chaps pull up over your legs, providing sufficient protection while still allowing plenty of ventilation. Full pants are also available in Gore-tex.

Cold-Weather Cycling

In cold weather, pay particular attention to your toes, face, fingers, and neck. Wool mittens or gloves are good, and if the temperature gets really cold a good pair of ski gloves or motorcycle gloves will keep your fingers warm while still allowing you to control the brakes and shifters. Wool socks are a must, and if you're a fanatic you can even buy cycling shoes made for winter riding.

A knit ski hat worn under your bike helmet will help keep your head warm, and, if your helmet is vented, blocking the vents with little chunks of foam rubber will also help. A knit ski mask, with holes for the eyes, nose, and mouth, goes a long way toward keeping your face from freezing.

Instead of wearing a heavy coat, try wearing several layers of clothing, such as a duofold insulated underwear top, followed by a long-sleeved wool ski sweater or jersey, followed by a snug-fitting windbreaker. If your chest gets cold from the force of the wind, a piece of newspaper folded under your jersey will make you more comfortable. Layered clothing is better than a single warm garment because you can shed whatever layers you need to be comfortable after you've started to heat up from exercise. With a heavy coat you get damp from your own perspiration, and eventually that makes you feel chilled and clammy.

For pants, you can use leg warmers with your cycling shorts. And if it's *very* cold, wear warmup pants designed for joggers.

Basic Rules of Bicycle Riding

Pay attention. Many accidents could be avoided if the cyclist paid attention to the flow of traffic, the condition of the road, and the terrain. All your senses help you stay out of trouble on the road. Vision is clearly the most important, but other senses play a role too. The sound of an engine behind you can help you judge the size of the vehicle, its speed, and whether or not the operator is driving recklessly. A car horn may be either a greeting or an order for you to get out of the way. The smell of exhaust fumes tells you to keep your distance from a bus or truck. The smell of asphalt tells you to beware of fresh or heat-softened pavement, which can gum up your tires. You can feel the vibrations of a heavy vehicle approaching from behind. You feel the wind of a bus passing you. Your senses and mental abilities work together when you're alert. Daydreaming detaches your mind from your senses, disconnecting you from the signals that would warn you of danger.

Ride predictably. Many accidents happen because bicyclists fail to observe traffic regulations. There is only one reason for traffic regulations, and this is to make it possible for each driver to predict what the other will do—at least to some extent. If you don't know official traffic regulations, go to the Department of Motor Vehicles and get a booklet that summarizes them. The rules will tell you what motorists are expecting. It's up to you to make your judgments accordingly.

Always signal your intentions to turn or stop. Extend your left arm straight out for a left turn; turn it up at the elbow for a right turn; and straighten it, pointing diagonally downward, for a stop.

Read motorists' minds. If you assume that the drivers around you have things other than you on their minds, you'll make your decisions more cautiously and defensively. You won't make turns in front of drivers who *should* see you but in fact don't. You'll assume that they don't see you and make your turn accordingly. Although you may feel conspicuous, you're usually not. Because the bicyclist can't hurt the motorist, while a nearby truck can, he'll notice the truck first and the bike later—if at all. Most drivers will do their best where you're concerned. But, to avoid injury, you need to take full responsibility for your own defense.

Establish eye contact. Though it may not always be feasible, it's helpful to establish eye contact with motorists whenever you can. By seeking eye contact you immediately discover whether or not there's an obstacle preventing the driver from seeing you. This may be a tree, a bush, a parked car, or even a passenger in the driver's own car. Sometimes the obstacle is in the driver's head; he or she gazes out on the world with a glazed, empty expression—preoccupied with a conflict at work, plans for a vacation, etc. Frequently, however, when you establish eye contact and flash a smile you'll get open recognition of your presence. With the wave of a hand, the motorist may even signal you to take the right-of-way.

Keep a safe distance from the curb. Ride as far to the right side of the street as is *safe,* but don't ride in the gutter. If you ride in the gutter you have no room to escape from hazards such as glass, rocks, etc. If you ride too close to the curb, your wheel may rub the curb or your pedal may strike the top of the sidewalk. Always ride on the asphalt a comfortable distance to the left of the gutter and the seam.

Choose safe streets. If the traffic is too heavy and the street is narrow or lacks a bike lane, use an alternate route. The time of day can make a difference in traffic patterns. Some streets that are jammed from curb to curb during rush hour can be delightful, wide open, and even enjoyable to ride on at other times.

Watch for a car doors opening. Be aware of doors opening from parked cars. Get in the habit of looking ahead into the cars before you pass them. If you see an occupant, expect the door to open. Adjust your speed through traffic so that you have room to swerve to your left should a car door be opened into your path. Check out the traffic to the rear frequently. Just a quick peek over your left shoulder will do; it only involves a quarter turn of your head. This can be done very fast. If you expect a door to open, focus on the seam between the door and the car body. The minute you see a change in this seam, stop or prepare to swerve. Don't hesitate to shout to warn the driver. Every cyclist should develop a good yell.

Don't weave. If cars are parked intermittently, don't weave into the empty spaces and then out again into traffic. This makes you very unpredictable to motorists, even though you may think you're being safe.

Always ride on the proper side of the street. Besides violating traffic laws, the wrong-way cyclist causes many accidents. Motorists do not expect a cyclist on the wrong side of the road. A motorist conditions his or her vision to look in the direction from which traffic is most likely to appear. Example: A driver is conditioned to look first to the left when leaving a driveway. The wrongway cyclist, approaching from the right, may well go unnoticed.

Ride single-file in traffic areas. It's all right to cycle two abreast if you are not impeding traffic, but in traffic it's much safer to stay in single file.

Use caution where there's a potential for side traffic. An approaching driveway or street means a vehicle may cross your path. If a car or truck is waiting to enter traffic and the driver is looking your way, don't assume that he sees you. The motorist is looking for other cars, not bicycles, and besides, you may be in the motorist's blind spot. Make eye contact with the driver, wave your hand as though to say "Hello," and be prepared to brake.

Watch out for pedestrians. Since a bicycle is a vehicle, always yield the right-of-way to pedestrians. Also, don't hesitate to shout a warning to a pedestrian if you think you could be a hazard to each other. Be pleasant in your comments. You'll get back whatever you put out.

Keep your head high. Keep your eyes moving, scanning the road ahead, at all times. Develop as "big" a picture as you can. A youngster riding his Stingray on the sidewalk might suddenly swerve and fly off the curb into your path. With your head up high and your eyes sweeping the area ahead, you'll see the potential for trouble long before it happens.

Keep your hands free. Do not carry items that will interfere with your vision or your ability to handle your bike safely. Riding in traffic with one hand on the bars and the other holding a grocery bag is dangerous and fool-hardy. Get yourself a bike rack and panniers or a backpack if there's something you want to carry.

Use caution at intersections. Always check cross traffic before passing through an intersection, even if the light is green. There may be a vehicle running a red light, or a pedestrian who didn't make it across the street in time, or an animal, or another cyclist either running the light or cutting it too close. Give yourself space to avoid collisions. Similarly, when waiting at a red light, don't dart out into the intersection when the light turns green without first looking in both directions. The law states that you must wait for both vehicles and pedestrians to clear the intersection before you proceed, even if your light is green.

Use caution in parking lots. Be very careful when riding through parking lots. Cars are frequently backing out of spaces, sometimes very quickly. They are looking for other cars, not bikes. If you wear toe straps, loosen them while riding in parking lots so that you'll have your feet free to keep from falling in case you need to stop fast. Watch for signals from cars—such as backup lights turning on—that will warn you what a car is preparing to do. But don't depend on that 100 percent, since backup lights don't always work.

Be on the lookout for sewer grates. Narrow tires can jam between the bars of sewer grates on the side of the road. Similarly, be especially cautious of expansion joints in steel deck bridges and approaches to bridges.

Watch the car passing you. A vehicle that has passed on your left may then turn to the right directly into your path. This happens to most cyclists at one time or another. The motorist either misjudges your speed or doesn't see you. Recognizing this possibility, always keep an eye on the right front tire of the car passing you. The moment you see it turn toward you, assume that the auto is about to cut you off. Slow down or stop to avoid a crash.

Never take the blinking lights of a vehicle's turn signals seriously. A motorist can change his or her mind at the last minute. Or the driver may not even know the signal is on.

Use skill and caution in turning left. Executing a left turn from the left lane is legal providing the bike doesn't impede the flow of traffic. Use practical and safe judgment when getting into the left lane, remembering that you must yield the right-of-way when changing lanes. If the traffic is heavy, and getting over into the turn lane would require a vehicle to slow down for you, forget it. Don't assume that cars have to stop for you. In this case they don't! If the intersection has two left-turn lanes, always use the lane on the right and complete your turn as close to the right side of the street as is safe. Watch for cars turning right, and yield to pedestrians. Another way to execute your left turn is to continue straight across the original intersection, stop, and turn your bike 90 degrees to the left; then wait for the green light and proceed with the flow of traffic.

Use caution in crossing railroad tracks. When you see tracks, slow down before crossing. Often the rails are an inch or two above the road surface. Crossing too fast can cause your wheel to bottom out on the track which can dent the rim or ruin a tire or both. Always cross at a right angle to prevent your front wheel from getting caught in the track groove. It's best to get up off your seat the instant you cross the tracks. This takes weight off the bike to provide a softer crossing.

Ride clear of debris. Glass, rocks, twigs, cans, nails, wire, potholes, and even wet leaves in the road are hazards. They can ruin a tire, cause you to lose control, or both.

Beware of dogs. Dogs have long presented a problem to bikers, especially on country roads where dogs are often allowed to run free. A dog may do any of several things (1) Run alongside you but not leave the property; (2) leap at you only once, then turn around and go back; (3) try to snap at your legs, feet, or wheels; or (4) dart across in front of you. Only rarely will an animal jump on you or run into your bike—but it has happened. There are several things you can do to discourage dogs:

Yell at the dog—say "No" or "Stay." Be very firm, as though you were giving an order to your own animal. Dogs perceive confidence and more often than not respect authority.

If yelling doesn't stop the dog, *use some repellent.* A well-aimed squirt of water from a water bottle can be effective.

Outrun the dog. In most cases the dog isn't really trying to hurt you; he's trying to chase you away. It gives his ego a big boost to see you go.

Never try to kick a dog. He'll take this as an attack and become very serious about biting you.

Watch out for gravel. Gravel is very hazardous, especially when it is scattered across pavement, because it can cause your bike to skid out from under you. It is particularly hazardous when turning; make your turns gingerly. Use your rear brake only in gravel.

Monitor downhill speeds. Do not take downhills with reckless abandon. Know the limits of your bike. The higher the quality of the bike, the faster the speeds it can handle. Occasionally, on a fast downhill run, you may experience what is called wheel wobble as the bike oscillates or vibrates excessively. If this ever happens to you, tighten your knees in close to the top tube, grasp the handlebars firmly on the hooks, and apply the rear brake gently and smoothly. Easy pressure on the front brake will then reduce your speed, and the vibration will stop.

Watch out for side-view mirrors on large vehicles. Note the extension of side mirrors on campers and pickup trucks. A passing vehicle can unwittingly bump you with a protruding mirror. Recreational vehicles and trucks from rental agencies are bigger hazards than semis. The drivers of RV's and rentals are generally inexperienced and subject to many distractions: kids in the camper, scenery, etc. It's always best to assume that they don't know you're there.

Note the number of occupants in a vehicle. Passengers in the back seat mean poor rear vision for the driver, who may also be less alert to traffic because he or she is conversing with friends. Beware of happy sightseers. Such things as conversation, scenery, or consulting a map are distractions that can take the driver's attention away from the road and from you.

"Understand" trucks. Professional truck drivers are the most skilled drivers on the road. Learn to respect them, if for no other reason than that they outweigh you a million to one. Understand the peculiar problems of the truck driver: Momentum is a major factor. A truck can have as many as 18 gears, and when it's fully loaded the driver may have to go through all of them to get up to highway speeds. After that, drivers don't like to lose speed, since that means losing time, and going through all those gears again is hard work. Keep this in mind when riding your bike. It may be far easier for the cyclist to give a little than for the trucker to slow down. If you hear a large truck approaching, check out the conditions ahead. Is another vehicle coming in the opposite direction, making it impossible for the truck to pass in the opposing lane? Are you approaching a curve or the crest of a hill, making it dangerous for a truck to pass? Slow down and get off the road if necessary. You'll be surprised at how many "thank you's" you'll hear in the form of quick double blasts on the trucks' air horns.

Dress for the road. Wear an approved bicycle helmet—white or yellow for greatest visibility. Wear bright colors—an orange, red, or yellow jersey, for example. Wear riding gloves, both to cushion your grip on the handlebars and to protect the palms of your hands in the event of a fall. Equip your bike with toe clips; they will prevent your feet from slipping off the pedals and will increase your speed and power. Lastly, wear shatterproof sunglasses to shield you from the sun and to prevent bugs, dirt, and small stones flung by car and truck wheels from injuring your eyes.

"Natural" Safety Hazards

Sometimes it's not motorists or other cyclists who threaten your safety so much as the forces of nature: rain, wind, fog, darkness, and the heat of the desert. On a bicycle you're obviously much more vulnerable to the natural elements than you would be in your car or at home with a good book. If you're planning on becoming an avid cyclist you'll want to acquaint yourself with potential natural hazards and the best ways to handle them.

RAIN

Bicycle brakes work poorly when they're wet. Water on the rims prevents friction—and friction is what makes you stop. Aluminum-alloy rims are more porous and therefore stop better than steel rims in the rain.

DARKNESS

A full 25 percent of all bicycle fatalities take place at night on narrow country roads. Based on those figures, it is wise to avoid such rides if at all possible, but, if you must ride at night, do everything you can to be visible.

FOG

We have one suggestion about riding in the fog: DON'T! There just isn't a way to make it safe. If you're in the city, take public transportation, or call a friend to drive you to your destination. If you're touring and you have your camping gear with you, stop and set up camp. Do everything you can to avoid riding in the fog.

DESERT RIDING – PREVENTING DEHYDRATION

The prime danger of riding in a desert is dehydration. The heat and the dryness of the air deplete your body fluids. The symptoms are progressive: You begin with a dry mouth, nose, and eyelids; then your skin becomes pale and clammy; next come dizziness and hallucination; weakness and nausea follow quickly.

Dehydration can happen within a few hours or a few days. The best treatment is prevention. Realize that you can act to prevent it, if you act wisely. Conserve your energy in hot weather. Ride slowly and steadily, maintaining a comfortable, almost leisurely pace. Get up with the first light of dawn—sometimes 3:00 or 4:00 *A.M.* in the Western Hemisphere—and put in most of your riding hours before 10:00 in the morning.

One of the best ways to prevent dehydration is by eating fruits. (Oranges, bananas, apples, and pears are excellent.) These contain large quantities of water as well as the vitamins and minerals you need in hot climates. Natural fruit juices are terrific in the heat. Celery helps prevent sodium loss. Tomato juice diluted with a little water provides good quantities of sodium and potassium.

Watch the pressure in your tires as you proceed. Heat will cause the air inside to expand, increasing the pressure. Let about ten pounds of air out when you begin, and then check it every couple of hours as you go.

Take reasonable precautions, but don't be afraid of the desert. It can be extremely beautiful. In the U.S. the roads across the deserts are well traveled, so that even if you get into some kind of trouble on your bike, it isn't difficult to hail a passing motorist and get a ride—bike and all.

Finally, wear a white helmet to keep the sun off your head. Wear good sunglasses, and use sunscreen on your face or any other bare-skin areas that need protection. You'll find that your arms, the tops of your thighs, and the backs of your calves get the most exposure.

Basic Riding Know-How

ONE OF THE MAJOR REASONS for the bicycle's wide appeal is that anyone—with or without athletic ability—can become proficient enough to really enjoy the sport. There are no unusual skills to learn . . . just ordinary movements we all use every day in the course of walking down the street, climbing stairs, or running. Moreover, the bicycle is its own athletic coach, since the frame itself guides you through the movements for proper form and peak efficiency.

The subtleties of pedaling, braking, shifting, and riding position can dramatically improve your efficiency and bicycling pleasure. Likewise, the often-neglected aspect of *training,* or tuning up your motor—your muscles and cardiovascular system—can let you fully enjoy bicycling whatever distances you choose to travel.

Pedaling

An experienced cyclist learns to extend the power stroke to a full 180 degrees. If you ride without toe clips, concentrate on the way your muscles feel when your foot reaches the top of the stroke, or just slightly beyond the 12-o'clock position. Think of this as the trigger point—the signal for you to pour on the power and push the pedal to the bottom of its stroke.

When you start riding with toe clips, you acquire a second trigger point. When your foot is in the 6-o'clock position you pull up on the pedal, using the toe clip to lift the pedal to the 12-o'clock position. Using your imagination, learn to visualize your feet spinning around in powerful, efficient circles. Actually form a picture of this in your mind. You'll be surprised to discover that this exercise of imagination really does influence your physical performance, since it programs your nervous system to send specific signals to your muscles. As every accomplished athlete knows, the mind plays a major role in perfecting every physical technique.

The Brakes

In all braking situations, the front wheel—not the rear—has the most weight on it and thus has the best traction. Because of the traction on the front wheel, the front brake is more effective and requires more pressure than the rear brake. Conversely, with reduced traction on the rear wheel, applying too much brake pressure can stop the wheel from turning altogether, causing it to go into a skid.

Riding Position

If your bike is equipped with dropped handlebars, your upper body gets to play an active role in maximizing pedaling effectiveness. Your arms, back, and stomach muscles make corrections for balance; they also flex to provide leverage for your leg muscles when you're climbing a hill or pouring on the speed. There are three basic hand positions provided by dropped-style handlebars, each with its aerodynamic as well as muscular advantages.

Shifting Gears

STEP 1 — Start by putting the bike in its lowest gear, with the chain on the biggest sprocket in the rear and the smallest sprocket in the front. This is the gear you'd use for climbing a hill. Notice how it feels to crank the pedals, and notice the positions of the shift levers.

STEP 2 — Put the bike in its highest gear, with the chain on the smallest sprocket in the rear and the largest sprocket in the front. You'd use this gear on flat, open road. Notice how it feels to crank the pedals, and notice the positions of the shift levers.

STEP 3 — Set your gears in a mid-range position: chain on the large gear in front and the middle, or third, gear in the rear.

Continue to experiment with your gears until you feel comfortable about the process of shifting. Then set your bike in its mid-range gear and remove the ropes so you can ride. Ride for 10 or 15 minutes in the mid-range gear so you'll become familiar with the way it feels. Shift into the low range and see how that feels. Then shift into high range and see how that feels.

Practice shifting from high to mid-range to low range, and then back again, as you ride. Repeat these patterns again and again, riding in a leisurely manner as you do so, until you feel comfortable.

Tips for Shifting Derailleurs

1. Anticipate the terrain. Think about the gear you'll want to be in when you get to the beginning of a long hill, for example. When you're bearing down on the pedals on a steep hill, the derailleur usually won't carry the chain to a lower gear. So get into that lower gear before you find yourself on a hill, sweating and cursing because you're in a gear that's too high and you can't get shifted into a lower one.
2. Shift into lower gears when approaching stop streets or signal lights. Remember, you can't

shift gears standing still, and you'll want that low gear when you start out again. Think ahead and drop into the lower gear by shifting a few yards before you stop.

3. Learn to recognize and adjust for the sounds made by the chain rubbing against the derailleur cage or improperly aligned on a sprocket. The chain should move noiselessly on the sprockets. If it makes a noise, move the shift lever—front or rear—in small increments until the sound goes away. With experience, you'll be able to tell from the sound which derailleur needs adjustment.

4. If your chain slips off either the front or rear sprocket, your derailleur needs adjustment. You can learn how to do it yourself (it's not hard), or take it to your bike shop, where they'll charge you a small amount to correct the problem.

5. If your bike slips out of gear, your shift levers probably need adjustment. Shift levers have an adjustment screw on the end of the axle shafts that hold the levers themselves. Better levers have wire loops, wing nuts, or knurled knobs so that the rider can easily make this adjustment while riding. However, a few brands of levers have a screw that requires a dime or a screwdriver to tighten it. Experiment with this adjustment and get into the habit of checking it routinely.

Tips for Improving Your Ride

The more you ride, the more you'll become aware of ways to improve your cycling form. You may feel that you're working too hard for the distance you travel. Or you may feel that certain parts of your body are more uncomfortable than they have to be. Or you may feel insecure in traffic. Here are five important tips to help you solve these and other problems:

STAY IN LOWER GEARS

Beginning and intermediate riders have a tendency to pedal their bikes in gears that are too high. This can cause knee pain because of the pressure exerted on joints and ligaments each time the rider bears down on the pedals. Faster pedaling speeds reduce this pressure by distributing the same power output over more revolutions. Thus these faster pedaling rates use energy more effectively. Try to keep up a regular cadence of 60 to 75 revolutions per minute. You can gauge your rate by counting the number of times your right knee comes up while the second hand of your watch indicates one minute.

PEDAL IN CIRCLES

As you pedal, try to visualize your feet making the full circle of the cranks through the complete pedaling stroke. This will have the effect of automatically sending a message to your muscles to do just that. The visualization trick will not work instantly, but the more you remember to practice it, the more efficient your pedaling will become. If your bike is equipped with toe clips, you will in fact be able to apply pressure on the pedals through the full circle of the cranks.

CHANGE HAND POSITIONS FREQUENTLY

Riding in one position for too long will cause your back and arm muscles to stiffen up. Change positions often as you ride, giving your muscles an opportunity to stretch and flex. This is the best prescription there is for preventing the kinds of stiffness characteristic of cycling.

PAY ATTENTION TO THE WAY YOU FEEL

As you ride, remind yourself to be aware of any discomforts you may be feeling. Are your hands numb or tingling? Do your shoulders feel tight? Is your rear end getting sore? While riding, make small changes in your posture to relieve pressure on the parts of your body that hurt. When specific discomforts persist, consider the equipment itself: Is your seat properly adjusted? Are your handlebars too high or too low? Would handlebar padding make your hands more comfortable? Would a different saddle ease that pain in your rear end? Are your toe clips the right size? When you feel pain or discomfort, assume that these sensations are signals to change something either in your bike or in your riding style.

GET OFF AND PUSH WHEN PEDALING GETS TOO HARD

False pride causes more sore knees, strained muscles, and other health problems than any other single factor in biking. This happens for one of two reasons: You overestimate your present physical capacities and bully the bike up a hill that's too steep, or you neglect to shift into a lower gear in time for a hill. When you find yourself in either of these situations, stop, get off, swallow your pride if necessary, and walk your bike up the hill. Remember, you want to finish your ride with good associations about the experience.

Getting In Shape

Now that you've got the techniques for riding down pat, don't be surprised if your body registers complaints in the form of aches, vague pains, and general stiffness after an afternoon on your bike. Although your bicycle is a vehicle, it's not like a car. You can't just get in and go without preparation.

You have to ride to get good on a bike, and for a while it may not be as much fun as you might like. You're going to experience some aches and pains, but that's okay. That's what's supposed to be happening.

There are a number of changes a new rider's body will go through on the way to full enjoyment of the sport. Eventually, every aspect of your life will benefit from your increased lung capacity, your improved muscle strength and tone, and the miles of new capillaries you'll grow to carry oxygen to your muscle tissue. But it takes time and patience for your body to respond to the new demands you're making on it. Keep pushing yourself so that your body's capacities grow, but not beyond the point where riding ceases to be a pleasure. If you take it slow and easy at first, tuning up your body over time, you may soon find yourself relishing the greater rigors of commuting or even cycle training for a triathlon.

Caring For Your Bike

KEEPING YOUR BIKE in top condition is essential to your continued riding pleasure. A wobbly wheel or loose pedal bearings can easily cause needless anxiety while sapping your energy. Regular bicycle maintenance also goes a long way toward preventing or minimizing costly repairs.

Luckily, bicycle maintenance is easy, and most of it can be done by anyone, with or without mechanical skill. The instructions that follow will help you keep your bike in top running condition between yearly tuneups by a skilled mechanic. For those of you who wish to do your own yearly overhaul and repairs, there are many excellent manuals available at your local bike shop. Instead of duplicating that information here, we've tried to stick to the basics.

The first rule of bicycle maintenance is "Keep your bike clean!" Grit tends to build up on moving parts, and, unless you clean it off, it has a way of getting into bearing surfaces and wearing them out before their time. Never use water to clean your bike. Use a solvent, such as kerosene (be careful, it's highly flammable), Bullshot, or WD-40. Avoid getting these solvents on brake pads and tires.

Tire Repairs

When you begin riding more than a few miles a week, you will inevitably have a flat tire sooner or later. You can postpone this eventuality by keeping your tires inflated to pressures recommended by the manufacturer; replacing your tires before the treads are worn thin; avoiding glass and metal objects in the road; and brushing your tires off to remove any tiny, sharp stones or glass that may be sticking to the tread and working their way into the rubber.

When you do get a flat tire on the road, you either change the tire or patch it, depending on whether your bike has clinchers or sewups.

CHANGING SEWUP TIRES

Tools required: Pump and spare tire.

Sewup tires are easier and faster to change on the road than clinchers. That's one reason why they were invented. With the tube sewn into the tire casing, both are easily removable as a unit.

Sewup tires are glued to the wheels of your bike. Begin by removing the wheel, which is usually accomplished by means of a quick-release lever.

If your brakes rub against the tire, release the brake's quick release, located on the brake lever or the brake assembly itself.

Locate the tire valve and release any pressure that may still be in the tire. Then start removing the tire on the side of the wheel opposite the valve by pulling it away from the metal rim. The glue used is a rubber-based adhesive that maintains a tackiness for months and sometimes years, so the tire is usually easy to peel from the rim.

To replace the punctured tire with your spare, first insert the valve stem in the hole provided for it in the rim. Press the rim against a tree, a wall, or a clean patch of ground so you can stretch the tire onto it. (Be careful not to pick up rocks and stones while you're doing this.) Starting at the valve stem, work the tire onto the rim evenly by stretching it around the wheel with both hands at once. Never use any kind of metal object or pry bar on a sewup tire. Not only is it unnecessary, but it can also destroy a good tire.

Inflate the tire to about half-pressure and check the tire to make certain it's mounted evenly on the rim. At low pressure, it is easy to twist the tire right or left to align it on the wheel.

Replace the tire on the frame. Lock the quick-release skewers in place on the axle. Re-engage the release mechanisms on the brakes. Inflate the tire with your hand pump until it is up to proper pressure or feels hard when you press your thumb firmly against it. That's it—you're ready to go! With practice, the average person can change a sewup tire on the road in less than five minutes.

About spares: Unless you plan to carry a spare tire with you, you're defeating the purpose of having a bike equipped with sewups. A spare weighs only ounces and can be clipped under the seat with a spare toe strap or one of several simple carrying devices sold for this purpose.

It's a good idea to get an old rim from your bike shop's junk bin to use for "seasoning" spare sewup tires. When you buy a new tire, glue it to the rim, inflate it, and let it stretch into shape. Whenever you need a fresh spare to carry on your bike, remove the seasoned tire and put it under the seat. A seasoned tire is much easier to install on the road than an unseasoned one.

If you season new tires in this way, you won't have to carry rim cement with you on your bike because the tire will already have its own glue on it. Hence, you won't end up with sticky fingers that pick up dirt, hair, and grime and just won't wipe off. The glue on the tire will be tacky to the touch by the time you need it, but it won't come off on your hands.

Patching sewup tires takes time and patience. For instructions, consult complete repair manual, which you can purchase from most bicycle shops.

CHANGING CLINCHER TIRES

Tools required: Pump, patch kit, two tire irons, and a 6-inch crescent wrench if you have bolt-on axles.

Wheels with clincher tires may be equipped with either quick-release axles or bolt-ons. In either case, remove the wheel from the frame. Begin by releasing the quick-release mechanism of the brake—a device that will be located either on the hand lever on the handlebars or on the brake caliper over the wheel.

Remove the wheel either by loosening the nuts that hold the axle to the frame or by releasing rhe quick-release skewer. Pump some air into the tire to locate the leak. Mark that area with a pencil, with a pen, or, if you don't have either of these, by scratching the tire with a stone.

Remove the wheel either by loosening the nuts that hold the axle to the frame or by releasing the quick-release skewer. Pump some air into the tire to locate the leak. Mark that area with a pencil, with a pen, or, if you don't have either of these, by scratching the tire with a stone.

Remove the tire from the rim. In some cases you'll be able to do this with your hands, but with the new high-pressure tires you may have to use tire irons.

Work one tire iron in between the rim and the side of the casing. Be careful not to catch the tube with the iron, as this can tear the rubber and cause another leak.

With one iron holding the tire, work the second iron around the rim until you've released one side of the tire from the rim for the full circumference of the wheel. Now you can reach in and remove the inner tube.

Inflate the tube with your pump and check for leaks. Mark the leak with a pen, pencil, or stone. Release the air from the tube.

Following the instructions that came with your patch kit, apply a patch over the hole in the tube and reinflate it. Check for leaks again. If you've run over a nail, the chances are good that you have two puncture holes—the first caused by the initial penetration, the second by the nail chewing up the tube as you rode for a few yards with the tire flat.

When you are satisfied that you've patched all the leaks, examine the inside of your tire casing with your fingers. You may find a nail or a shard of glass in there, so be careful. Examine the casing from the inside to see if there are any breaks or cuts that might pinch the tube. Temporary repairs can often be made by applying a regular tire patch over any break more than a quarter-inch long. But never trust such a repair job to carry you any farther than the nearest bike shop to buy a new tire.

Work one side of the tire casing onto the rim with your fingers. Then place the tube inside the casing, inflating it just enough to give it body. Smooth the tube neatly into the casing. Work the casing into the rim with your fingers, releasing air from the tube if necessary. Sometimes, especially with high-pressure clinchers, it may be necessary to work the last six or eight inches of the casing on with a tire iron. Do this only as a last resort, as it is easy to tear the tube using an iron. Be sure to check with your bike shop to determine whether or not you should use a tool on your particular type of tire.

Replace the wheel in the frame and inflate it to full pressure. Check to see that the quick release is re-engaged on the brake. Make certain that the axle nuts and skewers are tight. Then you're ready to go.

About spares: Some bicyclists carry a spare tube instead of a patch kit. Repairing the clincher on the road then requires no more than removing the punctured tube, examining the casing, and reassembling the whole. On a tour, it is also possible to purchase a spare casing that folds up to about the same size as a sewup tire.

Wheel Checks

Wheels need to be kept "true"—that is, free of wobble. Regular checks of your wheels will help you prevent broken spokes and bent rims. Since the condition of the wheel affects the brakes, a wobbly wheel will cause you to lurch to a stop. On wet pavement or gravel, your wobbly wheel can even cause a dangerous skid.

To check your wheel, have someone lift one wheel at a time an inch or two from the ground. Spin the wheel and watch for side-to-side play (called "wobble"). If the wheel wobbles more than a 16th of an inch from center, it needs attention. As the wheel is spinning, watch for up-and-down movement also. This is called "hop." Again, more than 1/16 inch of hop indicates that the wheel needs to be trued.

Any good bike shop will true a wheel for a nominal fee. There are books available to help you learn how to do this, but it does take a lot of practice to become good at it. Unless you're willing

2nd row top left: Bob Hogan, formerly a Los Angeles, California Life Guard, "Spinning 1.7 mile Kapiolani Park," Honolulu . . . 2nd row from top: Carol Hogan, now Sports Editor for the Honolulu Advertiser Newspaper, and husband Bob, listen to Max Telford's pre-workout class on Ultramarathon Triathlon Training. Carol and Bob are contestants in the October, 1982 Ironman Triathlon . . . Lower right: Max with arm raised, giving striding instructions to one of his classes . . . Remaining photos: Members of "The Bike Club" of Honolulu shown drafting and echeloning the park against strong North East Trade Winds that blow across park.

to put in several hours of practice, it's best to have the job done by your favorite bike mechanic.

TIGHTENING SPOKES

Tools required: A spoke wrench.

As you're checking your wheels, also check for loose or broken spokes. Every spoke in the wheel should "plink" when you pluck it as you'd pluck a stringed musical instrument. If a spoke wiggles instead of plinking, it's too loose. If the wheel hops or wobbles, there are probably one or more loose spokes. Tightening spokes is an integral part of truing a wheel. In fact, truing is accomplished by adjusting spoke tension.

However, sometimes you'll find one or two loose spokes even though the wheel is true. You can tighten these yourself if you use care. Tighten them by turning the spoke nipple clockwise.

The best way to get the right tension is to snug up the spoke—that is, to tighten most of the looseness out and then continue to tighten the spoke, a quarter turn at a time. Tighten a quarter, spin the wheel to check for true, tighten another quarter turn, etc. If the wheel wobbles after the spoke is tightened, it means that you've tightened it too much. Back off on the tension until the wobble disappears again.

Pay particular attention to the rear wheel. Spokes in that wheel get much more stress than those in the front wheel. Spokes stretch or the wheel distorts as a result of the power you exert on it when you climb a hill.

If you're conscientious about adjusting loose spokes, and you develop a good feel for it, this simple maintenance procedure can save you many dollars in more expensive repairs.

BRAKE SHOES

Tools required: A 6-inch crescent wrench or a 10-mm box-end wrench.

Every time you apply your brakes, a little rubber is worn from the brake pads and in time they need to be replaced.

Usually it's very easy to tell when your brakes need attention; your bike doesn't respond to your squeezing of the brake levers. However, if that is your only criterion for testing the brakes, you may discover your need for repair or adjustment only after you've injured yourself or your bike or both.

Instead, inspect your brakes regularly. With the hand lever in its released position, each brake pad should be 1/8 to 1/4 inch from the rim, depending on how finely tuned you keep your bike. If they're set wider than that, your brake pads are probably worn and need to be replaced.

Check the alignment of the brakes on the rim. To do this, squeeze each brake lever and examine the way the pad lines up on the rim. If it's not centered on the braking surface, this indicates excess wear and a a need for adjustment or replacement.

You'll notice that there's a slot in the brake caliper arm onto which the brake pads are bolted. You can center the pads on the braking surface of the rim by loosening the nuts that hold them and sliding the pad up or down. Be sure to adjust the pads for the position they will be in when the hand lever is squeezed and the pads are fully engaged on the rim.

Cable adjustment is usually necessary after adjusting or replacing the brake pads. You can adjust either the outer cable or the inner cable. (The outer cable is like a tube; the inner cable runs inside it.) On side-pull brakes, the outer cable adjustment is located on the brake assembly itself; on center-pulls, it's on a clip above the brake assembly.

Adjust the outer cable by first loosening the locknut and then turning the adjusting barrel until the pads are from 1/8 to 1/4 inch from the rim. Try the brakes by squeezing the hand-lever. When you're satisfied with your adjustment, tighten the locknut back in place.

Most minor adjustments can be accomplished with the outer cable adjustment. However, if the pads are badly worn or you are replacing them, you may need to adjust the inner cable. This is done by loosening the nut on the inner cable-adjustment bolt and either shortening or lengthening the cable. As you'll see when you get started, this is a three-handed job. Unless you're very good with your hands, have a friend help you or get a tool from your bike shop called a "third hand," which holds the brake pads against the rim while you adjust the cables.

Pads are easy to replace once you've mastered the technique described above. Each pad is held in place by a single nut. Unscrew that nut, drop out the old pad assembly, put in the new, and adjust. The only thing to watch is that some pad clips, or holders, are open on one end. Whenever you put in new brake pads, *make certain that the closed end faces forward;* otherwise the pad can fly out of its clip while you're braking.

Checking Bottom Bracket Bearings

Tools required: Wrenches designed for the specific make of bottom bracket (available from bike shops).

It is easy to overlook the bottom bracket bearings—that is, the bearings that carry the crankset of your bike. Unless you're doing a lot of wet-weather riding, these bearings won't require full servicing (disassembly and grease) more than once a year. But, to prevent bearing damage, you do need to check this adjustment every two or three months.

To check for play or looseness in the bearing, grasp either crank arm firmly and try to move it sideways. It should rotate freely without play. Then remove the chain from the front chainwheel and try spinning the crank. It should spin freely and smoothly. If you feel excessive side-play, looseness, or sloppiness in the bearing, it will need to be tightened. If the crank is hard to turn it will need to be loosened. If the crank turns roughly or you hear a gritty sound, that indicates that the bearings and parts need to be disassembled, examined for bearing damage, replaced if worn, greased, and reassembled.

Simple adjustments are done from the left side of the bike. You begin by releasing the "lockring" and turning the "adjusting cup" either tighten or loosen the bearing—clockwise to tighten, counterclockwise to loosen. Tighten the lockring and try the adjustment again. Sometimes the lockring will change the adjustment as it is tightened, requiring readjustment of the adjusting cup until the bearing runs smoothly with the lockring tight.

Each bottom bracket bearing is a little different, and each one requires tools designed specifically for it. Your bike shop can supply you with the right tools for adjustment.

If you don't wish to do the mechanical work yourself, take your bike to your bike shop when you discover that bearing adjustments are needed. The few dollars you'll spend now can save you money in the long run.

Checking Pedals

Tools required: A wrench (preferably a pedal wrench) to fit the pedals on your bike.

One of the simplest maintenance checks you can make is also one of the most expensive if neglected. On occasion, the pedal spindle, which is threaded into the crank, unscrews slightly. You may not feel that it's loose. As you ride with a loose pedal, the threaded end of its spindle rocks back and forth in the crank arm. This can strip the threads in the crank arm, and, once the arm is stripped in this way, you have no choice but to buy a new one. If your bike has high-quality alloy cranks, the damage can be an expensive proposition indeed.

Put a wrench on the pedals and tighten them snugly into the crank arm. Note that the pedal on the right is tightened by turning it clockwise, while the pedal on the left is tightened by turning it in the opposite direction.

While you're at it, check the pedal bearings. Grasp the pedal and feel for any looseness in the bearing. Spin it and make certain it spins freely.

Mid- to high-quality pedal bearings can be both adjusted and greased. To adjust them, remove the outer dust cap behind which you'll find a locknut and bearing assembly similar to those on the wheels and crankset. To adjust the pedal bearing, you loosen the locknut and adjust the cone (it is threaded like a nut) until the pedal runs free and smooth.

Checking Headset Bearings

Tools required: Wrenches to fit both the locknut and the adjusting nut of the headset.

The headset of your bicycle holds the bearings that support the front fork, allowing you to turn the front wheel. Unlike any other bearing, this one must resist the erratic pounding of the road. Because of the vibration transmitted to the headset, there is a tendency for the locknut and adjusting nut to loosen. For this reason, we recommend getting into the habit of checking the headset adjustment every time you ride. The procedure is so simple that you'll soon be doing it as a matter of course.

Straddle your bike as though getting ready to ride. Engage the front wheel brake and push the bike forward and back with the brake on. Do you feel any looseness in the headset? Does it make a clicking or rattling sound? In either case, it's time for an adjustment.

Loosen the locknut and turn the adjusting nut until the click or looseness goes away. Tighten the locknut against the adjusting nut to prevent it from working loose again. Now turn the front fork back and forth. Does it bind as you turn it? If so, the adjusting nut needs to be loosened.

When you can turn the fork smoothly from side to side while *not* producing a clicking noise in the headset, you'll know that the adjustment is correct.

Checking and Adjusting Wheel Bearings

Tools required: One cone wrench (a very thin open-end wrench which you can purchase at the bike shop). One wrench to turn the locknut.

Not all wheel bearings can be adjusted. Some high-quality bikes are equipped with bearings that are sealed at the factory. Even though you can't adjust these, you can check them, and if they're loose or otherwise defective they can be repaired by a bike shop or returned to the factory for new bearing assemblies.

To check your wheel bearings, lift the wheel a few inches off the ground and, grasping the tire, try to wiggle it from left to right. If the bearing feels loose, you'll want to adjust it or send the wheel into the shop for adjustment.

Spin the wheel and see how it goes. Does the bearing bind? If so, you'll need to adjust it.

To adjust the wheel bearings, remove the wheel from the frame. Fit the cone wrench into the adjusting nut as shown. Loosen the locknut. Now turn the adjusting cone until you can spin the axle in your fingers. Tighten the locknut against the adjusting cone to prevent it from coming loose. Put the wheel back on your bike and tighten it into place, either with the quick-release skewer or the axlenuts.

Cleaning and Adjusting Derailleurs

Tools required: Small screwdrive; spray can of Bullshot, WD-40, or similar lubricant/solvent; stiff 1/4-inch paintbrush.

Because they are close to the road and pick up dust, as well as grease from the chain, derailleurs can get filthy. The combination of grease and road grit gums up the works and causes excessive wear, so it's important to clean off the grime from time to time.

Using a quarter-inch paintbrush, brush away any grit around the moving parts and adjustment screws of both front and rear derailleurs. Then spray each derailleur with Bullshot or WD-40. Wipe away any excess solvent along with the grease, using a soft rag.

Clean the outer surfaces of the guide pulleys of the rear derailleur in the same way. Then go over all the shift cables and shift levers with the paintbrush, solvent/lubricant spray, and soft rag. Doing this once every couple of months will go a long way toward preventing expensive repairs.

Adjusting the rear derailleur. Does the chain ever slip off the freewheel cogs when you're riding? Or does it refuse to go onto the smallest or largest cogs? If you have any of these problems, your rear derailleur needs adjustment.

Suspend the rear wheel of your bike in such a way that you can crank it by hand and shift gears. Now find the adjustment screws on the rear derailleur. Sometimes these screws are marked with an "L" for low and an "H" for high. Remember that the high gear is the smallest one on the free-wheel, the low gear the biggest.

Turn the adjustment screw left or right until the chain centers perfectly on the corresponding cog. You'll see that the adjustment screws limit the travel of the derailleur cage, preventing the chain from slipping off the outer cogs. Altering the adjustment screws changes only these outer limits.

Adjusting the front derailleur. You will find the same two adjustment screws on the front derailleur. In this case, the screws limit the travel of the derailleur cage that positions the chain over the chainwheels.

After you have made your initial adjustments, crank the bike by hand, with the rear wheel suspended, and shift both front and rear derailleurs back and forth in various gear combinations. In certain extreme gear combinations you may discover that you need further adjustments.

Cleaning and Lubricating the Chain

Tools required: Bullshot or WD-40; chain lube or 20-weight oil; rags.

Chain care is extremely important. Because of its unique construction, any friction in the chain is greatly magnified. And this means taking more effort to move your bike forward.

To test for optimal chain efficiency, take a paper match and press the unlighted head against any roller. You should be able to rotate the roller using the match. If you can't, the chain needs to be thoroughly cleaned and lubricated.

Using a clean, soft rag and Bullshot or WD-40, alternately spray and wipe the full length of your chain. Spray, wipe, turn the crank forward to the next length, spray, wipe, etc., until the chain looks bright, clean, and slightly oily. Make the match test again on random links. When you are satisfied that the chain is clean, give it one more light spray without wiping it off with a rag. Let it dry for a few minutes and then treat the chain with 20-weight oil or chain lube. Wipe off the excess oil to avoid picking up dirt. Leave the bike standing for an hour or so, if convenient, to allow excess lubricant to drip off. Tip the bike to the right so the lubricant doesn't drip onto the tires and rims.

Whenever you use Bullshot, WD-40, or any other lubricant in a spray can, avoid getting it on the tires, rims, or brake pads, as it can affect braking performance. Also, some kinds of rubber and plastic may be adversely affected by lubricants.

Sometimes you'll hear people talking about their bicycle drive chains "stretching." This means that the inner bearing surfaces have worn down the distances between their centers elongate.

When a chain wears and stretches, the links no longer fit between the cogs of the gears. They ride high between the teeth, causing the teeth themselves to wear. So regular chain maintenance, including cleaning and lubrication, saves wear and tear on expensive moving parts.

Whenever you suspect excess chain wear—because the bike is hard to shift or slips out of gear, or because the chain constantly rattles against the derailleur cages—have it examined by your bike mechanic. A new chain costs under $10 plus a few dollars for installation. A chain that receives regular cleaning and lubrication every two or three months should give you many years of trouble-free service, so your time in periodic maintenance will indeed be well spent.

Taping Handlebars

Tools required: No tools are needed, but two rolls of handlebar tape are required for a complete job.

For some reason many people are intimidated by the idea of taping their handlebars. The process is simple, however, and can be done in about half an hour even though you've never done it before.

There are several kinds of handlebar tape available: plastic, rubber, leather, and fabric. The fabric tape is best for two reasons. First, unlike rubber or plastic, fabric tape absorbs perspiration, keeping your grip on the handlebars solid and secure. Second, fabric tape has its own adhesive backing, making the job of wrapping the bars relatively easy.

Using fabric tape, start wrapping at the end of the bars going *counterclockwise* on the left bar and *clockwise* on the right. Make two complete turns as you start. This will prevent fraying at the ends. As you spiral up the bar, overlap each turn about a quarter inch.

Stretch the tape smoothly past the handbrakes and continue wrapping, as before, on the top bar. Stop the wrap two to three inches from the stem. Tape down the end of the fabric tape nearest the handlebar stem with a band of plastic electrician's tape to prevent fraying and unwrapping.

As many cyclists leave the old tape in place when retaping their handlebars, it is not unusual to find three or four layers of tape. The extra tape provides additional padding and insulation from road shock.

Installing Handlebar Padding

To put on insulated sleeves, you must remove the hand brakes and clean all the old tape from the handlebars. Soap up the bars with shaving soap, or any other soap that will lather, and thus lubricate the sleeves as you work them over the bars. Keep the bars slippery and damp as you work. Then wipe off excess soap, replace your handbrakes, and you're ready to go.

The Training Log, Your Best Schedule

Long-range planning for your training is virtually impossible without detailed record keeping that can remind you exactly what you did during a certain day, week or month and allow you to make judgments about its worth. The best way to be sure that such information is at hand when you need it is to keep a cycling diary.

Nearly all advantages of keeping a training diary derive from the comparisons it makes available. If you keep a record of your workouts from year to year, you can see the results of different training methods, dietary changes and equipment modifications. Let's look at some specific information the diary can give you and what you can learn from it.

RECORDING AND ANALYZING DATA

One obvious advantage of record keeping is that you can chart your total miles for the year and for any period within it—the pre-season buildup from January to March, for instance. Compare this to your racing performances as the season wears on. Perhaps you'll find that more pre-season miles would give you the aerobic base to ride the early races more competitively while still retaining enthusiasm for later in the summer.

The most useful tool in evaluating mileage data is a graph. Make up a homemade one with miles from 0 to 400 on the vertical leg and the weeks of the year on the horizontal. Chart bike miles in blue and off-season running miles in red. At the bottom, next to the appropriate week, list top performances and notable disasters. Especially watch the curve of my buildup from January to April to see if you are adding mileage too fast. Such graphs are fascinating over a period of years.

Diaries provide a way to judge the effects of endurance work other than cycling. For instance, you can determine the difference in your riding performance after a winter spent cross-country skiing compared to one spent running long distance, grunting through circuit training or sweating the cold weather away on rollers.

During the season, entries can reveal the change in racing performance due to high-intensity work like intervals or motorpacing. It is important to know how many weeks it takes to reach your peak through a given training regimen—say anaerobic sessions twice a week—so you can hit your top performance level for specific events in the future.

For example, by looking back over a period of several years you might see how doing intervals once a week brings you along slowly to a peak in about 12 weeks, while a schedule of three interval sessions per week gets you there in half the time. With a solid aerobic base and this information, you know exactly how long it will take to reach top form. But this can be calculated only if you've kept a record of past training and racing performances.

The data you accumulate will allow you to see the results of a winter weight program. Careful entries will let you know from one year to the next how many sets, reps and how much poundage you have used for each exercise. Comparing yearly race results helps you assess the value of specific exercises, as well as the relative benefits of different weight routines, such as circuit training versus a power program.

Training diaries are also a great place to record your race results. Put in the name of the event and starting time, the weather, the category you rode, your placing and time, along with the names of dedicated racers who finished ahead and behind. In this way you can compare your accomplishments in the same race from year to year and also see if you are improving or regressing in relation to other serious riders. You think you will remember results forever as you relive the competition after the event, but over the years the races will tend to run together in your mind. The diary never forgets.

Diaries let you analyze peaks and valleys in performance. You can do this through evaluation of race results or with periodic time trials. Once you have ridden either a PR (personal record) or a PD (personal disaster), you can look back at the preceding weeks and months to find out why it happened. In the case of great rides or a series of races in which you were consistently in top form, you can reproduce that preparation later.

Another valuable reason for keeping records is that you can track down the causes of injuries more easily. If you are having knee problems that cropped up for no apparent reason, an analysis of the diary may give you some clues. Did you change your shoes, cleat position or saddle height last month? How about that long ride two weeks ago? Maybe it irritated ligaments and you haven't recovered because, as the diary shows, you got inspired and rode 300 miles in the next six days with one race and two interval sessions. One thing diaries reveal in cold-hearted, objective and brutal style is the way we tend to get excited and overdo our training just when we are rounding into top form. Diaries mirror our ego, our stupidity, our unwillingness to accept our limits. Maybe that is why some racers don't keep them, and why those who do are often loath to act on what the records show so clearly.

Body weight fluctuations over a year or a career can also be charted. You can find out if you really do climb better when you are lighter or if you tend to lose some strength after your weight drops below a certain level. Knowing the poundage at which you function best is a great help in the struggle to achieve consistently good performances.

A diary allows you to see the effect that time of day has on training. If you have to ride for three months from 5:30 to 7:30 a.m. due to a change in your work or school schedule, you can compare the results of that routine to the afternoon workouts you're more accustomed to, particularly in relation to injuries. A current theory holds that your body is coldest and, therefore, more susceptible to injury early in the morning. Does this account for that bothersome tightness in your left thigh? A carefully kept record can help you figure it out.

Riders can present all sorts of reasons and excuses for not keeping a diary, even though they know it could help their cycling. Some can't remember to make daily entries. This problem can be conquered by keeping the diary on the nightstand and filling in the day's proceedings before going to sleep. Some riders stash their diaries in the bathroom next to the toilet paper and are able to make extremely regular entries. Or the diary can be kept near the bike's resting place and the data recorded upon return from each training ride. Any excuse for not writing down your workouts is just that—an excuse. If you really believe that keeping a diary can help you be a better rider, you will have no trouble remembering to fill it in.

There are some pitfalls of diary keeping, a main one being the recording of too much data and getting lost in trivial detail. You don't need graphs of daily caloric intake, a complete biorhythm chart, three pulse and blood pressure readings per day or a four-page narrative account of your mental processes during the ride. Just stick to a few important items.

Another danger some riders have encountered is the "diary miles syndrome." It is easy to get trapped in the belief that more miles equal better performance, the result being a constant struggle to make this week's total more than last week's, which was more than the week before that, and so on. For a while there is great satisfaction in the mere recording of these ever-larger totals, but the time will surely come when the physical and mental strain causes a breakdown. Don't let the diary become an end in itself; make it an aid, not a tyrant.

INFORMATION TO ENTER

Here are some suggestions for actual entries. Although it looks like it will take you longer to write down the information than it took to do the workout, all these notations can be made in about three minutes a day.

Weight. Some riders weigh themselves every day under identical circumstances—before breakfast is standard—but this is too frequent. Your actual weight won't fluctuate appreciably in 24 hours, although scale weight may vary as much as 5-8 pounds depending on your state of hydration. If you are training hard every day or riding a lengthy stage race, daily weight checks will help you determine if you are adequately replacing lost fluids. But during normal training, morning weigh-ins are unnecessary. Instead, step on the scale about once a week to check for any weight-loss trend. A steady decrease past your best racing weight may indicate that you are dipping into muscle reserves and in danger of falling victim to overtraining.

Heart Rate. This should be taken once a month—immediately after waking up is best—after you have trained long enough for your heart rate to stabilize. The newcomer to fitness will see his resting heart rate fall steadily during the initial months of training, from about 75 beats per minute in sedentary life to the low 50s as exercise strengthens the cardiovascular system and makes it more efficient. Once it reaches a stable rate (determined by heredity as well as training volume) there is usually no need to check it frequently. The exception is during periods of heavy training, especially when you are doing intervals. Then heart rate should be recorded daily because an increase (at rest) of more than five or six beats may be signaling the onset of staleness. Remember that a variation can be caused by so many factors that it is not a very reliable indicator of overtraining, though it certainly won't hurt to see if daily pulse checks have any predictive value for you. Here again the importance of recording exact figures over several years is obvious.

Workout. Record what you do on the bike each day. Note miles, route, gears and cadence, along with any special features of the ride, such as intervals, riding companions and weather conditions. Also include data on any timed sections. For example clock yourself on a certain hill. This is not a scheduled time trial but maybe you have gotten into the habit of jamming it in training. Over several years you've found that your time going up is an accurate gauge of your fitness.

New Factors. Make note of any special circumstances like saddle or handlebar height adjustments, new components or wheels, and clothing. For instance, unfamiliar shoes can cause knee trouble if the cleats vary the position of the foot on the pedal. Even if the resulting irritation is barely noticeable after one ride, the training diary helps you spot the pattern.

Evaluation. Include a brief subjective appraisal of how the ride felt. You could rate its quality A to F like school grades, or include a descriptive phrase: "Felt lousy first 20 miles—sleepy and heavy legs—but better during last 30." This entry is important because it helps you remember how your body and mind responded to riding on a given day, allowing you to more accurately assess the effects of previous days and weeks of training.

Stress Load. This pertains to things not related directly to cycling. Included are happenings in your off-the-bike life that can affect either training or racing performance, such as job or school stress, staying up late at night, illness and injuries, changes in diet, etc. Example: *"54 miles— Ridgway and return—*tired last 20 from bout with flu Monday. Felt okay rest of day."

Although the volume of information in my training diary helps me plan my workouts, it is a worthwhile journal for its own intrinsic merit. In the final analysis you need no excuses to justify keeping it. You might like to browse through the entires you have made over the last five years, not to uncover any patterns but rather to re-experience the ride or race sketched out so sparely in terms of miles ridden, intervals completed and how the weather was. Keep a workout diary because it records an important part of each of the days of your life for reflection and remembrance.

Bicycle Racing

THE WORLD'S FIRST OFFICIAL bicycle race was held on May 31, 1868. Pedaling his 100-pound, iron-wheeled "Ordinary" over a rough gravel path in a park, James Moore, an Englishman, established his place in bicycling history by crossing the finish line ahead of the other contestants. The following year, this same bicyclist won the world's first long-distance trial, riding the 83 miles from Paris to Rouen in 10 hours, 25 minutes. At a scorching average speed of a little under eight miles per hour, he amazed the world.

France was the center of the world cycling competition almost from the start. In 1903, the world's greatest sporting event, the Tour de France, took place for the first time. The 2,600-mile course winds through villages and city streets, up through 7,500-foot mountain passes in the Alps and the Pyrenees—a test of human endurance that lasts for 22 days. This race is run with teams, each team including experts in sprinting and mountain climbing. Although several team members contribute to the win, the final glory goes to the first person across the finish line. It is customary, however, for the winner to turn over the entire winnings—as much as $25,000—to teammates.

The history of cycle racing in Great Britain is a curious one. Although there have been many great world-class British bicycle racers, organized racing had a rocky beginning in England. From 1890 until 1942 there were no "mass-start" races in Great Britain. The police, appalled by large groups of men racing on bicycles through the countryside, often arrested the racers for dangerous driving, which, of course, did little to encourage the sport.

Then a man by the name of F. T. Bidlake figured out a way to get around the police. Instead of having 50 men starting in a pack, Bidlake sent the racers off at intervals of one minute, timing each participant individually. This style of racing—called the "time-trial" race—has since become recognized the world over. "Mass-start" races were not officially allowed in Great Britain until 1942.

Bicycle racing has a colorful history, and in Europe it is the most popular competitive sport. In France, England, Spain, Switzerland, and Belgium, thousands of spectators line the streets for days, as racers, working in teams or individually, compete over distances ranging from a few miles to nearly 3,000 miles.

One of the world's best-known bicycle-racing heroes is the Belgian-born Eddy Merckx. In the early 1970s, at the height of his career, this man's paycheck from his Italian sponsors topped $10,000 per month! With advertising contracts, personal appearances, and prize money, it is estimated that he earned $500,000 per year, making him the highest-paid athlete in European history. During 1971, Merckx won 50 races, including the classic Tour de France for the third year in a row.

Not until 1958, however, were women officially recognized in the sport of cycle racing when British racing women got the women's world championships established. In 1969, a California woman by the name of Audrey McElmury went to Czechoslovakia and brought back America's first Gold Medal for world-class cycling competition in nearly 57 years.

Curiously enough, bike racing in the U.S. and Canada has not enjoyed the popularity it has in Europe. Yet this was not always true. Indeed, worldclass cycling, with different nations competing against each other, started in Chicago in 1893, with the Chicago-born Arthur Zimmerman taking a first place in the popular one-mile race. Up until the early 1930s, bicycle racing enjoyed greater popularity in the U.S. than baseball and horse racing.

Then, for nearly 50 years, bicycle racing fell into relative obscurity in the Western Hemisphere as auto racing overshadowed the bike. But in recent years there has been a growing interest in bike racing, with Canada's Tour de la Nouvelle France and the United States' Red Zinger competitions. The latter, held in Colorado, draws racers from all over the world. Similarly, after an interval of 75 years, Montreal hosted the world cycling championships in 1974; in 1976 the same city became the site of the Olympic bike races.

Over the years many different forms of racing have evolved, challenging the athletic efforts of men and women of all ages. The following are the main racing events officially sanctioned by world-class cycle-racing organizations.

Time Trials

This is the form of racing invented by F. T. Bidlake in 1942 to avoid conflicts with the police over "mass-start" races. Any number of cyclists can enter this race; each one is started at a different time. Usually there is a minute's space between racers. In the end, the person with the lowest elapsed time takes the prize.

Wherever you find bike clubs the world over, you'll find time trials. They usually take place on the open road, starting very early in the morning on days when traffic is light, such as Sundays and holidays.

Time trials are staged in terms of distances of 10, 20, 30, 50, or 100 miles; durations of 12 or 24 hours; or hill climbs from 300 yards to 3 miles, depending on the grade.

Average speeds are highest in the 10-to-30-mile category. Racers may cycle at speeds around 27 miles per hour, which they sustain for an hour without letup.

Mass-Start Racing

Mass-start racing is when all the participants start in one pack. In some of the European classics, such as Canada's Tour de la Nouvelle France, or Belgium's Het Volk, there are literally thousands of participants. With each racer pitted against all the others and the prize going to the first athlete to cross the finish line, such races generate a great deal of excitement.

Mass-start races come in a variety of shapes and sizes. A *criterium,* for example, may be held in a populated area, with a mile-long circuit of road sealed off from regular traffic for the duration of the race. Often taking place in small towns, these races—which last only a few hours—draw huge crowds of excited onlookers.

Other mass-start races, such as the Tour de France, take as long as 22 days to complete, yet there is never any lack of spectators to cheer on their favorite heroes.

Professional entrants in the great European road races are usually members of teams sponsored by various companies. It is not uncommon for the riders' jerseys to carry names like Perrier, Cinzano, or Michelin, along with names like Peugeot, Simplex, and Campagnolo, which are more directly associated with the bicycle industry.

Track Racing

Nowhere in cycle racing are the wits and tactical abilities of the participants more important than in track events. Official tracks range in size from the smallest, in Ontario, Canada, with 13 laps to the mile, to the largest, in London, England, with about three laps per mile.

Tracks may be banked or flat. Depending on the size of the oval, the banks may be shallow or steep. On the Ontario track, the banks slope up at a dizzying 55 degrees on the turns.

Track racers use stripped-down racing bikes with a fixed gear and no brakes. These machines weigh from 16 to 20 pounds and are designed so that the cyclists must crouch very low over their front wheels maximizing muscular control and power for sprinting.

There are several types of track races: sprint, pursuit, scratch, Devil-take-the-hindmost, unknown distance, Madison, and motor-paced riding. Let's describe each one briefly.

SPRINT

This race takes place over 800- to 1,000-meter courses, but only the last 200 meters of the race count. Until that point, it's all tactical. Sprint races usually involve two or three cyclists who are so closely matched physically that the only way to win is by outwitting one's opponents. One tactic is to act as though you're going all out, forcing your opponent to put on the steam and waste his or her best efforts before you've actually made your best move. While he or she gets thoroughly worn out, you are waiting for the last minute to put on your reserve power and pass your opponent in the last 200 meters. Another tactic is to box in your opponent on the turns, maintaining your slight edge not by sprinting, but by outmaneuvering your challenger and preventing him or her from passing you.

MOTOR-PACED RIDING

This race involves two cycles, one motor-driven and one pedaled. Riding ahead, a special motorcycle breaks the wind, creating a slipstream and reducing air resistance for the teammate pedaling inches behind. Speeds of up to 50 miles an hour are often reached on small, banked tracks.

Track racing is one of the most exciting and tense sports you can experience as an onlooker. In many ways it's a perfect spectator sport, since you can see the entire track from the grandstands as you urge on your favorite riders. The race itself calls for mental discipline as well as brute strength, as riders see new ways to psych out their opponents or maneuver into position for the final assault on the finish line.

Cycle-Cross Racing

Originally this race was invented in Europe as a way of staying in shape during the off-season, but now it's become a serious event in itself, with athlete specializing in this single form of racing. The length of the race varies from one to eight miles. The racers go over hills, through streams, over fallen trees and boulders, and through mud, sand, tall grasses, and woods. The rider rides whenever possible. But when the going gets rough you simply have to hop off and carry your bike. It's a wonderful sport if you like to wallow in the mud, plunge head first into freezing-cold creeks, scramble up hills too steep to climb on a bike, and do all this in a frenzy of competition with a dozen or more other riders.

PURSUIT

In this race, two riders start on opposite sides of the oval track. On a signal from the judges, each rider tries to catch up with, or pass, the other, usually over a distance of about 4,000 meters. Because riders are so closely matched in the official races, they seldom do catch up with each other, and the winner is determined by the clock—sometimes by hundredths or even thousandths of seconds.

Similar principles are applied in team pursuits, involving teams of up to eight riders each. Any racer passed by another is eliminated. The prize goes to the cyclist with the best time who is still on the track after completing the full distance of the race.

Mountains are earth's undying monuments. —Hawthorne

SCRATCH

This competition is run like a horse race, with all racers beginning on the same line. The first one across the finish line wins. Scratch races are generally three, five, or ten miles long.

DEVIL-TAKE-THE-HINDMOST

As each circuit is completed, the last rider in each lap is eliminated. On the last lap of the race there's a mad sprint to the finish line, with the first rider across taking the prize.

UNKNOWN DISTANCE

When the race begins, the cyclists don't know how long they'll have to ride. Suddenly a gong is sounded, signaling the last lap. Wit, muscle, and courage explode on the track as each rider presses himself or herself to the limit to be the first one across the finish line.

MADISON

Although it has been rebuilt several times, New York's Madison Square Garden was originally constructed, at the turn of the century, for bicycle racing. One form of bicycle racing still takes its name from that place. The original Madison races were six-day affairs, with riders dropping of exhaustion toward the ends of the races, causing dramatic and sometimes bloody crashes. Thousands of spectators came to watch the racers, just as they came to watch the infamous marathon dances of the era. Although the original version of the Madison is banned, the race is still run with paired riders; one rider rests while the other races, shifting back and forth in this manner for as long as six days.

Ultra-Marathon

There is one other type of organized bicycle racing, and that is what I call "ultra-marathon time trials." These events take the cyclist to the outer limits of physical and mental endurance. The long-distance cyclist can be compared to an ultra-marathon runner, who runs continuously for 24 to 48 hours. But whereas the runner may be competing for a full day or two, the ultra-marathon cyclist may be competing for periods up to two weeks. I am talking, of course of competitions like the transcontinental ride in which I participated.

The United States Cycling Federation recognizes the Transcontinental ride as the longest event—in terms of miles covered—on the record books. USCF rules state that a cyclist must ride from coast to coast, either west to east or east to west, with the terminal points of the ride being the New York City Hall on the East Coast and either San Francisco or Santa Monica California, on the West Coast.

There are different categories of ultra-marathon: (1) Solo—that is, one person unassisted and riding without the aid of windfoils or any other device to cut wind resistance; (2) two or more riders, riding as a team on separate bikes and taking turns riding in front to draft the other rider, giving the rider in the rear a period of relief from the wind; and (3) one cyclist riding solo, with a motorcycle riding just ahead to break the wind for the bicyclist. Within these categories, records are also kept for cyclists riding tandem bikes.

At the present time, Kevin and Kris Kvale, of Minneapolis, Minnesota, hold the record in the second category (two or more bicycles drafting each other) with a time of 14 days, 9 hours, and 19 minutes (August 9, 1977).

Similarly, four men from Southern California—Brooks McKinney, Bruce Hall, Pete Penseyres, and Rob Templin—hold the record for the dual tandem ride, with a time of 10 days, 21 hours, and 49 minutes (June 27, 1979).

I hold the world's record for the solo category for crossing the continent in 12 days, 3 hours, and 41 minutes (June 28, 1980)—a record I took from my friend Paul Cornish, also a Californian.

Another notable ultra-marathon for cyclists in the U.S. is the ride from Seattle, Washington, to

A view of the great expanse of volcanic ash that makes up the greater part of the bicycle course scenery out and back to Havi on the Big Island of Hawaii.

San Diego, California, a distance of 1,600 miles. This record is currently held by Michael Shermer, from Tustin, California, who covered the distance in 7 days, 8 hours, and 28 minutes (September 22, 1980).

You do not have to belong to a team or pass any tests to enter these competitions. As an ultra-marathon cyclist, you make all decisions on your own—including which route to take and when to leave—in challenging a record. The one thing that is required is a tremendous amount of preparation. This involves not only getting your own body in shape, but also putting together a "support team": people you can trust to follow along behind you and take care of such things as food preparation, sleeping facilities, and mechanical work on the bike.

My own transcontinental rides have demanded a lifelong commitment—a commitment that has necessitated great sacrifices in all areas of my life. In spite of the fact that I am a college graduate with a teaching credential, I have worked odd jobs at night, sold vacuum cleaners from door to door, and worked as a custodian so that I could have my days free to train. Every cent I earned—and then some—went toward achieving my goal. So if you are considering a transcontinental challenge, be prepared to give your life over to it. The goal can be achieved in no other way.

The real rewards of the long-distance challenge may well be invisible to the general public. It is not one's name in the record books that excites the marathoner, but something much deeper and more personal. It is the satisfaction of pushing oneself to the outer limits, of proving one more time that the limits we perceive are never absolute. Perhaps in all forms of athletic competition the ultimate goals are to explore the physical and mental potentials of the human race, to redefine our capacities over and over again.

Triathlons and Biathlons

An exciting sport that is emerging is the combining of biking with swimming and/or running, called the Triathlon including 3 sports or the Biathlon with two sports in combination.

Many new faces are seen out on the bike runs and bike ways these days. These are the runners and swimmers that are taking up bicycling in an effort to compete in these multi sport events.

With the tremendous increase in the number of multi sport events being scheduled each year together with greater numbers of participants in each event from year to year, Training Triathletes and Biathletes will soon crowd the serious bike racer off of the course. In Hawaii, for example, within 3 years of the inception of the Ironman World Triathlon the serious bike racing population has increased over 600% as evidenced by the number of Bicyclists spinning around Kapiolani Park, Wednesday and Friday afternoons.

These exciting and demanding sports involve, swimming a distance, jumping on a bicycle and riding a given distance and then running a few miles. The distances are set so that the Triathlete has to have trained well in all of the sports involved to be able to complete the event. Even with a substantial period of time spent in training to be able to complete one of these events in a respectable time requires a strong athlete.

The Bicycle industry is still asleep. They cannot believe that Triahletes will account for the majority of the serious competing bicyclists within a short period of time. Triathlons will put the bicycle in the forefront of participating sports in America. This is something that bicycle racing has not been able to do in over 100 years.

Winter Training

When the racing season is over in your area—perhaps in October or November—you are faced with the question of what to do in the winter. If you plan to race the following season, you should not just hang up the bike and get fat. Your next season will be much easier if you maintain a certain level of fitness. If you quit completely you will have to start building all over again in the new year and might waste several months that could have been more productively spent.

Over the winter you want to maintain your oxygen uptake, keep fat off your body, and keep your muscles conditioned. It is good for you to relax from competition, and a week or two of doing nothing won't hurt you.

WINTER TRAINING EQUIPMENT

For the program described here you'll need an indoor bicycle with a speedometer, an odometer, and a device for varying the workload. The latter is usually a knob on the handlebars which, when turned, will apply pressure to a band around the wheel or to a brake rubbing against the rim of the wheel. This device makes it harder or easier to turn the pedals; the harder you pedal, the more energy you'll expend per minute of riding. In addition, you should have a watch or timer to measure the length of your workout.

You can also set up an indoor cycling system with what are called "bike rollers." These are operated by placing an ordinary ten-speed bike on a frame with rollers which turn in unison as you pedal. Although there is no way of varying the workload, by equipping the bike with a speedometer/odometer you can measure the "distance" and speed of each workout. This lets you keep a record of each ride and duplicate workouts that meet your own particular needs. If you now own a good ten-speed bike, and your main interest is racing or riding on the road, consider bike rollers. By using your regular bike on rollers, you'll continue to use the muscles you employ on the road, whereas an exerciser will probably fit your body differently and therefore bring other muscles into play.

Indoor bicycles come in a variety of shapes, sizes, and prices. Depending on your pocketbook, you can spend anywhere from $150 to $3,000.

Cycle Training for Indoor Wheels

The program presented here is designed for people in good health, with no known health problems. It is presented with the understanding that it is not a prescription for a rehabilitation program. As with all other exercise programs, it is recommended that you consult your physician and get a complete medical checkup before beginning.

APPLYING THE PROGRAM

A healthy adult has an at-rest pulse of 70 or less beats per minute. Begin your program by taking your pulse after you have been inactive for ten minutes. If your at-rest heart rate is between 50 and 70, you are within the range of normalcy.

In order to exercise your heart, lungs, and vascular (blood-carrying) system, you'll want to exercise hard enough to raise your pulse rate to certain minimum levels. The World Health Organization recommends the following exercise guidelines:

Age	Exercising Pulse Rate
20–29 years	160–170 beats per minute
30–39 years	150–160 beats per minute
40–49 years	140–150 beats per minute
50–59 years	130–140 beats per minute
60–up years	120–130 beats per minute

You can also use formulas for aerobic exercise levels, as provided in the previous chapter, to estimate your work levels. Learn to take your pulse while exercising, either at your wrist or at the carotid artery—a couple of inches to the right or left or your windpipe, just under your jaw line, as described in the swimming chapter.

Set your exerciser at a low workload level and get on. Pedal easily for three to five minutes to warm up. You should just begin to sweat.

Then begin pedaling at a rate of 60 to 75 revolutions per minute. (You can establish your rate by counting each time your right knee comes to the top of a stroke for each sweep of the second hand.) Take note of the speed your speedometer needle registers when you are pedaling at the 60-75-rpm rate, and this will save you from having to count revolutions again.

After five minutes, take your pulse as you continue to pedal. This is tricky at first, but with a little practice it'll become easy and automatic. Is your pulse rate below the exercising pulse rate for your age group, as described in the chart a few paragraphs back? If it is, increase your workload by tightening the adjustment knob on your exerciser. Is your pulse rate too high? Reduce the tension. Experiment until your workload is adjusted so that you can maintain your exercising pulse rate at the level matched to your age group.

Note the setting on your tensioner knob and the speed on your speedometer while you are pedaling at 60-75 rpm. These readings will give you accurate gauges for measuring the intensity of your workout each day.

Work out on your stationary bike for 20 minutes a day, three to five times each week. Do this for a month and you'll begin to notice changes in your body. For example, after a few weeks of riding you'll find that your pulse rate at rest will be lower than before you started working out. As your capacity improves, you'll find that you'll have to keep increasing the tension on your adjustment knob in order to keep your pulse to the exercising pulse rate recommended for your age group. Check your pulse rate at least every two weeks. Make adjustments for new work levels as you continue to improve.

You can also raise your pulse rate by the speed at which you pedal. Increasing the duration of your workout—that is, the period of time you exercise each day—will also increase your endurance.

FOR OUTDOOR CYCLISTS ON INDOOR BIKES

If you are an outdoor cyclist using a stationary bike to keep up your training levels in the winter months, you'll want to adjust the workloads to fit higher cadences than we have instructed above: i.e., if you ordinarily train outdoors at 90-100 rpm, set the tension on your indoor machine so that you can maintain your aerobic pulse rate at that cadence.

Because the stationary bike maintains a constant tension, while outdoor cycling usually gives you opportunities to coast, an hour of indoor cycling is usually more strenuous than an hour outdoors. As a rule of thumb, estimate that half an hour indoors will be approximately the same as a full hour outdoors.

Most noncompetitive cyclists who are in top shape seem to agree that half an hour on the stationary bike, three to five times a week, keeps them in shape for their favorite sport. Competitive cyclists double that, working at higher cadences with more tension to build strength and endurance.

Rollers are used by most cyclists at various times and in various ways. At the track, or before a road race where space is limited, they are used to warm up for events. People train on rollers when the weather is bad or if there's not enough time to go out on the road. Use them to loosen up after a short cold outdoor session. Groups of rollers can be linked with dials for competition.

Either a road or a track bike can be used, but be sure to adjust the rollers to the wheelbase of your machine. The back wheel centers itself naturally between the two back rollers and the front axle should be directly above the axle of the front roller. If the front wheel is positioned too far back, the bike will wobble; if it is too far forward, you might ride right off the front when accelerating.

Wear full-length warm-up pants and a long-sleeved jersey when you ride the rollers. Place the rollers in a door frame or near a wall so that you can support yourself if necessary; you can use a chair for mounting. Ride in the usual training position with the hands on the top of the bars, not down on the hooks. You'll be able to breathe better and stay smoother on the bike.

Tires should be inflated a little more than would be normal for the road. Soft tires make the ride bouncy and mushy. Gearing for a road bike should be 52 x 14 or 53 x 14. On a track bike, use 49 or 50 x 14. Staying upright is just a matter of balance, and you will soon learn to ride no-hands.

When beginning, remember not to hold on too tight and don't panic. Falling doesn't really hurt when you're not going anywhere.

In cold weather, if you want to train seriously but can only get outdoors for short rides, it's good to use rollers during another part of the day. If you ride the road in the evening, for example, then use rollers in the morning. Spending half an hour or an hour on the rollers after coming in from a ride can help fitness.

Last Words

All the dietary ideas and suggestions offered previously apply equally to indoor cycling. Just as with outdoor cycle training, the physical demands of regular rigorous indoor cycling require that you treat your body kindly. That means reducing the amount of fatty foods and refined carbohydrates (white sugar and flour) in your diet and drinking plenty of fluids to replace those you lose in sweat as you exercise. For extra insurance, it doesn't hurt to take a vitamin/mineral supplement.

If there's a long stretch of time when you can't get out on your bike, perhaps four days or more, then you should get on rollers every day. Do a hard interval workout for an hour one day and a shorter, easier ride at moderate tempo for about half an hour on alternate days.

For a good one hour workout, start with a slow tempo and ride ten or 15 minutes until you are just starting to sweat. Then do 15 or 20 minutes of fast tempo, with the last five minutes extra fast. When you finish, you should be so exhausted that you can't go another 30 seconds at that pace. Roll slowly again for five minutes to rest. Then do 15 interval sprints, 30 seconds on and 30 seconds off. Spend another five minutes at slow tempo to finish the hour.

You should be quite tired at the end of this workout. If you are still getting in shape or don't have an hour to spend, cut down the number of minutes spent on each activity to make perhaps a 45-minute training session.

Roller racing is done with a track bike and the competition distance is usually one mile. The maximum gear allowed is 50 x 14 and maximum wheel size is 27 inches, with a minimum crank length of 165 millimeters. Tilt the hooks forward and upward to provide a more level surface on the top of the handlebars. Position yourself directly over the pedals for better spin by dropping the saddle and moving it forward. Be sure to have the ball of the foot directly over the axle of the pedal; this is a farther-back foot position than some road riders are used to.

More speed work is necessary if you plan to race on the rollers. The standard one-hour workout can be alternated with a more specialized routine. Begin with the warmup, then do five interval sprints of 15 seconds each with 30 seconds' rest between each one. Roll ten minutes then do a mile (about one minute) flat out; roll another ten minutes and do another one-mile sprint. If you're feeling all right, do this a third time as well, then end with ten minutes at a moderate tempo.

THE WEEKLY SCHEDULE

The weekly training schedule for a nationally ranked rider might go something like this:

Monday, after a Sunday race, a 50- to 65-mile ride in a fairly small gear of about 75 inches over fairly flat terrain.

Tuesday, a very rapid tempo ride of about an hour and a half in that same gear, very fast. You might warm up for 15 minutes and then just twiddle along, breathing and sweating for about half an hour, take a five-minute break, do another half hour, and then roll down easily for fifteen minutes.

Wednesday, another long ride. If you are fairly far along into the season, you might do over 100 miles, mostly in a small gear. If you had some nice stretches of road or were feeling good, you'd start going up into your racing gears (53 x 13, 14, 15, 16, etc.) for half an hour or so, just to get the feel of it.

Thursday, repeat what you did Tuesday.

Friday, 80 miles or so, not too hard. If you feel good, then step into it a little bit.

Saturday, before Sunday's race, an easy 40 miles just riding around.

Earlier in the season or.for juniors and women these distances can be halved, then gradually increased, depending upon the individual and category of his or her racing. The 100-mile ride might only be 60 miles, and Monday's 60 miles might be only 30. The tempo ride on Tuesday you probably wouldn't even do at all; you'd probably just go out and ride around.

If you're racing both Saturday and Sunday, your Friday ride would be a little easier. The best riders get on the bike every day; there's no off-day. But the day before a race you don't want to be knocking your brains out; that's why you do about 40 or 50 miles of nice riding, with a little bit of brisk effort in there just to feel good.

The only reason to spend any real leisure days is if your legs are tremendously heavy. Perhaps over the weekend you've ridden some super-hard races with great big gears and you're tired and disgusted. Then you might even take Monday off, and do 50 miles of easy riding on Tuesday.

When there are short club races or training races during the week, in the evening you should still get out in the morning and do some riding. Put in 35 to 40 miles of brisk pace in a small gear, about 75 inches. The little gear won't hurt you; it makes you breathe and work hard, but you recuperate. You recover immediately and it doesn't bother your legs.

The alternation of slow and fast and short and long days gives you different types of training. Long slow days work on leg muscles and take fat off the body. Short fast days are for the cardiovascular system and breathing. Both types of fitness are necessary for road racing. You have to be able to make a quick hard short attack, to sprint a little bit and be able to bridge gaps. But you have to be able to finish the race; your legs have to be in good shape at the end of the race, too.

A technique that is good for your cardiovascular system is interval training, which can be done during part of the ride. Intervals are used in training for many sports and can be described as a series of sprints that build up strength, tax the system, and teach recovery. You don't put out absolute maximum effort for each sprint because you'd be finished after two or three times. You use about three-quarter effort. The length of the sprint can be determined by time or by leg revolutions or by distance, and different people prefer different length intervals. I find that in cycling a good interval to choose is about 400 yards, or perhaps the length of four telephone poles alo the side of the road. A series of five or ten of these with equal amounts of rest in between can help build heart and lungs, endurance, and speed.

WHAT TIME OF DAY TO TRAIN

Ideally training should be done in the morning. Get up at 7:30, have breakfast at 8:00, and then go out on your ride an hour later at about 9:00. You can take another ride in the evening about 4:30. This is the ideal situation, of course, but people can't do that; they have to work. When I have things to do during the day, then I go out at 7:00 in the morning.

The morning seems to be a good time to train because, although by 9 o'clock it's arming up a little bit, the air is still fresh out and nice. It seems cleaner. By the end of the day it can get hot and there are a lot of auto fumes around. There is less wind in the morning, too; the wind seems to come up and go down with the sun.

Midday doesn't seem to be a good time to train, especially in the summer when it's hot. Also it's getting around lunchtime and you've either just eaten or you're getting hungry.

Evenings are nice for training, especially on the track. But often you can't pick and choose the ideal training time, and must make the best of your own situation. So be flexible.

Improvement makes straight roads; but the crooked roads without improvement are roads of genius.
—William Blake

INDIVIDUAL TRAINING SCHEDULE

Training is a building process. You start out with shorter rides and the tempo builds, the gears build and the mileage builds. All riders start out with basically the same training program, but part way through the season they begin to specialize. The road rider keeps on increasing his gears and his mileage (or, if he's doing a lot of hard racing, he's taking it easy between races), while the track rider, especially the sprinter, starts to cut down on his miles. He goes shorter road distances because when he climbs on his bike at the track his legs have got to be absolutely fresh.

The time to start specializing is dictated by the time when the specialty races are due to start. If they are important ones the rider might start six or seven weeks before.

The amount of training to do seems to depend on the toughness of the individual's character and physique. You could take two different people and put them on the same training program. One person goes out and does it and feels terrific, and he wants more. But the other can't go out and do it again or perform properly the next day. Perhaps he needs a little different schedule; he should cut down while the other man should do a little bit more.

Improvement is a long slow process and it's not a thing you can feel. When you first start training two weeks will go by and you don't even feel as fresh as when you started. It actually feels like you're down a little bit. But keep on doing it. It'll take four or five or six or seven weeks before you'll be able to go out there and feel like you can conquer the world.

After the weeks go by you're going better. You don't even realize it until all of a sudden one day you've made a tremendous ride in a big gear, which you couldn't have done a few weeks before and you still feel light on the pedals. Or on the track you're sprinting for three or four weeks and all of a sudden you don't even realize it but you're going faster.

The important thing is to get out and do something; not something that's making you exhausted every day, but something you can do again and again and again. Whether you're the kind of person who has to sit down and make up schedules and follow them or the kind of guy who likes to go out for long rides and just tempo away mile after mile, what's important is spending time on the bike.

When the races start coming along they're going to fill in the gaps that you've left in your own training. If you're not somebody who can sit down and see where your weaknesses are and work on them, the racing after a few weeks is going to fill in these gaps. Racing is an important part of training because you get all kinds of riding there, whether you like it or not.

CAN YOU OVER TRAIN

A person can get run down from not eating good food or not getting enough rest or sleep and so forth. You might get anemic, with a low blood count, and would have to eat foods that are going to help build up your red blood cells. Don't train hard until your blood count starts coming back up, because training in a weakened state is too frustrating; you tire quickly and get discouraged. Just go through the motions by doing a little riding, and visit a doctor. When your blood count improves, then you can increase your training and do a little more.

I don't think you can really hurt yourself by training, except that if you take a hundred-mile ride every day you might get a little bit tired. Or you might go out riding with someone who is fitter than you are and blow yourself apart for a couple of days. Then you would have to start building yourself up again by maybe taking a day off or a few real easy days. Get back into your regular schedule a few days later, when everything's back to normal.

If you go out and do something you're not ready for, you will feel the effects for several days. For example, if you take a tremendously long ride that you haven't built up to—say you've been doing 25 miles and you try 100—on that ride you might feel very light and very nice, especially in the first part of it. But if the miles just aren't in your legs, you can wind up with cramps—your legs just won't turn over. Your muscles are not conditioned to perform for that long.

You cannot train too much if you build up to it.

Cycling and Sex

Bicycling reduces sexual prowess!

From time to time riders have problems. The following letter describes one of the more extreme instances.

I have an unusual problem, I am 32, weigh 195 pounds and am in good physical shape. I began bicycling after a series of foot ailments caused by too much long-distance running. After moderate cycling for a couple of months, I went on a moderately paced tour of 700 miles in nine days. The only trouble that I encountered was that the plastic-molded seat that came on my bicycle was too hard. I seemed to have more than the usual tired rear end after one or two hours of riding. After the fifth day I then bought an Avocet Touring Seat, which I found very comfortable during the rest of the trip and had no more pain (especially to my pelvic bones) other than the usual discomfort which seems to be relieved by taking a five-minute rest break every two hours of riding or so. I never had the "numb crotch" syndrome.

Upon arriving home I found that I was unable to have an erection. I waited a month (no change), then went to a urologist who determined that I had no bladder or prostate problems. He stated that little was known about the exact mechanism of erections (for example, whether a chemical is released by one of the glands or if it is a stimulation by nerve impulses) except that some blood vessels seem to contract so that more blood flows into the penis than out. He told me just to wait and see for a return of natural functioning or come see him in six months. Now, two months later, I seem to have improved to a sort of feeble half-erection.

Have you any experience with this sort of dysfunction? Any explanation? Should I stop riding? I've only ridden twice since.

Here is the answer. You must have damaged the very last portion of the pelvic plexus nerve, which controls the blood circulation through the penis. There is nothing I know of that will speed up the regeneration of the nerve. I certainly do not advise cycling until healing is complete, but your change of saddle already may have solved the problem. The Avocet Touring saddle is probably helpful for this type of problem, as it is grooved in the area of the nerves and blood vessels. Make sure that you are riding on the posterior grooved portion, not on the tongue.

"After full function has been recovered, you should go back to cycling gradually, with initial rides of ten miles or less, followed by progressively longer rides until you are sure that there is no further damage to the nerve. I also advise getting down in a racing or semi-racing position, to take as much weight off the saddle as possible.

Do you need to lose some weight? Unfortunately, it is not possible to depend on a "numb crotch" or pain as warning signals, since it is possible to damage this nerve without any warning whatsoever. (If you're not okay by now, go to another urologist.)"

This sort of problem is the exception rather than the rule, however. Obviously, a person who is exhausted from bike riding is not at the moment the most enthusiastic sex partner, but the sense of well-being gained from a state of physical fitness may be an incentive to lovemaking. And the psychological benefits of bicycling—getting out in the fresh air, that exhilaration and feeling of freedom on a bike—help one's activities in general, including sexual activities.

Furthermore, it's been found that vigorous exercise actually stimulates the production of the hormone that scientists feel is responsible for the male sex drive in the first place—testosterone.

Dr. J. R. Sutton of the Garvan Institute of Medical Research in Australia measured testosterone levels in two groups of men (athletes and nonathletes) before, during and after a period of vigorous exercise. He found that the levels of this hormone were greatest *after* the workouts, and that they were higher in the athletes than in the nonathletes.

These findings can be explained by the fact that testosterone is important in muscular activity. The hormone makes it easier for muscles to store glycogen, their favorite fuel, and so the more active your muscles are, the more testosterone you are likely to have at your disposal—for exercise or sex.

Just because one man has a higher level of testosterone than another, that he will necesarily have a higher level of sexual function. But it seems reasonable to assume that a man who raises his testosterone level may have a higher level of sexual function than he had before. Of course, psychological factors can enter in here, too.

Now the following is an account of just how much the psychological benefits of his riding as opposed to the physical ones are responsible for the change in this man. It is probably a combination of increased physical vigor, fitness, and testosterone, and psychological well-being, too.

At any rate, a Japanese doctor, Rokuro Koike, who had been a bicycle racer in his youth, took a teaching position at age 47 in a medical college in Tokyo. He decided to commute by bicycle, though at first a daily trip of 40 kilometers (24.8 miles) both ways was too strenuous. So he cycled two or three times a week and used public transit the rest of the time. As he got in shape he increased the frequency gradually until seven years later he finally reached his goal, pedaling to work and back home every weekday.

Thus far, there was nothing unusual. But what he discovered, to his and his wife's pleasant surprise, was that he was making love more often than before and with greater vigor than when he was first married. He confided that the frequency had increased to two or three times a week, whereas until two years before it had been once or twice.

So how do you maintain your potency after 50? According to Dr. Koike, the basic requirement is to improve your general physical condition through well-balanced nutrition combined with proper exercise. Understandably, he has said that exercise twice a day is the charm, with bicycling being particularly effective. Why? One of his theories is that the testes are cooled as you breeze along the road, which is certainly true in cooler weather. The position of the cyclist on the bicycle, if he takes a crouched position, means the wind hits his front and is funneled between his legs and around the saddle. (In fact, it's important for a cyclist in the wintertime not just to wear a pair of leg warmers but to wear sweat pants or something to keep the entire crotch area warm.) And the testes do function better in making sperm when they are a few degrees cooler than body temperature.

As far as cycling is concerned, there is probably a good bit of truth to the saying, "If it feels good, do it."

Where Do You Get Started?

To become a serious contender in the world of bicycle racing, you must train 12 months out of the year. This means riding 50 to 150 miles a day, five to seven days a week, regardless of the weather. When you absolutely can't train because of snow or ice, get on an indoor bicycle or take up an alternative sport such as speed-skating, which develops leg muscles that are important in bicycling and maintains the capacity of the cardiovascular system. Weight lifting or weight training is also popular with serious competitive cyclists.

There are many opportunities open for the aspiring cycle racer. Bicycle clubs in your community sponsor races and/or training rides. You can get the names of local clubs through your bike shop or by writing to:

Bicycle Institute of America
122 East 42nd Street
New York, NY 10017

In the U.S., the League of American Wheelmen sponsors both local and national bicycling events. Membership in that club provides you with a monthly magazine of touring and racing events. Write to:

League of American Wheelmen
10E. Read St.
Baltimore, MD 21202

Information about the Olympic bike-racing programs, the Amateur Athletic Union, and the Union Cycliste Internationale (the world governing body for bike racing) is available from:

Untied States Cycling Federation
Box 669
Wall Street Station
New York, NY 10005

or:

Velo-News
Box 1257
Brattleboro, VT 05301

Names and addresses of local bike clubs change from year to year as new officers are elected. For this reason, you should ask at your local bike shop for the most current information and addresses of clubs in your area. Most bike shops have a bulletin board on which are posted cycling events and the dates of club meetings.

United States Triathlon Association
P.O. Box 7708
Burbank California 91510

Bibliography

Following are a few of the many helpful books available for further information on bicycle racing, bike maintenance, physiology, diet and the activities that help make up a good winter program for cyclists: weight training, running and cross-country skiing.

All About Bicycle Racing. Mountain View, CA: World Publications, 1975.
Anderson, Robert. *Stretching*. Box 1002, Englewood, CO 80110. 1975.
Ballantine, Richard. *Richard's Bicycle Book*. New York: Ballantine Books, 1974.
Burke, Edmund. *Toward an Understanding of Human Performance*. Ithaca, NY: Movement Publications, 1977.
Caldwell, John. *The Cross-Country Ski Book*. Brattleboro, VT: Stephen Greene Press, 1981.
Cycling. Central Sports School (CONI). Rome, Italy: 1972.
DeLong, Fred. *DeLong's Guide to Bicycles and Bicycling: The Art and Science*. Radnor, PA: Chilton, 1978.
Fixx, James. *The Complete Book of Running*. New York: Random House, 1977.
Food for Fitness. Mountain View, CA: World Publications, 1975.
Inside the Cyclist. Brattleboro, VT: *Velo-news*, 1979.
Kolin, M. and D. de la Rosa. *The Custom Bicycle*. Emmaus, PA: Rodale Press, 1979.
Kolin, M. and D. de la Rosa. *Understanding, Maintaining and Riding the Ten-Speed Bicycle*. Emmaus, PA: Rodale Press, 1979.
McCullagh, James, Ed. *American Bicycle Racing*. Emmaus, PA: Rodale Press, 1976.
Mirkin, G. and M. Hoffman. *The Sports Medicine Book*. Boston: Little, Brown and Co., 1978.
Osler, Tom. *Serious Runner's Handbook*. Mountain View, CA: World Publications, 1978.
Reynolds, Bill. *Complete Weight Training Book*. Mountain View, CA: World Publications, 1976.
Simes, Jack. *Winning Bicycle Racing*. Chicago: Contemporary Books, Inc., 1976.

Periodicals

American Cyclist, Box 11628, Milwaukee, WI 53211. General interest cycling plus some cross-country skiing. Twelve issues per year.
American Wheelmen, Box 988, Baltimore, MD 21203. Official publication of the League of American Wheelmen (LAW), the organization for serious tourists. Sent to all members; not available by subscription. Twelve issues per year.
Bicycling, 33 E. Minor St., Emmaus, PA 18049. Covers all aspects of bicycle riding and equipment. Nine issues per year.
Cycling USA, c/o U.S. Cycling Federation, 175 E. Boulder St., Colorado Springs, CO 80909. Official USCF publication sent to all licensed riders and also available by subscription. Twelve issues per year.
Velo-news, Box 1257, Brattleboro, VT 05301. Photos, news articles and features about national and international racing, including calendar of events and results. Eighteen issues per year.

Bibliography

Ald, Roy. *Cycling: The Rhythmic, Respiratory Way to Physical Fitness.* New York: Grosset & Dunlap, 1968.

Alth, Max. *All about Bikes and Bicycling: Care, Repair, and Safety.* New York: Hawthorn Books, 1972.

Arkhipov, Evgenii, and Sedov, A. *Na Olimpiiskih Trekah* [On Olympic Tracks]. Moscow: Sovietskaya Rossiya, 1961.

———. *Odnodnevnye Shosseinye Gonki*]Short, One Day Road Pursuits]. Moscow: Fizikultura i Sport, 1960.

———. *Velosipenye Gonki po Shosse* [Bicycle Pursuit on the Road]. Moscow: Fizikultura i Sport, 1958.

Asa, Warren. *American Youth Hostels' North American Bicycle Atlas.* 3rd ed. New York: American Youth Hostels, 1973.

Ballantine, Richard. *Richard's Bicycle Book.* New York: Ballantine Books, 1974.

Technical Mechanical Glossary

Agrati—an Italian company that produces many frame-building parts such as bottom brackets, lugs, and dropouts.

anodized—metal subjected to electrolytic action to coat it with a protective and/or decorative finish.

baking oven—a large structure with variable temperature controls that is used to bake paint finishes on bicycle frames.

balloon tire—a tire 2 or more inches wide with a low pressure capacity.

Bearing race—the circle that the balls in bearing cones and cups make as they contact the axle.

Bivalent hub—a Cinelli-designed hub for bicycle wheels. Bivalent hubs permit a quick rear-wheel change since the freewheel remains with the frame—not with the hub. Front and rear wheels are interchangeable. Unfortunately, because of high production costs, Cino Cinelli has withdrawn the hubs from the market.

bottom bracket—a short round tube on a bicycle frame to which the down tube, seat tube, and chainstays have been brazed or welded.

bottom bracket cup—a part of the bottom bracket bearings that screws into the frame's bottom bracket and in which the crank axle's bearings run.

bottom tube (on tandem)—tube connecting the two cranksets.

brazing—a process by which two metal surfaces are joined by means of heating and melting a third substance such as brass or silver.

brazing with pins—the use of "nails" in frame construction to keep the tubes in the proper position in the lugs.

bronze brazing—melting bronze in order to join two metal surfaces that have higher melting temperatures than the bronze.

Brox—French brazing material used in frame building.

butted tubing—catchall term given to all tubes that are either double butted, single butted, or taper gauge.
  a. double butted—refers to a tube that is thicker at the ends than in the middle without an increase in its outside diameter.
  b. single butted—same as double butted, except only one end is thicker.
  c. taper gauge—refers to a tube whose thickness is gradually diminished through highly mechanized industrial operations. Forks are always either taper gauge or straight gauge; they are never double butted or single butted.*Campi*

Campi—term used when referring to components made by S.P.A. Brevetti Internazionali Campagnolo.

carbon fiber—a chemical term which refers to a composite of fibers of a pure element, in this case carbon, that are woven and distributed randomly and are bound together to form a strong lightweight material.

cast bottom bracket—a bottom bracket that is formed in a mold and, as a result, does not have a seam.

caster—a word used interchangeably with tail and trail. Caster angle is formed by the intersection of a vertical line drawn through the front fork ends and a line which is parallel to the head tube and is extended to the wheelbase.

cast lug—a bicycle lug that is formed in a mold and, consequently, does not have seams.

Solitude is as needful to the imagination as society is wholesome for the character. —*James Russell Lowell*

cast seat lug—seatpost lug molded to precision.

century—100-mile ride.

chainstays—two tubes which go from the bottom bracket to the rear dropouts.

chrome plating—applying a thin coating of chromium on frames or other bicycle parts.

cold setting—aligning frame while it is cold (after brazing).

Columbus—Italian-produced special frame tubing.

cone and locknut—bearing parts that attach to axle on which bearings run around. The nut is screwed down hard on another nut to prevent slacking back.

Continental fork section—refers to wide oval fork blades.

copper-tacked or coppered—initial step in frame-building procedures in which tubes and lugs are held together by torchin copper.

crankarm—rotating portion which holds the pedal.

criterium—a multilap road race that is held on a short circuit varying in length from one to ten miles. The criterium course utilizes public roads that are temporarily closed to normal traffic. This race is designed to allow the spectator to see the riders as they pass by each lap.

custom frame—bicycle frame that is built by an artisan to fit the various needs of the individual customer.

cyclo-cross—cross-country race event on special course featuring obstacles.

derailleur—a mechanical device that is bolted to the bicycle frame. Its purpose is to shift (or derail) the chain from one gear to another, allowing variable gear ratios.

down tube—that part of the bicycle frame which connects the bottom of the head tube with the bottom bracket.

drop-forged handlebar stem—stem made from aluminum alloy and forged to shape under high pressure.

dropouts—slots into which the front and fear wheels fit.

ergonomics—biotechnology or the application of biological and engineering data to problems related to man and machine.

faced bottom bracket—edges of the bottom bracket are faced with a special tool to make sure that they are squared.

facing—squaring edges with a special tool.

flash-weld—using heavy electrical current at high speed an frequency to weld tubes.

flat top crown—a fork crown on which the top part is flat.

fork—that part of the bicycle that holds the front wheel in place and is attached to the frame by the headset. The fork assembly includes a fork steering column, a fork crown, fork blade and the fork dropouts. There are three types: semi-sloping, fully sloping, and flat.

fork blades—curved tubes that connect the fork crown to the front dropouts which hold the front wheel in place.

fork crown—that part of the fork that attaches the fork blades to the fork steering column.

    a. stamped or pressed—fork crown which has been cut, bent, and stamped into shape by a die.

    b. forged—a fork crown that is produced with the grain of the steel "in line" by heating and hammering with highly refined machines.

    c. cast—similar to the cast lugs and the cast bottom bracket, the cast fork crown is formed in a mold and, as a result, does not have a seam.

fork rake—each bicycle fork is bent or curved on the bottom, just before it attaches to the fork dropouts. The fork rake is the amount the tube is bent.

freewheel—a mechanism with one, two, three, four, five, six, or even seven individual sprockets with varying numbers of teeth on each sprocket. The freewheel threads onto the rear hub and, together with the chain and crankset, permits the rider to propel his bicycle. The various number of teeth on the freewheel sprockets determines the gear ratios for a particular bicycle. The name "freewheel" is given to this gear mechanism because it is built to enable the rider to coast when not pedaling, as opposed to a direct-driven mechanism which requires the cyclist to pedal all the time.

front-wheel expander brake—brake with a hub shell and an internal expanding brake shoe.

gear ratio—To calculate a gear ratio, multiply the diameter of the wheel in inches by the number of teeth on the front chainwheel and then divide by the number of teeth on the rear sprocket. For a 10-speed these calculations must be done ten different times; once for each of the different chainwheel/freewheel sprocket combinations. Gear ratios can also be calculated in meters.

glass beading—cleaning the surface of a metal with tiny glass beads propelled by a jet of compressed air.

Haden blank—an oversize lug manufactured by Haden Brothers, Limited, of Birmingham, England. It is intended for the builder who wishes to file the lug to a final shape that varies from those commercially available.

hanger bracket—another name for bottom bracket.

head angle—refers to the angle which is formed by drawing a straight line through the head tube to the ground.

headset—parts of bearing mechanism in the head tube that secure the fork to the main triangle.

high-wheeler—bicycles of the late 1800s with large-diameter front wheels (approximately 50 inches) and smaller-diameter rear wheels (approximately 17 inches), straight handlebars, and spokes radiating directly from the hub (no crossover); vehicle was mounted via a small step above the rear wheel.

hot setting—aligning frame while it is still hot.

investment cast lug—mold is made of lug to precision then filled with wax. The wax is melted out, leaving the mold to be filled with the material for the lug.

Italian section fork—a term synonymous with the large, sectioned fork blades.

jig—a metal fixture that firmly holds various frame parts while the builder brazes them together.

lug—metal sleeve that holds the frame tubes at the joints.

lug cutout—designed pattern that is incorporated into the lug.

main triangle—that part of the frame which is made up of the head tube, top tube, seat tube, and the down tube.

mandrel—a spindle or metal bar around which tubes are shaped.

mass start race—any race on either the track or road where the competitors start at the same time.

microfusione—term used in describing investment cast products.

mitered tube—a tube which has been precisely cut so that the entire diameter of the tube sits flush against the tube it butts up against.

Nervex—the brand name of quality lugs, bottom brackets, and fork crowns produced by the French company Ets. Aimé Dubois in Yssingeaux, France.

pannier—saddlebag that is mounted on a bicycle by means of a carrier over the rear or front wheel. It is generally constructed of heavy-duty canvas or reinforced nylon.

pinning—drilling holes through tubes and lugs and inserting wire pins or "nails" to hold alignment during brazing.

pinstriping—decorative paint trimming on tubes.

plain gauge tubing—tubes in which the walls are of uniform thickness.

pressed steel lug—a lug which has been cut, bent, and stamped into shape by a die.

Prugnat—the brand name of quality lugs, bottom brackets, and fork crowns produced by the French company of the same name located in Moret-sur-Loing, France.

pursuit—track race with two competitors (individuals or teams) starting simultaneously on opposite sides of the track and trying to catch one another.

quick-release mechanism—a device used to quickly tighten or loosen a cable, wheel, or seat without the use of any wrenches.

racing frame—a frame designed for performance rather than comfort.

Reynolds tubing—the name of the tubing produced by TI Reynolds, the world's largest manufacturer of quality bicycle tubing.

    a. 531DB—tubing made of manganese-molybdenum steel. This designation usually refers to the fact that the entire frame is built with the appropriate butted tubings.

    b. 531SL—same as the 531DB except that the gauges are lighter, making the tubing "Special Lightweight."

    c. 753—also a manganese-molybdenum steel butted tubing. The tubing wall has been reduced in thickness to make it lighter than the 531SL, yet its composition makes it 50 percent stronger. A frame built with 753 is generally 20 percent lighter than one built with 531SL.

ring-braze—inserting a ring of brass between the tube and the lug when brazing.

Roto—an Italian firm that produces frame-building parts such as fork crowns, lugs, and bottom brackets; especially known for their investment cast products.

saddle angle—the tilt of the saddle as it is positioned on the seatpost.

saddle height—the distance from the top of the saddle to the top of the pedal when it is near the bottom of its rotation as it is in line with the seat tube.

safety bicycle—bicycle with wheels of equal size and with a chain gearing setup so that the wheels go faster than the pedals.

seatstays—two tubes that run from the top of the seat tube to the rear dropouts.

    a. fully wrap—seatstays that are attached and wrapped around the front of the seat lug as far as possible. The two ends of the seatstays are then connected by filling the space with braze.

    b. semi-wrap—seatstays are attached to the side of the seat lug.

    c. fastback—seatstays that butt up against the seat tube or are attached to the rear of the seat lug.

seat tube—the tube running from the top tube to the down tube.

seat tube angle—the angle formed by the seat tube and the ground.

sew-up tire,—a tire in which the inner tube has been stitched inside the tire's casing. This tire is always glued onto the rim.

side-loading—force perpendicular to center line of frame caused by off-center foot pressure on the pedals.

Sifbronze—name used when referring to brazing materials made by Sifbronze, a division of Suffolk Lawn Mowers, Limited, in Suffolk, England.

silver solder—any braze material with a high mixture of silver.

spoke nipple—tip that is inserted through the rim and is threaded onto the spoke.

spot tack—joining the lugs and tubes together by brazing in various spots before a final brazing of the joint. This method is used as a preliminary step in the brazing process since it allows for easy corrections if any misalignment is noted.

standard drawn tubing—tubing accurately sized by drawing over a mandrel.

stove-enamel finish—another name for a baked-on enamel finish.

stress—a force being applied on a frame and the frame's ability to resist it.

Super Vitus—quality butted tubing produced by Ateliers de la Rive in Sainte Chamond, France.

tack brazing—same as spot tacking.

tensile strength—the greatest stress a substance can bear without disintegrating or breaking.

threads—the size and number of threads per inch that appear on a fork column and in the bottom bracket.

    a. English—an English fork column has a headset with a 1-inch opening and 24 threads per inch (1″ x 24 tpi). An English bottom bracket has cups that are 1.370 inches wide with 24 threads per inch (1.370″ x 24 tpi). The adjustable cup has right-handed threads while the fixed cup has left-handed threads. English-threaded components are sometimes referred to as having BSC threads.

    b. French—a French fork column requires a headset with a 25-mm. opening with 1 thread per millimeter or 25.4 threads per inch (25 mm. x 1.0 mm.). A French bottom bracket has cups that are 35 mm. wide with 25.4 threads per inch (35 mm. x 1.0 mm.). Both the adjustable and the fixed cups have right-handed threads.

    c. Italian—an Italian-threaded fork column would require a headset with a 25.4-mm. opening with 24 threads per inch (25.4 mm. x 24 tpi). An Italian bottom bracket has cups that are 36 mm. wide with 24 threads per inch (36 mm. x 24 tpi). Both the adjustable and the fixed cups have right-handed threads.

    d. Swiss—same as French threads except the fixed cup on the bottom bracket has left-handed threads.

titanium—a grey, lightweight metal used in frame construction and in the manufacture of high-quality components.

toe clip—metal piece attached to front of pedal which secures the foot, and together with a strap, buckles around the middle of the foot for increased pedaling efficiency.

top eye—small fitting that is inserted and brazed on semi-wrapped seatstays.

top tube—the tube on a frame that connects the head tube to the seat tube.

touring frame—frame designed for comfort and stability when laden with touring packs.

tracking—making sure that wheels are both in a direct line and parallel from front to rear.

tubing gauge—the thickness of tubes.

tubular tire—another name for a sew-up tire.

wheelbase—the distance from the center of the bicycle's front wheel to the center of its rear wheel.

Biking Bibliography

Bicycling Book, John Marino, Lawrence May, and Hal Z. Bennett. J.P. Tarcher, Inc. 9110 Sunset Blvd. Los Angeles, California, 90069, 1981.

Beginning Bicycle Racing, Fred Matheny.. Whitman Press Inc. Lebanon, New Hampshire, 1980.

The Custom Bicycle, Michael J. Kolin and Denise M. de la Rosa. Rodale Press. Emmaus, Pennsylvania, 1979.

The Practical Book of Bicycling, Frances Call with Merle E. Dowd. Elsevier-Dutton Publishing Co., Inc. 2 Park Avenue, New York, New York, 10016, 1981.

Winning, Jack Simes. Contemporary Books, Inc. 180 North Michigan Ave. Chicago, Illinois, 60601, 1976.

The Bicycle Racing Book, William Sanders. Quality Books Inc. Northbrook, Ill. 60062.

Publications

"American Wheelman", 8053 Sykes Rd. Richmond, Virginia, 23235.

"Bicycling", 33 E. Minor St., Emmaus, Pennsylvania, 18049.

"American Cyclist", P.O. Box 11628, Milwaukee, Wisconsin, 53211.

"Bicycle Forum", P.O. Box 8311-K, Missoula, MT, 59807.

"Velo-News", Box 1257, Brattleboro, Vermont, 05301.

"Cycling USA", 1750 E. Boulder, Colorado Springs, CO, 80909. (The United States Cycling Federation newspaper)

"Bicycle Paper", Box 842, Seattle, Washington, 98111.

"The Law Bulletin", League of American Wheelman, Box 988, Baltimore, Maryland, 21203.

Organizations

Bicycle Institute of America, 122 East 42nd St. New York, NY, 10017.

League of American Wheelman, 10 E. Read Street, Baltimore, MD, 21202.

United States Cycling Federation, Box 669, Wall Street Station, New York, New York, 10005.

American Bicycling Association, P.O. Box 718, Chandler, AZ, 85224.

International Bicycling Touring Society, 846 Prospect Street, La Jolla, CA, 92307.

Further Readings

Bicycle Frames, Building Bicycles Wheels, Complete Bicycle Time Trailing Book and *Serious Cycling for the Beginner* are available through Anderson World, Inc. 1400 Stierlin Road, Mountain View, CA 94043.

"The authors are indebted to Michael J. Kolin and Denise M. de la Rosa and Rodale Press for permission to reprint portions of 'The Custom Bicycle'. The bottom illustration on page 350, portions of the text on pages 356, 357, 359, 360, 361, 419, 420, 421, 422 and 432, the Bibliography on page 396, and the Technical Mechanical Glossary on pages 396-399 used in this book are taken from 'The Custom Bicycle copyright 1979, by Michael J. Kolin and Denise M. de la Rosa, published by Rodale Press, Inc., Emmaus, PA 18049."

Today I have grown taller from walking with the trees. —Karle Wilson (Mrs. Thomas Ellis Baker)

The longing to be primitive is a disease of culture. —George Santayana

Sylviane Puntous of Montreal, Canada seals her second crown in the Women's Division of the 1984 Ironman Triathlon World Championship with a record time of 10:25:13. Her twin sister Patricia finished less than two minutes later taking second place.

No. of Teeth on Chain-wheel	12	13	14	15	16	17	18	19	20	No. of Teeth
24	2.00	1.85	1.71	1.60	1.50	1.41	1.33	1.26	1.20	
25	2.08	1.92	1.79	1.67	1.56	1.47	1.39	1.32	1.25	
26	2.17	2.00	1.86	1.73	1.63	1.53	1.44	1.37	1.30	
27	2.25	2.07	1.93	1.80	1.69	1.59	1.50	1.42	1.35	
28	2.33	2.15	2.00	1.87	1.75	1.65	1.56	1.47	1.40	
29	2.42	2.23	2.07	1.93	1.81	1.71	1.61	1.53	1.45	
30	2.50	2.31	2.14	2.00	1.88	1.76	1.67	1.58	1.50	
31	2.58	2.38	2.21	2.07	1.94	1.82	1.72	1.63	1.55	
32	2.67	2.46	2.29	2.13	2.00	1.88	1.78	1.68	1.60	
33	2.75	2.54	2.36	2.20	2.06	1.94	1.83	1.74	1.65	
34	2.83	2.62	2.43	2.27	2.13	2.00	1.89	1.79	1.70	
35	2.92	2.69	2.50	2.33	2.19	2.06	1.94	1.84	1.75	
36	3.00	2.77	2.57	2.40	2.25	2.12	2.00	1.89	1.80	
37	3.08	2.85	2.64	2.47	2.31	2.18	2.06	1.95	1.85	
38	3.17	2.92	2.71	2.53	2.38	2.24	2.11	2.00	1.90	
39	3.25	3.00	2.79	2.60	2.44	2.29	2.17	2.05	1.95	
40	3.33	3.08	2.86	2.67	2.50	2.35	2.22	2.11	2.00	
41	3.42	3.15	2.93	2.73	2.56	2.41	2.28	2.16	2.05	
42	3.50	3.23	3.00	2.80	2.63	2.47	2.33	2.21	2.10	
43	3.58	3.31	3.07	2.87	2.69	2.53	2.39	2.26	2.15	
44	3.67	3.38	3.14	2.93	2.75	2.59	2.44	2.32	2.20	
45	3.75	3.46	3.21	3.00	2.81	2.65	2.50	2.37	2.25	
46	3.83	3.54	3.29	3.07	2.88	2.71	2.56	2.42	2.30	
47	3.92	3.62	3.36	3.13	2.94	2.76	2.61	2.47	2.35	
48	4.00	3.69	3.43	3.20	3.00	2.82	2.67	2.53	2.40	
49	4.08	3.77	3.50	3.27	3.06	2.88	2.72	2.58	2.45	
50	4.17	3.85	3.57	3.33	3.13	2.94	2.78	2.63	2.50	
51	4.25	3.92	3.64	3.40	3.19	3.00	2.83	2.68	2.55	
52	4.33	4.00	3.71	3.47	3.25	3.06	2.89	2.74	2.60	
53	4.42	4.08	3.79	3.53	3.31	3.12	2.94	2.79	2.65	
54	4.50	4.15	3.86	3.60	3.38	3.18	3.00	2.84	2.70	
55	4.58	4.23	3.93	3.67	3.44	3.24	3.06	2.89	2.75	
56	4.67	4.31	4.00	3.73	3.50	3.29	3.11	2.95	2.80	

Gear Ratios

21	22	23	24	25	26	27	28	29	30	No. of Teeth on Chain-wheel
1.14	1.09	1.04	1.00	.96	.92	.89	.86	.83	.80	24
1.19	1.14	1.09	1.04	1.00	.96	.93	.89	.86	.83	25
1.24	1.18	1.13	1.08	1.04	1.00	.96	.93	.90	.87	26
1.29	1.23	1.17	1.13	1.08	1.04	1.00	.96	.93	.90	27
1.33	1.27	1.22	1.17	1.12	1.08	1.04	1.00	.97	.93	28
1.38	1.32	1.26	1.21	1.16	1.12	1.07	1.04	1.00	.97	29
1.43	1.36	1.30	1.25	1.20	1.15	1.11	1.07	1.03	1.00	30
1.48	1.41	1.35	1.29	1.24	1.19	1.15	1.11	1.07	1.03	31
1.52	1.45	1.39	1.33	1.28	1.23	1.19	1.14	1.10	1.07	32
1.57	1.50	1.43	1.38	1.32	1.27	1.22	1.18	1.14	1.10	33
1.62	1.55	1.48	1.42	1.36	1.31	1.26	1.21	1.17	1.13	34
1.67	1.59	1.52	1.46	1.40	1.35	1.30	1.25	1.21	1.17	35
1.71	1.64	1.57	1.50	1.44	1.38	1.33	1.29	1.24	1.20	36
1.76	1.68	1.61	1.54	1.48	1.42	1.37	1.32	1.28	1.23	37
1.81	1.73	1.65	1.58	1.52	1.46	1.41	1.36	1.31	1.27	38
1.86	1.77	1.70	1.63	1.56	1.50	1.44	1.39	1.34	1.30	39
1.90	1.82	1.74	1.67	1.60	1.54	1.48	1.43	1.38	1.33	40
1.95	1.86	1.78	1.71	1.64	1.58	1.52	1.46	1.41	1.37	41
2.00	1.91	1.83	1.75	1.68	1.62	1.56	1.50	1.45	1.40	42
2.05	1.95	1.87	1.79	1.72	1.65	1.59	1.54	1.48	1.43	43
2.10	2.00	1.91	1.83	1.76	1.69	1.63	1.57	1.52	1.47	44
2.14	2.05	1.96	1.88	1.80	1.73	1.67	1.61	1.55	1.50	45
2.19	2.09	2.00	1.92	1.84	1.77	1.70	1.64	1.59	1.53	46
2.24	2.14	2.04	1.96	1.88	1.81	1.74	1.68	1.62	1.57	47
2.29	2.18	2.09	2.00	1.92	1.85	1.78	1.71	1.66	1.60	48
2.33	2.23	2.13	2.04	1.96	1.88	1.81	1.75	1.69	1.63	49
2.38	2.27	2.17	2.08	2.00	1.92	1.85	1.79	1.72	1.67	50
2.43	2.32	2.22	2.13	2.04	1.96	1.89	1.82	1.76	1.70	51
2.48	2.36	2.26	2.17	2.08	2.00	1.93	1.86	1.79	1.73	52
2.52	2.41	2.30	2.21	2.12	2.04	1.96	1.89	1.83	1.77	53
2.57	2.45	2.35	2.25	2.16	2.08	2.00	1.93	1.86	1.80	54
2.62	2.50	2.39	2.29	2.20	2.12	2.04	1.96	1.89	1.83	55
2.67	2.55	2.43	2.33	2.24	2.15	2.07	2.00	1.93	1.87	56

Selected Inch-Wheel Numbers for Gear Ratios

Gear Ratio	Inch-Wheel Number 26-Inch	Inch-Wheel Number 27-Inch	Gear Ratio	Inch-Wheel Number 26-Inch	Inch-Wheel Number 27-Inch
.80	(21) 20.8	(22) 21.6	1.73	(45) 45.0	46.7
.86	(22) 22.4	(23) 23.2	1.74	45.2	(47) 46.9
.89	(23) 23.2	(24) 24.0	1.77	(46) 46.0	47.7
.92	(24) 23.9	(25) 24.8	1.78	46.3	(48) 48.0
.96	(25) 25.0	(26) 25.9	1.81	(47) 47.0	48.8
1.00	(26) 26.0	(27) 27.0	1.82	47.3	(49) 49.0
1.04	(27) 27.0	(28) 28.1	1.85	(48) 48.1	(50) 49.9
1.07	(28) 27.8	(29) 28.9	1.89	(49) 49.2	(51) 51.0
1.11	(29) 28.9	(30) 30.0	1.93	(50) 50.2	(52) 52.0
1.15	(30) 29.9	(31) 31.1	1.96	(51) 51.0	(53) 52.9
1.19	(31) 31.0	(32) 32.1	2.00	(52) 52.0	(54) 54.0
1.23	(32) 32.0	(33) 33.2	2.04	(53) 53.1	(55) 55.0
1.26	(33) 32.8	(34) 34.0	2.08	(54) 54.1	(56) 56.1
1.30	(34) 33.8	(35) 35.1	2.11	(55) 54.9	(57) 56.9
1.33	(35) 34.6	(36) 35.9	2.15	(56) 55.9	(58) 58.0
1.37	(36) 35.6	(37) 37.0	2.19	(57) 57.0	(59) 59.1
1.41	(37) 36.6	(38) 38.1	2.23	(58) 58.0	(60) 60.2
1.46	(38) 38.0	(39) 39.4	2.26	58.8	(61) 61.0
1.48	(39) 38.5	(40) 40.0	2.27	(59) 59.0	61.3
1.52	39.6	(41) 41.0	2.30	(60) 59.9	(62) 62.0
1.54	(40) 40.0	41.5	2.33	60.6	(63) 62.8
1.56	40.6	(42) 42.1	2.35	(61) 61.1	63.4
1.58	(41) 41.1	42.6	2.37	61.6	(64) 63.9
1.59	41.3	(43) 42.9	2.38	(62) 61.9	64.2
1.60	(42) 41.6	(43) 43.1	2.41	62.7	(65) 65.0
1.63	42.4	(44) 44.0	2.42	(63) 63.0	65.3
1.66	(43) 43.1	44.8	2.45	63.7	(66) 66.1
1.67	43.4	(45) 45.1	2.46	(64) 64.0	66.4
1.69	(44) 44.0	45.6	2.48	64.5	(67) 66.9
1.70	44.2	(46) 45.9	2.50	(65) 65.0	67.4
2.52	65.5	(68) 68.0	3.50	(91) 91.0	(94) 94.4
2.54	(66) 66.0	68.5	3.53	91.8	(95) 95.3
2.56	66.5	(69) 69.0	3.54	(92) 92.0	95.6

Selected Inch-Wheel Numbers for Gear Ratios (Continued)

Gear Ratio	Inch-Wheel Number 26-Inch	Inch-Wheel Number 27-Inch	Gear Ratio	Inch-Wheel Number 26-Inch	Inch-Wheel Number 27-Inch
2.58	(67) 67.0	69.5	3.57	92.8	(96) 96.2
2.60	67.5	(70) 70.1	3.58	(93) 93.0	96.5
2.62	(68) 68.1	70.6	3.60	93.5	(97) 97.0
2.63	68.4	(71) 70.9	3.62	(94) 94.0	97.6
2.67	(69) 69.4	(72) 72.0	3.64	(95) 94.6	(98) 98.2
2.69	(70) 70.0	72.5	3.67	95.5	(99) 99.0
2.71	70.5	(73) 73.0	3.69	(96) 96.0	99.5
2.73	(71) 71.0	73.6	3.71	96.5	(100) 100.0
2.75	71.5	(74) 74.1	3.73	(97) 97.0	100.5
2.77	(72) 72.0	74.7	3.75	97.5	(101) 101.2
2.78	72.3	(75) 75.0	3.77	(98) 98.0	101.9
2.81	(73) 73.0	75.7	3.79	(99) 98.5	(102) 102.4
2.82	73.3	(76) 76.0	3.85	(100) 100.0	(104) 104.0
2.84	(74) 73.9	76.5	3.92	(102) 102.0	(106) 106.0
2.86	74.4	(77) 77.0	4.00	(104) 104.0	(108) 108.0
2.89	(75) 75.1	(78) 77.9	4.08	(106) 106.0	(110) 110.1
2.92	(76) 76.0	78.8	4.15	(108) 108.0	(112) 112.0
2.93	76.2	(79) 79.0	4.17	(109) 108.5	(113) 112.7
2.95	(77) 76.7	(80) 79.6	4.23	(110) 110.0	(114) 114.1
3.00	(78) 78.0	(81) 81.0	4.25	110.4	(115) 115.0
3.06	(79) 79.5	(82) 82.5	4.31	(112) 112.5	(116) 116.4
3.08	(80) 80.0	(83) 83.0	4.33	(113) 113.0	(117) 117.0
3.11	(81) 80.9	(84) 83.9	4.42	(115) 115.2	(119) 119.2
3.15	(82) 82.0	(85) 85.0	4.50	(117) 117.0	(122) 121.5
3.19	(83) 83.0	(86) 86.0	4.58	(119) 119.0	(124) 123.7
3.23	(84) 84.0	(87) 87.1	4.67	(122) 122.0	(126) 126.0
3.27	(85) 85.0	(88) 88.1			
3.31	(86) 86.0	88.2			
3.33	(87) 86.5	(89) 88.7			
3.38	(88) 87.9	(91) 91.1			
3.42	(89) 89.0	(92) 92.2			
3.46	(90) 90.0	(93) 93.3			

NOTE: Inch-wheel numbers in () are rounded to whole numbers.

Setting saddle angle. The front of the saddle should be slightly higher than the back of the saddle. Placing a yardstick on the saddle makes this critical adjustment easier to set. *Never* allow the tip of the saddle to be lower than the back of the saddle.

Setting saddle height. The saddle height should be adjusted with the rider on the bicycle with *both* heels on the pedals <u>and not the toe as illustrated.</u> Adjust the height of the saddle to allow for a *slight* bend in the knee at the bottom of the stroke. Quick Check: Pedal backwards with both heels on the pedals. If the hips sway, the saddle is too high.

2

Advanced Triathlon Cycle Training

Growing numbers of people are dedicating at least a part of their lives to what can be called high-level fitness — that is, a level of physical conditioning that goes far beyond what is needed for a leisurely ride on a weekend or even for commuting 10 or 20 miles to and from work each day. Thousands of cyclists quietly training for "centuries" and "double centuries" (100- and 200-mile rides) held in nearly every major city in the U.S. High-level fitness, and the challenge of a century ride, satisfies something in the human spirit that cannot be satisfied within one's profession or family life. It touches something deep and personal in one's being, providing a source of self-expression, pride, and a power that reaches beyond the bounds of everyday existence.

Bicycle training the aerobics war

To understand high-level fitness, we need to take a look at "aerobics." The term refers to exercise that is continued for a sufficient intensity and duration, such that it produces changes in the various systems and organs of the body. this, of course, is what we call being fit or being in condition.

Aerobic exercise does the following:

1. It strengthens the muscles of respiration and tends to reduce the resistance to air flow, ultimately facilitating the rapid flow of air in and out of the lungs.
2. It improves the strength and pumping efficiency of the heart, enabling more blood to be pumped with each stroke. This improves the ability to more rapidly transport life-sustaining oxygen from the lungs to the heart and ultimately to all parts of the body.
3. It tones up muscles throughout the body, thereby improving the general circulation, at times lowering blood pressure and reducing the work of the heart.
4. It causes an increase in the total amount of blood circulating through the body and increases the number of red blood cells and the amount of hemoglobin, making the blood a more efficient oxygen carrier.

Many changes must take place in your body before you can feel the benefits of aerobics or comfortably ride a bicycle 50, 100, or more miles per day. You are never fully conscious of these changes occurring, any more than you are conscious of lungs and chest expanding, or hormonal constitutions altering, or volumes of blood in the cardiovascular system increasing, or the production of blood cells speeding up, or the capacities of muscle cells to absorb nutrients and oxygen improving. You are conscious that your physical abilities are broadening, that you can do a lot more with less effort than before, and that physical challenges that once exhausted and distressed you are now highly invigorating.

One of the first things you'll need to develop is a way of judging how much exercise you should be getting and how hard you should be working at it.

How much and how often?

The intensity, duration, and frequency of your workouts must all be taken into account when designing or evaluating a training program.

Intensity. You must exercise at between 60 and 90 percent of your maximum heart rate (based on age) before you can enjoy aerobic benefits — that is, exercise resulting in the

Some material in this chapter has been reprinted from The Custom Bicycle, copyright 1979, by Michael J. Kolin and Denise M. de la Rosa.

healthy growth of your cardio-vascular and oxygen-collecting systems.

To determine your maximum heart rate, subtract your age from the base number of 220. For example, let's say you are 40 years old. Subtract that from the base number to get 180, and 60 to 90 percent of that gives you the figures 108 and 162. In simple terms, that means you should exercise intensely enough to keep you heart working at between 108 and 162 beats per minute.

Counting you pulse beats while riding your bike isn't easy. Here's how it's done: Hold the handlebars with the same hand on which you wear your wrist watch. With the first two fingers of your other hand, feel the pulse in your carotid artery, located about two inches to the right or left of your Adam's apple. Count the beats for 10 seconds. Multiply that number by 6, and you've found the rate at which your heart is presently beating. This number should fall within the range you've previously calculated as you maximum-heart-rate range. If you are working below that rate, you need to bicycle harder. If you are working over that level, slow down.

Duration. Try to get between 15 and 60 minutes of continuous aerobic exercise each time you ride. Duration and intensity are interrelated. That is, using the example of the 40-year-old rider again, he or she would derive the same aerobic benefits riding 60 minutes at 106 beats per minute as riding 15 minutes at 162 beats per minute. You can adjust duration and intensity as you wish, as long as you maintain at least the lower end of your maximum heart rate.

Frequency. Plan to exercise between three and five days each week. Few training benefits can accrue unless you exercise a minimum of three days per week, and, interestingly enough, there is little or no measurable physiological benefit derived from riding more than five days per week.

How riding style affects training

There are two basic styles of riding through which you can achieve the levels of training we're discussing here. These are represented by the acronyms LSD and POT — terms coined by Joe Henderson in his *Long Slow Distance Training*. LSD stands for "long, slow distance, and long, steady distance" while POT stands for "plenty of tempo." Let's explore these one at a time.

LSD was derived from work showing that aerobic benefits are best achieved not by sporadic, heroic efforts, but by regularly sustaining a rather moderate output over a minimum duration of 20 to 30 minutes.

The basic principle of long, slow distance is that your body will adjust and grow, reaping the benefits of physical exercise best when you establish a program where you are exercising for relatively long periods of time, covering distances of sufficient length, even if your pace is fairly slow. You must, even with LSD, work hard enough to give your heart and lungs a good workout, but you need not be heroic in your efforts.

The form of training Henderson calls POT is based on the principle that after you have achieved a certain level of conditioning, you can expand you capacities past that point only through *stress*. In this case, stress means putting new, higher demands on your body for short periods of time until your heart, lungs, and vascular system grow up to the capacity you desire.

Let's say, for example, that you're riding three days a week, 10 miles each day, at an average speed of 15 miles per hour. You feel comfortable doing this, but you want to double your output in preparation for a week-long bicycle tour you are planning with friends. The POT advocate would tell you to keep doing your usual routine of 10 miles a day at 15 miles per hour, but with short POT (plenty-of-tempo) sessions added to those rides. What would this mean exactly?

At the end of your ride, you might add another two miles over flat terrain. In this additional two-mile stretch you'd push yourself all out. Instead of riding at your regular rate of spped, covering the extra distance in about 8½ minutes, you'd double your output, covering the same distance in 4¼ minutes.

The extra push at the end of your ride presents your body with a new level of stress. Your heart and lung capacities will grow to meet that new challenge.

From time to time, popular sports magazines carry articles arguing the advantages of LSD, over POT, or vice versa. But making a choice between the two training styles misses the point. The important thing to note is that LSD allows you to maintain a particular level of conditioning, while POT provides you with an effective tool for increasing that level to a new plateau. The bicycle training program, which follows, integrates the two philosophies.

Before committing yourself to this or any other strenuous physical training program, however, we suggest that you discuss your plans with your doctor. many physicians now have equipment available for testing you cardio-vascular system under stress.

By measuring your present capacities in this way, you can get a clear picture of the way you should begin training — how much, how soon? — and the speed at which you can progress. This is especially important if you're over 40, if you haven't been exercising, for a number of years, or if you're known to have heart disease, diabetes, or any other condition affecting your heart, lungs, and vascular system.

Oxygen Uptake

In speaking of "aerobic capacity" or "oxygen uptake" we are rather talking abou the rate at which oxygen is delivered to the muscles doing the work. Oxygen is absorbed through the lung membranes — a process which smoking seriously inhibits, so no serious racing cyclist should go near cigarettes, or even frequent smoke-filled places — and is then carried to the muscles by the blood.

The capacity of the blood to carry oxygen is determined by hemoglobin content; anemic people should get medical treatment before trying to raise aerobic capacity, and any cyclist should be careful to get enough iron.

The oxygen-carrying blood is pumped to the muscles by the heart, and I suspect that this is the biggest single factor in determining fitness for aerobic effort. It is certainly one which can be developed by training, and in which changes can be monitored.

It was once believed that there was a pathological condition called "athlete's heart." Well, a trained athlete does have a bigger heart than average, and hard training over a period of time will cause the heart to enlarge, but this is far from a bad thing. A big heart doesn't have to pump as fast for normal operations; it can thump along in the 50s and 60s at rest, and this means it doesn't wear out as fast as a heart that runs 80 or 90 all the time. So in addition to making you a fast rider, aerobic training will also help you live longer. A bigger heart is not only a more efficient oxygen delivery pump, but a healthier organ.

All this assumes the rider is moving at a steady speed within the limits of his or her aerobic capacity, having first warmed up gradually. If, however, the body is called upon to make a sudden hard effort, either from starting fast with no warm-up or from a sudden increase in speed during a race, the system must respond with more oxygen, and there is an unavoidable time lag built in. During this delay, the demand of the muscles for oxygen exceeds the supply, and after a mere 20 seconds or so of this, the body shifts into anaerobic metabolism to produce energy. This, of course, refers to the process of breaking down glycogen without oxygen.

Here we encounter the Free Lunch Principle: you pay for this brief period of freedom from oxygen dependency. Anaerobic metabolism has a byproduct: lactic acid. And lactic acid, in a word, hurts. If you keep pushing, so that the body never catches up but remains in the anaerobic state, the pain will eventually stop you with paralyzing cramps.

Lactic Acid buildup

At less extreme levels, cyclists encounter this at the start of a race; you haven't warmed up and the pace is pretty fast off the line, so there's a period during which your legs hurt and your lungs burn. But if you can hold on, the body can usually stabilize things pretty soon, and this is what happens when a rider speaks of "getting my second wind" or "getting warmed up." When somebody tells you that if you'll just hang in there a bit you'll start feeling better, don't dismiss this as pep-talk nonsense; there's a valid medical principle behind it.

Unfortunately it's not just a question of the aerobic system catching up with oxygen demand; another nasty thing about lactic acid is that the process by which the body gets rid of the stuff demands oxygen in its own right. So you get what is called an "oxygen debt" — the system has to labor extra hard both to supply ongoing oxygen needs of the muscles and to flush out the lactate. This is why even after you have slowed down you keep fighting for air for some time.

You can train the body to tolerate lactic acid, to some extent, by doing anaerobic intervals (to be explained shortly). Actually I suspect this is to some extent a matter of teaching the mind to endure certain levels of discomfort — what runners call "breaking the pain barrier." Some training along these lines is needed. Because other riders with high pain thresholds will frequently attack and force the whole pack to go into the painful anaerobic state in order to keep up. On the track, some events are largely anaerobic, particularly the kilometer.

Indeed mental aspects are present in all types of training. The mind can be taught to interpret certain stimuli in certain ways, and it is possible to raise the level at which it interprets discomfort as outright pain. Racers put it more bluntly; they say, "You learn that pain won't kill you."

You can take this too far, of course; there is normal body pain which can be ignored for the moment, and then there are danger signals, such as the twinge of pain from a ligament about to pop. Learn to recognize the difference, and never try to tough your way through it if something is clearly wrong. Get off the bike immediately and go see a doctor.

But a good mental attitude during training will go a long way toward making you a winner. Nobody ever learned to actually like lactic acid, but you can change the way you think of it. Insted of thinking, "Oh, this hurts," try thinking, "Hey, if it hurts this much, think how those other turkeys are going to be hurting when I go like this in that race next weekend."

Editor's Note:

In our chapter on Running and Ultra Marathon Training we deal with the controversial subject of Interval Training. We offer this alternative to those that might feel the need for additional anerobic effort in their training also as a training alternative. John Marino, Arthur Lidyard, Max Telford, and many more trainers prefer the aerobic Long slow distance, concept followed by strength and speed training in that order. In any event listen to your body for signs of fatigue brought on by excessive intervals.

Interval Training

The interval system of training has been the subject of so much controversy that one hesitates even to bring it up; yet there's nothing that difficult or strange about the concept. Interval training consists simply of alternating periods of moderate effort with short bursts of very strong, near - maximum output. While interval training is usually associated with timed schedules, it can be entirely free and unstructured, as in the Swedish "fartlek" or speed-play system. Riding briskly over a course with numerous closely-spaced steep hills will indeed produce an interval effect, as will riding in urban traffic with frequent stoplights. (This last is worth thinking about if you ride your bike to and from work or school; instead of avoiding streets where you have to stop a lot, maybe you should seek them out.)

Interval training works on the "progressive overload" principle. Regular application of maximum stress to the body, with periods of lesser effort to permit recovery, will develop the entire system very powerfully in a remarkably short period of time. The heart is particularly benefitted; interval training also simulates the highly irregular, on-and-off stress pattern of most racing. (Much of the anti-interval criticism has come from runners and their coaches. Runners, however, compete at a much more unform pace than cyclists; a road race over varying terrain with an aggressive pack induces fluctuations in stress patterns that would demolish the average runner.)

Theoretically, intervals should be done according to pulse rate. That is, the period between intervals of effort should be just long enough to let pulse rate fall to 60 to 70 percent of maximum. During the stress interval pulse should be pushed up close to maximum.

Most of the time, any experienced rider can tell subjectively when it's time to get going again. You should rest long enough to be able to go hard again, but you should remain out of breath; in fact "rest" is a misleading term, because you should be exerting some sort of effort at all times. Don't freewheel in the "rest" periods.

If you want some sort of guidelines, one-minute intervals are pretty good — a minute on, a minute off. Do about 12 or 15 of these, more if you find you can. For particularly good effects and a bit less boredom, do alternate big-gear and low-gear intervals. That is, do one in a gear of 82 inches or higher, the next in 70 inches or lower. (With most setups you can do this simply by switching back and forth between chainwheels.) The great John Howard, who was U.S. National Champion in Road and Time Trial more times than any other rider so far, used to use this alternating-gears system of doing intervals, sometimes doing as many as 25 repetitions in a session.

It is strongly recommended that the use of a speedometer and/or a watch be used. A clip to hold a stopwatch (or ordinary pocket watch) on the bars is an inexpensive and useful accessory, as you can use the sweep hand to time your pedal rpms and interval duration; it comes in handy on time trials, too. The speedometer is trickier; some makes are incompatible with a quick-release hub, and the ones that run off the tire are inaccurate in the upper ranges. Best is the electronic type which also gives pedal rpms, a very useful thing to be able to read; this is also, unfortunately, a very expensive piece of equipment, but it is worth it. With a speedometer you can really tell what you're doing; you can keep yourself from fading toward the end of the "on" period by resolving not to let the needle fall below a given point for one minute, or whatever.

Longer intervals, two minutes' duration or so, are harder on the system and exhaust you fast, so do fewer repetitions to a set, and expect a longer recovery period — three minutes on, two off, for example.

You can also do free-form intervals, like going hard when you feel like it, or picking arbitrary points like telephone poles. But don't let the "off" periods get too long or you'll just be doing some sprint and jump training.

Anaerobic intervals

Also called "pain intervals," involve "on" periods of three minutes or more. In these you deliberately go into the anaerobic state and hold it for several minutes. The concentrations of lactic acid are hard on your body, so it is unwise to do these too often; no more than once a week, and I would say every other week, is plenty. It is terribly hard to force yourself to maintain that level of effort all the way through the interval, so it helps to have some way to give yourself a little extra push — the speedometer again, or a strong training partner, even a cranky coach.

Never do any sort of intervals two days in a row, and three interval sessions a week should be maximum. Without sufficient recovery time, intervals are very destructive.

Steady state training

Interval training is great for developing the ability to produce a sudden surge of power, but a road cyclist also must be able to ride at a strong steady pace over distance. This is particularly valuable in time trials or on solo breaks, but in any sort of race it is an advantage to be able to set a hard pace and maintain it. In any case, steady-state riding at 75 percent or so of maximum pulse for an hour is a great aerobic workout and good mental discipline, too.

The best way to get this is simply to ride time trials. Set up your own; just measure a course and time yourself. (If you live where you can get at a course which is used for real time trials you will be able to plan for the real event while doing your training, a great advantage.) You might also like to get together with some friends and hold unofficial time trials to introduce the element of competition.

A 25-mile (40-km) time trial once a week is strongly advised; if you lack the time for that, then at least do ten or 15 miles (15 or 20 km) and go hard. And keep track of your times in your notebook; this way you can measure the results of your training.

Despite the claims of a few overenthusiastic LSD messiahs, nobody has ever learned to go fast by going slow.

Many of these people point to European riders as exemplars of this system; Merckx doesn't do intervals, Coppi didn't do intervals, and so on. What is ignored is that Europeans race four or five times a week during the height of the season. They naturally don't need to train for speed; they hardly need to train at all as Americans use the term. They can rely on early-season races to get in shape; their training rides are merely for basic conditioning, getting in miles to toughen up their fannies and loosen up the legs.

It is certainly possible to train effectively doing nothing but long, steady-paced endurance rides, if you have the time. Hardly anybody I know does. Anything less than two and a half hours in the saddle, by LSD standards, is pointless; the hard-core LSD freak will hardly consider anything under four or five; impractical for the average part-time rider, not to mention boring as anything for most of us.

But all-interval training is unbalanced; ideally you need some distance training for endurance. If at all possible, each week should include at least one ride of 60 miles (90 km) or more, done at a steady but not exhausting pace. This should be done in the middle of the week, no later than Thursday, to give the body time to rest for Sunday's race.

If your schedule won't accept a ride of such duration, though, don't despair. While endurance training is indeed valuable, and absolutely necessary for the rider aiming at national and international competition, the beginning or part-time racer can get along fairly well without it. After all, most novice and lower-category events are run over short distances. Why train over 100 miles (160 km) if you're never going to race over 30 miles (48 km)?

You can in fact go pretty high without racing all that far. There are lots of big, prestigious criteriums in which the top classes go only 50 miles (80 km) or so, and of course there's always the track. California star Ron Sharin, with job commitments to limit training time, has had a remarkable career as a pursuiter and short-criterium racer, including national titles and records and participation in international events.

If you do go on a long training ride, go hard. Keep pedal rpms above 80 at the very minimum; 90 to 100 is more like it. Slogging along at low rpms over long miles is terrible.

Carry plenty of food and water and a spare tire; don't stop for anything but flats, mechanical problems, or illness. Most riders prefer to go with a friend or two of similar abilities; then they can work together to keep up the pace.

Cycling: The world's toughest sport?

In many sports like running or skiing, the athlete who gets to the point of exhaustion has to stop because he can no longer support his own weight. He falls down. In cycling the bike is holding you up and, although this means that you don't need as much energy to support yourself, it also means that all the energy is going into the activity itself. You can suffer much more just doing your thing because you don't have to fight gravity. A rider will sometimes get off the bike after his event and not be able to stand up.

A cyclist can get to the point of exhaustion, where he doesn't have the energy to support his own weight, and still keep on going. He may rest and recover and then reach that point again later on. In many other sports you reach the limit just once.

Cycling events also take longer in terms of hours than most other sports. A marathon runner will race two or three hours one day and then again two or three weeks later and think he's done something. A rider in a stage race has to do two marathons a day every day for a week.

People don't realize how much the human body can do. You can do two marathons a day — you are physically capable of doing it — and the world's top professional and amateur cyclists do it practically year 'round.

TIME TRIALING

The challenging ''race of truth''
is the perfect event for beginners

Quite a few experienced road riders profess that they hate time trials. They say the excitement of mass-start events is missing: no strategy, no teamwork, no tactics. In some cases this distaste is mental. Compared to time trialing, it is psychologically easier to ride a mass-start race because you are too busy thinking about strategy, position in the pack and avoiding a crash to dwell for long on how badly you are hurting. A TT, on the other hand, requires that you concentrate intensely on your pain and discomfort so that you can go at your maximum speed for the distance.

It is perhaps due to a quirk in my character that I like time trials very much. For me their fascination arises from the fact that I must tread on the edge all the time — the anaerobic threshold, the fine line between lightness and durability in equipment, and the mental line that defines just how hard I can push myself. As I see it, the time trial is the event for the limit-seeker, the rider who accepts personal challenge and enjoys meeting it in the toughest arena there is: the battlefield of oneself. The ideal effort will put you on the red line of your capabilities where it is physically painful and mentally excruciating.

There are no excuses in a time trial. Road racing results, however, are frequently influenced by luck or by factors other than one's power and fitness. Crashes, wheelsucking, the refusal of some riders in a break to work — all these and more have been offered as reasons why the strongest rider sometimes doesn't win. But time trials have no place for alibis. Barring a puncture, it's just your fitness and your will against the unyielding clock. No wonder Europeans call time trials the ''race of truth.'' In this and the following two chapters we'll look closely at this event and see why it offers so much to cyclists interested in improving riding strength, cardiovascular capacity and certain racing skills.

An event for everyone

Because of the nature of the event, a time trial is the perfect medium for exposing riders of all ages to cycling competition. If you are fascinated by racing and want to try it, you don't need an expensive bike to ride TTs because you can compete against yourself against your previous best time. you are spared a major investment that may be wasted money if you find that the sport isn't for you. You don't need to be accomplished at drafting, riding elbow to elbow, sprinting and all the other road racing technsiques that take time to learn. Since such skills must be practiced int he company of others, time trialing is a natural choice for the cyclist who lives far from population centers and cannot often train in a group.

Time trials are an ideal way to gauge your strength and improvement. It's not the same in mass-start racing. For example, in a certain road event last year you might not have been especially fit but you placed well due to the lackluster competition and the vagaries of the unfolding race situation. In the same event this season you might be in peak form, but because you miss a break have a puncture or get elbowed off the road in the sprint you wind up way down the finishing order. Against the clock, however, you can see objectively the state of your fitness and evaluate the effectiveness of your training.

Most beginning competitors fear the loss of self-determination when surrounded by dozens of riders in road races, where spills can be totally unavoidable due to the actions of others. But in a time trial the chances of accident are small. It is hard to crash unless you take the turnaround too fast or blot out everything but the mesmerizing spin of the front wheel and ride right off the road. There's really no doubt, though, that a time trial is the safest way to introduce new racers to the thrill of going fast on a bike.

As in all open-road events, one danger a time trialist does face is vehicular traffic, a point sadly underscored by Alan Kingsbery's nearly fatal collision with a cement truck going through an intersection during the 1978 National Championship. For this reason tight course marshaling is a must. However, the racer must still take on the difficult responsibility to ride alertly even as all resources are being thrown into going fast. Whether you are competing in a time trial, mass-start event or are simply out training, you have to ride defensively and with awareness.

For all the advantages the event offers to both new and experienced racers, time trialing is going to increase in popularity in years to come. Running has built an enormous participation base because foot races are essentially time trials. People who don't have a chance in the world of winning like to compete because they can race to beat their own previous times. But for a beginning cyclist who is already sold on the sport and whose primary interest is to become a road racer, what precise benefits can be gained from hard and lonely efforts against the clock?

Importance to road racers

If you are thinking about riding your first USCF road event, time trials can give you a graphic measure of your fitness. Some prospective racers never make it to the line because they are unsure if they have the speed and endurance to stay with a pack. Others try sanctioned events before they have a sufficient mileage base, get dropped or suffer inordinately and never race again. By riding TTs you can compare your results with those of successful racers and see if you are ready to take the plunge or if more training is needed.

Once you have started racing, good results in time trials against riders in the next higher category may help you decide whether to advance. Quite a few riders qualify through their race placings to move up, but they are hesitant to do so. If your time trial results are comparable to those who would be your new opposition, there is a good chance you can advance and be competitive.

Time trials are a valuable training technique for a rider any any stage of development. John Howard, who has won four National Road Championships and one 25-mile title (55:36 at the 1976 Nationals), is among those who believe in TTs as a training method. In a Velonews interview he asserted that time trials help "to develop a rhythm and . . . determination." Howard knows that in order to ride a time trial at maximum speed you have to train your body to operate at its anaerobic threshold. This is the level of exertion where you are working so hard that the slightest increase in effort would cause more lactic acid to accumulate than you system can eliminate. It is exercise at the brink. When the anaerobic threshold is crossed, the body's response is to slow down almost immediately.

Training at the anaerobic threshold — precisely the sort of workout you get by riding time trials — is important if you want to achieve top results. Dr. Ed Burke says that "your potential to be a successful endurance cyclist appears to be related to your anaerobic threshold." Another physiologist, Dr. Ben Londeree, comments that "a significant portion of training should be done at a pace which exceeds your current anaerobic threshold." An excellent way to achieve this is to ride time trials of 10 miles or less at a fast pace than you could sustain for 25, the USCF championship distance. This sort of training will make you a better time trialist and will also improve your motor for road racing.

The ideal way to incorporate time trials into your training program is to ride them in low-key competition, such as in a club TT series. The reason this works well is because it is hard to get mentally up for a training time trial done alone, the result being that you don't go as fast as you could and, therefore, you don't stimulate as much improvement. If your club sponsors midweek 10-milers, you'll find it much easier to put out in that competitive situation.

In addition to general fitness, time trialing develops specific road race skills. If you are a strong solo rider you are better equipped to get back to the pack after a crash or a puncture. As Howard observed in the aforementioned interview, you will also be able to bridge the gap to a break without needing half the pack to help. Finally, TT ability may allow you to get away and stay away for long periods. Unless you are a devastating road sprinter, an escape based on time trialing power may be the best chance you'll have to win.

Equipment modifications

Time trialing is the last refuge of the hard-core equipment freak and many riders make drastic modifications in favor of lightness, but this can be carried too far. It is alluring to think that an ounce saved here and a bit of rolling resistance eliminated there will result in significantly lower times. It won't happen. You may save a few seconds with some judicious weight paring, but going overboard all too often leads to equipment failure. Light wheels and tires are an example. You can save some rotating weight by using a radially laced 28-spoke front wheel, a 32-spoke rear and 200-gram tires, but the price you pay for the ounces saved (besides what the cash register demands) is a greater likelihood of punctures and wheel malfunctions.

In the same way the search for component and frame lightness is often counterproductive. A very light frame may flex so much that the advantage of weight reduction is negated by its absorption of your energy. Drilled cranksets are visually impressive but also may flex too much. The result of an obsessive search for lightness looks great on the scales but often loses its luster on the road.

However, equipment gimmickry can have a positive psychological effect on riders who need that sort of boost. Sometimes a few ounces saved can artifically raise confidence, and if the event is important enough you may want to take the chance. I suspect that this is what happened with our four riders in the 70-kilometer team time trial at the 1980 Junior World Championships.

YOUR CYCLE TRAINING PROGRAM

Setting Goals

Goal-setting is essential to any fitness training program. It is only through continually achieving and surpassing your goals that gorwth takes place. You first goal should be to attain an aerobic training level — that is, to attain your maximum heart rate and sustain it over the desired period of time.

To achieve this basic goal, you will have to give some thought to your training route. If you live in the flats of Kansas, you may be able to maintain your maximum heart rate by traveling a 20-mile course in an hour, while a person living in hilly terrain might achieve the same effect by pedaling a strenuous 12-mile course in an hour. You will have to determine your course by trial and error, trying out different routes until you find one that works for you. If traffic is a problem, causing you to lose intensity by stopping and starting too often, try riding early in the morning when traffic is light.

Once you have achieved and maintained your aerobic level for a period of time, you will find that your heart rate begins to drop as your body's strength and endurance grow. As your heart rate drops, you will have to keep adding new challenges — increasing your miles, cutting down the time you take to complete your course, or taking on a new and difficult grade — in order to maintain your maximum rate.

Goal-setting gives you a target, a point toward which you can direct your mental and physical energies. Set these goals consciously, writing them down with dates in a notebook. For example, "June 15. Rode canyon loop in three hours. Goals: to cut time to 2½ hours." Later you can look back and see that you accomplished your goal as you said you would. That is one of the most powerful incentives to keep you working at your program.

Warming up

Before you throw yourself into an all-out workout, warming up can help get your blood flowing at a rate at which it can liberally supply your muscle cells with the oxygen and nutrients they need. Higher body temperatures allow oxygen to be transmitted from your blood to your muscle cells at a higher rate, causing chemical reactions that result in a release of energy within your muscles. In addition, nerve responses are quickened, and the force and speed at which a muscle cell can respond is vastly improved. Warmups are especially important for middle-aged and older people, who, according to studies conducted by Dr. Paul Fardy, otherwise do not generally have sufficient coronary circulation for strenuous exercise.

Finally, warm-ups are one of the best ways to prevent athletic injuries. When a person starts out cold, muscle strain, tears of muscle tissue or ligaments, or simple muscular stiffness or soreness are much more like to occur than when you warm-up first.

One of the advantages of bicycling is that the warm-up can take place during the first 15 minutes of your ride. Choose a comfortable gear and ease into your pedaling without attempting to achieve your training level of output. Warm-ups should be intense but not fatiguing. When you begin to perspire, that's the sign that your body temperature has risen sufficiently to start your workout. Usually a 15-minute warmup is sufficient.

Some people prefer to begin with warm-up exercises. Stretching exercises, (see our chapter on Bicycle Stretching by Bob Anderson) warm-up and limber your muscles gently and effectively while stretching the muscles beyond their normal range. When stretching, stretch each muscle group to the point where you just begin to feel the pull; then go a little further and hold the position for 30 seconds. Avoid sudden bouncing, violent stretching, or rigorous calistenic routines; these can create muscular contractions and accomplish just the opposite effect from the one you want.

After doing the stretching routine, do leisurely situps or run in place until you begin to feel yourself heat up. At that point you're ready to ride.

The Ride

Start each ride slowly. Take several deep breaths and relax, letting your body and mind come to terms with the bike. Enjoy these early moments of the ride and the sensation of the air on your skin. Feel the strength of your body as you propel the bike forward.

At some point within the first five or ten minutes you'll begin to feel fully focused on the activity of riding. This is what we call "centering." You and the bike are now working together as a unit.

Look for a clear space of a block or more in the road. Take your pulse using the method we described. If your pulse-rate is too low according to the maximum-heart-rate schedule you worked out, speed up your pace. Take your pulse at different exercise levels until you become familiar with what your output must be to achieve the training level you want.

Once you know how it feels to exercise at an aerobically beneficial level, it is a simply matter to sustain that intensity for the duration you wish. But go slowly at first. Work at rates that are comfortable and enjoyable. If you learn to associate pleasure with each ride. you'll find yourself highly motivated to do it again the next day.

Cornering

I think everybody who gets on a road with a lot of turns really likes to swoop in and out of them. You do it almost naturally and don't even think about it. There is a cooperation between your mind and body; you get your balance.

The line to take through a turn is much the same as in other sports such as auto racing, skiing, and so on. Make the widest are possible, which means coming up to the turn on the outside, sweeping through as close to the inside corner as possible, and then continuing on to the outside again. Of course you have to be careful when riding on public roads.

As soon as you can see the turn, set up your line. It's like a car driver on a track. Although he's going well over 100 mph, when he sees the turn approaching it's almost coming in slow motion and he can feel his body going right around it.

It's the same way in cycling. You adjust to the speed and the situation. Things start happening in your mind and you see exactly where to go and you do it.

As you come into the corner, change into the gear you will want to be in when coming out on the other side and brake a little bit if you have to. When coasting, the inside pedal is up and the outside one is down.

Sit back a little over the rear wheel, because this gives better balance when you turn and helps you to steer through. You can also let your inside knee hang out a little bit, to bring the center of gravity down. It's bad to get that knee caught on anything, of course, but it does help make you more stable and go faster.

Pedaling in and out of the turns is good to practice. Don't take chances by pedaling farther and farther into the turn until you scrape, to see how far over you can go. But do make an effort to judge pedal clearance, which determines when to stop and when to begin pedaling as you approach and come out of a turn.

Climbing

If a hill is not too steep, it will help develop strength in the legs to stay in the saddle as long as you can keep the gear turning. When it gets to be a real forcing effort, then get out of the saddle.

Climbing specialists are usually always out of the saddle and in small gears. The Spanish climbers, for example, don't push large gears up a hill. They're very relaxed and bobbing right out of the saddle, almost as if they were running on the pedals.

When climbing, the bike shouldn't move too much from side to side. As you push down on the pedals, your body moves from side to side a little bit and the bike does move slightly, corresponding with the effort of pulling on the bars with your arms.

But it's more important, when climbing, that instead of throwing your weight and bike from side to side, you throw it forward. You're hammering on the pedals and it's like lunging forward. Going from side to side is just lost motion.

Years ago a European professional who had observed American riders told me that Americans don't seem to use their back muscles as much as Europeans. If you notice, most good bike riders have muscle in their lower backs, even the skinny ones. It looks almost like they have a little roll around their waist, but it's muscular and probably comes from pulling on the bars and a little bobbing from side to side.

How To Fall

Crashes happen so fast that often there is no time to do anything about them. But through the years you learn that there are certain things to do to protect yourself when you crash. When it happens, the best thing to do is take your hands off the bars, grasp your head, and fold your arms around it. Even on the ground, again, cover up your head by folding your arms around it. Ribs and other places grow back together but your head can stand only so many injuries.

Some people seem to have an extra talent for being able to ride through an accident and stay on the bike. A lot of this is luck, but some of it is reflexes and some of it is bike handling. There was one fellow we called "The Magician," because no matter what happened he could stay upright. He could ride across an entire bike and not fall. People in front of him fell down and people in back of him fell down, but he could do it.

Horizontal adjustment of the saddle. The saddle position from front to back is adjustable to compensate for individual variances in upper leg length and riding style. To correctly adjust the saddle, sit on the bicycle with both feet in the toe clips. The saddle is correctly adjusted when a plumb line from the indentation just behind the knee cap to the pedal axle.

Champion Dave Scott, winner of the 1984 Ironman Triathlon World Championships.

Photo by David Epperson

418

All riders do fall once in a while and I think it happens more when you are just beginning. Even in training sometimes you can't help it. If the front tire blows out there's not much you can do; usually you will go down. If someone else crashes in front of you, it's not your fault, but usually you crash, too.

In this country I don't think you will encounter really bad road conditions in racing, especially in the beginning. But an experienced rider, particularly if he goes to Europe, might find difficult conditions once in a while. If a race is coming up over known bad roads, like on breadloaf cobbles where you slide right off the sides, then go over some similar road and see what it feels like.

Usually on bumpy roads you should push yourself back over the saddle to put a little more weight on the rear wheel. Especially on rough uphills the wheel can skip. A farther-back position seems to give more control. Ride relaxed with elbows bent to take up the shock of the road and keep pushing. Sometimes it seems to stabilize you a little more to use a bigger gear than you normally would.

The most common mistakes of beginners are riding too big a gear, being tense, and riding erratically or wobbling. The wobbling seems to come from chopping on the pedals instead of pedaling in a circle. Beginners also grip the bars too tightly. You have to grasp them firmly but be relaxed, too. From your upper body and shoulders right down tot the wrists, you should be relaxed. If you stiffen your whole body and arms, you will ride erratically.

Being tense wastes energy and also makes a bad style of riding. With a smooth, relaxed pedal stroke, the bike will go fairly straight and will not hae to travel as far because of any zigzagging from one side of the road to the other. This will make you a safer riding companion and competitor.

Have a plan

The mental attitude for entering a bicycle race is not very different from any other sport. Don't get too up-tight before the race, at least not until about five minutes before the start, because that drains your energy. But you do have to have a plan for the race.

The plan is not something you're going to follow by the book. You have to play it by ear, whatever happens. It's like a sprinter who comes to the line for a match sprint with several different stock plans of what's going to happen. If this opponent does such-and-such he knows what he's going to do, and if the opponent does something else, then he knows what he has to do in return. He doesn't really have to think about it, he just does it.

So keep the possibilities in mind. A good sprinter might say, "I'm going for the prize at the end; I'm not going to go for any primes; I'm going to go with anything that looks like a good break, and when we get to the end I'm going for the win." A strong road rider may force the pace throughout the race and then figure, "Okay, I'm going to make my attack with three or four laps to go and ride alone to the end." An all-'rounder might have three or four plans.

Bike riding style is speed and distance

It has been with great amazement that I have noticed the lack of riding technique on the part of the majority of contestants in the U.S. Triathlon series being held on the Pacific Coast. We have made an extra effort to try to impress our readers of the importance of top riding style as a prerequisite to speed and distance on the bicycle. Here again we will try to steer the reader into a more acceptable and correct style of cycling.

While it is very difficult to "coach" a rider without being familiar with his or her individual style, there are basic rules of thumb which generally have universal application.

Gear selection

Countless pages have been written about gear selection: for mountains, the flats, racing, training; but in the final analysis, the "correct gear" depends on the specific anatomy and style of the rider. Stocky,heavily muscled individuals tend to pedal larger gears at lower rpm's than slim, lightly muscled persons. But, what is the correct gear for you?

Generally, a rider should attempt to pedal between 80 to 100 rpm's on a tubular-tired, lightweight bicycle and 60 to 80 rpm's on a clincher tire bicycle. The recommended rpm's vary because of the difference in the revolving weight of the wheels which affects your pedaling speed. Variations within that range will reflect individual anatomy, conditioning, and how much practice at pedaling the rider has had. The argument in support of high pedal rpm's with a "low" gear is simple — the rider will be able to ride longer. Let's look at an exaggerated analogy to clarify this point. Which exercise could you best perform: lifting a 2-pound weight with one hand over your head 50 times, or lifting 100 pounds with one hand over your head once? This analogy is not perfect since it does not take the time expended into account. It does, however, demonstrate the point that a muscle is only capable of exerting a limited amount of force and, most importantly, the muscle can be conditioned to perform a large number of light repetitions in a shorter period of time than it takes to condition the muscle to double or triple the amount of force exerted. Accepting the fact that "high rpm's" are desirable, we arrive at the problem of defining "how high is high?"

Rule of thumb: If the gear you have selected is too high, your legs will fatigue before your lungs. If the selected gear is too low, your lungs will fatigue first. This rule can easily be verified by performing two test rides. First, select the lowest gear on your bicycle. Pedal as fast as you can and maintain that pace for 15 seconds. you will notice that your legs will not be tired, however, your lungs will be "burning." After resting, perform the second test. Select the highest gear on your bike and again pedal as fast as you can for 15 seconds. Your lungs will not be "burning," instead, your legs will feel "tight." Practice using this rule of thumb to maximize your output whenever you ride. If you experience abnormal fatigue in your legs, reduce the gear you are riding. If you find yourself breathing too hard, increase the gear. Proper attention to your gear ratio will result in the optimum relationship between energy expended and the speed maintained.

Riding Position

The three basic positions of the hands on the handlebars are reviewed in figures 22-1A to 22-4 on pages 232-36. Let's continue our analysis of positions to include the proper use of the body while riding the bicycle.

Maintaining a relaxed position is one of the key elements in cycling. Many people ride with their hands gripping the handlebars as if someone were trying to wrench the bars from their grip. Although you must maintain a grip on the bars, remember that the bicycle is designed to ride in a straight line without any effort except pedaling. If the bicycle requires your attention to ride in a straight line, something is probably misaligned. (Chapter 21 reviews the steps to insure that the frame is tracking correctly.) You should not be expending energy on the bicycle unless it benefits your pedaling. Imagine how tired you would be just sitting in your living room if you had a "death grip" on a pair of handlebars for two hours. All of your energy should be aimed at making the bicycle go faster; don't allow your energy to "run out" through your handlebars.

In all three handlebar positions (on the tops, behind the brake levers, and on the drops), the rider should have bent elbows. One resting his weight on the bars because it is the most comfortable position for the back, the same position of the upper body can be maintained if the hands are moved to Position 2 and the amount of bend in the elbows is increased. Position 2 will also provide the shock absorber effect without any loss of efficiency.

Many riders unconsciously perform miniature "push-ups" as they ride. This is an indication that the rider is not using the arms properly and it actually tires the rider more than if the upper body is kept relatively still. Imagine, for instance, how many of these miniature push-ups are performed during a two-hour ride. Now imagine sitting at home with your hands on a table performing the same push-ups for two hours. None of that energy expended was used to make the bicycle go faster. The push-ups are usually performed unconsciously by the rider, but they should be eliminated because they result in an energy loss without any increase in efficiency.

Pedaling

Strictly speaking, intentional "ankling" is incorrect in spite of the many books and magazine articles that tell of its benefits. None of the dozens of coaches that we have spoken to about pedaling advocate ankling. A review of the many good European cycling books will reveal that there is no mention of ankling as a benefit to cycling. The motion that has often been incorrectly described as ankling, is an exaggeration (or misunderstanding) of the motions used in walking. Let's review the motion of a person's foot during a single step before we discuss proper pedaling technique.

1. As the foot is lifted, the heel naturally precedes the toe in the upward motion of the leg. No one makes a conscious effort to raise the heel first. It moves first because the muscles controlling the foot are relaxed and the lifting motion of the leg is done by the muscles in the upper leg.

2. As the foot descends, the heel begins to lead the toe, in readiness to make contact with the ground, since the heel will touch the ground first — not the toe.

3. the heel touches the ground first and as the body moves forward the weight is transferred to the ball of the foot and the process continues. If one is to believe the proponents of ankling, the rider should move the toes of the foot down at the bottom of the pedal stroke. This is no more correct than it is to recommend the saem motion when walking. Our muscles have functioned in a relatively fixed manner since we initially learned to walk — the most efficient pedal stroke utilizes the natural motion of the foot. The proponents of ankling are usually not cycling coaches. Instead, they are persons who have attempted to analyze the motions of the foot in the pedal stroke of the expert cyclist. It is easy to become misled when looking at the motions of a foot during the pedal stroke because, when a high rpm is maintained, the toe will precede the heel at the bottom of the stroke. It does not precede the heel because the rider consciously "pushes" the toe through first; it occurs because the centrifugal force of the high rpm's does not allow the full drop of the heel. The opposite is true in the use of a high gear at low rpm's — the heel will often be as low as the toes.

There is one foolproof method to determine if a rider is ankling or if his lower leg is operating properly — that is to watch the calf muscles expand and contract during the pedal stroke. Watching from behind, check to see when the calf is under pressure (tight). It should occur only on the down portion of the stroke. If the calf is tight on the up part of the stroke, the rider is still pushing with his toes instead of concentrating on pulling his whole foot up. Muscles "rest" by receiving fresh supplies of oxygenated blood; therefore, the rest period is greatest during the relaxed position of the muscle. Obviously, a muscle that is under tension during twice as much of the stroke will tire faster than a muscle that is given more opportunity to rest.

Although all serious cyclists have toe clips and straps on their pedals, most riders do not use them to their full advantage. You can prove this to yourself by watching the pedaling stroke of the average cyclist. Imagine the circle scribed by the cyclist's foot is the face of a clock. Most riders do not actually apply pressure to the pedals for more than three "hours" (from four to seven o'clock when the rider is viewed riding from left to right). It is impossible to assist individual riders with their pedal stroke in a book — that is the job of the coach. Understanding and being able to analyze the theory of efficient pedaling will hopefully benefit all riders who do not have a coach available.

Cornering

Although many riders have no intention of racing, learning how to corner at speed is important to reduce accidents. The tourist often requires these skills when descending mountains. There are two basic techniques for high-speed cornering — pedaling through the corner and coasting through the corner. Before a rider attempts to negotiate coasting through a corner at high speed, the method of efficiently pedaling through the corner should be mastered.

421

Pedaling through a corner

This method is important to master because it is necessary to achieve the proper position and confidence before attempting to learn the fastest way around a corner which is coasting. When pedaling around a righthand corner, the rider should attempt to keep the bicycle as upright as possible to reduce the possibility of hitting the pedal on the ground. To best accomplish this, the rider should bend the elbows slightly more than usual and move the upper body to the right until the rider's nose is approximately over the right hand. On lefthand corners, the procedure is reversed. The body should lean to the left with the rider's nose over the left hand.

Coasting through a corner

To better understand why the recommended position is so effective, let's look at the two primary factors that act on the bicycle when cornering at speed — the center of gravity of the bicycle and the traction of the tires. The weight of the rider is primarily resting at the level of the bicycle seat. The amount of weight on the seat decreases, of course, as the rider increases pressure on the pedals. The traction of the tires is affected by the tire construction, road surface, weight of the bicycle and rider, and the centrifugal force caused by going through the turn. To increase cornering speed, the center of gravity of the bicycle must be lowered. That is best accomplished by placing the majority of the rider's weight on the pedals.

Specifically, a right-hand turn should be accomplished as follows:
- Rider's nose over right hand. (This means that if a plumb line were to be dropped from your nose, it should fall just over the right hand.)
- Inside crank (right foot is in uppermost position) should be in the up position.
- Outside crank (left foot is in lowest position) will be in the down position.
- Rider should concentrate his weight on the outside leg — effectively lowering the center of gravity as much as possible.

A left-hand corner is negotiated similarly:
- Rider's nose over left hand.
- Inside crank should be up.
- Outside crank should be down.

Some riders prefer to allow the inside knee to drop from its normal position near the top tube for improved balance, however it is not required.

It's just as important to cool down after the ride as it is to warm up before. This prevents muscular stiffness and also gives your heart and lungs a chance to come gradually and naturally back to at-rest heart and respiration rates.

Use the last five minutes of your ride to cool down. During this five-minute period, lower your output to a leisurely pace. Drop to a lower gear, where you can pedal at a fast but not strenuous rate.

After you get off your bike, run through some warmup exercises in a leisurely fashion. Cooling-down exercises help clear your system of toxic by-products, which are normal in all forms of exercise. They will also reduce your chances of having aching muscles the next day.

Understanding pain

The most painful part of any exercise program is the first two or three weeks. The activity itself may seem uncomfortable — an odious task at best — during that early period. Muscles ache or are stiff each morning after you exercise.

It may surprise you to learn that this is a normal course of events for most people when they start on a demanding exercise program, or when they start over after laying off for the winter.

When one begins an exercise program, muscles need to stretch, strengthen, and become more resilient. Capillaries need to grow, both to carry the increased supplies of nutrients your body demands and to cleanse away waste products from muscle cells that are metabolizing at a more rapid rate than before you started exercising. In the beginning your heart and lungs must work doubly hard to supply blood to your muscle cells through an inadequate network of blood vessels. After the new capillaries grow, as indeed they will, the blood supply reaches the muscle cells with far less effort.

And what about the aching muscles and stiffness after exercise during the first weeks of the program? Most of this stiffness is caused by a buildup of lactic acids and waste products around muscle cells.

Lactic acids are part of a chain of chemical events that take place when cells are asked to produce energy in the absence of adequate oxygen supplies. Discomfort resulting from lactic-acid buildup will disappear as you grow more numerous capillaries and increase your ability to take in oxygen and feed it to your cells. Once your cells are receiving adequate oxygen supplies through your bloodstream, stiffness and pain will disappear. Exercise then literally fills you with energy.

When you're aware of the changes one's body goes through to be comfortable and invigorated by exercise, you can design a program to get into top physical condition with a minimum of discomfort. The secret lies in starting slowly and gradually increasing the amount of exercise as your body grows to meet each new demand.

A major cause of discomfort is breaking your training schedule — that is, laying off for a week or two and then expecting to go back to the same training level you left without gradually building back up to it.

Keep exercising regularly

It is important to understand that fitness is maintained only by exercising regularly. High-level fitness deteriorates after you've laid off for two weeks or more. You'll lose half the improvement you've gained through the kind of program we're describing if you suspend it for 4 to 12 weeks. You'll fall back to your fitness level prior to starting your exercise program, if you go without exercise for eight months or more. So, unless you want to start all over again, stick with it.

Too often, as doctors know only too well, people who exercise occasionally try to make up for lost time on weekends or during vacations. Because they've been exercising a little during the week (though usually not as much as they think they have), they overestimate their capacities and push themselves past safe physiological limits. The consequences of this error of judgment can be as serious as herat attacks and as benign as simple lethargy or depression the day after.

If you're ill for a couple of weeks, even with nothing more than a cold, it's important to build back up to your previous training level gradually. Many people make the mistake of trying to pick up exactly where they left off, which can prove to be both too strenuous and discouraging.

Interruptions of any kind cause your aerobic capacities to backslide, especially if you're over 30. In addition, infections — even minor ones, like colds, or immunizations given by your physician — take energy from the muscles you use for cycling and divert it to organs needed for healing or producing antibodies. Switching back to vigorous exercise after an infection takes time.

How do you catch up after you've been away from your training schedule? First of all, everyone has a slightly different rate for catching up. And if you're just getting over a cold, or you've been under unusual emotional stress, you rate of catching up will be different than if you've been relaxed and well since you last exercised. Thus you need some personal guidelines to follow, and these can be found in signals from your own body.

Recognizing overexertion

Our bodies and minds have ways of telling us when to slow down, when we're pushing ourselves too hard. Learn to recognize and heed the signals summarized below.

Upper left: Claire St. Arnaud and friend Jan . . . Santa Barbara Triathlete a long way from home . . . Max Telford, Scottish-born New Zealander, has run over 100,000 miles in his running career. Next two rows: "Spinning the Park" . . . Those comfortable Champers . . . Dave Bending of Dave's Quality Bikes in Santa Barbara and Kona gets a massage in exchange for a straight wheel . . . Waikiki Swim Club . . . 2 Bikers and a Swimmer's legs . . . Bob and Carol Hogan, training Triathletes, "Spinning the Park."

- **Physical symptoms.** Stop exercising and rest if you feel: lightheadedness, severe breathlessness, chest pain, nausea, dizziness, or loss of muscle control.
- **Heart recovery rate.** Take you pulse five minutes after you've finished a workout. If it's over 120, you've pushed yourself too hard for your present capacities. Take your pulse again ten minutes after exercise. If it's not below 100, ease up on your exercise program and build up more gradually.
- **Breathing recovery rate.** Do you find yourself still short of breath ten minutes after you've exercised? Normal breathing rates are from 12 to 16 breaths per minute. If it's more than that, it's a good sign you need to ease up a bit and start building up more gradually.
- **Emotions after exercising.** Although this factor varies a great deal from person to person, most people feel self-satisfied and even elated in the first hour or so after a good workout. If you feel agitated, anxious, restless, or discouraged after a ride, that's a good sign that you should cut back and build up more gradually.

Let these signs be your guides, both in your initial training period and during any period of catching up after a layoff.

Tips for improving performance

Training rides provide an excellent means for getting to know your body and its capacities. You'll find out more about the impact of diet, rest, climate, weather, and other factors on your body when you are giving it a challenging workout than when you are just going about the rest of your daily routine.

Keeping a log book of your rides will enable you to record and measure your progress and its effects. Some riders log in only their times, mileages, and pulse rates. We recommend keeping more extensive notations, including thoughts that occur to you along the way about how you can improve your performance or your bike; feelings you have before, during, and after the ride; information on your diet, the kinds of warmups you are doing, or anything you notice that particularly improves or handicaps your ride.

The more you ride and the higher your level of training, the more you'll want to have all your powers working for you. Accordingly, there are certain tools for refining your ride and for increasing your pleasure in the experience of high-level cycle training. These tools fall into three categories: diet, breathing, and motivation. Although each of these categories is important, diet is listed first because in some ways what you eat has more dramatic effects on your performance than the other two categories combined. (See our chapter on Diet)

Diet and High-Level Fitness

Nothing is more controversial among athletes and their trainers than the subject of diet. But if there is agreement on any one point, it is that the good old American meat-and-potatoes diet is not conducive to optimal fitness.

The more you exercise, the more your body dictates certain dietary changes. The folly of eating large quantities of anything at all just before or during a long ride, for example, quickly becomes apparent to the cyclist through such symptoms as cramps, stomach ache, nausea, diarrhea, headache, a sudden, unexpected drop in energy, and even anxiety and depression. You'll also notice that too much meat in your diet makes you feel listless during a ride, that a high sugar content in your diet causes uneven energy cycles — with extreme highs and lows — and that too much salt in your diet increases your heart rate in an unhealthy way and causes your body to retian more water than it needs.

In recent years serious athletes have discovered that they can perform best on vegetarian diets — in some cases fully vegetarian, and in other cases augmented with small quantities of meat, especially fish and fowl.

The subject of diet among any group of people, athletes or not, is an emotional one. However, athletic people find themselves in a unique position. In order to increase their pleasure and improve their performance, they must be willing to put aside their biases and take a closer look at diet. One of the first revelations that comes to such people is that they have been bombarded by false information about diet most of their lives. Many of their own biases and habits have been shaped by food packagers — by cereal companies, large commercial bakeries, and milk lobby, the meat producers, the fast-food chains, etc. As Dr. John W. Farquhar points out: "We have received much nutritional misinformation about our true need for protein and calcium, and we are surrounded by a culture that encourages us to consume far more calories, sugar, fat, and cholesterol than is healthy."

Foods To Be Wary Of

Milk. Many people, especially those from the Mediterranean, the Middle East, and Africa, are particularly intolerant of milk. In addition, about 8 percent of all Caucasians have milk allergies. Digestive problems such as gas, bloating, and stomach pains can occur after eating foods that had even a small amount of milk used in their preparation. If you simply don't care for milk, don't drink it. In fact, you should avoid it. Your body is telling you something — that is just doesn't get along well with milk. No one requires milk after the first decade of life in any case.

Grain. Dr. Sheehan tells of a runner who experienced diarrhea and blood in this stool whenver he ate bread before a race. The cause of this was traced to wheat, the culprit in which is gluten — protein found in all grains except corn and rice. It can even be the cause of a disease known as "sprue," or chronic diarrhea. According to Dr. Sheehan, many ahtletes develop this disease and/or intolerance to gluten when placed under stress. To avoid gluten, keep the following out of your diet: bread and all baked goods, cereals, gravies, sauces, and soups that may contain flour or gluten as a thickener. In addition, avoid mayonnaise, ice cream, ale, and beer, which can all contain gluten and gluten derivates.

Coffee. Coffee, caffeine-containing tea and cola drinks frequently cause hyperacidity of the stomach, stomach spasms, and spasms of the colon in people who are sensitive to caffeine. It also stimulates bowel action and acts as a dieuretic.

Excessive Roughage. Athletes with irritable, sensitive, or spastic colons may experience pain, gas, bloating, and thin, pencil-shaped stools after eating large quantities of raw fruit, raw vegetables, baked beans, cabbage, nuts, or corn.

Hyperallergenic Foods. Foods known to cause allergic reactions — such as minor rash, headaches, nasal congestion, itching, bloating, diarrhea, and hives — include shellfish, chocolate, melons, nuts, citrus fruits, strawberries, egg white, and pork.

In addition, there are a number of food additives that can affect your performance: MSG (monosodium glutamate), often used in restaurant sauces, especially for Chinese and Italian foods, can cause headache, itching, or burning sensations throughout your body, even a general sense of disorientation. Refined sugar can leach B-vitamins from your system. Citral, a lemon flavoring, and other artificial flavorings and colorings can make it impossible for your body to use vitamin C. Nitrites, implicated as carcinogenic, are sodium and, at the very least, can cause your body to retain fluids. Alcohol leaches B-vitamins as well as electrolyte minerals (magnesium, potassium, calcium, and sodium) from your system, disrupting natural controls on fluid exchange between cells, impeding metabolic processes within muscle cells, and interfering with the transmission of electrochemical impulses in nerve cells.

You'll find few packaged foods available that aren't filled with chemical additives, including the ones above as well as literally hundreds of others that we don't have the space to list here.

Foods That are Good for You

Now that you know what you shouldn't eat, what about what is good for you? Let's turn to some general guidelines for a training diet.

The human body's fuel system is indeed complex. In an article published in *Bicycling* magazine, Tracy DeCrosta points out that your muscle cells get energy from three basic sources.

1. ATP (adenosine triphosphate): Stored in muscle cells and immediately available for short, strenuous bursts of activity, these energy sources are quickly used up.

2. CP (creatine-phosphate): Also stored in muscle cells, this substance regenerates ATP as it is used up.

3. Glycogen: Stored in muscle tissue and in the liver, it is processed by our bodies to produce more ATP and CP.

Glycogen is made in your body, mainly through the digestion of carbohydrates. Its production, storage, and utilization are very efficient. Fats from meats are also used as fuel, but their conversion to energy for the muscle cells is quite inefficient. As DeCrosta tells us, the waste products of meat and high-protein foods ". . . are processed through the kidneys, and that extra digestive stress during an activity like cycling can be a hindrance."

A conditioned athlete can store up to 70,000 calories of fat in his or her body. this storage of fat need not be supplemented by large quantities of meat. The fact is that we can satisfy all our needs for fat from vegetable sources and from small quantities of oils used in food preparation.

So what kinds of foods are best for athletes in training? The answer is simple, natural carbohydrates. Here's why: Even though our bodies convert carbohydrates to glycogen very efficiently (glycogen being rapidly convert carbohydrates to glycogen very efficiently (glycogen being rapidly converted to energy in our muscle cells), our bodies can store only 2,000 to 3,000 calories' worth of carbohydrates. Because of this high utilization and low storage ratio, John Farquhar recommends that at least 55 percent of a person's diet consist of carbohydrates.

- Eat foods with "life" in them: raw fruits and vegetables, or vegetables that have been cooked only for short periods of time.
- Eat dried legumes (lentils, beans, etc.) for your main protein source. Instead of large quantities of beef or pork, eat small quantities of fish or fowl.
- Eat whole grain rather than refined grain products: whole-wheat bread, brown rice, granola breakfast cereals, etc.
- Eat small quantities of food frequently rather than large quantities less frequently. Never stuff yourself, especially prior to or during a ride.

Don't suddenly change your diet. Both body and mind will rebel if you do. Rather, set goals for yourself and work into new nutritional habits gradually. Here are some goals for cyclists who want to improve their training diets. Try one goal at a time, advancing to the next goal only when you feel satisfied with achieving the previous one:

1. When you feel a craving for a sugary snack, grab an apple or other fruit instead.

2. When you feel the need for a cup of coffee, a beer, or a cola drink, reach instead for an herbal tea drink (hot or iced) or a glass of fruit juice. Most stores now carry a stock of individual, chilled bottles of fruit juice, which you can drink down as you would a bottle of pop.

3. For your lunches, try vegetarian sandwiches such as avocado and tomato; tomatoes, sprouts, and lettuce; or peanut butter with grated carrots and apple slices — always made with whole-wheat bread or pita bread.

4. Buy a vegetable steamer and wok, and experiment with cooking fresh vegetables instead of canned or frozen ones.

5. Instead of eating ham and eggs for breakfast, have a bowl of fresh, whole-grain granola or "Familia" with slices of fresh fruit on top.

6. Eat meat for only one meal a day. Avoid red meat. Fish or poultry is easier on your digestion.

7. Replace beef, pork, or lamb in your diet with fish or fowl (skinned to reduce fat).

8. Look in recipe books for vegetarian main courses, and have these in place of meat-centered dinners at least twice a week.

9. Try out meat substitutes such as falafel and soy-burgers, which are available at health-food stores; let them replace meat in your diet two or three times a week.

10. Replace snack foods such as ice cream with yogurt and fresh fruit; replace cakes or candies with oatmeal cookies (made from any recipe, but with sugar reduced and raisins or dried fruits added).

Improved nutrition will reward you not only in higher athletic performance, but in better overall health as well. The American Heart Association tells us that cutting down on our intake of meats, dairy foods, and eggs will reduce our risk of heart disease. In addition, the higher bulk content of foods such as fresh vegetables fruits, and whole grains reduces one's risk of a long list of digestive diseases. Also proper diet stabilizes our energy levels, freeing us from the extreme highs and lows in mood and motivation that are caused by eating high-calorie, low-nutrition foods.

Feeding and "The Bonk" on the Road From Kona to Havi

Except in a very short race, you must drink liquid during an event; this is carried in a water bottle on the bike or in a back pocket of the racing jersey.

Liquid is important because the body is much more efficient when operating in its normal temperature range. If you continually consume liquids, taking on a little bit at a time, you're operating probably about two degrees lower than if you let yourself get into a condition of dehydration. So keep sipping when you can and you will perform much more efficiently. If it's very hot, for example, you might use two bottles of fluid in fifty miles.

There are a number of replacement drinks that contain some of the substances lost in perspiration. These are good but they can leave a saccharine taste in the mouth. Some people like water with a little bit of lemon. Some people take tea during a race, but if you spill this on yourself it's sticky. That's why I feel plain water is the best. You can do everything with it. If it's hot you can sprinkle it over your head or your feet or your neck.

If a race lasts more than 70-75 miles, you may also need to eat at about the 40-mile point. Your body wears down like a battery. Ask any cyclist what it's like to run out of energy in a race; you get what they call "the bonk." You pedal in triangles and see black spots in front of your eyes. This comes from not eating, and you can prevent it by training for the event properly and by taking food after a certain amount of time.

Fruit is good to eat during a race because fruits have salts and other things that you lose in sweat. Carbohydrates are necessary, too. They're like firewood — instant energy. I wouldn't recommend eating anything that has a lot of acid.

Bananas are a favorite. Raisins are difficult to digest. Things that have skins on them, like apples, you should peel and cut up. A lot of people like oranges because they clean out the mucus and the buildup in your mouth, but other people can't eat oranges because they're too acid. Riders also carry sandwiches made of honey or cheese or other concoctions. It all depends on the individual.

As soon as you feel the slightest bit hungry, you should definitely eat something. After a while you'll learn how long you can ride until you start feeling bad; you should eat just before this happens so you won't go through any period of weakness.

In training you can actually change your metabolism. I've found that if I'm sprinting regularly and then try to start training for a long-distance event, I'll start to get that weak feeling after two and a half hours. But as I train over a period of time, I can go longer and longer without getting that. I believe your metabolism adapts to the event you are training for. A sprinter has to consume his energy in eleven seconds. He burns it up immediately and his metabolism is geared to that. So when a sprinter goes on a road ride his metabolism is working faster and it utilizes the food he has eaten in a shorter period of time.

Even famous riders get the bonk if they don't eat and go out riding. It's not a thing to be

Determining length of the stem (handlebar Position 3). The stem is correctly sized if a plumb line from the nose drops approximately 1 inch behind the handlebars in Position 3. The elbows should be slightly bent. The rider's weight is comfortably divided — 45 percent front, 55 percent rear. The arms are relaxed and the rider's weight is supported by the arms and shoulders combined.

This illustrates the negative effect of riding stiff-armed as all the road shock is transmitted through the arms to the body.

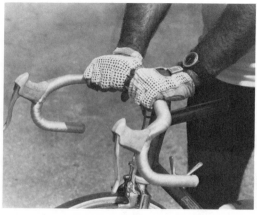

(A) The hands are placed on the "tops" of the handlebars. Always keep one hand in this position when riding one-handed — this position provides the greatest stability. (B) Variation on above position with hands a little further apart.

The hands are on the "tops," behind the brakes. However, this variation utilizes the top of the brake lever as a rest. All good-quality hand brakes include a rubber hood to insulate the hands against road shock. This position allows use of the brake by merely extending the fingers. This position is recommended for climbing when out of the saddle. This position is very stable, allows free breathing, and the levers can be used to increase pedal pressure when hill climbing.

Proper placement of the hands in this position varies according to the physique of the rider. There is one rule of thumb: The wrist should be straight. If you hold your wrist straight before you touch the bars and then grasp the bar at the spot where your wrist is straight, you have found "correct" position.

If the feet are pointed in, the knees will point in. Although this is an exaggeration of the correct position, the cleats should be mounted to position the foot with the toes pointed slightly inward.

If the feet of a rider are pointed out, the knees will also point out. Obviously incorrect.

This position does not encourage the "knees to the bar" aerodynamic position.

ANKLING POSITIONS "BY THE CLOCK"

Ankling can be learned and practiced by clock positions. Beginning at the top or 12 o'clock position (as viewed from the left side of the bicycle), the foot with the ball centered over the axle of the pedal should be tipped up relative to the leg and pushing forward on the pedal. As the pedal approaches the three o'clock position, the foot approaches a flat or square position and force is straight down. At 6 o'clock, toes are almost curled under, tipped down relative to the leg and pushing backward. As the pedal rotates through 6 o'clock, the toes begin pulling up on the toe-clips as the foot again approaches the flat position at nine o'clock. Approaching the 12 o'clock position, toes are tipped up and getting ready to push forward as the pedal rotates through 12 o'clock. Ankle action results from tipping the toes up to tipping them down and back again through the 360-degree motion of the pedal.

Although all serious cyclists have toe clips and straps on their pedals, most riders do not use them to their full advantage. You can prove this to yourself by watching the pedaling stroke of the average cyclist. Imagine the circle scribed by the cyclist's foot is the face of a clock. Most riders do not actually apply pressure to the pedals for more than three "hours" (from four to seven o'clock when the rider is viewed riding from left to right). It is impossible to assist individual riders with their pedal stroke in a book — that is the job of the coach. Understanding and being able to analyze the theory of efficient pedaling will hopefully benefit all riders who do not have a coach available.

432

Here we show an illustration of "Standing On It" meaning getting out of the saddle and pumping hard, either for a fast getaway from the pack or for hill climbing. Notice the head position is directly over the front hub, the weight is forward. The arms are used by pulling on the grips, to assist the legs in applying torque to the pedals. Good standing style permits some lateral bike motion but not to the extreme.

433

Diane Giebel, 1968 U.S. Olympic Team Member demonstrates the proper method for taking Heart Rate Count. Place the hand on the neck under the jawbone, where one can feel the pulsation of the carotid artery. The swimmer should take his pulse for 6 seconds and multiply by 10 (or take it for 10 seconds and multiply by 6 seconds). The pulse should be taken as soon as possible after an effort since the pulse rate decreases very quickly.

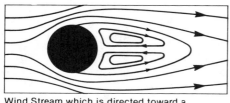

Wind Stream which is directed toward a cylindrical object disturbs air flow.

Smooth wind stream with streamlined object.

CONVERSION TABLE OF CENTIMETERS TO INCHES

CM	IN.	CM	IN.
46	18.11	56	22.04
47	18.50	57	22.44
48	18.89	58	22.83
49	19.29	59	23.22
50	19.68	60	23.62
51	20.07	61	24.01
52	20.47	62	24.41
53	20.86	63	24.80
54	21.25	64	25.19
55	21.65	65	25.59

ashamed of. It's just a fact; if you don't eat any food you're not going to have anything to burn.

There is a funny thing that happens, though. Let's say you get stuck out on the road with no money and no food, or you're in a race and didn't get fed. You'll go through a super-weak period, but if you can get through that then you seem to come back again a little bit. I think this is when your body begins to utilize fat reserves. Even a very fit athlete still has over ten percent fat. So you definitely experience some kind of revitalization.

Feeding Technique

Originally, it was difficult to get to the places on the course to feed riders. This is why there were pockets in the front of their jerseys, to carry more food. But now a lot of the races aren't that long, the roads are better, and riders can carry most of what they need in their rear pockets.

Whether to carry all your food with you or pick it up along the way depends on how long the race is, how many feeding stations there are, and whether you can depend on people to feed you.

If you have complete faith in the people who are working for you, and their job is to be there at the feeding zone, then it's nice not to carry the weight. You know for sure that you can get fed along the way. Perhaps your trainer explains the route and says, "This is where we're going to feed you." He'll have everything ready and you won't have all that bulk in your jersey.

But in a smaller event without so much support, it's better to carry your own food. In a lot of races you're not really sure what's going on and the people who work for you are not really sure what's going on and nobody knows the course. So you should carry as much as you can.

Feeding is usually done at a place on the course where the race isn't going very fast. It might be just at the crest of a little grade, for example. It can be difficult to get fed if the riders are bunched together when they come into the feeding area, so you should try to spread out a little. Sometimes you will see riders grabbing for other people's food, or even trying to knock other people's food to the ground.

It's always a good idea to plan out what you do, whether it's the race itself or the feeding. If you decide beforehand to be fed on the left side of the road, then you'll only have to look to the left. Your trainer could wear a certain color jersey — pure white or pure red — or use a yellow musette bag or the team colors. All that is helpful.

To hand up a water bottle, your trainer should place his fingers around the neck and hold it from the top, then run along with it, looking where he is going. For instance, if he is on the right side of the road he should hold the bottle in his left hand and glance over his left shoulder. He trots along and you just come by and pluck it right out of his hand. The trainer should be sure to hold the bottle steady and to watch out that other people don't grab it or knock it down.

Food is handed up in a musette bag, a square cloth bag with a long loop. The trainer holds the loop out and you must stick your arm through it and throw it around your back as you come by. It's not necessary to run with the musette bag; it's just held.

However you do it, feeding is important in the race. A water bottle is a lifeline and even an apple tastes like a feast when you've been out there for a long time.

Breathing for Increased Performance
See our Chapter on Super Breathing

While food is essential in producing the stuff that allows us to use our muscles, without oxygen our bodies would be unable to convert the things we eat into energy. For this reason it is important to develop our lungs' capacities to their fullest.

**Most people breathe shallowly, never fully inflating their lungs.
In the following exercise, the objective is to increase your lung
capacity by concentrating on your lower abdominal area.**

1. Sit cross-legged, either on the floor or on a wide-couch. Loosen your belt and pants. Let your hands relax on your knees. Take a deep breath. Hold it. Let it out. Do this a second and third time to loosen up your chest and abdominal muscles.

2. Take a deep breath. Deeper! Expand your abdominal muscles. Let your belly balloon out. Breathe in still more air, expanding your chest. Slowly raise your shoulders, keeping your hands on your knees. This complete inhalation should take about seven seconds. When your lungs are filled, hold that breath for a moment.

3. Exhale for seven seconds, lowering your shoulders while your chest and abdominal muscles are relaxing.

Do this complete exercise several times over for about ten minutes at a time. Practice it two or three times a day, whenever the opportunity arises — while waiting for an appointment, while stopped in heavy commuter traffic, or even while working at your desk. It's an excellent exercise to combine with watching television or listening to music.

Deep Personal Rewards

High levels of physical training need not involve world-record challenges or heroic efforts to compete against the best. On the contrary, for most of us, achieving a high level of physical training and proficiency as a cyclist is a quiet and personal thing. Still, there is a part of each of us that shares the feelings of victory that the greatest of athletes experience each time they complete a particularly fine performance. For me, the greatest feeling of victory came at the conclusion of my 1980 ride, I remember when the red ribbon marking my finish line came into view. I broke through it and was instantly mobbed by my crew. They raised me on their shoulders, cheered, and hugged me; together we wept with joy and relief at our joint accomplishment. I was the happiest man in the world. There are no words that will ever explain how I felt. The thrill of being able to cover distances with the energies of one's own body that most people would consider covering only in a motor vehicle sparks something deep and basic in everyone who has ever done it. While the exact source of the unparalleled excitement of this experience remains an elusive and seductive mystery, most cyclists who have acquired high levels of fitness understand that they've touched and expressed parts of themselves which perhaps lie sleeping in everyone and may be as essential and universal as friendship and love.

I like to walk about amidst the beautiful things that adorn the world. —George Santayana

If you pick 'em up, O Lord, I'll put 'em down. —Anon, The Prayer of the Tired Walker

To Compete or Not To Compete While Training

This subject will keep the conversation around the pool, bike shop, or water fountain, going for hours! Max Telford says *No* . . . stick to your training schedules. If you participate in a 10k or half marathon, it will take you out of your routine for 2 or 3 days; a full marathon will remove you from your schedule for as much as a week or more. And of course there is always the possibility of injuries that could keep you from training for an extended period of time.

I believe that there is a happy medium where a competitive swim, bike or run event, whether individually or in combination, is beneficial. If triathlon training is on schedule, it is helpful to the triathlete to get the feel of the crowd while swimming, biking or running. Chances are that he has been training alone and is not aware of the problems that he could run up against with other competitors: a mass swim start with a large number of contestants all trying to round the first buoy together . . . the problems created by out and back bike course traffic . . . and mixing bike and running on the same out and back course!

Competing against time is not important in these preliminary events . . . but care to avoid injury is very important! You will want to race another day, so take care.

A Sample Twelve Month Biking Schedule

Many have asked why it takes 12 months to learn how to ride a bike 112 miles. It does not take twelve months to accomplish this feat. A recreational rider may do it on his first try, although I would advise that he has bus fare home. From this first attempt at a century ride, the biker will improve in strength and stamina. Until a year later he will not only make the ride but will do it in 5 to 6 hours as opposed to his sub 12 mile per hour finishing time of his first ride, if he finished at all. As practice and training progresses he will continue to improve in distance and strength until a year later or two years after his first century ride attempt, he can be considered a competition rider. This is providing, however, he has put in the weekly miles and applied training concepts necessary to achieve this goal.

The same aerobic training concepts adopted for the runner apply equally for the biker. The hard, easy riding day formula also applies. The Long Slow Distance concept now called the Long Steady Distance, incorporating POT (Plenty Of cranking Tempo), is the basis of building staying power. Strength training is applied to biking much in the same way that it is in running — doing hill work, weight training, and aerobic intervals to the anerobic barrier. Here also we will use the heart rate per minute or BPM as the controlling level of our individual effort. Time trialing and speed play (just as in running) can be used to a great advantage in bicycle training.

We will first assume that the rider does not have extensive riding experience. The more accomplished rider may join in at the level of his skill.

MONTH 1:
Hard days are for distance riding starting with 5 miles per day, keeping in low gears and spinning the pedals smoothly at 90 R.P.M.'s, 3 days per week. Locate a suitable course, out and back, that has a few hills, preferably away from automobile pollution and traffic. Easy days are for strength training, practice hill climbing by sitting in the saddle as long as possible, spinning in the lowest gears you have.

MONTH 2:
Distance should be increased to 10 miles per day, 3 days per week, incorporating speed play and hill climbs. Nautilus weight training on the 3 easy days.

MONTH 3:
Increase to 20 miles per workout day, 3 days per week, increasing hill climbing. Nautilus weight training.

MONTH 4:

Increase distance to 30 miles per day for the three days alternating with Nautilus Weight training. We will now begin to integrate biking with either the swimming schedule or the running period, depending upon the individual's time schedule. In combining two events, endeavor to tie them as closely (time-wise) as possible to get the maximum benefit from the transition of muscle usage from event to event.

MONTH 5:

Distance should remain at 30 miles per day, but should include plenty of spinning tempo and moving up on gears on all terrains. This will tend to start building strength into the spin. Pedal RPM's might drop to 80 but will increase as your strength builds. Nautilus Weight Training 3 days per week.

MONTH 6:

Thirty miles per day for the 3 easy days should increase to 4 days per week, maintaining the 90 pedal RPM's but striving for higher gears on all terrains. Heavier hill work should be included in each workout. If you cannot find a steeper hill use higher gears. For those who live in a hill-less countryside, invest in a 12 or 13 point high gear for your cluster and spin these gears with the 52 point chain ring on the flat stretches at 90 RPM. Nautilus Strength Training.

MONTH 7:

Thirty miles per day, 4 days per week, combining swim or run schedules with each workout. The weight training schedule, as set for the swimming and running easy days, is the same schedule thereby reducing the number of hours spent on the easy days for each event. Where the weight training day conflicts with a hard day's distance swim, bike or run, schedule it for an early or late time of day.

MONTH 8:

We will now start to increase mileage and combination of training modes to include 3 events in one day. For example, an early AM 2000-meter swim followed by a bike ride of 15 miles and a 10 K run or a total workout of 2 to 3 hours, with a 20- to 30-mile bike ride in the evening. Nautilus strength training on the off or easy day.

MONTH 9:

As in Month 8, increasing the mileage and workout time a minimum of 3 hours and 120 miles per week on the bike, may be split up over the 4 days but with not less than 20 miles in any one day with possibly a 50-mile ride on the weekend. Swim-Bike-Run combining should include more distances in each event. Nautilus Strength Training.

MONTH 10:

Increase mileage to 160 per week with a century ride on the weekend thrown in. Plenty of hill work striving for higher gears maintaining 80 to 90 pedal RPM's. Multi-sport combining should include increased times to at least a 4-hour consecutive workout in the three events. Nautilus Strength Training.

MONTH 11:

Increase mileage to 200 per week with a century thrown in on the weekend. The transition from the bike to the run should be smooth now, no binding calf and quad leg muscles going into the run. Combined training should occupy all of your spare time and then some, at least 4 to 5 hours. Running mileage after your first marathon should be averaging 60 to 80 miles per week, swimming distance at 7 to 10,000 meters, and biking 300 miles. Plenty of combination training and Nautilus Strength Training should be thrown in.

MONTH 12:

You have sharpened your skills in all events, your distances are running 10,000 meters swimming, 100 miles running and 300 biking. Care should be taken at this point to avoid injuries and not to over train or to peak out too early prior to your first big triathlon!

BIKE RACING GLOSSARY

Ankling: Changing the angle of the foot when pedaling.

Apron: The optional flat area, specially surfaced, on the infield just inside and below the banked or racing part of a track.

Atmospheres: A measure of air pressure in the tires, which is described as a multiple of that at sea level.

Attack: To go at a faster pace in order to get away from another ride or group of riders.

Australian pursuit: An event on the track in which three or more rider start evenly spaced around the track and at the same time. Riders who are caught are removed from the race, which continues until there is only one man left.

Balancing: Maintaining the bike motionless on the track with the feet still in the pedals, a technique used by sprinters.

Banking: The main surface of a track, or more particularly the steepest area.

Blocking: To get in the way of other riders, as a tactic.

Blow up: To overexert oneself, run out of energy, or give up.

"Bonk, the": A feeling of complete physical collapse that comes when the rider runs out of energy.

Bottom bracket: The tube at the bottom of the frame that holds the crank assembly.

Break or breakaway: A group of riders that leaves the main group behind.

Bridge (a gap): To cross the space between one group of riders and another.

Bunch: See Field.

Chasers: Small groups or single riders trying to catch other groups.

Chucker: See Jamming tool.

Clinchers: A conventional bicycle tire with tube, which resembles an automobile tire in the way it is mounted on the rim.

Cluster: A group of gears fastened together and mounted on the rear wheel. Also called a block.

Cone nuts: Thin nuts that are screwed on the axle shaft to adjust and lock the wheel bearings.

Crank: The arm extending from the spindle of the bottom bracket assembly, upon which the pedals are mounted, or more properly the entire assembly (which includes those arms).

Criterium: A multilap road race on a short, usually closed, course.

Cross-three or cross-four: Refers to the pattern of spokes and how many other spokes each one crosses in its path from the hub to the rim.

Cups: Placed in the top and bottom of the head tube to hold the bearings in position.

Cyclocross: A bicycle event in which part of the course contains obstacles or difficult sections that must or may be covered on foot, carrying the bike.

Derailleur: A mechanical device used to shift the chain from one gear to another.

Drafting: Being protected from the wind by riding close behind another rider. Also called sitting in or pacing.

Echelon: A staggered line of riders, each one downwind of the one ahead.

Field: The main group of riders, also known as the pack or the bunch.

Field sprint: The finish among the main group of riders.

Fixed gear: A direct-drive chain and cog setup in which the rider cannot coast or shift gears.

Force the pace: To ride harder or attack.

Freewheel: The element in the rear gear setup that enables the rider to coast when not peddaling.

Half-wheeling: Staying a few inches ahead of another rider while riding alongside him in training.

Hammering: Riding hard.

Handicap: On the road, an event in which groups of riders start at different times, giving the slower ones an earlier start, etc. On the track, this is usually done by starting the riders on different lines instead of at different times.

Handsling: A method of changing partners in a team race.

Hang in: Barely keeping contact at the back of a group of riders.

Headset bearings: the small bearings located at the top and bottom of the head tube, which allow the fork to be held in position and move freely.

Hook: To move your back wheel as a threat, or by mistake, against the front wheel of another.

Interval training: A method, used in many sports, of short periods of near maximum effort interspaced with rest periods of minimum effort.

Italian pursuit: A form of team pursuiting on the track, with two teams of four or more men starting on opposite sides; each man drops out after he pulls a lap. The race ends with single riders on each team and the winning team is the one whose rider crosses his team's line first.

Jamming: Riding hard.

Jamming tool: Also called a chucker. In team racing, an object that fits in the left hip pocket and is grasped by the partner to throw or relay the rider into the race.

Jump: To get out of the saddle and accelerate.

Kilometer: 1,000 meters, or the time trial event for one rider that covers this distance on the track.

Lay-back: The amount by which the seat is positioned behind the center of the cranks, or the angle of the seat tube that controls this.

Lead-out: A tactic or training activity in which one rider sprints for the benefit of the one behind him, who then comes by at an even greater speed.

Limit rider(s): In a handicap event, the rider or riders who have the shortest distance to travel.

Madison: A team race on the track in which riders on the same team relay each other into the race and take turns being in contention.

Mass start: Any event on the track or the road in which everyone starts at the same time and place. A scratch race.

Match sprint: A track event of two to four riders over the number of laps closest to 1,000 meters. The winner is the rider who crosses the line first. Time is taken on the last 200 meters.

Minute man or rider: In a time trial, the rider who starts one minute ahead of you is called your minute man.

Miss-and-out: Also called Devil-take-the-hindmost. A track event in which the last rider over the line on each lap or given number of laps is removed from the race.

Motorpace: To follow behind a vehicle with an engine; particularly, the event on the track involving pairs of motorcycles and bicycles.

Out-and-back: A course that goes to a certain point, makes a 180-degree turn, and comes back the same way. Usually used in time trials.

Pace line: A string of riders who alternately ride at the front and sit in.

Pack: See Field.

Pedal action: The turn of speed on the pedals.

Pick-up: Changing partners in a team race.

Point race: An event, on the track or the road, in which riders earn points by their placings in several finishes or primes throughout the race. The winner is not the first man to finish the race, but the one with the most points after the finish.

Point-to-point: A road race that is run from one place to another and that covers the course only once.

Pole line: The innermost line on the track, around which it is measured.

Pole, the: The area on a track between the pole line and the sprinters' line.

Prime: A sprint for points or prizes within a race. Not the finish.

Pull or pull through: To take a turn going hard at the front of a pace line or the field.

Pull off: To move to the side in order to let another rider come to the front.

Pursuit: A track event in which riders start on opposite sides and try to catch each other.

Road bike: A bicycle used for road racing and training on the road and that has several gears and at least one handbrake.

Road race: A general term for all events on the road, including time trials, criteriums, stage races, etc., but usually referring to a race of 25-100 miles over a large course.

Roller racing: Events, usually indoors, in which two or more sets of rollers are attached to some kind of distance recorder for the purposes of competition.

Rollers: An apparatus consisting of three cylinders joined by a drive belt and fitting the wheelbase of a bicycle, on which the cyclist can ride in place. Used for home training or exercise, for racing, and to warm up before events, especially at the track.

Runner: A dished section of the track between the banking and the apron or infield.

Sew-up or tubular (tire): A tire in which the tube is sewn into the tire casing. It is attached to the rim with adhesive.

Sitting in: Drafting, or staying close behind another rider to be protected from the wind.

Six-day: An indoor track race, similar to a stage race on the road, which takes place over six days and is contested by teams of two or three riders, mostly in madison-style racing. The winner is the team that covers the greatest distance and/or wins the most points.

Sleigh riding: Sitting in, without doing any work at the front. Also called wheel-sucking.

Slipstream: The area of least wind resistance right behind another rider.

Snap: quick acceleration ability.

Spindle: A central shaft in the bottom bracket assembly upon which bearings are mounted and to which the crank arms are attached. Can also refer to the axle in the hubs.

Sprint: A high-speed finish to a race or for a prime. Also, in track racing, the match sprint event.

Sprinters' line: A line 70 centimeters to the outside of, and running parallel to, the pole line. In the final 200 meters of some races, once the lead rider goes to the inside of the sprinters' line he is considered to have entered the pole and must stay inside of that line for the remainder of the race.

Stage race: An event consisting of several races — road, criterium, and time trial — which takes place over one day or more and in which the winner is the rider or team with the shortest total time for the combination of events.

Stayer bike: A bicycle used in the motorpace event, with a small front wheel, special fork, and other unique features.

Stayers' line: A line circling the track about halfway up, used in the motorpace event and in team racing.

String: In a race, a line of riders going off the front of the field or attacking.

Humor and knowledge are the two great hopes of civilization. —*Konrad Lorenz*

Upper Left: Filming, Feb. 1982, Spring Ironman Triathlon Movie . . . Kona Bay, Ironman Swim Course out past Hilton and return . . . Friday evening before big day—casual conversation hides anxiety . . . Tom and Ironman friend from Detroit . . . Dr. Scaff lectures Honolulu Marathon Clinic, after finishing grueling 50 mile run around the Island . . . Waikiki Swim Club starting their 9:00 A.M. Saturday Weekly Swim of 1000 and 2000 meters . . . Swim start of the 4 mile Rough Water Invitational Waikiki Swim, Kaimana Beach . . . Dr. Paul C. Bragg Memorial Cross . . . Wild Boar Ham Cum Wild Pig Pu Pus . . . Start of the '81 Santa Barbara 1/2 Triathlon. 3 pictures vertical row: USTS San Diego Start . . . Bob Johnson, Author, finishing Santa Barbara 1/2 Triathlon . . . USTS San Diego Start, splashing into 56 degree water . . . Co-Author Patricia Bragg.

VIII

Marathon and Ultramarathon Training for the Triathlon

Upper left: Diane Giebel, 1968 Olympic Team Member—Top Swimmer in '81 Santa Barbara Triathlon. Upper right: Bob Fox, Triathlete and contestant in Oct./82 Ironman . . . '82 Goleta Beach Run Swim run scenes . . . Carol and Kim, "Tri Manual" staff with Diane Giebel in the center.

1

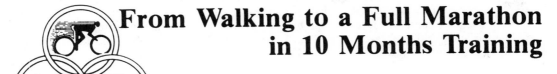

From Walking to a Full Marathon in 10 Months Training

Most Triathletes are from the Running Sport

RECENT STATISTICS HAVE PROVEN that the greatest majority of aspiring Triathletes are running specialists. This fact makes it difficult to lay out a training program that experienced runners and non-runners alike can adhere to. In truth, I will not attempt to. For every runner there is a formula, the faster the runner the more positive he is that he has the only key to successful marathon training. I will not argue with this. I would only bid him best wishes, good running, and be on his way! I wish to direct this chapter to the 95 to 99% of the rest of us who have an open mind and are interested in the alternative viewpoint from which to make a personal judgement based on our inherent strengths and weaknesses, and not Mr. 1% who is running down the road preceded by the T.V. camera truck.

Fortunately for us, we will be able to utilize this simple, but well-practiced training method, in all phases of Triathlon training be it Swim, Bike, or Run. Your stop watch and your heart rate is your training chart, your training log will in essence be your schedule in retrospect.

The last event in Triathlon, the marathon, is only a running race for the sub 4 hour finishers. For the remainder, at best, it is a run-walk effort, at worst, survival.

The training concepts that are applicable to swim and bike as well as run are based on distance strength and speed work in that order. This formula will build stamina that will carry you through the full Triathlon in a good style.

On Starting from Scratch

During recent years few contemporary phenomena have enjoyed more diligent scientific scrutiny than running has. In laboratories, medical schools and athletic departments the world over, researchers have been busily searching out the most arcane secrets of the sport. A decade ago the typical athlete was largely on his or her own in ferreting out a training system. Today, by contrast, a great deal of information is available about how the body responds to various regimens. Moreover, as a result of a burgeoning array of journals, both lay and scientific, much of this lore can be studied by any athlete with a modest curiosity. This chapter is based largely on what scientists are currently telling us about running.

When first undertaking a running program, don't assume that just because you're more active than some people you'll have an easier time of it. Rudolph H. Dressendorfer of the Department of Physical Education at the University of California at Davis tested a group of healthy men, twenty-five to thirty-eight years old, who regularly played tennis or golf, surfed, or went skin diving. They adapted to running exactly as if they had been totally untrained. If you're over thirty-five, incidentally, be sure to get a doctor's approval before you start running. This is important because you can feel fine and nonetheless have cardiac or other abnormalities that may cause trouble when you're under physical stress.

The Uses of Patience

In the mind of the typical beginner, getting into shape is a simple matter. The muscles become stronger. Endurance increases. Breathing as you exercise becomes easier. What more could there possibly be to it than that? There is quite a bit more. Profound and fundamental changes occur throughout the body. Since these changes can't be rushed, getting into good condition is likely to take longer than you think it will, especially if you're over thirty. This is particularly true because most such changes require not just exertion but rest as well; it is during the resting intervals that strengthening and rebuilding take place. Thus you may be improving at the very time common sense would suggest you are least likely to be doing so: when you are doing nothing.

On Not Overdoing It

There *is* such a thing as overtraining. When you overtrain, you lose rather than gain ground. Dr. William P. Morgan whose views on running as an addiction were put the matter this way in a recent issue of *The Physician and Sportsmedicine:* "Running should be viewed as a wonder drug. . . . It has profound potential in preventing mental and physical disease and in rehabilitation after various illnesses have occurred. However, just like other wonder drugs, running has the potential for abuse, and the runner who appears in the physician's office on crutches or in a wheelchair as a result of the crippling effects of excessive running can be compared to the hard-core drug addict who overdoses."

The Uses of Warmup

Before a race some runners warm up by running for a few minutes. Others don't. Recent research shows that a warmup really does help, particularly in short, fast runs. Bruce J. Martin and several other researchers at Indiana University's Department of Anatomy and Physiology tested trained runners in ninety-second treadmill runs with and without preparatory warmups. In the efforts following warmup, lactic acid production was lessened an average of 52 percent, creating greater efficiency. In addition, the temperature of the calf muscle was raised, also improving physiological function.

Presumably warmup is less important in longer runs, where the first few minutes can in effect constitute a warmup. Nonetheless, one top marathoner told me, "I always warm up plenty before a race. When you want to start right in moving at five minutes a mile, your body had better be ready to go."

Shoes Matter

Some runners wear lightweight racing flats in competition, while others use heavier training shoes. Does the difference in weight matter? Yes, according to the findings of M. J. Catlin and Rudolph Dressendorfer. When the two researchers tested a group of runners they found that while shoe weight had no discernible effect on stride length, an average of 3.3 percent more energy was required to run in training shoes than in racing flats. In races, wear flats.

Feeling Better Faster

Accumulated lactic acid contributes to the persistence of fatigue after a run. To rid the body of lactic acid, according to studies by Arend Bonen and Angelo N. Belcastro, the best remedy is gentle jogging. Movement, they report, is more effective than rest.

Ill Winds

The typical competitive runner pays diligent attention to his or her weight, diet and training, yet gives little thought to a factor that under some circumstances is just as important: the wind.

Like jet pilots, top runners are aware of wind conditions and use guile, cunning and experience to make the most of them. It is no accident that in 1975, when Bill Rodgers set his first Boston Marathon record, he was pushed along by a friendly tail wind. (Nor, of course, is it an accident that four years later, when he set his second record on the course, his improved abilities required no such help.)

Studies show that in middle- and long-distance races from 15 to 25 percent of a runner's energy is used to overcome wind resistance. If, therefore, such resistance can be reduced, higher speeds can be attained with no increase in energy expenditure. As it turns out, the simplest way to lower wind resistance is to tuck in close to another runner. From 4 to 9 percent of your energy can be conserved in this way, according to calculations made by Chester R. Kyle of California State University at Long Beach.

Running in another runner's lee doesn't always mean, incidentally, running directly behind him. In a crosswind you'll have to run to one side. And in a following wind, try not to stay directly in front of other runners. Get out in the open where the tail wind is strongest.

How to Breathe

Runners sometimes wonder how they should breathe while they run. Should they synchronize their breathing with their footsteps or what? Most authorities say breathing rhythm requires no thought; it takes care of itself without any deliberate attention. One suggestion some coaches, including New Zealand's Arthur Lydiard, make is that air be inhaled and expelled by using the stomach muscles. That way, breathing will be as deep as possible and the maximum amount of oxygen will be available.

Many Running Formulas to Choose From

Many running books on the market offer directions for the beginning runner. Top athletes in the field of distance running have set forth personal running programs and formulas, and systems of training which have probably proven successful in their own personal training program and in some cases that of their students and followers. At the outset of this important chapter in this Triathlon Training Manual, we wish to advise and urgently request that the beginner avail himself of the unlimited sources of excellent material available elsewhere and expand upon the basic information offered in this chapter. Space does not permit extensive coverage of this complex subject because running is just a segment of the triathlon event.

Running for the Beginner

Our responsibility is to take the non-athlete who wishes to become active, away from the T.V. spectator sport environment and encourage him to become a participant. We must assume that he is to start from scratch, meaning that he has read the Chaper on Walking, has been out on the road, getting the feel of putting distance behind himself by foot, and is looking for a new adventure. Triathlon aspirants for the most part are coming out of the ranks of running athletes. Recent polls prove this to be true. Of a thousand quiries into the multi-sport of Triathlon from swimmers, bikers, and runners . . . runners comprised 80% with the remainder being evenly divided between swimmers and bikers. Practicing runners and participating marathon contestants might find some of the material in the running chapter somewhat redundant, however, please bear with us. We know you will find many tips and running helps well worth your reading time and will lead into the training for the ultimate participation sport, the triathlon.

Beginning marathon training concepts are many and varied, as previously stated; however, we particularly like all of Jim Fixx's material now in publication combined with some of the tried and proven basic beginner's concepts of the Honolulu Marathon Clinic under the direction of Drs. Scaff and Wagner.

The Honolulu Marathon boasts being the "Beginners' Marathon," and earns its reputation honestly as over two-thirds of the contestants year in and year out are first-time marathon runners. All ages of men and women have commenced basic training in March and run a full marathon in December, each year for the last 9 years. Many are first-time contestants for any type of distance running competition. It is possible to win the Honolulu Marathon in two ways, the first one to cross the finish line and the last one. Aid stations and timers wait out the very last contestant, regardless of the hour.

As the runner becomes more experienced with a few 10-kilometer runs, half marathons, and his first marathon in his runner's log, it is then time to take up running more seriously if he expects to substantially bring down finishing times. Without advanced training, a runner will reach a plateau of achievement and never progress beyond that point.

Percy Cerutty's Australian Training Concepts

For some reason all eyes turn to the Southern Hemisphere when advanced distance training is mentioned, specifically Australia and New Zealand. Many tiring but profitable days were spent with the late Percy Cerutty at his Runners Training Camp, officially known as The International Athletics' Center, and unofficially by friend's and students as "Ceres." The camp is located near Portsey on the southern tip of Australia near Melbourne, Victoria. I would like to share some of the knowledge gained while I trained with Percy at Portsey. For those who are unaware of Percy's prestigious achievements in the field of distance training, he is credited with training runners who brought back to the 6 million people of Australia over 30 Olympic Gold Medals and scores of lesser awards! The one great name that will live forever in running history is that of Herb Elliot, who stands as a tribute to the training skills and expertise of Percy Cerutty of Portsey.

In the eyes of some, Percy's unique training methods and his personal philosophy prevented them from seeing the gems of wisdom and knowledge from this man with a diminutive stature, weighing scarcely over 145 lbs., with sparkling wit and often cynical candor radiating from his crackling gray eyes. Percy could strip the greats of their pomp and raise up a lanky unknown student to be the greatest name in world running history through his love and dedication to that person and the sport.

An Emphasis on Strength Training

The one great ingredient lacking in most training methods used today for distance running is strength training. The Cerutty training system includes extensive training in weights, gymnastic equipment, swimming, and most of all, hill climbing (not the type of hill climbing most of us are familiar with but "Sand Hill Climbing"). Portsey is situated on a sandy headland projecting out into the Bass Straights of the Great Australian Bight and consists of steep, drifting sand dunes. Percy prided himself on his ability to lead his running class up the sandy hills. Every visitor to "Ceres" simply had to "have a go" at this taxing climb, combined with deep sandy-road and beach running just to get the feel of what it is like to train at Portsey.

Percy was highly criticized by North American and European trainers for this sand hill training concept as well as many of his other innovative ideas. His record stands up against the best trainers with many successes such as world record holders, Herb Elliott, Albert Thomas, Dave Stephens, and an extensive list of Gold, Silver, and Bronze Medal Olympic runners and athletes.

In the profitable time I spent at Portsey with Percy Cerutty, I came away with training concepts which are indelible in my physical, mental, and spiritual being. It is my desire to portray much of Percy's philosophy of life, hoping some of it will rub off on the readers of this book! Percy was not only a sports trainer . . . but a philosopher and teacher. He inspired his athletes to live fuller lives. Part of his daily training program was an inspirational talk, ranging from a combination of Stoicism and Spartanism to Christian beliefs. **In these informal talks, Percy endeavoured to raise the spirit of the athlete and inspire the soul to a higher state of spiritual** consciousness! As the athlete grows spiritually, his physical performance will gradually unfold to new heights and personal records!

At this point we will start with the basics of running, and as we progress, we will inject "Ceruttyisms" where they will best be assimilated into the running routine. A number of publications have come out on Percy's life and training methods including Larry Myers' Training with Cerutty. This is must reading for every distance athlete, especially aspiring marathon runners and triathletes. Upon each reading of this book, one can feel Portsey and the electricity in the air radiating from the energy expended daily from teacher and student alike. We know you will enjoy the same experience I had, without ever having been there. By reading the book, running and life will take on new dimensions that you will not acquire in any other way.

New Zealand Training Concepts

From New Zealand comes the great Arthur Lydiard. Arthur has coached runners in Finland, Mexico, Venezuela, and Denmark as well as his native New Zealand. His training system, perfected over more than 30 years, has been responsible for new records in middle class and especially distance events.

His conditioning and speed training methods are practiced world wide. These methods are largely responsible for the triple success of Barry Magee, Murray Halberg and Peter Snell at the 1960 Rome Olympics and for the triumphs of other New Zealanders and Finns at the 1972 and the 1976 Olympic Games. The Lydiard training method is a common sense approach for running and stamina building, speed work and a good knowledge of physiology.

Running the Lydiard Way. By World Publication, Box 366 Mountain View, California, 94042 . . . is an excellent book to train by and gives the Lydiard philosophy of distance training fully . . . also Arthur Lydiard holds running seminars in the U.S. Date and location available from P.O. Box 589, Glen Ellyn, Illinois, 60126.

World Class Runner Max Telford

The leading proponent of the Lydiard method of distance training is another New Zealander, world class runner, Max Telford. Max, though Scottish born, has spent most of his 44 years in New Zealand and has been the ultramarathon leader since 1968. Max is listed in the *Guinness Book of World Records* for his 186-mile non-stop endurance record in 31½ hours, increasing the existing record distance by 55 miles for that period of time. He holds more unusual long-distance world running records than anyone else and is one of only three men to have run more than 100,000 miles in his career including a 5,180-mile run, plus two-way transits across both Death Valley and the Grand Canyon.

Max Telford is presently a distance running instructor in Honolulu, Hawaii. While the Telford distance training method is strictly his own, Max is partial to his old teacher, and brother New Zealander, Arthur Lydiard, and his proven training philosophy.

Max believes that the ultramarathon is the fastest growing side of the sport of running. He feels that marathons are getting too big . . . serious runners are being lost in the crowd, and the challenge is lost. He is excited about the swim, bike, and run triathlon as an emerging multi-sport and has priceless counsel and help for the training triathlete! Telford's training method is based on distance stamina, strength and speed in that order . . . developing one before going on to the next. His method is to develop mileage and then move into strength and speed training. These concepts are directly applicable to biking and swimming.

Hawaii — Traithlon Trainer's Paradise

It was with great pride that I was accepted into Max's weekly training class at Kapiolani Park, Honolulu. I cannot think of a better year-round training situation for the serious distance runner or biker than Honolulu, Hawaii. The Waikiki Swim Club, the originating originization of the triathlon, offers extensive opportunities to perfect the distance swim: the beautiful new pool at the University of Hawaii; a Saturday morning group swim of 1,000 to 2,000 meters in the Ala Moana Basin followed by a friendly get together around the breakfast table. Every Sunday 2.5 mile buddy-system rough water swims are planned for distance swim training . . . all of this in 70° to 80° clear blue water.

Would You Like to Run a Full Marathon in 10 Months?

Well, back to the business of training to run a marathon in 10 months. There are as many methods to train for a marathon as there are sub-three marathon runners. When they are hot and in their prime, their formulas and advice is well received; but as they begin to lose their speed, their books and running counsel begin to wain as does the distribution of their publications. For the serious runner, with a few full marathons under his or her belt, there are few names that have survived the test of time in the running field, as I have stated, and those are, Arthur Lydiard, Percy Cerutty and the world class distance athlete, Max Telford. Their names and formulas will pop up regularly in books and publications on the subject of running which is a true test of the staying power of their training concepts. Even though Percy Cerutty has passed on, his Ceruttyisms of distance training live on. Arthur Lydiard and Max Telford are sharing their priceless gems of over distance training concepts with interested students at the training locations mentioned.

From a pure beginner's point of view, I personally like the Honolulu Marathon Clinic's approach to training. Drs. Scaff and Wagner, both qualified sports medicine doctors, have perfected a system of training that seems to best suit the novice and are exporting these concepts around the country. Of the nine marathons held in Honolulu, with as many as 7,000 contestants each year, two-thirds are usually first timers. If a person of reasonably good health of any age will come down to Kapiolani Port at 7:30 Sunday morning on the first day of March and each Sunday morning thereafter until the first week in December, following the simple weekly instructions given at each early morning pre-run briefing, he will be ready to run a full 26.238 mile marathon in early December.

Now this is basic training at its best, considering the time frame and the intensity of the training. You are trained to survive and to complete the marathon, speed is not a training consideration, this is left up to the individual, which I believe is as it should be, finishing is the main consideration in the first marathon for most beginners. Speed will come in its own time.

Max Telford, looks at this subject of basic training another way which is also very effective. Again I would urge everyone seriously interested in excelling in the sport of running, beyond just surviving, to go to Hawaii and become involved in the excellent running environment and teaching of the Telford method.

The Importance of a Runner's Log

The first consideration in running is the use of a Runner's Log. Rather than use valuable space in this book for the layout of schedules, we suggest that you duplicate the page, "Basic Runner's Log" at your local duplicating store. This will give you a daily, weekly, and monthly account of your training activities.

It is extremely important to take your "before rising" heart rate each morning. You will begin to notice a change in heart rate for the better in the ensuing months. To establish a complete medical record and to check out any signs of abnormal physiological function or cardiac condition, you should take a treadmill stress test. These tests will establish blood pressure, etc. for the beginning of your training. An annual follow-up of this stress test will indicate the overall cardiac efficiency improvement made as a result of your training routines.

All pertinent information involved in the daily training routine should be included. This will become your running history and your best training manual for years to come because it will show areas for you to work on for improvement, be it strength, speed or long, slow distance.

FIVE MILE SPLITS AT SPEEDS RANGING FROM 4.50 MIN. TO 10.00 MIN. A MILE

Mile	5 Miles	10 Miles	15 Miles	20 Miles	Marathon
4:50	24:10	48:20	1:12:30	1:36:40	2:07:44
5:00	25:00	50:00	1:15:00	1:40:00	2:11:06
5:10	25:50	51:40	1:17:30	1:43:20	2:15:28
5:20	26:40	53:20	1:20:00	1:46:40	2:19:50
5:30	27:30	55:00	1:22:30	1:50:00	2:24:12
5:40	28:20	56:40	1:25:00	1:53:20	2:28:34
5:50	29:10	58:20	1:27:30	1:56:40	2:32:56
6:00	30:00	1:00:00	1:30:00	2:00:00	2:37:19
6:10	30:50	1:01:40	1:32:30	2:03:20	2:41:41
6:20	31:40	1:03:20	1:35:00	2:06:40	2:46:03
6:30	32:30	1:05:00	1:37:30	2:10:00	2:50:25
6:40	33:20	1:06:40	1:40:00	2:13:20	2:54:47
6:50	34:10	1:08:20	1:42:30	2:16:40	2:59:09
7:00	35:00	1:10:00	1:45:00	2:20:00	3:03:33
7:10	35:50	1:11:40	1:47:30	2:23:20	3:07:55
7:20	36:40	1:13:20	1:50:00	2:26:40	3:12:17
7:30	37:30	1:15:00	1:52:30	2:30:00	3:16:39
7:40	38:20	1:16:40	1:55:00	2:33:20	3:21:01
7:50	39:10	1:18:20	1:57:30	2:36:40	3:25:23
8:00	40:00	1:20:00	2:00:00	2:40:00	3:29:45
8:10	40:50	1:21:40	2:02:30	2:43:20	3:34:07
8:20	41:40	1:23:20	2:05:00	2:46:40	3:38:29
8:30	42:30	1:25:00	2:07:30	2:50:00	3:42:51
8:40	43:20	1:26:40	2:10:00	2:53:20	3:47:13
8:50	44:10	1:28:20	2:12:30	2:56:40	3:51:35
9:00	45:00	1:30:00	2:15:00	3:00:00	3:56:00
9:10	45:50	1:31:40	2:17:30	3:03:20	4:00:22
9:20	46:40	1:33:20	2:20:00	3:06:40	4:04:44
9:30	47:30	1:35:00	2:22:30	3:10:00	4:09:06
9:40	48:20	1:36:40	2:25:00	3:13:20	4:13:28
9:50	49:10	1:38:20	2:27:30	3:16:40	4:17:50
10:00	50:00	1:40:00	2:30:00	3:20:00	4:22:13

Open any book on running and you will find charts, all kinds of training charts, charts so complicated, even for a daily run, that you would need notes before going out on the road to be able to follow these training plans. Our method of scheduling will be carried in your head, whether at work or out on the road training. You will know what you are doing and why you are doing it. Your body will dictate the repetitions, the aerobic and anaerobic effort. Simple isn't it? It's efficient, it works, and has been used for years by top athletes the world over.

It's All in Your Head

Well, almost anyway. Let's add the heart, the lungs, the legs, the feet and we will have a foolproof, easy-to-follow training system patterned to our bodies and our available time which will accelerate your distance and intensity as your body improves in strength and ability, not some structured schedule which does not take you as a person, a being, with a job and family, into consideration. This custom-fitted training schedule, when applied to swimming and biking, will work as well for running. Remember the real schedule—your schedule, the one that will be priceless to you in the future is Your Personal Training Log—maintain it diligently, accurately, and you will enjoy the results of this effort as your training improves and your competitive event times start to drop!

An investment in a good watch with a sweep second hand or a digital minute and second reading is important. There are a number of good products on the market today, one particularly good model has a pace beeper that allows the runner or biker to set the cadence for his stride or pedal R.P.M.s. This rate can be increased or decreased as required.

The Gerschler-Reindel Training Method

Monitoring the heart rate is the essence of this method of training for all multi-sport events including Swim, Bike, and Run. This tried and proven method does not require endless printed pages of activity schedules to be memorized prior to training runs as stated, but make it possible for the athlete to train to whatever degree of effort he desires carrying his schedule in his head and using time elapse, distance and heart rate to set his pace. All of the three triathlon events training schedules will be based upon this formula.

The Heart Rate Schedule

The heart rate for a training athlete should be periodically monitored after a period of training. In time, the individual will be able to judge his rate without the use of a stop watch; but to start, we must know what our maximum rate should be, based upon our age. We have included a chart for this purpose setting minimum, optimum and maximum heart rates for both men and women. By dividing each one of the three limits by six, you will get the 10 second rate which is all you need to monitor the heart rate while exercising or training. For example, a 30 year old man's maximum heart rate is 180 BPM, divided by six gives a 30 beats in a 10-second period, or another method is to take a 6 second count and add a zero to give a BPM rate.

THE PULSE TEST: HOW HARD TO TRAIN

WOMEN

Age	Minimum	Optimum	Maximum
25	130	157	185
30	126	153	180
35	123	149	175
40	119	145	170
45	116	140	165
50	112	136	160
55	109	132	155
60	105	128	150
65	102	123	145
70	98	119	140
75	95	114	135

MEN

Age	Minimum	Optimum	Maximum
25	137	166	195
30	133	162	190
35	130	157	185
40	126	153	180
45	123	149	175
50	119	145	170
55	116	140	165
60	112	136	160
65	109	132	155
70	105	128	150
75	102	123	145

The calculation for the maximum heart rate is computed by taking the age from a figure of 220, for men but adding 20 to the age of women before computing the maximum rate.

This maximum rate count is the area that we are not to exceed as established by our age. The optimum rate is set at 85% of this figure and the minimum rate at 70%. Our training method will involve working within the minimum and optimum range but mostly to the higher rate pushing into the anaerobic threshold in our strength and speed play sessions.

Changes in Body Function While Training

1. We increase our capacity for using oxygen.
2. Our hearts are able to pump more blood at a lower pulse rate and blood pressure.
3. Our lung capacity increases.
4. Our heat-dissipating ability increases.
5. After exercise, our pulse rate and blood pressure return to normal more quickly.
6. We develop greater muscular strength.
7. We produce less lactic acid—a work-limited substance—for a given amount of work.
8. Our bodies become more efficient mechanically, using less oxygen per unit of work.
9. We develop greater endurance.

The aerobic method of taking the pulse is by placing the index and the middle fingertips just behind the windpipe at the level of the Adam's apple; instantly you will feel the artery pulsating. The blood pressure may be taken at this point on either side of the windpipe while running or biking or swimming ... however, in the case of running, a better count may be taken while walking. Prior to embarking on an extensive training program such as this, there is an added advantage to a treadmill test at this time. It will be a starting point for a periodic check on your heart rate, decline both resting and under stress and other areas of improved well-being.

Now we have established our minimum, optimum and maximum heart rate for the age group we are in. We should start our warm-up with a brisk walk for a period of time necessary to raise our BPM to 100 to 120, depending on our age. The 120 rate is for the youngest.

From a Crawl to Walk to Race Walk to a Jog

If you have followed our book from the beginning, you will have progressed through the Chapters on Breathing, Crawling, Walking and Race Walking. With this as a background we can now proceed into a faster rate of movement, a jogging rate or a slow run. It is important that you select a practical place to run upwind and away from heavy traffic, fairly level, on turf, in a park or on a golf course fringe, if possible. Establish distances by the use of a pedometer, a bicycle mileage gauge, or using your own stride of approximately 1,320 paces to the mile.

Month One

You are now ready to go out on the course. Start with a fast walk and increase the cadence until you are into a slow run, letting your heels make contact with the ground gently, in a rolling gait. At this point, it is important to maintain this gait as it will start the development of calf and leg muscles gently and avoid excessively sore muscles. Maintain this gait for as long as possible until you feel the need for more oxygen than you can comfortably inhale. Then slow down to a brisk walking gait. When you feel comfortable breathing again, break into a slow run. Maintain this form for at least one-half hour each day the first week.

5-50-Mile Pacing

Mile	5 Miles	10 Miles	15 Miles	20 Miles	Marathon	50 Miles
4:50	24:10	48:20	1:12:30	1:36:40	2:07:44	
5:00	25:00	50:00	1:15:00	1:40:00	2:11:06	
5:10	25:50	51:40	1:17:30	1:43:20	2:15:28	
5:20	26:40	53:20	1:20:00	1:46:50	2:19:50	
5:30	27:30	55:00	1:22:30	1:50:00	2:24:12	
5:40	28:20	56:40	1:25:00	1:53:20	2:28:34	
5:50	29:10	58:20	1:27:30	1:56:40	2:32:56	
6:00	30:00	1:00:00	1:30:00	2:00:00	2:37:19	5:00:00
6:10	30:50	1:01:40	1:32:30	2:03:20	2:41:41	5:08:20
6:20	31:40	1:03:20	1:35:00	2:06:40	2:46:03	5:16:40
6:30	32:30	1:05:00	1:37:30	2:10:00	2:50:25	5:25:00
6:40	33:20	1:06:40	1:40:00	2:13:20	2:54:47	5:33:20
6:50	34:10	1:08:20	1:42:30	2:16:40	2:59:09	5:41:40
7:00	35:00	1:10:00	1:45:00	2:20:00	3:03:33	5:50:00
7:10	35:00	1:11:40	1:18:20	2:23:20	3:07:55	5:58:20
7:20	36:40	1:13:20	1:50:00	2:26:40	3:12:17	6:06:40
7:30	37:30	1:15:00	1:52:30	2:30:00	3:16:39	6:15:00
7:40	38:20	1:16:40	1:55:00	2:33:20	3:21:01	6:23:20
7:50	39:10	1:18:20	1:57:30	2:36:40	3:25:23	6:31:40
8:00	40:00	1:20:00	2:00:00	2:40:00	3:29:45	6:40:00
8:10	40:50	1:21:40	2:02:30	2:43:20	3:34:07	6:48:20
8:20	41:40	1:23:20	2:05:00	2:46:40	3:38:29	6:56:40
8:30	42:30	1:25:00	2:07:30	2:50:00	3:42:51	7:05:00
8:40	43:20	1:26:40	2:10:00	2:53:20	3:47:13	7:13:20
8:50	44:10	1:28:20	2:12:30	2:56:40	3:51:35	7:21:40
9:00	45:00	1:30:00	2:15:00	3:00:00	3:56:00	7:30:00
9:10	45:50	1:31:40	2:17:30	3:03:20	4:00:22	7:38:20
9:20	46:40	1:33:20	2:20:00	3:06:40	4:04:44	7:46:40
9:30	47:30	1:35:00	2:22:30	3:10:00	4:09:06	7:55:00
9:40	48:20	1:36:40	2:25:00	3:13:20	4:13:28	8:03:20
9:50	49:10	1:38:20	2:27:30	3:16:40	4:17:50	8:11:40

Grow up as soon as you can. It pays. The only time you really live fully is from thirty to sixty. . . . The young are slaves to dreams; the old servants of regrets. Only the middle-aged have all their five senses in the keeping of their wits.   HARVEY ALLEN

We are now going to establish hard days and easy days. Each week should include three hard workout days and three easy days with one day of rest. These days should alternate and should be selected to fit into your pattern of everyday family living. Select a time of day when you will not be missed, such as early a.m. while breakfast is being prepared or p.m. while dinner is being prepared or grocery shopping is taking place.

At this point, at the outset of your running career, there is no reason to create a confrontation. By being considerate of other family members a supportive role for your running interests will be established.

The hard days are for building long slow distance and the easy days are for recovery and the seventh day is a day of rest. Select one of the hard days for the big one, the day you explore territory you have heretofore not covered in your runs. Make this run twice as far as any previous run, endeavor to go the distance in a running gait as opposed to a run-walk gait.

Your goal at this point is to reduce the number of minutes walking, and increase the number of minutes running until you are able to maintain a steady pace. Speed is not important to a point . . . go out by time, not distance.

Next, increase the total amount of time spent jogging each week to at least one hour, with at least 20 days of serious effort each month interspersed with alternate days of walking. Make an extra effort to reduce excessive body weight and resting pulse. Maintain your exercise pulse rate at or near the optimum rate as set forth earlier. If you are one of those fortunate individuals who can maintain a steady jogging pace from the outset, revert to the pulse rate for your speed control, maintaining it near the optimum BPM for your age group.

The first week's work-outs should build to a steady pace and should increase until you are completing up to a full hour's time without rest stops or a walking rest period. You should be covering from four to six miles in this period, on your hard days . . . easy days should include at least ½ hour of brisk walking.

An excellent pacing test is to attempt to carry on a conversation with a fellow runner. See if you can carry on a conversation while you are running. If you are gasping for breath, you are running too fast, regardless of what your friends may say to shame you. Most of us must start out at a very slow rate, perhaps 12-14 minutes per mile in order to maintain a conversational pace. Your pace will usually pick up a little automatically as your body becomes accustomed to the exercise, but the primary factor is the one-hour time period of running. Whenever you do increase the time you spend running or your mileage, always decrease your pace and then allow it to build up gradually. Never push it. Don't let anyone try to humiliate or harrass you out of your body's comfortable pace.

Drink Plenty of Water During Training

Another important point to remember is to consume at least 20 ounces of water prior to going out on the run on warm days, half that much on cooler days (a gulp of water from a fountain or container is one ounce). Drink 10 ounces of water every 20 minutes during a run. This is especially crucial in warm weather. It is impossible to finish a warm weather marathon without regular water stops. The danger of heat stroke is omnipresent. Therefore, now is the time to train your stomach to accept fluids on the run, as well as to establish the water-stop habit for all time in your running routine. Stop to drink. This allows you to take a quick break (while not choking on your water or feeling foolish). More importantly, it allows the blood, previously restricted by contracting muscles, to resume a free flow through your muscles, thus replenishing their energy supply. This circulation and the fluids give you that refreshed feeling. After drinking your water, walk a few steps and resume your running.

Importance of an Hour's Run

Do not think in terms of miles: think *hour*. An hour might take you four miles one day and five the next, but the object remains the same—to keep you running for at least one hour. Your body is tackling its initial task. It needs to learn to slip into fat metabolism efficiently and effectively and this training will not occur in anything less than one hour's time. Why an hour? Noting that we burn up most of our carbohydrates (the energy source available from ingested food) within 40 minutes of sustained exercise, it becomes obvious that no one can eat enough the night before a marathon to sustain him or her throughout the distance. The body, therefore, must be trained to utilize stored body energy which is in the form of fats. Primitive man, going for days between animal kills, lived constantly from his stored body fats, a state called fat metabolism. In modern man, the enzyme system for converting fat back into energy has virtually disappeared from lack of use. The body must be retrained to enter into this state. By the time you have run 40 minutes, your body is learning to literally switch gears. This explains the feeling of exhaustion about this point in your run (it will pass!)

EFFORT-ADJUSTED PACING TABLE

Total Time (Ave./mile)	5 miles (19%)	10 miles (37%)	15 miles (55%)	20 miles (75%)	Last 6+ (25%)
2:30 (5:43)	28 min.	55 min.	1:22	1:52	38 min.
2:35 (5:55)	29 min.	57 min.	1:25	1:56	39 min.
2:40 (6:06)	30 min.	59 min.	1:28	2:00	40 min.
2:45 (6:17)	31 min.	1:01	1:31	2:04	41 min.
2:50 (6:29)	32 min.	1:03	1:33	2:07	43 min.
2:55 (6:40)	33 min.	1:05	1:36	2:11	44 min.
3:00 (6:52)	34 min.	1:07	1:39	2:15	45 min.
3:05 (7:04)	35 min.	1:08	1:42	2:19	46 min.
3:10 (7:15)	36 min.	1:10	1:44	2:22	48 min.
3:15 (7:26)	37 min.	1:12	1:47	2:26	49 min.
3:20 (7:38)	38 min.	1:14	1:50	2:30	50 min.
3:25 (7:49)	39 min.	1:16	1:53	2:34	51 min.
3:30 (8:01)	40 min.	1:18	1:55	2:37	53 min.
3:35 (8:12)	41 min.	1:20	1:58	2:41	54 min.
3:40 (8:23)	42 min.	1:21	2:01	2:45	55 min.
3:45 (8:35)	43 min.	1:23	2:04	2:49	56 min.
3:50 (8:46)	44 min.	1:25	2:06	2:52	58 min.
3:55 (8:58)	45 min.	1:27	2:09	2:56	59 min.
4:00 (9:09)	46 min.	1:29	2:12	3:00	1:00

Select a goal from the total times at left, then attempt to run the corresponding times at each of the checkpoints. The percentages indicate how much of the total time the intermediate distances should occupy. The "splits" are rounded to the nearest minute, so they may vary 30 seconds on either side of the figures indicated.

AGE-GROUP EQUIVALENTS

Marathon runners generally have maximum performance potential between ages 25 and 30. This chart, based on statistics provided by Ken Young and Dan Moore, gives approximate equivalent times at other ages.

Age	2:08:33*	2:20	3:00	3:30	4:00
5	3:24	3:43	4:46	5:34	6:22
10	2:50	3:06	3:59	4:39	5:19
15	2:28	2:42	3:28	4:04	4:38
20	2:16	2:28	3:11	3:43	4:14
25	2:09	2:21	3:02	3:32	4:02
30	2:09	2:20	3:00	3:30	4:00
35	2:09	2:21	3:02	3:32	4:02
40	2:13	2:26	3:07	3:38	4:10
45	2:18	2:31	3:14	3:47	4:19
50	2:23	2:37	3:22	3:55	4:29
55	2:31	2:45	3:23	4:08	4:43
60	2:38	2:53	3:45	4:20	4:58
65	2:46	3:02	3:54	4:33	5:12
70	2:55	3:12	4:07	4:48	5:29

*2:08:33 is the current world record for men; 2:20 is considered a "world-class" time; 3:00 is the most common goal of marathoners; 3:30 is the Boston marathon qualifying time for men over 40 and all women; 4:00 is a time 90% of marathon finishers are under.

Your hard days for the first month should include at least one hour's run. The distance will increase in this period automatically as you drop the need for the walking pace. Do not let speed be a factor because it will result in injuries that will be discouraging to you at this early point in your running career. The easy days will consist of a brisk walk, calisthenics, weight lifting with an emphasis on the abdominal muscles. The easy day gives time for the body to heal between the hard day's run and will avoid the chronic fatigue syndrome.

Month Two

Continue the first month's routine, maintaining a slow, steady pace. The distance day (being one of the hard days preferably a day off from work or the spouse's day to do their thing) should consist of at least 1½ hour's long slow distance run. Starting out with a slower pace than normal, steadily build up to your normal pace. Remember to drink ten ounces of water every 20 minutes, maintaining a steady sub-optimum BPM heart rate and a comfortable aerobic breathing rate either through the nose or the mouth, whichever is more comfortable. The easy days can now increase to a jog walk, relaxed, gait pace for one hour.

Side Pain

Should you develop a side pain while running, stop and go into a deeper breathing mode, forcing air out through tight lips, tightening the diaphram muscle causing the pain. Also sometimes

Triathlon competition can extend well into the evening hours, as can be seen in this spotlit view of the 1984 Ironman Triathlon World Championships in Hawaii.

More than 1,000 athletes gather in Kailua Bay in Kona, Hawaii to start the 2.4-mile swim portion of the 1984 Ironman Triathlon World Championship. Water temperatures approching 75 degrees and one to two-foot waves can make the first leg of the race the most difficult.

Photo by Noël Black

PER-MILE AVERAGES

This chart indicates the per-mile pace of various marathon times. The times on the left are for the marathon (two hours to 4:37 in even minutes). Beside each is the average mile time (to the nearest tenth-second) that it takes to run that fast. To find the pace of marathons slower than 4:37, add approximately 2.3 seconds per mile for each additional minute of marathon time. A 4:38 marathon would equal about 10:40.8 per mile, etc.

2:00 = 4:34.6	**2:10** = 4:57.5	**2:20** = 5:20.4	**2:30** = 5:43.3
2:01 = 4:36.9	2:11 = 4:59.8	2:21 = 5:22.7	2:31 = 5:45.6
2:02 = 4:39.2	2:12 = 5:02.1	2:22 = 5:25.0	2:32 = 5:47.8
2:03 = 4:41.5	2:13 = 5:04.4	2:23 = 5:27.2	2:33 = 5:50.1
2:04 = 4:43.8	2:14 = 5:06.7	2:24 = 5:29.5	2:34 = 5:52.4
2:05 = 4:46.1	2:15 = 5:08.9	2:25 = 5:31.8	2:35 = 5:54.7
2:06 = 4:48.3	2:16 = 5:11.2	2:26 = 5:34.1	2:36 = 5:57.0
2:07 = 4:50.6	2:17 = 5:13.5	2:27 = 5:36.4	2:37 = 5:59.3
2:08 = 4:52.9	2:18 = 5:15.8	2:28 = 5:38.7	2:38 = 6:01.6
2:09 = 4:55.2	2:19 = 5:18.1	2:29 = 5:41.0	2:39 = 6:03.9
2:40 = 6:06.2	**2:50** = 6:29.0	**3:00** = 6:51.9	**3:10** = 7:14.8
2:41 = 6:08.2	2:51 = 6:31.3	3:01 = 6:54.2	3:11 = 7:17.1
2:42 = 6:10.7	2:52 = 6:33.6	3:02 = 6:56.5	3:12 = 7:19.4
2:43 = 6:13.0	2:53 = 6:35.9	3:03 = 6:58.8	3:13 = 7:12.7
2:44 = 6:15.3	2:54 = 6:38.2	3:04 = 7:01.1	3:14 = 7:24.0
2:45 = 6:17.6	2:55 = 6:40.5	3:05 = 7:03.4	3:15 = 7:26.3
2:46 = 6:19.9	2:56 = 6:42.8	3:06 = 7:05.6	3:16 = 7:28.5
2:47 = 6:22.2	2:57 = 6:45.1	3:07 = 7:07.9	3:17 = 7:30.8
2:48 = 6:24.5	2:58 = 6:47.3	3:08 = 7:10.2	3:18 = 7:33.1
2:49 = 6:26.7	2:59 = 6:49.6	3:09 = 7:12.5	3:19 = 7:35.4
3:20 = 7:37.7	**3:30** = 8:00.6	**3:40** = 8:23.5	**3:50** = 8:46.4
3:21 = 7:40.0	3:31 = 8:02.9	3:41 = 8:25.8	3:51 = 8:48.6
3:22 = 7:42.3	3:32 = 8:05.2	3:42 = 8:28.0	3:52 = 8:50.9
3:23 = 7:44.6	3:33 = 8:07.4	3:43 = 8:30.3	3:53 = 8:53.2
3:24 = 7:46.8	3:34 = 8:09.7	3:44 = 8:32.6	3:54 = 8:55.5
3:25 = 7:49.1	3:35 = 8:12.0	3:45 = 8:34.9	3:55 = 8:57.8
3:26 = 7:51.4	3:36 = 8:14.3	3:46 = 8:37.2	3:56 = 9:00.1
3:27 = 7:53.1	3:37 = 8:16.6	3:47 = 8:39.6	3:57 = 9:02.4
3:28 = 7:56.0	3:38 = 8:18.9	3:48 = 8:41.9	3:58 = 9:04.7
3:29 = 7:58.3	3:39 = 8:21.2	3:49 = 8:44.2	3:59 = 9:07.0
4:00 = 9:09.2	**4:10** = 9:32.1	**4:20** = 9:55.0	**4:30** = 10:17.9
4:01 = 9:11.5	4:11 = 9:34.4	4:21 = 9:57.3	4:31 = 10:20.2
4:02 = 9:13.8	4:12 = 9:36.7	4:22 = 9:59.6	4:32 = 10:22.5
4:03 = 9:16.1	4:13 = 9:39.0	4:23 = 10:01.9	4:33 = 10:24.8
4:04 = 9:18.4	4:14 = 9:41.3	4:24 = 10:04.2	4:34 = 10:27.1
4:05 = 9:20.7	4:15 = 9:43.6	4:25 = 10:06.5	4:35 = 10:29.4
4:06 = 9:23 0	4:16 = 9:45.9	4:26 = 10:08.8	4:36 = 10:31.7
4:07 = 9:25.3	4:17 = 9:48.2	4:27 = 10:11.1	4:37 = 10:33.9
4:08 = 9:27.6	4:18 = 9:50.5	4:28 = 10:13.3	4:38 = 10:36.2
4:09 = 9:29.9	4:19 = 9:52.7	4:29 = 10:15.6	4:37 = 10:38.5

raising the arm on the side of the stitch helps. This condition is a sign that you are running too fast and not breathing deep enough. Percy Cerutty, the Gold Medal trainer of Australia, stated that a marathon runner never uses over 1/3 of his long capacity. In his running instruction, Percy encouraged his students to push both arms out low in front, exhaling, raising them with the shoulders into a shoulder shrug, and inhaling, repeating this movement several times. This opens up the lungs to an increase in air intake and is especially beneficial when climbing hills or when you experience an anaerobic or oxygen-starved condition.

Month Three

Proper Running Form

A distance runner should develop the proper running form in the beginning of his training. Arms should be carried low near the belt line with a relaxed, propelling motion, shoulders relaxed, hands not clenched but partially open and relaxed. The belt area should be over the legs or a bit forward, trunk erect, head back. This position allows for an increase in stride distance as you advance. As a long distance runner, you will become energy conscious and learn to conserve energy by doing away with any motion that is inefficient.

Our schedule will increase in distance now that you are comfortable with a steady pace, for a full hour's run on two of the hard days and a run of 1½ to 2 hours on one day of the week. The easy days now will take on a new purpose—to build strength. By this time what superficial hurts and minor running injuries you have had should be healed and you are now ready to proceed.

Strength Training

Find a hill in your training area. If hills aren't available, use building steps or stair wells. Spend at least 30 minutes after your warm-up running inclines. The proper motion is "bounding," using the balls of your feet raising the knees high (only swinging the arms relaxed and low for balance). Make a number of assaults of from five to ten minutes each, with a slow descent as a rest period. Here again, monitor your heart rate at the top of the climb to establish your maximum pace based upon your cardiovascular system's capacity at the optimum BPM rate. You will soon begin to notice an improvement in the pace as the heart and leg muscles gain strength.

Every exercise day should start with a warm-up of first, a brisk walk, moving into a slow jog, and end with another brisk walk. This cool-down is important so that the lactic acid build-up in the muscle tissue, as a result of the workout, will have a chance to be removed from the muscle tissue during the slower pace to facilitate oxygen transfer. This will go a long way to relieving the soreness experienced the day following a good run.

To Stretch or Not to Stretch

I personally believe in stretching, if properly done. Stretches should not be attempted when the body is cold or the muscle tissues and the tendons have not had first a chance to be mildly stimulated by a brisk walk or some calisthenics. See our Chapter on Stretching, written especially for the Triathlon Training Manual by one of the authors, Bob Anderson, as taken from his most recent complete compendium on this very important subject, "Stretching." This book covers stretching for every sport including Swim, Bike, and Run.

Contrary to this statement, The Honolulu Marathon Clinic made a survey of participants and out of the computer came the fact that those that stretched had a higher degree of running injuries than those that did not stretch. I participated in this survey and am of the opinion that here again the stretches were made on cold muscle and tendon tissue. The survey did not qualify whether the stretches were made before or after the warm-up. The result of the study was held as inconclusive by the clinic until a more accurate sampling could be made.

Weight Training for Runners

The modern weight room is well suited for weight training for the runner. Nautilus, Universal and the free bar weight gyms should be an important part of the runner's training.

While visiting Percy Cerutty, at Portsey, Melbourne, Australia, I was impressed with the array of equipment of all vintages and home manufacture that Percy invented for his running students. His weight routines were a very important part of his training system.

The most obvious problem with most running styles is a lack of strength, particularly upper body strength. Of all the several means of building strength that Cerutty advocated and which will be discussed in this chapter, the most crucial is weight lifting. Percy Cerutty was the first athletic coach in history to advocate that lifting heavy weights is an essential part of developing a distance runner. He was once vice-president of the Victorian Weight Lifting Association.

"Good running starts in the upper body and is then transferred to the legs," Percy said. "Strength is the main factor that will enable a person to reach his potential."

The Basic Lifts

Much as Percy devised the five basic movements to develop full-lung aeration, he had five basic lifting exercises for developing tensile strength. They were: (1) one-arm swing; (2) cheat curl; (3) bench press; (4) dead lift and (5) sit-ups.

One-arm swing. This lift is not only beneficial as a warm-up for the other exercises, but is also extremely valuable in building a neural pattern in the athlete's brain to enable him to lift his center of gravity out of his pelvis and be in perfect balance when he runs with the five basic movements.

In this exercise, the runner should work with a heavy dumbbell, approximately 1/3-1/2 of his body weight. The dumbbell should be held firmly in one hand and then swung in an arc on one side of the body.

Cheat curl. This lift is just what the name implies. The athlete bends the lower part of his back to help him curl a weight that is as much as three-quarters of his body weight. This lift is important in strengthening the muscles in the arms that are crucial in the five basic movements (supinators, pronators, biceps and triceps). This added strength allows the runner stronger and more varied arm movements, which leads to full-lung aeration and faster running.

This can be done with either an underhand or overhand grip, though the underhand grip is preferable. Some athletes alternate grips to develop different muscles.

Repetitions per set should be limited to five, with no more than two or three sets. At first, three-quarters of one's body weight might prove to be too difficult, but the athlete can build to this.

Dead lift. The dead lift is the exercise for leg development, although it also strengthens the upper body and the back.

The athlete begins this lift by firmly planting both of his feet under the bar, directly below the shoulders. He should be lifting twice his body weight in this move. A reverse grip should be used, in which one hand wraps over the bar while the other wraps under it. The back should be bent at a 45-degree angle to the horizontal while the head is facing forward. The lifter should then bend his knees and lower his body almost to a sitting position. Good lifting posture is essential with this exercise. The runner can suffer from groin strain if he pulls the heavy weight off the ground with his back or stomach weights and build up to twice your body weight.

Sit-ups. This is the ideal exercise to end a weight training session. It is not actually a weight lifting exercise, but is the best means of strengthening the abdominal muscles, which are among the most neglected muscles in track and field athletes.

"Most all runners neglect to develop abdominal strength," Percy said, "and because of it they lack the leg power they should have when their legs are being lifted by the abdominal muscles."

Hurdlers need this exercise more than any other athlete, although all athletes should do them.

Sit-ups should be done on an incline board with a weight held behind the head. This should start out as five pounds and steadily increase. As the sit-ups become easier, the athlete should not try to do more; he should increase the weight. This increase should be gradual. Many athletes at Porsea did these with weights of 25 pounds and more.

A good number of sit-ups is 20 or 25. During the conditioning period, three sets of these should be done in a day with 10, 20 and 25 pounds.

There are a number of other exercises Cerutty recommended for building strength. Running up hills, particularly sand hills such as the ones at Portsea, was one. This develops the upper body movements and the thighs.

The Cerutty Method of Hill Training

"Other than dead lifting a very heavy weight, I strongly recommend running up steep hills," Percy said.

Most runners bend their elbows with a high arc on a hill. This defeats the purpose of hill training by encouraging an awkward running style and wasting energy. When an athlete reaches a hill, he should *lower* his arms and thrust them in a low arc. The lower the arms are carried, the faster he can climb the hill.

Another error runners make on hills is bringing their knees up too high. This is a totally wasteful movement. If the arms are carried low, this is automatically discouraged.

Developing the low arm position on hills is extremely beneficial when the runner comes to a track. Running with the proper movements and running *fast* will seem easier than if all training had been on the flat.

Hills should be run intensively, with several repetitions. The number of repetitions is based on the grade of the hill, of course. At Portsea, where the main hill was 80 feet of sand, some runners had trouble running up it once with full power. The hill should be grade of at least 1-2.

When running downhill, most runners have the tendency to come down very hard with each step. This is inefficient and wastes energy. It causes the runner to come downhill too fast, and leaves him tired on the flat. This is especially harmful when the downhill section is followed by another uphill climb, because the runner will have little energy for it.

The proper downhill running technique involves keeping the body straight with the strength of the abdominal muscles. Athletes who run a lot of cross-country should work on strengthening these.

The runner should always be in total control of himself when he is running downhill so he won't fall and injure his knees. He should rest shortly while the momentum carries him down the hill. This will conserve his valuable energy and improve his surging power for a race.

A good hill workout involves hard uphill running, then an easy controlled descent before starting uphill again.

Your goal should be to get on and off the hill comfortably without injuring yourself. How?

1. Maintain an even pace, up *or* down a hill. Most injuries occur on the downhill slope. When you have caught your breath from ascending the hill, you are feeling good and your tendency is to fly down it. This is a good time to listen to your feet since silent feet are a sign of appropriate downhill behavior.
2. Shorten your steps. This is more efficient and prevents injury.
3. Remain upright. Do not lean into a hill.
4. Picture yourself climbing stairs or a stepladder. Swing your arms parallel to your body and not across.

Striding

Striding is of extreme importance in the runner's future and should be incorporated into his training at this point. Care should be taken to avoid injuries by over striding or over stretching muscle mass in the groin and upper leg area.

After the warm-up, prior to a distance or hard day's run, 5 x 200 yard intervals of a striding pace should be accomplished. Remember we used a rolling gait to build our distance to this point. Now it is important that we begin to step out and extend our stride gradually. There are approximately 49,000 yards in a full marathon. If your stride is 30 inches each foot will hit the road about 57,000 times. If your stride is 36 inches, only 49,000 times. Roughly, for every inch you increase your stride, you reduce the footfall number by roughly 1,300 in full marathon. If at the same time you can maintain your cadence, you will appreciably improve your completion time.

Striding should also be a part of your Fartlek "Speed Play" run, thereby breaking the monotony of the steady pace. Striding should not be at a fast pace but should offer a long stretch in each stride. Start out gradually and increase the stride distance and the running distance gradually until it becomes your regular running stride.

Heat Stroke

The minute you are thirsty, the race is over. Thirst is the final symptom indicating the onset of heat exhaustion and heat stroke.

After 20 minutes of running, your core body temperature rises from its resting temperature of 98.6° to about 102°, which is the most efficient temperature for running. For every three miles you run, your body loses one pound of water. When you've lost 2-3% of your body weight, your core temperature begins to rise again. For a 180-pound man, 3% of his body weight is about 5½ pounds, or 15 miles without water. One indicator that you are not getting enough fluid replacement is the loss of more than 5% of your body weight on a run. At a core temperature of 105°, heat exhaustion begins to set in. In warm weather this can be dangerous. It is 85% fatal if not properly treated. The most important consideration is that all fluids must be taken early, which is why you have become accustomed to drinking water every 20 minutes. At about 16 miles, absorption of liquids from the stomach decreases, as more and more blood is shunted to the legs, becoming unavailable for circulating fluids. At about 18 miles, absorption ends. If you have not taken sufficient liquids in the first 10 miles, this is when trouble develops. It is too late to correct the problem by this time. The time to take in plenty of cool water is when your body is cool. It will then be available to serve the body as it heats gradually and it will prevent overheating.

Month Four

You are getting strong by this time and are conditioned for more time on the course. The hard days increase to four, no day of rest, and the easy days to three. One of the hard days will be a two-hour run of moderate effort using again the BPM formula. As you have noticed by this time, your early morning resting heart rate has decreased as much as five BPM. This is excellent and is proof that the body is adjusting to the increased work load. The heart action is more efficient at this stage, pumping an adequate flow of blood with less effort. Also your BPM's out on the course will allow you to increase your running distance in the one-hour period. Your breathing is coming in easy deep breaths, and conversation while running is a joy instead of the breathless pain experienced at the start.

Weight . . . Losing It

There is only one sure way to lose weight—eat less. All the rest is luck. You are lucky if your body metabolizes fats efficiently. You are unlucky if it does not. Though it varies according to build, your body will be burning at least 100 calories per mile regardless of how long it takes you. Simply speaking, then, it will take you five miles of running to burn off three cans of beer! It follows, then, that you can always eat more than you run off, and most of us try just that. If you have entered a running program to lose weight, don't count on it (although it will probably work for your best friend). The good news is that running will reshape and firm up your body, regardless of weight loss. In conjunction with a sensible diet, of course, running can *help* you to lose weight. As we know, after 40 minutes of running, the body shifts into fat metabolism until we begin to eat again. It would make sense, then, to diet on those days, allowing this phenomenon to operate. Eat selectively on non-running days. Bear in mind, however, that dieting is a stress state involving weakness and fatigue. It is important to stabilize your weight no less than six weeks before a marathon. No dieting should be done after that. The best time to diet, of course, is *now* while your weekly mileage is low.

Why Lose Weight?

Obviously it will take less energy to propel your lighter body across the finish line than your heavy one. Given equal height and weekly mileage, the lighter person will always come in first. If you are working as hard as you can, the only difference between you and the front runner is simply weight.

Extra weight, of course, puts added strain on injury-prone pivotal areas such as the hip, knee, ankle, and foot. Furthermore, extra weight interferes with heat exchange. In lay terms, it takes longer for the internal heat to reach the surface through extra layers of fat increasing the chances of heat exhaustion and heat stroke.

Distribution of Weight

The closer the weight problem is to your feet, the harder it is to run. A pound on the foot requires four times the energy to carry than a pound on the back. This explains the phenomenon of the spindly-legged fat man running well. It may not be fair, but there is not much we can do about big legs. You'll have to accept running a little slower or concentrate your exercise program on your legs. (It might be worth mentioning that taking shorter steps is easier for those with bigger legs.)

As a word of caution: See our Chapter on Running Injuries as it pertains to excessive weight loss. This is becoming a serious problem with runners as well as all distance athletes. Disturbing the basic body's metabolism can be fatal. A properly monitored food and mineral intake is extremely important because excess weight is lost through low caloric intake and increased calorie expenditure through training.

Month Five

You are now ready for distance in miles. To this point we have only been interested in training hours, but as you have noticed, in the given period of time, say one hour, you have increased the distance substantially over month two's distance traveled. Your Log Book is beginning to show how your strength and stamina are building.

The four hard days are planned for 30 miles per week minimum Long Slow Distance. A word of caution . . . to strive for speed now could cause unnecessary injuries, so maintain the LSD mode of training for these 4 distance days with the easy days concentrated on strength training, hill or step climbing, (start taking two steps at a time) weight training, sit-ups, leg extensions, leg presses, bench presses, arm curls, and breathing and stretching exercises.

10 Marathon Training Commandments

1. Thou shalt run at least 3 times per week
2. Thou shalt not run more than 7 times per week
3. Thou shalt not run less than one hour
4. Thou shalt not run farther than 15 miles
5. Thou shalt run 2 hours or more, one time per week
6. Thou shalt listen to thy body for signs of injuries
7. Thou shalt consume 9 ounces of liquid every 2½ miles or every 20 minutes of running time
8. Thou shalt diligently build strength, *after* Long Slow Distance
9. Thou shalt strive for speed *after* distance and strength training
10. Thou shalt build to 60 miles per week for 8 weeks before your first Marathon

Your thirty miles or more per week may be made up in any number of ways 3-1 hour runs at a 10 minute per mile rate = 18 miles with a 2 hour run on one day gives 12 miles or a total of 30 miles.

Month Six

You are now in full training for that marathon of 26.238 miles which is only 5 months away. Thirty miles per week is the base to start from for serious training. You will now start stretching out your weekly mileage slowly to 40 miles per week. Care should be taken not to advance too rapidly—remember to slow your pace to allow for the increased mileage, then work back up to the new mileage goal slowly.

The Anaerobic or Interval Training Alternative

At this point in your training you may like to venture into anaerobic training. This is an alternative to the method you are now using the aerobic system as taught by the great trainers of World Class distance athletes.

Your hard days are increasing in distance as your body conditions for this extended effort and distance.

The easy days now take on a new effort called anaerobic training. Move from a brisk walk into your running pace with a heart rate of 110 to 120 BPM. Move up your BPM to your optimum rate during your strength training sessions, bounding up hills or steps pushing the Anaerobic Barrier, for as long as is comfortable anerobically; meaning that you have gone briefly into oxygen debt, BPMs have exceeded your optimum and you can feel mild lactic acid pain in your legs. Now slow this pace down to allow the heart rate to return to the starting rate of 120. This might be from 3 to 5 minutes of a slow jogging pace or a walk back down the hill or steps to the start.

As the BPM rate returns to the 110 to 120 base, stride out again into your strong pace for another time period and so forth for at least 8 sets or 2 running miles. You will notice that this BPM rate returns more slowly after each set. This is normal and will improve with time. The maximum benefit to the heart for this form of anaerobic training comes during the rest period. This is when the heart pumps increased volumes of fluid at a declining rate. This subject is fully covered in the Interval Training Chapter and is applicable to Swim, Bike, and Run Training.

The anaerobic system of strength building varies only to the degree that you enter that anerobic threshold zone. A little for short durations will open up an increased capacity that will continue to expand. Trainers that oppose this system do so only when excesses occur that could be a short or long term danger to health and training ability.

The Lydiard-Telford Formula in a Nut Shell

In theory, you're now doing a lot of your running at speeds just within your maximum steady state. This places the utmost, aerobic *safe* pressure on your heart from the cardiorespiratory and cardiovascular systems, and offers the best possible progressive development. You should run over each of your measured courses at your best steady rate of speed—hard but evenly—but still finish with the knowledge that you could have run a little faster.

Your aim is to find your best aerobic speed over the various courses. If, during any of these runs, you find you have to ease back a little to recover, you'll know that you've moved into the anaerobic phase. This is neither economical nor desirable. You could go on running your courses anaerobically and quite evenly for several days, but then you would find yourself unable to continue because of the gradual breakdown of your whole system. So take careful note of any early warning signs and move your speed back if necessary. Once you've established approximately the best aerobic effort for each course, you can cover successive runs. Try to maintain a strong, even pace all the way, at previously planned times.

This way, it becomes possible to maintain the utmost economical pressure on the cardiac system without creating excessive waste products in the body that could slow progress and dishearten you. As your maximum steady state rises, the runs over the courses will become progressively faster, and you'll be working aerobically at speeds that earlier would have been anaerobic—or even impossible.

Running is the best exercise for runners, and the more you do in a balanced aerobic-anaerobic ratio according to this overall system, the better you'll be. Conditioning running helps to develop strong upper-leg muscles, which are the only ones powerful enough to make the heart work at the effort and for the lengths of time necessary to gain the desired results. The longer and more steadily you use those big muscles to lift your body against gravity, the better.

Now You Can Become Competitive

To acquaint yourself with the vagaries of competitive running, we suggest you enter a *few* (no more than 10% of your training mileage should be spent in races), *short* (never over 15 miles) official races between now and then just to see what it's like. Run these races for education and to see how it feels to be a racer, *not to win* (if you do, you are asking to be injured).

Month Seven

Moving into increased distance from the previous month to a minimum of 30 miles to a maximum of 50 should not be difficult now but will involve more training time out on the road. Include your easy day mileage in this count and an estimate of your strength training distance. One of the hard days in the week should now include a time trial. After a good warm-up and two or three miles of a comfortable run, set a distance that you think you can go at your maximum rate, say one quarter mile or even a half mile. Move out at your steady rate, just pushing into the anaerobic barrier for the distance, carefully taking a count of your elapsed time for this distance. Each week hereafter you will duplicate this time trial to show you your pace improvement.

Listen to Your Body for Signs of Injuries

Special attention should be given to injuries that may develop as you start to increase weekly mileage. Slow down your running gait and reduce the distance for a few days until the injury heals. Severe injuries might require complete rest for a week or two. This is good insurance . . . use this time constructively. If you are a triathlete in training, there is always an alternate training mode that you can concentrate on such as biking or swimming. If severe weather conditions prohibit the extensive training on either of these two sports, there is always the weight room and the stationary bicycle. See our Chapter on Injuries.

Fartlek or Speed Play Running Variation

Long Slow Distance running can be boring unless you have a running companion or the scenery and the passing points of interest hold your attention. Many well-adjusted runners find that this is an excellent time to meditate or go into prayer, do mental gymnastics, balance the check book, work out business problems, etc. . . . An alternative to the boring pace of the runner is a Swedish idea that is interesting called the Fartlek. This consists of a varied pace such as a sprint, fast unlimited runs over varied distances and terrains alternating with slow runs. The name Fartlek is Swedish for "Speed Play." The different paces are as varied as the runners. Percy Cerutty had his version of this event by including a childlike skip, then a lope, and an occasional "shake out" of arms and leg muscles. This running method is particularly good in cross-country running where speed can be applied on good turf, slowing for inclines, and skipping or loping through a flower strewn forest path.

Month Eight

At this point your ideal weekly mileage is 60 miles. The hard day runs are averaging 10 to 12 miles. The easy days from 6 to 8. This still leaves you wondering how you can accomplish a 26.238 mile full marathon run. You are building toward this goal perfectly, providing you have maintained a good log of your miles and the log is accurate. A tried and true formula for determining your ability to go the distance is as follows: Add up the total training mileage you have put in for 60 days prior to the Marathon and divide that figure by 20. This will give you the distance you will go in your first marathon before "Hitting the Wall" or coming to a complete stop. Now maybe you will think twice about taking a day off from your training routine, as every day's run is being counted on your training clock. As you see for a 26.2-mile race, a collapse point at the finish line (and not before) requires over 60 miles per week training for 60 days previous. Staggering? It is comforting to know, then, that you can *slow* your pace during the race and enjoy a comfortable marathon with less training mileage. The inherent danger in pushing that weekly mileage up past 50 is injury. This is a decision you must make for yourself (and soon, in order to plan your increase in training increments to culminate in the mileage you want to attain for the 60 days prior to the marathon).

More mileage = ease in approaching "your pace" in the marathon + greater risk of injury during training and not being able to run the marathon at all. We advise 40-50 miles per week and a slow steady pace (10-15% slower than your training pace) to get your first marathon behind you safely and happily. The simplest minimum program which will prepare you to finish a marathon with the least amount of training, while simultaneously decreasing the risk of serious injury, is two hours of continuous running every other day (42 miles/week for a 10-minute mile). By limiting your running to every other day, you have the greatest protection against injuries. At the same time the two-hour runs provide more training effect for the time you invest than the shorter, more frequent runs. Here is a partial list of where you can expect to collapse or "hit the wall" if you remain obstinate and do not slow to below your training pace during the race:

For 60 days before the marathon, if you have trained for:

30 miles/week	you will hit the wall at:	12 miles
40 miles/week	you will hit the wall at:	16 miles
50 miles/week	you will hit the wall at:	20 miles

Since so many runners do get around 50 miles per week in, and this is considered good mileage, hitting the wall at the 20-mile mark is extremely common. (This explains why you hear so much about the dread 20-mile mark "wall"). It occurs because with 40-50 miles a week, the runner is well trained. He will feel *too* good in the early stages of the race and will ignore our instruction to

Hill climbing for strength training. Max Telford's Running Class bounds up the slopes of Diamond Head.

The Telford Running Class in Kapiolani Park, Honolulu.

keep his pace down and save energy for the later stages of the race. So, regardless of how good you feel, in the marathon you will need to keep your pace below your training rate unless you are training 60 miles/week for the 60 days prior to the marathon. Knowing this, plan your goal for those 60 days now and work up to it gradually.

Set Your Pace

There are three ways to pace yourself during a race or even a training run.

1 — Start out as fast as you can while you're feeling great, confident that you can slow down when you feel tired. It doesn't really work this way.

This method of pacing accounts for the many world class runners who have been known to walk off marathon courses without finishing. You'll find in any race or training run that you'll often wind up walking in the end if you push yourself in the beginning.

2 — Start out very slowly, then finish the race sprinting, using what energy you've saved. This is very difficult to do. It requires experience and in-depth familiarity with your body's limits and capabilities. The biggest danger lies in starting your sprint too soon. Then all you can hope for is that you do not get your stitch until you are within walking distance of the finish line or the end of your run. It might be a good idea to experiment, though, with this method during training to learn a little more about your capabilities.

3 — Maintain an even, steady pace from start to finish. This is your best bet. You can determine your natural pace during training runs by running known, measured distances and dividing them by the number of minutes it takes you to run them. Or enter a number of "Predict-your-finishing-time" races. Then, with pencil and paper in hand figure your splits for the marathon. These are the times you should arrive at certain course marks (e.g., the 5-, 10-, and 20-mile marks) if running at your planned steady pace.

NOTE: In the marathon, the "Creepers," the really slow runners, often eventually bypass the fast runner who must slow down later in the race because of his mistakes. By going out even 20 seconds a mile too fast, it is possible by the 19-mile mark to hit the wall, bringing in the "faster" runner an hour slower than he had anticipated. It's that crucial. If you are running a four-hour marathon and pacing yourself, you can count on passing 20-30% of the field in the last six miles. Learn to pace yourself.

Will I Ever Be Able to Finish a Marathon?

Trust me, if you are following the recommended program, you can. Thousands of others have gone through this successfully. But be aware that 26.2 miles of running is an injury in itself, and there is only one marathon in your body during the first year of training. If you choose to use up your marathon on a training run, it's up to you.

What you *can* do, however, to test your capabilities, is to try one 18-mile run this month. This will be your longest run of the year outside of the marathon itself.

If you "hit the wall," consider yourself injured and pamper your body accordingly. At the end of this run, ask yourself: "Could I go another nine miles at this pace?" This gives you an excellent opportunity to assess and adjust your marathon choices. It is comforting to know it is not too late. If the marathon seems like an impossible dream after this ordeal, you will know you are remiss in one or both of two areas:

1 — You are not getting in enough training miles

2 — You are running too fast

You have enough time now before the marathon to learn to pace yourself sensibly and to think twice about taking "just today" off for questionable excuses.

Month Nine

At this point you wonder why you are into this marathon mania. Don't fret! You are at the leveling off stage in your training program. Hopefully, you have reached this stage of your training without re-occurring injuries and 60 miles per week is possible without a great amount of extra effort. Your running routine has hit a groove that is comfortable for you, your family and your job. Now is the time to begin to enjoy your body's function as a runner, do not try to increase mileage over the 60 miles per week. This could bring on injuries that could lay you up before that cherished marathon date.

Running Pace Test

Now is the time to consider pacing your run. As in the Triathlon, Marathon running success or failure will depend on proper pacing of the event. By this time you have set a pace for yourself that feels comfortable for 10 to 12 miles. To prove to yourself that you have this pace down pat, do your regular run without the use of your watch to see how evenly your pace comes out. You will be pleasantly surprised, in that you will probably not be off over one minute in an hour and a half to 2 hour run.

Month Ten

This is the most crucial month of all the months when many things can happen to make useless all of these endless days of training, such as falling down, catching a cold, and nagging running injury. Maintain your steady routine—now is not the time to experiment with new stride, foot action, arm swing, or shoes.

Continue with your 60 miles per week, hard and easy day routines as in the last 2 months with one exception—one hard day should be a slow run of close to 18 miles during the middle of this month. This is the longest run you will make before the full marathon. If you can run 18 miles you can run 20 or even 22. For the last 4 to 6 miles of your first marathon you will be so psyched up by the fact that you have passed 20 to 30% of the field in the last 10 miles that nothing can stop you now. The adrenalin shot from the cheering spectators urging you on will guarantee a finish, in a time that you will be proud of.

The last run you will make will be a deplition run prior to or during the first days of your Carbo depletion period of approximately 10 miles. This is an excellent time to check your pace so that you will know how to compute your first 10 marathon miles at 20% off of your regular pace.

CAUTION

A cold can be dangerous, even lethal. It can cause potentially dangerous irregular heartbeats. There is really very little you can do to prevent the onset of a cold or flu outside of taking special care of your body.

There are, however, risks that you do not need to take when you are within three weeks of a marathon. We advise that you lay off vigorous contact sports such as rugby and football. You do not have time to recover from an injury at this point. The final 2-3 weeks before a marathon are a slow-down period. For all intents and purposes you are already trained to run the race. The main object now is to *avoid injury*.

The Week Before the Marathon

CARBOHYDRATE LOADING

The merits of carbohydrate loading remain a favorite topic of conversation among runners. The pros and cons seem equally divided. Carbohydrate loading, or glycogen muscle stuffing, is simply an effort to trick the muscles into taking up to 50% more glycogen than they normally do. This extra energy will then be available as fuel during the latter stages of the race. This is accomplished by observing a period of carbohydrate depleting, or a protein diet, followed by a few days of eating large quantities of carbohydrates.

It will not hurt you to try this and if nothing else it takes your mind off the marathon!

DAY BY DAY: diet and training

Sunday (one week prior to the marathon): By this time all your homework has been done. Further training is of negligible consequence. A long, slow, "depletion" run of about 15 miles is on the agenda, simply to trigger the process of carbohydrate starvation. Beginning on this date, one curtails his intake of carbohydrates, concentrating on fats and protein.

Monday through Wednesday: Continue to "deplete" through a daily short, slow run, and a diet consisting solely of fats and protein—exclude all carbohydrates. Expect to feel fatigued.

Thursday: Running workouts are now finished. Limbering up exercises and perhaps one- to two-mile short, easy runs to maintain flexibility are all that are necessary. Continue to eat some fat and protein, but the stress now is on carbohydrates. Be careful, though, not to increase total calories (avoiding unnecessary weight gain). A sense of logginess and a bloated feeling accompany this phase since, for each gram of carbohydrate stuffed into the muscle, four grams of water follow. This sensation will pass as you get into the race and the added liquid has the hidden benefit of being available for bathing the tissues in the later stages of the race.

Friday: The most important thing you can do physiologically is to get a good night's sleep. The sleep you get the night before the race will make no difference, since the benefits of sleep work on a 48-hour cycle. Theoretically, you could stay up all night Saturday and your performance would be unaffected if you had rested well on Friday.

1) *to be humble,* and to place yourself where you belong in the starting line-up. You will experience an irresistable urge to keep up with those around you. So, if you find yourself kneecap to kneecap with Bill Rodgers when the gun goes off, you're in big trouble.

2) *to pace yourself*—beginning slowly, at your training pace (below, if your race is longer than five miles)—evenly throughout the race. You will probably learn this in your first race when you start out too fast and burn yourself out. Remember that even when you situate yourself where you think you belong in the starting line-up, most of those around you will be losing their heads and sprinting off. You need to think for yourself and will find that you catch up with and pass the majority of those who left you behind before the race is over.

3) *to stop at every single water stop,* both for the water and for the rest. Since they are set up by the race officials, you know the water stops are spaced according to your requirements for water.

4) *to tell if you are training properly.* If you run sensibly, drink water and still fall on your face before the finish line, you haven't been putting in your training time.

5) *to enjoy the camaraderie of the race!*

RACE DAY

1 – Do not eat within a three-hour period before the race. Stop drinking liquids within an hour of the start. Try to empty your bladder a half hour before the start.

2 – Get there early. Don't miss the marathon looking for a parking place. Have a plan for parking.

3 – Have your running number pinned on all four corners directly to the front of your shirt. Normally there is a check point midway and at this time your number *must* be visible, as well as at the finish.

4 – Bring a can of cola and some Vaseline. The cola is your first aid station. About 10 minutes before the race is due to start, pop the top, allowing it to defizz. Then a minute or two before the

gun goes off, take a big drink and discard the rest. The Vaseline, strategically and liberally smeared, can help you avoid serious chafing during the 26.2 miles.

5 — Position yourself where you belong in the pack. Be modest. In most marathons, entrants are divided according to predicted finishing times. Stand behind the sign that indicates the time in which you have planned to finish the race. Even then, when the gun goes off, do not be influenced by the group's lunge forward. You know your own pace.

6 — Carbohydrate load. It is based on physiological principles. It can't hurt. If nothing else it will take your mind off the impending marathon!

7 — Do not go on a starvation diet on the assumption that it will be easier to run with a little less weight. You will be weak and injury-prone. The time to have lost that weight was six months ago. Forget it.

8 — Remember, your shoes should have 200 miles on them. Break in the shoes in which you plan to run. Make sure you have assembled a comfortable, well-worn outfit for race day. It's nice if your shirt has some kind of message or identification. Spectators enjoy it and it's a good feeling to know that someone (your sponsor, perhaps) cares whether you finish or not.

9 — Get plenty of rest two nights before the marathon.

The Race

1 — HAVE A GAME PLAN (AND STICK TO IT)

First, do not ask too much of yourself. If your training mileage is 30 miles per week, plan your marathon pace about 20% slower than your training pace. If training at 40-50 miles per week, about 10% slower. With 60+ training miles per week, you can plan on running the race at your training pace. Allow yourself time for water stops.

At 20 miles, you can pick it up again (go into your sprint if you like) if you're still feeling good. If you have saved yourself, you can end up running a good race. But pride goeth before the wall. If you have run over the last part of the marathon course a few times, it will feel familiar to you.

This race is between you and your ego, your racing shoes and the road. Ignore other racers' speed and comments. You are basically on your own. Use your own judgment. *Pace yourself.*

2 — FOLLOW YOUR GAME PLAN

Give yourself room, but if you find yourself *ahead* of your game plan, slow down to get back on the track. It isn't recommended to get ahead of your plan for the first 15 miles. Ten seconds per mile can make a tremendous difference over a distance of 26 miles. It could be just enough for you that it causes you to hit the wall and have to walk for the last few miles, thus adding an hour to your time. If you are following your schedule, say for a four-hour marathon, remember that you can expect to pass upwards of 20% of the field in the last six miles. At 15 miles, do an inventory. If you are feeling good, *then* pick up your pace a little. If you have run out too fast, by 15 miles you will not be feeling good and will not have to worry about picking *anything* up.

3 — DO NOT PASS UP ONE SINGLE AID STATION

The minute you are thirsty, the race is over for you. Walk into the aid station (avoid feeling resentment for the other 2,000 runners who have arrived at this aid station with you). Drinking on the run does not save a lot of time. You will have to stop anyway to stop choking. *Drink* the diluted cola. Drink whatever water you need and pour the rest over your head if you like. The aid stations should also be stocked with cold, wet sponges with which to refresh yourself. Medical staff will be on hand as well, and do not hesitate to share any problem you may be developing with them.

Thirst may be the only warning you have of ensuing heat exhaustion. Do not let it happen. At about the 16-mile mark, absorption through the stomach decreases and by the 18-mile mark is complete, so the water must be in your body early in the race. At the 18-mile mark it is best to drink water only, and in small amounts, maybe just to wet your mouth. Absorption is difficult at this point. Stay in tune with your body. Check for amber warning lights. If you get dizzy, have blurring vision or swelling, check with the aid station doctor. He might be able to wrap your ankle or set your mind at ease (or pull you out of the race before you kill yourself).

4 – RACE PSYCHING

You know how to run 13-17 miles because you have done it. Look at it this way: you are going out for another 13-17 mile run. The first half of the marathon should be fun, or at least not intimidating, because you have done this before. At about the 17-mile mark, your body starts to tell you that it is exceeding its normal limits. You are not in any trouble, perhaps just a little uncomfortable or tired. At this point, tell yourself, "Well, there's another aid station in about another mile and a half. Can I make it that far? Sure I can run a mile and a half." Then you are at the 19-mile mark. Ask yourself again, "Can I make it to the *next* aid station? Sure I can!" Then all of a sudden you are at the 22-23 mile mark and you say, "The hell with it. Even if I *walk* I can make it to the finish." So you go from aid station to aid station, making up your mind along the way.

If you have done your homework and remember the basics—fluids and pacing—you are a sophisticated runner and will run a fine race. GOOD LUCK. You deserve it.

Marijuana and the Distance Athlete

Several researchers have looked into the question. They report that marijuana produces a marked reduction in work capacity and increases the resting heart rate; in one study heart rate averaged 73.7 when marijuana was not smoked, 105.8 when it was. Similar results were obtained in an experiment carried out at the University of California at Santa Barbara. Researchers there found that smoking marijuana didn't have any apparent effect either on blood pressure or on the body's oxygen-processing capacity. It did, however, increase the heart rate 34 percent while at rest, 18 percent during exercise, and 50 percent afterward. The increase had no appreciable effect during exercise of only moderate intensity. The researchers said it would, however, limit performance at higher intensities. Perhaps this is why, when I asked one top athlete about the incidence of marijuana smoking among elite runners, he told me he knew of none who used the drug!

Running with Jet Lag

If you're planning to race in a distant time zone, arrive early. Many bodily functions are sent askew when you travel across time zones that it takes several days to readjust.

If you can't avoid doing so, however, you can race with no such adjustment period. Two other researchers report that a runner's aerobic capacity, probably the chief factor in running success, "appears to be an extremely stable function exhibiting no circadian periodicity." In other words, you can feel terrible but nonetheless race well.

Preparing for Hot-Weather Racing

If you're getting ready to race in a hot climate but the weather is cool where you train, you can nonetheless achieve partial adaptation, according to experiments conducted by Carl V. Gisolfi and Judith S. Cohen at the University of Iowa. It will, however, take several weeks. You can enhance the adaptation process by bundling up, thereby creating your own private tropics as you run.

High Altitude Training

If you go to the mountains to train, you will find that you can run faster when you return to a lower altitude. The best altitude for mountain training is 7,000 feet. Below that, the amount of

An Seinor, finisher of the 1981 Honolulu marathon. Over two thirds of the contestants are first time marathoners.

Japanese couple, contestants in the 1981 Honolulu Marathon. Over 1,000 Japanese runners compete in this event.

Ken "Cowman" Shirk, just prior to the swim in the 1980 Ironman Triathlon. Ken manages the whole event without his horns getting out of place. Cowman has participated in 79-80-81-82 Hawaii, Traithlons.

Kim Bushong, 1982 leader of the mens bike race, shown here returning to Kona, for the start of the Marathon. Kim was in top 100 in the 1981 Triathlon.

Photo Credit: Carol Hogan

oxygen is too close to the concentration found at sea level. At a higher altitude, oxygen is so scarce that training must be greatly curtailed.

Many old wive's tales and theories have been discounted regarding high altitude training and competition. A Swiss team, working in the Swiss Alps at over 4,000 meters or 12,000 feet have come up startling new concepts regarding blood adaptation and metobolic responses of the body to rarified atmosphere.

The tests were made with the use of runners and bicyclists. The results proved that in the exposure to the altitude and a continued maintenance for a forty-eight hour period, the body immediately adapts to rare air, sufficiently for athletes to achieve maximum results in their training efforts.

This information was passed on to the Honolulu Competitors for the 1979 "Run to the Sun," an annual test of Ultramarathon staying power. This event is held on the Island of Maui, Hawaii and is a run of 37½ miles from sea level at the Kahalui Airport to the top of Haleakalau Crater at 10,500 ft. elevation. The team maintained an altitude exposure of 8,000 ft. average for 24 hours and experienced no appreciable loss of stamina during this grueling run.

The Physiology of Exercise

It is impossible to be explicit about the physiological reactions of hard training. But I offer the following reasons for my training approach, based on thirty-five years experience as an athlete and coach and several years of lay study of physiology in conjunction with physiologists and sports medicine institutes.

I have tried to simplify the theory into practical terms, because it is important to know why exhausting exercise affects you, and how it can be used to maximize athletic efficiency.

Fundamentally, my training system is based on a balanced combination of *aerobic* and *anaerobic* running. Aerobic running means running within your capacity to use oxygen. Each person according to his physical condition, is able to use a certain amount of oxygen each minute. But this limit can be increased by proper exercise.

ANAEROBIC EXERCISE

The aerobic limit, known as the maximum steady state, is the level at which you are working to the limit of your ability to breathe in, transport, and utilize oxygen. When you exercise beyond that maximum steady state, you begin running in an anaerobic state. This is made possible by chemical changes in your body's metabolism. This supplies the oxygen you need over and above the amount you can breathe in, transport, and utilize. This is a reconversion process with strict limits, so the body is always limited in its anaerobic capacity. The reaction that takes place creates an *oxygen debt,* which can be incurred quickly. Oxygen debt is the amount of oxygen required to counteract anaerobic exercise over and above the oxygen you can gain through your lungs. This is accompanied by the accumulation of lactic acid and other waste products leading directly to neuromuscular breakdown or, simply, tired muscles that refuse to function as you wish. The absolute limit when you are exercising anaerobically is an oxygen debt of approximately 15 liters, although the average athlete will have a limit considerably less than this until he has trained properly.

As exercise increases in intensity, the oxygen debt doubles, squares, and cubes. Experiments by Morehouse and Miller graphically show how dramatically the oxygen requirement increases as the speed of running is raised:

METABOLISM

Metabolism refers to the chemical reactions in living cells by which energy is provided for vital processes. It often refers to the oxidations that are the ultimate source of energy. A muscle converts chemical energy into mechanical activity. It is stimulated by nervous impulses produced through chemical changes. The heart is a muscle. This nervous energy is thought to derive from the breakdown of high-energy compounds, such as adenosine triphosphate (ATP), which results from the oxidation of food stuffs.

Exercise requires continual adjustments in respiration, circulation, temperature-regulating mechanisms, and kidney functions. In fact, the entire body is affected by the metabolic activity that provides energy for exercise.

LACTIC ACID

The energy yields vary widely between aerobic and anerobic exercise. Morehouse and Miller have shown that aerobic exercise is nineteen times more economical than anaerobic exercise. The more intense the exercise, the quicker and less economically the body's fuel is used, and the faster the waste products accumulate in the form of *lactic acid*. This accumulation increases cell activity, interfering with the activities of *enzymes*. These organic catalysts produced by living cells speed the rate of chemical reactions in the body and assist in the recovery from exhausting work.

Lactic acid also upsets the *blood pH*, the measure of the blood's degree of alkalinity or acidity. The point of neutrality between alkalinity and acidity is 7.0, and normal blood pH is between 7.46 and 7.48, indicating that it is slightly alkaline. Under severe physical tests and hard anaerobic exercise, however, increased acidity can lower the pH level to 6.8 or 5.9. If the pH stays at low levels it can upset the nutritive system, destroying or neutralizing the benefits of vitamins and retarding general development. The pH range within which vitamins function effectively is comparatively small, so any lowering of the level can be deleterious. Under such circumstances, recovery from training is poor and subsequent training is more difficult. The fall in pH level can also affect the central nervous system, causing loss of sleep and irritability, and producing loss of interest in training and competition. It's a physiological reaction that can become seriously psychological.

Cardiac Efficiency

The two important measures of heart capacity with which we are concerned are *minute volume* (the quantity of blood the heart can pump each minute) and *stroke volume* (the quantity of blood pumped during each contraction). Again, it is a function of my training system to progressively increase both capacities.

Your general efficiency and ultimate results in running depend basically, as we have said, on your ability to absorb oxygen from the air, to transport it to various muscles and organs, and then to utilize it in the operation of muscles and organs. Normally, people take far more oxygen into their lungs than they're able to use because they lack the necessary blood tone to assimilate it. This is due to a deficiency of *hemoglobin,* the pigment in red blood cells that combines with oxygen and transports it. So the aerobic section of the training system is directed toward improving the efficiency of all these factors, separately and collectively.

Through aerobic training, the heart becomes larger and improves its minute and stroke volume. It not only becomes capable of pumping greater quantities of blood with each contraction, but it also pumps faster since increased blood circulation allows it to fill faster. During rest, your heart is able to pump about 4 liters of blood a minute, but it can increase its capacity eight or ten times, according to your condition. An athlete who runs daily for long periods maintains a reasonably high blood pressure in the circulatory system, and steadily develops faster circulation and increased ability to transport greater quantities of blood to various parts of the body.

This harder work and continued pressure bring a steady improvement in *pulmonary ventilation,* the periodic renewal of air in the lungs. The lungs become more efficient because they develop more active pulmonary capillary beds, enabling the blood to absorb oxygen faster and more easily. At the same time, the heart sends greater quantities of blood to the lungs through an improved arterial system, so that the absorption of oxygen into the blood rises markedly and, with it, your ability to use oxygen for exercise.

A consequence of this general improvement is that the heart begins to work more efficiently. This is reflected in a progressive decrease in the basal pulse rate. This rate is influenced by many factors—posture, emotion, body temperature, and exercise—so it is difficult to use it as an exact guide to fitness. It is also misleading for comparisons of athletes because the normal heart rate at rest varies widely, from 50 to 90 beats a minute, from person to person. However, whatever your normal pulse rate, if it is taken while at rest under similar conditions from time to time during training, you will note a steady drop in beats per minute. The rate eventually decreases as much as 25 beats a minute.

Another facet of improved efficiency—circulatory development—has been clearly shown in scientific photographs of muscles. In athletes and manual workers, the arterial network is clearly defined in many well-developed channels for the blood to circulate through. The muscles of sedentary workers, particularly those who don't exercise, show little development, preventing fast and thorough blood circulation. Continued use of the muscles for long periods not only develops underdeveloped capillaries within the muscles, but also new ones. This increases the efficiency with which the muscles can use oxygen and leads to the development of the endurance we seek.

Youngsters of fourteen, fifteen, and even younger who regularly achieve new swimming records are a perfect example of how this theory works in practice. They can outswim mature people to the marks because they do a great deal of aerobic training (long, slow swimming). They couldn't do it if they had to lift their body weight against gravity as runners do. But the buoyancy of the water means they essentially use their muscles solely to propel themselves along. Because their ability to use oxygen efficiently is greater than an adult's in comparison with their body weight, they can manage considerably larger volumes of aerobic exercise. They don't become strong in the sense that they can lift heavy weights. But they are capable of continuing for a long time at comparatively fast swimming speeds without suffering muscle tiredness. This is muscular endurance.

In West Germany, physiologists experimenting with endurance athletes showed that if muscle groups are exercised continually for long periods—particularly for periods of two hours or more—fine muscular endurance results. They established that this was directly due to the expansion of neglected capillary beds and the formation of new ones. It is often asked by runners with a daily two-hour program whether it is all right if they split the period into two one-hour sessions. Continued exercise is needed for capillary development, so two short periods will not be nearly as effective as one long one.

This is an argument that long slow distance (LSD) runners sometimes use in favor of their particular approach to training. However, while they will gain from long runs of several hours at a slow pace, they are not going to obtain the finest results. Greater circulatory development will be gained with a higher aerobic pressure than that of LSD training. For best results, aim for a level of 70 to 100 percent of best aerobic effort.

Summing up, athletes, by taking sensible aerobic exercise every day, stimulate their bodies' metabolism into providing progressively richer oxygenated blood, developing:

1. improved absorption of oxygen
2. faster blood circulation from the heart through the arteries, arterioles, capillaries, and veins to the lungs and muscles, and back to the heart
3. more efficient pulmonary ventilation and capillarization, as well as improved utilization of oxygen in the muscles

The quicker the heart can pump blood through the body, the better the performance.

Creating Oxygen Debts, an Opposing Viewpoint

While aerobic exercise develops general cardiac efficiency and a higher maximum steady state, it is also necessary to develop anaerobic capacity to increase the body's ability to withstand maximum oxygen debts. This means you must create fatigue rates that will stimulate your metabolism to react against them. This metabolic activity can compensate for lack of oxygen up to a limit of about 15 liters. At this level, neuromuscular breakdown—or complete exhaustion—can be withheld until the lactic acid concentration is as high as 200 milligrams to 100 milliliters of blood.

Let us assume a runner has a steady state of 3 liters a minute and can sustain a 15-liter debt. If the workload being performed requires 4 liters a minute, he can maintain the effort for 15 minutes—using 1 liter of his debt capacity each minute. If the workload is increased to 5 liters a minute, he can maintain the effort for only 7.5 minutes—using 2 liters of debt capacity each minute. The oxygen debt doubles, squares, and cubes as the effort increases.

It is essential to understand the extent, intensity, and regularity of these fatigue rates. A lot of training programs are based on this broad principle. But many coaches and athletes go to extremes to create excessive oxygen debts, in the hope that the body's metabolism will be overstimulated to develop more efficiency against fatigue. They try to hurry the process, forgetting that anaerobic exercise is always uneconomical and that when fatigue rates are created, the body must recover before further fatiguing effort is applied.

It has been mentioned that aerobic exercise is nineteen times more economical than anaerobic exercise. It's necessary, therefore, to conserve energy and use it with a maximum economy. When the maximum steady state is low, an athlete can run anaerobically at a comparitively easy speed. As the maximum steady state rises, slower anaerobic speeds become aerobic (and economical). And as training progresses on this principle, the possibilities of running farther and faster aerobically—and therefore with economy—increases.

A daily program of sustained running is essential to achieving correct respiratory and circulatory development. The longer the periods of running, the better the results of the sustained effort will be. Running speed, in theory, should be just below your maximum steady state at all times, so you can maintain runs of long duration. Over this level, long-duration running will be beyond you because you will be running anaerobically.

The anaerobic stage of your preparation should only be tackled after you have developed your aerobic capacity and maximum steady state to the highest possible levels. Then it must be fairly extreme for a defined period to develop a matching high anaerobic capacity. At this point, you should aim to create a big oxygen debt and lower the blood pH to stimulate your metabolism to build buffers against fatigue. Once you've built those buffers to maximum efficiency, it's pointless and even risky to go on.

Level of Anaerobic Work

Four weeks of hard anaerobic training is usually enough. You may need even less. This training involves going hard for, say, three days to lower the blood pH, training lightly for a day to let it return to near normal, and then pulling it down again with anaerobic effort the next day. Let it come up then pull it down. Keep it fluctuating. If you keep it low, you upset the entire system.

Continual creation of large oxygen debts accumulates lactic acid and other wastes, upsets the nutritive system, reduces the benefits of vitamins, reduces nourishment from food, disrupts enzyme functions, slows recovery, makes further training difficult, upsets the nervous system, makes you disinterested and irritable, induces insomnia and low spirits, endangers your general health, and makes you vulnerable to injuries and illness. Train, don't strain.

This applies more accurately to running at faster aerobic speeds than are implied by LSD. East German physiologists have shown that it's better to do long aerobic running at between 70 and 100 percent of your maximum steady state. Lower aerobic effort, while it may be fine for joggers, does not exert the same desirable pressure on the heart and the cardiac and respiratory systems that an athlete needs.

Bowerman also maintains that overtraining can result in staleness and loss of interest in practice and competition, and suggests that the ideal solution is regular competition. I see staleness as a physiological reaction caused by excessive anaerobic work. This becomes psychological through the effects of continual low blood pH on the central nervous system. Lots of competitive racing won't cure that.

I've never noticed athletes who train aerobically over varied courses to lose interest. They do not usually have problems maintaining 160 kilometers a week of fast aerobic running throughout the required conditioning period. When they move into the anaerobic phase, when the physiological problems could again be encountered, they are at a level of cardiac efficiency enabling them to handle the constant fluctuation of blood pH without that staleness side effect.

For a practical example, assume we work with conditioned A until he has the capacity to use 3 liters of oxygen a minute, and runner B up to 5 liters. We then give them the same volume and intensity of anaerobic training. Because his maximum steady state is lower, runner A will level off and begin to lose form, fighting a continually larger oxygen debt. Runner B, on the other hand, will continue to maintain his best form, since he can use oxygen more effectively and for longer periods. It's easy to see how this physiological effect on runner A can become a psychological problem. He's never going to beat runner B and he can see it.

Let's start these two runners off the same mark in a 1500-meter race. They'll be together at the end of the first lap, and neither will be feeling any strain, since neither has yet experienced the effect of oxygen debt. But, because runner A's capacity to use oxygen is only three-fifths that of runner B, by the time they're into the third lap, A will be feeling the pace. He'll be building an oxygen debt to keep up with runner B, lactic acid will be accumulating, and neuromuscular breakdown will be underway. When runner B fires in his finishing burst, runner A won't be able to answer. And if, by the time they met in this race, runner A's physiological inferiority had also become psychological, he's in real trouble. Which of the two do you want to be?

Interval Training

One of the greatest difficulties in persuading coaches and athletes to accept the anaerobic system is that the majority are chained to the principles of interval training. They emphasize anaerobic interval training or repetition work as the most important aspect of the training program.

The object is simple: to lower blood pH by running into big oxygen debts, to allow blood pH to recover again, and then to lower it once more. This can be done in 101 different ways, since it is only a matter of the athlete becoming tired by hard anaerobic running. He doesn't have to do it by the stern disciplines of running so many times over a certain distance in a particular time.

There is no coach in the world who can say exactly what an athlete should do as far as number of repetitions, distances, and intervals are concerned. Not even physiologists can tell an athlete that. The important point is that the athlete knows what he's trying to achieve and goes out and works at it until he does.

This is why marathon running is such a fascinating and demanding sport. A marathon runner must use his anaerobic capacities economically, controlling his running so that he gets just barely into an anaerobic state and stays there. If he runs into it too quickly, he accumulates lactic acid too fast and curtails his possibilities of continuing. This is what most marathon runners do when they run against a superior runner. They match pace with him and run into a big initial oxygen debt and then wonder why they're forced to drift back, why they can't maintain the pace. They'd do better to let the superior runner go and hold a pace at which they can ration out the oxygen debt very slowly. There's always the chance that the superior runner will misjudge his own pace and come back. In a marathon, you're racing to your own capacity as much as anyone else's.

I have purposely offered these two divergent viewpoints on the question of interval training, involving large-scale oxygen debt, passing far over the anaerobic barrier or threshold. This gives the reader two options and at least one hundred variations of both to work with. Each system should be tried to determine which is the most comfortable and productive for the individual runner.

Max Telford leads the class down the hill to the start, and then back again for another bounding session up the hill.

Winners of the Honolulu Marathon being congratulated by Hawaii 50 T.V. Celebrity.

Shimano and fellow riders biking through the lava fields.

Max Telford, (on the right) World Class Runner with over 100,000 miles of running to his credit, discusses training plans with members of his running class.

Hill Training: The Telford Method

Try to find a hill at least 300 meters long, rising at a gradient of near one in three, on a road, in the country, or on a forest trail, with 400 to 800 meters of reasonably flat ground at both top and bottom. The best alternative is a circuit with a smallish, steep hill for uphill work, a less steep hill for downhill running, and flattish areas both top and bottom between them for speed training and jogging. When you begin training on this hill circuit, run first at warming-up speed for about 2 kilometers. If temperatures permit, unnecessary clothing should be discarded to allow freedom of movement—most important in this phase of training.

At the base of the steeper hill, start springing up, on your toes, not running up, but bouncing. You must lift and drop the center of gravity, using your body weight as a form of resistance to the leg muscles. This gives you muscular development and flexibility through the extreme actions of the legs in first driving upward with a high knee-lift, and then taking the force of your body weight as it comes down again. Drive hard, pushing upward with your toes, flexing your ankles as far as possible and landing on the forepart of your foot. The heel should come down below the level of the toe as the weight is taken. This action stretches the calf muscles both upward and downward as far as possible. It also applies resistance, thoroughly exercising muscle fibers, so that flexibility and power are added simultaneously to build an economical stride length.

If you want to develop fast strides or increase stride frequency, your feet will have to follow through as close to the buttocks as possible. If you move your feet through close to the ground, it will result in a much slower stride. But you can't bring your feet through with a high action unless you run with your hips farther forward. Some of the world's best sprinters run with a seemingly backward-leaning action. While this action should not be exaggerated, you must lean such that foot strike is comfortable, economical, and makes for fast leg action.

Concentrate on running with your head up and looking straight ahead. If your head falls forward, your hips will tend to be held back. They should be sufficiently forward to allow the knees to rise high, which in turn allows the feet to follow through high. If your hips are back, there is no way you can get your knees up high enough.

As you spring up that hill, your arms, shoulders, neck, and facial muscles should be relaxed. Keep your head up and looking ahead, with hips slightly forward, and legs driving down forcefully. Push hard with the toes, raise the knees high, and then apply body-weight resistance to the leg muscles as your feet hit the ground. Your progression up the hill will be gradual, not fast. Do only as much hill springing as your condition allows, and only increase the work load as your muscles become accustomed to it.

At the top, take a recovery period by jogging easily. You should not stop running. When you hit the downward hill, you should run fast, with relaxed, slightly longer strides. With no resistance against them, your muscles will be able to recover further, and you will feel stretching in the legs, the stomach muscles, and the hips. You should do some exercises for your stomach muscles to make them more supple for easier breathing when you're running under pressure, with your heart and lungs expanded. Unless your stomach muscles are supple, you'll apply pressure to your diaphragm, pulling at the ligaments that attach the diaphragm to the bone. This results in stomach cramps or stitches, the sharp pains that can force you to stop or ease up.

The downhill running tends to throw the body backward a little further, stretching your stomach muscles and increasing pressure on the diaphragm. You can help offset this by doing backward-bending exercises as muscle stretchers. If you use a road for this training, it is imperative to wear shoes with thick rubber soles and heels, not shoes with the heel cut away.

Leg and Lower Body Development

There are two kinds of muscle contraction—*isometric* and *isotonic*. The contraction is isotonic when the muscular effort results in movement, such as lifting, pushing, or pulling something that moves. It is isometric when force is applied by pushing, pulling, or trying to lift an immovable object. Both forms of resistance have value in exercise, so athletes should evaluate and apply them to specific needs.

When speed development is the aim, you should concentrate on the white muscle fibers. In sprinting, these muscles are required to work for a short period in a series of short, sharp contractions. Therefore, they require exercise that allows for quick resistance pressures in a series of repetitions that aren't too fatiguing, but are sufficient to impel all the fibers to work. An isotonic exercise is best, and that springing up hills is an isotonic exercise similar to the movement needed in the eventual competition.

Developing the Stride

Fundamentally, speed is developed in two ways: through longer strides and a faster stride frequency. To develop longer strides, you have to increase the power and flexibility of the legs. Increased stride frequency will come with greater reflex actions, better coordination, and more flexibility, relaxation, and technique. Applying resistance to the muscles to increase the size and strength of the fibers will help achieve strength.

It is important, in all types of running, to have strong quadriceps to maintain good knee-lift throughout the entire distance. Knee-lift is relative to the speed at which you are running. Though a marathon runner shouldn't keep the knees high during a race, he should run with his knees at a height that gives him the most economical stride length and frequency. A sprinter, however, must bring his knees up high, not only because it lengthens his stride, but because it brings his feet through high and fast.

Run regularly on steep hills to activate the upper leg muscles. Work until your muscles feel the exercise, and keep at it steadily. Suppling and loosening exercises should also be done on a regular basis at this stage, with particular attention to ankle flexibility. Too many runners have inefficient ankle action. Look at the ankles of gymnasts and ballet dancers, and you'll realize what great ankle flexibility can be attained. The increased striding efficiency on the quadriceps or front upper-leg muscles. The next time around again, you can run uphill, pushing mostly with the ankles, while lifting the knees. Then return to the hill springing. All the leg muscles, including the quadriceps, benefit from this training.

Another valuable exercise for this phase is frog hopping, with or without the addition of resistance weights. Go right down on your haunches and spring in hops for 50 to 100 meters. You must get low and spring high, returning to your haunches each time. A bag of sand on your shoulders will add resistance; it's better than holding weights as you jump, because it doesn't upset the balance.

The hill circuit program lasts six weeks. During this period, you should spend two days a week on the hill, alternating with one day of leg-speed running and three of long-distance running.

Feel your way into a pattern that suits you. Only well-conditioned athletes will get through the six weeks properly and successfully. This will halt all achilles tendon trouble, an injury quite prevalent in sport today. Athletes are always running into hamstring and tendon trouble because they haven't done enough suppling and stretching exercises, or hill work to build resistance and to extend important muscles and tendons.

In a six-week period, there is an almost total renewal of red cells in your body. Since this coincides with the length of the initial anaerobic training, there will be a significant change in your general metabolism.

Your mileage during this period will be about 40 miles a week, including warming up and cooling down. Try to fit in other easy running each day to supplement this, since light aerobic exercise aids recovery. Ideally, you should aim for about 30 minutes of supplementary running each day.

For the leg-speed training, you need a flat area, 100 to 120 meters long, preferably with a slight gradual decline. Warm up for at least 15 minutes, and then run over the course up to ten times, thinking only about moving your legs as fast as possible. There should be a 3-minute interval between each run; it is important not to rush this exercise. Don't be conscious of stride length. Keep your upper body relaxed and the knee action reasonably high. You'll have the feeling your legs aren't moving fast enough. So run with a subconscious stride, thinking about pulling the legs through fast using the quadriceps and lower abdominal muscles. The exercise is designed to overcome stress in the legs and to develop fine speed. Avoid running into the wind as resistance is not desired. After the last repetition, cool down for at least 15 minutes, jogging easily.

This exercise will give you tired legs, but if you keep at it, it will become progressively easier after about two weeks. By then, you should be getting excellent results. So there it is: hill training two days a week, leg-speed running 1 day and a long aerobic run on 3 days.

Upper Body and Leg Action

During conditioning running, always try to relax, particularly the upper body. Keep the head up and the hips comfortably forward; this allows you to stride longer and more economically. Never waste energy.

Try to keep your arm action low. Runners with a high arm action aren't relaxed and tend to throw their torsos from side to side. They don't get over their driving legs and lose some forward momentum. Test yourself by running on sand and then checking your footprints. If you're running balanced, your feet should fall directly one behind the other; if you're not, they'll vary either side of a straight centerline. If they're unbalanced, you'll lose forward motion.

I don't belong to the clenched-fist or air-clutching school of studied stylists. The late Hec Hogan, the Australian sprinter and former co-world record-holder, was my mirror of the perfect running action. He was fully relaxed, even under extreme pressure, with arms driving straight through and carried easily at a natural height. The minute you clench your fists you tense arm and shoulder muscles, and encourage swaying and loss of balance. Tensed muscles also waste energy.

Don't run on your toes. This works calf muscles unnaturally, which is uncomfortable and tiring over long distances. It is most economical and natural to come down with a nearly flat foot, with the heel hitting first and a slight roll in from the outside edge of the foot. There are many good runners who run on their toes, but I contend they would run better still, in distance work, with a nearly flat footfall.

Arm Action

The best form is the low-swinging arm action, with the thumbs skimming the seams of the shorts. This keeps them moving straight through and guides balance—the essential value of arm action. Arms don't assist the distance runner much, apart from aiding balance, and the low action is natural, relaxed, and automatic. It takes energy to hold the arms up high.

Physiological Changes

If you haven't done marathon conditioning before, you must think deeply about it from the start, and try to understand just what you're trying to achieve. You must relate it to physiological changes, making sure there's no confusion in your mind about the effects of various types of exercise on you. You've got to sort these exercises into their various compartments, balance your schedules, and get rid of any doubts about the approach during each developmental stage, right up to the climax of your racing season. Tackle each stage as a separate exercise, distinct from all others, but with the ultimate target fixed firmly in your mind. Only when you're quite clear about the physiological and mechanical aspects of your training will you develop the confidence you need to become a champion.

The fundamental principle of training is to develop enough stamina to enable you to maintain the necessary speed over the full distance at which you plan to compete. Many runners throughout the world are capable of running 400 meters in 46 seconds or faster. But remarkably few of them have sufficient stamina to run 800 meters in 1:44, or 52 seconds for each 400. That clearly shows the vital part stamina plays in the middle- and long-distance racing. Consider those relative times again. It will help you realize what could be achieved by fast runners if they concentrated on endurance development and shifted their attention to longer distances.

Building Stamina

Quite simply, it means putting your body into a near-tireless state so that oxygen debts are not created quickly and the ability to recover rapidly is at a high level. Stamina is general cardiac efficiency and the best way to develop it is by running. That running is best done at just under your maximum steady state, for approximately 60 miles a week. This is quite apart from any easier supplementary running, such as jogging, that you feel inclined to do.

Running is without question the best exercise for runners and, provided you watch the degree of effort, you can't really do too much of it. Certain physiologists have said that unless the pulse rate is brought up to 150-80 beats a minute, the athlete gains very little cardiac development. This is absolutely wrong. I have never believed it. If an athlete with a normal pulse rate of 50 to 60 lifts the rate to 100, he will get cardiac development. So *all* supplementary jogging, while it may not impose the pressure on the system to the degree that near maximum steady-state running does, affords extra benefits to the cardiac system, as well as aiding the athlete's recovery.

The long steady running that I term marathon training is designed to create a state of fatigue, though not so great as to interfere with the next day's program. You should be able to recover reasonably quick.

Determining Your Capability

First you have to find your own basic capability. The best way to do this is to run an out-and-back course for, say, 30 minutes. Run out for 15 minutes at a steady pace; then turn and run back again, trying to maintain that pace without forcing yourself. If it takes you 20 minutes to get back, it shows you've run the outward leg too fast for your condition. If you're back inside 15 minutes without apparently increasing your effort, you haven't run fast enough to begin with. Next time, you should adjust your pace according to your insights about your condition and capability, so that you return in the same time as the outward journey. It's good discipline, and that's something you have to acquire early because you're going to need a lot of it later on.

As you learn more about yourself and improve your general physical condition, you'll be able to run both farther and faster. But you should understand that it's the speed of the running that stops you, not the distance. Running that breaks the even passage of time and distance is anaerobic, not aerobic, and it must be avoided. It's much better to go too slowly at first than too fast. If you can recognize that as important and discipline yourself to it, you're on the way to becoming a greater runner than you believed possible.

Winterize Your Running

When the snow falls, the temperature drops and ice forms, runners must begin to take certain preventive measures against these winter conditions. Many of these winter elements may seem innocuous, but they can cause injury due to their effects on the road or sidewalk and the runner.

When snowfall hits the Washington area the entire city shuts down. This does not mean you have to interrupt your running schedule. Bear in mind that snow is impressionable and soft, as well as slightly slippery. More energy is required to run on snow due to the decrease in surface friction, and the leg muscles trying to stabilize the foot in the snow. This can lead to an overuse of the lower leg, which usually presents itself as generalized leg fatigue or skin splints. Another problem with running in the snow is that the heel sinks lower than the front of the foot, causing the Achilles' tendon to stretch beyond its normal limits during running. A strain is placed on the tendon from this motion.

Eventually tendonitis may develop. Some measures that can be taken to help prevent general leg fatigue and shin splints from occurring are the following.

1. Wear waffle-bottom shoes. These will act as "snow tires" and increase the shoe-to-snow friction.

2. Walk on the outsides, insides and heels of your feet for two minutes in each position every day. This will help strengthen your lower leg muscles. Achilles' tendinitis or strain is avoidable by simple stretching exercises for the muscles in the back of the leg that form the Achilles' tendon complex. All of these exercises must be done regularly to be effective.

Ice is the most hazardous of all the winter elements. Many times it is not seen until you have slipped and injured yourself. Steps that must be taken when an iced surface is suspected are to shorten your stride and look for a salted or sanded route.

The most uncomfortable weather to run in is rain. When temperatures are just over freezing, the rain will dampen both shoes and socks. This will cause a lowering in temperature of your feet by a considerable amount. A numb sensation will develop due to inadequate blood supply in the chilled feet. The loss of feeling is usually noticed in the toes and heels first. If you feel these symptoms in your feet, head home and place your feet in warm water. Never hot! Even though there is no feeling in your feet, they can still burn by the use of extremely hot water. Leave your feet in water until they have warmed up and most of the feeling has returned. Running shoes made of gore-tex uppers and waterproofing of shoes may help for a short time, but ultimately the water will soak in.

By initiating the proper strengthening and stretching program before the winter season and taking certain precautions every run, winter running won't plague you with injuries.

Summary of Running Schedule for the Marathon Chapter

GENERAL RULES:

Run not fewer than 3 times per week, not more than 6 times per week. Run at least one hour, but no farther than 15 miles at one time. After month two run at least 2 hours at one time.

Month One:	Walk-run one hour 3 times per week, walk 3 times per week
Month Two:	Run one hour 3 times per week, walk-run 3 times per week
Month Three:	Run one hour 3 times per week, run hills or steps 3 times per week adding weight training and striding to the easy days
Month Four:	Run one hour 3 days per week 2 hours on Sunday, with strength, striding and weight training on 3 days
Month Five:	Strive for distance at least 30 miles per week on the distance runs. Strength and striding, and weight training on 3 easy days.
Month Six:	30 to 40 miles per week, including strength, striding and time trial workouts
Month Seven:	40 to 50 miles per week
Month Eight:	50 to 60 miles per week
Month Nine:	50 to 60 miles per week
Month Ten:	30 miles per week, one hour run for three days for 3 weeks. The last week should include a 10 mile depletion run and limbering exercises while Carbo Loading
Month Eleven:	Run a full 26.2 mile marathon.

If one advances confidently in the direction of his dreams, and endeavors to live the life which he has imagined, he will meet with a success unexpected in common hours.

THOREAU

I speak truth, not so much as I would, but as much as I dare; and I dare a little the more, as I grow older.

MONTAIGNE

A weary marathoner after the Honolulu Marathon

Over a million dollars worth of top quality bicycles from around the world ready for the 1982 spring Ironman Triathlon

DISTANCES AND
METRIC CONVERSIONS

(NOTE: A kilometer is 1000 meters)

50 meters = 54 yards 6.5 inches	50 yards = 45.72m
60 meters = 65 yards 1 foot 10.2 inches	60 yards = 54.864m
100 meters = 109 yards 1 foot 1 inch	70 yards = 64.008m
110 meters = 120 yards 10.7 inches	100 yards = 91.44m
200 meters = 218 yards 2 feet 2 inches	120 yards = 109.728m
300 meters = 328 yards 3 inches	220 yards = 201.168m
400 meters = 437 yards 1 foot 4 inches	300 yards = 274.32m
500 meters = 546 yards 2 feet 5 inches	330 yards = 301.644m
600 meters = 656 yards 6 inches	440 yards = 402.336m
800 meters = 874 yards 2 feet 8 inches	500 yards = 457.2m
1000 meters = 1093 yards 1 foot 10 inches	600 yards = 548.64m
1500 meters = 1640 yards 1 foot 3 inches	660 yards = 603.504m
2000 meters = 1 mile 427 yards 8 inches	880 yards = 804.672m
3000 meters = 1 mile 1520 yards 2 feet 6 inches	1000 yards = 914.4m
4000 meters = 2 miles 854 yards 1 foot 4 inches	1320 yards = 1207.008m
5000 meters = 3 miles 188 yards 2.4 inches	One mile = 1609.344m
6000 meters = 3 miles 1281 yards 2 feet	2 miles = 3218.688m
7000 meters = 4 miles 615 yards 10 inches	3 miles = 4828.032m
8000 meters = 4 miles 1708 yards 2 feet 8 inches	4 miles = 6437.376m
9000 meters = 5 miles 1042 yards 1 foot 6 inches	5 miles = 8046.72m
10,000 meters = 6 miles 376 yards 4.8 inches	6 miles = 9656.064m
12,000 meters = 7 miles 803 yards 1 foot	7 miles = 11,265.408m
15,000 meters = 9 miles 564 yards 7.2 inches	8 miles = 12,874.752m
20,000 meters = 12 miles 754 yards 9.6 inches	9 miles = 14,484.096m
25,000 meters = 15 miles 940 yards 1 foot	10 miles = 16,093.44m
30,000 meters = 18 miles 1128 yards 1 foot 2.4 inches	15 miles = 24,140.16m
35,000 meters = 21 miles 1316 yards 1 foot 4.8 inches	20 miles = 32,186.88m
40,000 meters = 24 miles 1504 yards 1 foot 7.2 inches	Marathon = 42,195m
50,000 meters = 31 miles 120 yards 2 feet	30 miles = 48,280.32m
60,000 meters = 37 miles 476 yards 2 feet 4.8 inches	40 miles = 64,373.76m
70,000 meters = 43 miles 872 yards 2 feet 9.6 inches	50 miles = 80,467.2m
80,000 meters = 49 miles 1249 yards 2.4 inches	60 miles = 96,560.64m
90,000 meters = 55 miles 1625 yards 7.2 inches	70 miles = 112,654.08m
100,000 meters = 62 miles 241 yards 1 foot	80 miles = 128,747.52m
	90 miles = 144,840.96m
	100 miles = 160,934.4m

Marathon Training Bibliography

Best of Runner's World, The Complete Marathoner, The Complete Runner, Jog, Run, Race, The Long Run Solution, Marathoning, Run Farther, Run Faster, Run Gently, Run Long, Running After 40, available through Anderson World, Inc., 1400 Stierlin Road, Mountain View, California, 94043.

Running and Your Body, Bernie Dare, Tafnew Press, Book Division of Track and Field News, Box 296, Los Altos, California 94022, 1979.

Running the Lydiard Way, Arthur Lydiard and Garth Gilmour. World Publications, Inc. P.O. Box 366, Mountain View, CA 94042, 1978.

Your First Marathon, Jenni Gordon. Running Wild, 111 Rahara Dr., Lafayette, CA. 94549, 1979.

Long Distances, Less Jarver Tafnew Press, Box 296, Los Altos, CA. 94022, 1980.

Training with Cerutty, Larry Meyers. World Publications, Box 366, Mountain View, CA. 94042, 1977.

A Scientific Approach to Distance Running, David L. Costill. Track and Field, 1979.

Jog, Run, Race, Joe Henderson. World Publications, Inc., P.O. Box 399, Mountain View, CA. 94042, 1977.

The Complete Marathoner, Joe Henderson, ed. World Publications, Inc., P.O. Box 399, Mountain View, CA. 94042, 1978.

The Complete Book of Running, James F. Fixx. Random House, New York, NY, 1977.

Jim Fixx's Second Book of Running, James F. Fixx. Random House, New York, NY, 1978.

Indian Running, Peter Nabokov, Capra Press, P.O. Box 2068, Santa Barbara, CA. 93102.

Anderson, Bob, and Henderson, Joe, eds. *Guide to Distance Running.* Mountain View, Calif.: World Publications, 1971.

Andrew, G. M., Guzman, C. A., and Becklake, M. R. "Effect of Athletic Training on Exercise Cardiac Output." *Journal of Applied Physiology,* no. 21 (1966).

Balke, Bruno. "Effects of Altitude on Maximum Performances." *Track & Field News.* Track technique, no. 18. Los Altos, Calif., 1964.

Bowerman, William J. *Coaching Track and Field.* Boston: Houghton Mifflin Co., 1974.

Costes, Nick. *Interval Training.* Mountain View, Calif.: World Publications, 1972.

Haggard, H. W., and Greenberg, L. A. *Diet and Physical Efficiency.* New Haven: Yale University Press, 1933.

Merton, P. A. "Problems of Muscular Fatigue." *British Medical Bulletin,* no. 12 (1956).

Meyers, Larry *Training with Cerutty* World Publications, Box 366, Mountain View, Ca., 94042.

Morehouse, Laurence, and Miller, Augustus T. *The Physiology of Exercise* St. Louis: The C. V. Mosby Co., 1967.

Morehouse, L. E., and Rasch, P. J. *Sports Medicine For Trainers.* Philadelphia: W. B. Saunders Co., 1963.

Potts, Frank C. "Running at High Altitude." *Track & Field Quarterly,* January 1968.

Runner's World, eds. *The Complete Diet Guide: For Runners and Other Athletes.* Mountain View, Calif.: World Publications, 1978.

Runner's World, eds. *Runner's Training Guide.* Mountain View, Calif.: World Publications, 1973.

Runner's World, eds. *Running with Style.* Mountain View, Calif.: World Publications, 1975.

Sterner, John. "Stroke and Heat Exhaustion in Athletes." *Track & Field News.* Track Technique, no. 25. Los Altos, Calif., 1966.

Van Aaken, Ernst. "Running and the Chemistry of the Blood." *Track & Field News.* Track Technique, no. 3. Los Altos, Calif., 1961.

Watts, D.C.V., and Wilson, Harry. *Middle and Long Distance, Marathon and Steeplechase.* London: British Amateur Athletic Board, undated.

Zierler, K. L. *Mechanism of Muscle Contraction and its Energetics.* St. Louis: The C. V. Mosby Co., 1961.

Health is the soul which animates all enjoyment of life. —Temple

2

Ultramarathon and the Triathlete

The Ultramarathon in History

THE HISTORY OF ORGANIZED RUNNING probably got its start in Britain. Athletics seemed to be better organized in Britain than anywhere else in the world during the nineteenth century. And there was this tradition of running footmen which goes right back to the seventeenth century. The lord of the manor would say *his* footman was far better than the other bloke's at carrying messages. Then they would run against each other over quite long distances. A running man in those days was quicker than a man on horseback or a coach because of the state of the roads. Men could travel much longer distances and were far more reliable. Later on they became the first professional athletes.

There got to be a few traditional distances—10-mile races were the great thing in the 1700's. One man actually died an hour after setting up a record of 54½ minutes on Richmond Green. He just wasn't trained for that sort of effort. While the time may seem ludicrous nowadays, it still seems tragic, doesn't it? By modern standards, most of these people on into the nineteenth century weren't well trained. Even over the shorter distances they frequently would collapse after a race was over and be insensible for a time. These people would put tremendous efforts into their running. In terms of effort they might be doing more than the modern superathlete does to run themselves into unconsciousness. I think that's quite heroic, really.

Early Day Ultramarathons Were Walkers

Most of the ultra feats in the eighteenth century involved not runners but walkers, usually men, who covered distances as far as 300 to 400 miles. Hundred-mile walks in 24 hours were sometimes done on the roads or around a horse-race track, although Lovesey . . . the British running authority says there is some question as to how reliable the watches were. Around 1823 a seven-year-old girl ran for four hours at a time on several occasions. Another young girl in the nineteenth century apparently ran and walked 30 miles three times—in a little less than eight hours on each occasion—taking wine and water for sustenance and remaining in excellent spirits throughout. A man named Captain Barclay walked 1,000 miles in 1,000 hours—covering one mile each hour. He was never able to rest very long, and he had to endure abysmal weather. Thousands came to watch and Captain Barclay earned about £16,000—the equivalent today of $400,000. Clearly, there was what one might term an exceedingly thin tradition for such events, but considering how hard people worked, how different and how difficult it was to travel around and how little was known about training, such a sprinkling of endurance events was at least a beginning.

According to Lovesey, pedestrianism was at its social heyday about 1810 when it was very much a high-class affair, but by the 1860's and the era of the Industrial Revolution it had become considerably less fashionable. The predominant sports in England now, such as cricket, rugby and soccer, hadn't yet been established on a regular basis, so pedestrianism had a large following among the working class in the big cities, each of which had its own track for such events.

The First 6 Day Race

The earliest six-day race apparently took place about 1874, and soon the colorful, dynamic figure of Sir John Astley, sports promoter par excellence, dominated the scene. At one time a bit of a runner himself, as well as a Member of Parliament, he set up a championship belt and money prizes to encourage interest and organized races both in London and New York. Both the grander and lesser lights who actually hoofed around the tracks under Sir John's auspices were a varied lot. One "Corkey," whose Christian name was William Gentleman, was a one-time record holder who was described by Sir John in his autobiography, *Fifty Years of My Life,* as "a very quaint-looking old chap of 46 . . . had a peculiar high action. He didn't look a bit like staying, was as thin as a rail and stuttered very funnily, but in Mrs. Corkey, he possessed a real treasure. She never left him day or night and was always ready to hand her sweetheart a basin of delicious and greasy eel-broth he loved so well and which, obviously, agreed so famously with him." Henry "Blower" Brown, also a record holder, who had been a brickmaker, had "early distinguished himself by the rapid manner he trundled his barrel of bricks to the kiln and back again for another load; and like all brickmakers, he was wonderfully fond of beer. Therefore, when old Jack Smith wished to get an extra spurt out of his protege he used to yell at him on the track with the same exhortation and promise whenever his instinct told him it was needed: 'Well done, Blower. Go to it, Blower. You've got 'em all beat, my beauty. Yes, Blower shall have a barrel of beer all to himself if he wins. Go to it, Blower.'

One day Blower showed signs of shutting up; and he was more animal than angel. Smith and I agreed that it would be a good thing to wake him up a bit by putting him in a bath, quite a new sensation for him. So we took him to my lodgings hard by, and I ordered two chops to be got ready for him and then put him into a hip bath of real hot water which livened him up considerably, fairly making him sing out. When we got him nicely dry, the chops appeared. At last I was helping Blower into his running suit, I was horrified to observe old Smith busily employed gobbling up all the best parts of the chops, leaving only the bone, gristle and fat. When I expostulated with him on his greediness and cruelty to his man, he replied: 'Bless yer, Colonel, Blower has never had the chance of eating the inside, he likes the outside.' And sure enough, the brickmaker cleaned up the dish, with the result that he won first prize, doing 542 miles, a grand performance, and what is more, his appetite and thirst were in no way impaired."

Weston Pioneered Ultramarathon

Several other men were quite extraordinary for their persistence, talent and longevity in the sport. Edward Payson Weston, a Rhode Islander, originally a news vendor on a railway, walked from Boston to Washington, D.C., in order to get to Lincoln's inauguration in 1861. He was then just 21 years of age. Although he arrived late after his 443-mile trek he drew an enormous amount of attention. Six years later he walked over 1,300 miles from Portland, Maine, to Chicao, in 26 days. Forty years later he did it again, bettering his time over the first trip by 29 hours. In 1874 at Madison Square Garden he tried in May, September and October to become the first walker to break 500 miles in six days but got no further than 436 miles on his third attempt. In December he tried it in Newark, New Jersey, and made it with 26 minutes to spare.

Dan O'Leary, who was seven years Weston's junior and a little heavier although they were both the same height (5' 8") emigrated to the States when he was 20 years old. He sold books and pictures on installments to the poor of Chicago. His athletic career led to a changed and more prosperous life—he was to cross the Atlantic 44 times in pursuit of world records and long-standing rivals like Weston. In addition to holding the world record for a time, his career best was a 525-mile wobble in 1880 in San Francisco. Years of competition did not interfere with his friendship with Weston, and when O'Leary was 50 years old he walked 2,500 miles across America with Weston in 9 weeks. O'Leary celebrated his *81st* birthday by walking 100 miles to win a $100 bet.

Much as Sir John Astley enjoyed the success of American ultrawalkers, he looked around restlessly at the close of the 1870's for a local lad who could win back the championship belt from O'Leary. Charles Rowell, a boat boy at the Guards Club in Maidenhead, showed some promise as a runner and was promptly taken under Sir John's sponsorship. Rowell, then in his early twenties, "a very clean made, muscular young fellow," was to revolutionize the wobbles by introducing longer and longer spells of running. Since the other peds kept in shape by frequent competitions, Rowell set about training with a vengeance. He ran on a treadmill to strengthen his legs, dashing along the towpath following the Cambridge crew shells as they were out training on the river. Rowell sometimes ran up to London one day and back the next—60 miles each way in under eight hours, still impressive training of a kind that very few ultrarunners ever do nowadays. In Rowell's first wobble in New York City in March 1879, he earned back the belt and was $20,000 richer, a very considerable sum in those days. He lost to Weston in London that summer but in New York again in the fall he won and earned himself another $30,000.

Wagering Promoted Ultramarathons

Such sums of money—in addition to the public adulation—did much to encourage a number of men to try their hand at such things. It must have been intoxicating in spite of the grinding tedium to be occasionally pelted with flowers and presented with six-foot-high horseshoe flower bouquets. Rowell, flush with his earnings, took three trotting horses back to his newly acquired farm in England. On his return, reporters went straight to Charles Rowell, ignoring the disembarking actors and politicians. Sadly, when Rowell died almost three decades later he had lost all his wealth and was living in poverty. (He was not the only pedestrian who came atangle with fortune. George Hazael, a fellow countryman and for a while world champion who made "barrels of money," was later reduced to the hard life of a bottle-and-scrap-iron peddler.)

Charles Rowell was undoubtedly one of the most remarkable men to ever circle those tiny tracks. At the end of February 1882, he participated in his last race in New York. In a little-known monograph entitled "Six-Day Races," Tom Osler and Ed Dodd (themselves ultrarunners from New Jersey) described Rowell's intentions and achievements on that occasion:

"He intended to make it memorable by establishing an unbreakable world record. He almost succeeded. His first three days saw the following:

1882 Charles Rowell's Three Day Unbreakable World Record

- **100 miles—13:26:30** • **200 miles—35:09:28**
- **24 hours—150 miles 395 yards** • **48 hours—258 miles 220 yards** • **72 hours—353 miles 220 yards**

"Of these marks, only the 100 miles and 24 hours have been bettered today. Rowell proved by these marks that he was the greatest ultramarathoner of all time. Even today the world record for 24 hours is only 11 miles further than Rowell's 1882 mark, and Rowell faced another five days of running!

"At the close of the third day, poor Rowell accidentally gulped down a cup of warm vinegar. His stomach became sick and he retired from the race on the fifth day. George Hazael won with a new world record of 600 miles 220 yards."

There are a number of interesting sidelights on these 6-day affairs. For one thing, there were frequently two separate tracks set up in the same arena. The inside track was the domain of the better, higher status competitors, while the outer track was for the less experienced ordinary working men who, as Lovesey suggests, "probably came in off the streets and thought they might make a little money by trying to walk around the thing for a few days." The reason for this isolation of the separate tracks, he suggested, was to avoid any possible interference, since a certain amount of hacking and kicking went on.

491

The start of the "Run to the Sun" on the island of Maui, Hawaii. Mount Haleakala, an extinct volcano is in the background, 10,600 ft. elevation above sea level, is the finish line, 37½ miles away.

The Ultramarathon to stop them all, 90 humid degrees at the start, 45 cold, windy, cloud swept degrees at the top.

Wagering Insured Accurate Timing for the 6 Day Ultras

"You see, one thing about professional athletics that you can argue in its favor *is* accuracy. There was a lot of money at stake and I think the people who were betting would have wanted a pretty strong assurance that the distance was accurate. The track was measured with a sort of surveyor's wheel before the start, usually in the presence of the crowd. I can see that the system of lap scoring could have been confusing and lead to all sorts of mismanagement. But for these major events, it was probably reliable. And the way the record was edged up from a little more than 500 miles steadily to 623-odd miles is the way records improve nowadays. As for how much running they did, they did quite a bit sometimes but you can't be sure from the accounts just how much."

Number One, Dave Scott of Davis, California, wears the number befitting his performance during the 1983 Ironman Triathlon World Championship. Scott captured his third crown with a record time of 9:05:57. In the October 1984 Ironman, Dave's fourth win was clocked in at 8:54:20.

Photo by Reggie David

The reason for the races being 6 instead of 5 or 7 days, Lovesey added, was that in Victorian England Sunday was a strictly observed day of rest and time for church, family worship together, etc. Therefore a race had to be sandwiched in between two Sundays. Hence, the races began early Monday morning about 1:00 a.m. and finished around 10:30 or 11:00 the following Saturday night. Sunday-morning judges and participants alike were reverently seated in church.

In the mid-1880's, the wobbles plummeted in popularity, although a brief renaissance took root for some reason or another in Philadelphia from 1899 to 1903. Six were held in the space of one year. Sir Astley's weakness for gambling led to his getting "skinned" and he was no longer able to promote the races as he had in the past.

Cycling 6 Day Races Replaced the Ultras

"Another reason was that cycling was beginning to come in," Lovesey said. "Cycling had more to offer the spectators and the gamblers, since there was more change of fortune. Maybe people began to suspect in the later eighties that the races were fixed so that certain people would be allowed to win. There were various permutations on the six-day contest, and it went on in one form or another until well into the pre-World War One period."

Certainly their gradual disappearance from the sporting scene must have greatly satisfied newspaper correspondents and editorial writers, who were dubious about their value. Witness this concluding paragraph from the *Illustrated London News,* 9 November 1878:

> We cannot take leave of the subject without expressing an earnest hope that we have seen the last of these painful struggles against nature. It may be an advantage to know that a man can travel 520 miles in 138 hours, and manage to live through a week with an infinitesimal amount of rest, though we fail to perceive that anyone could possibly be placed in a position where his ability in this respect would be of real use to him . . . So, what is to be gained by a constant repetition of the feat? As long, however, as prizes are offered, so long will men come forward to compete for them; and we suppose the public will continue to flock to these races until a man dies upon the track. Then there will be a sudden revulsion of feeling, a howl of virtuous indignation, and such exhibitions will be sternly repressed. But why not repress them before anything so serious has occurred? We have no hesitation in stating that prizefighting is mild and humane, compared with such sport as six-day races; and that the one should be rigidly put down and the other encouraged, in the same country, is a gross and glaring inconsistency.

There had been scenes of brutality on the track, one of the more notable taking place in 1884 in New York when Patrick Fitzgerald was racing against Charles Rowell. Fitzgerald's slim lead over his opponent grew slimmer during the last day. In desperation his handlers had him bled by making incisions in his thighs to reduce the stiffness.

"It worked," the two authors noted dryly, "and Fitzgerald staggered to a new world record of 610 miles." It was also the end of Fitzgerald's running career. His weight shot up in four years from 160 to 240 pounds. During George Littlewood's 623-mile-plus effort at Madison Square Garden in 1888, he retired briefly from the track and was reposing in an alcohol bath when someone dropped a match in, burning him rather badly. But he still finished the race, in spite of the injury one of his feet sustained. One American journalist who witnessed some of these affairs took pity on "the poor, jaded, abused bodies" of the runners and said not only did they make him sick, but the memory of them would play havoc with his sleeping hours for days to come. There was even a bill introduced in the Pennsylvania legislature to outlaw the sport entirely.

Transcontinental Race Walkers

As for Edward P. Weston, that "Yankee of extraordinary staying powers," his career as a pedestrian outlasted the decline of the wobbles. In 1909, when he was 70, he walked from New York to San Francisco, and the next year walked from Los Angeles to New York, averaging 37 miles a day the first trip and 46 miles daily the second time around. At the age of 74 he legged it from New York to Minneapolis. Two years before his death at the age of 90, he was struck by a cab and left partially paralyzed. His comrade, O'Leary, died at the age of 88.

During all this flurry of dramatic activity in the last thirty years of the past century, ultrarunning in a quiet way finally began to come of age.

Andy Milroy, a schoolteacher who lives in the quiet rural town of Trowbridge in the English county of Wiltshire, is another remarkable ultra buff who breathes statistics. His passion led to the publication of the authoritative mimeographed publication entitled: "Distance Running Progressive Bests." This thin booklet lists each of the record holders since the nineteenth century for various events: 50 miles, 100 kilometers, 24 hours, and so on through the usual litany. In a brief foreword, Milroy explains why most of the records begin in the 1870's and 1880's. The running footmen of the 1600's, he notes, gave rise to professional pedestrians.

By the eighteenth century races were frequent but they were run on roads, between milestones, or on race-courses. Measurement of distances was inconsistent. It was not until the early 1850's that accurately measured circular running paths began to appear. The means of timing improved as well. In 1855 a watch with an independent second hand was invented, enabling events to be timed to 1/4 or even 1/5 of a second ... Records had been established by the early 1860's and there were professional athletes specializing in track distance running.

Further, the growth of amateur "athletics," as track and field are referred to in England, began to take hold in the 1860's. The British Amateur Athletic Union began to recognize distances from 10 to 50 miles as legitimate for record attempts. Surely, there were some simple human dynamics at work as well. Word gets around among men who had a taste for trying such things that someone might have run such and such a time under the auspices of a certain pub, or for a running club. A chance to earn a few pounds, or the simple factor of competitiveness, most likely explained the occasional attempts at those difficult distances. And surely the 6-day affairs must have been an added stimulus—for one thing, to run 50 miles must not have seemed quite so terrible or beyond one's own capacities when compared with the distances regularly posted at the Islington Hall.

The British Fostered Amateur Athletics

In 1879, a Mr. F. W. Firminger, an Englishman, ran 50 miles in 6 hours, 38 minutes and 41 seconds at the Stamford Bridge track. Five years later John Fowler-Dixon, who later appeared at ultra record attempts when he was much older to cheer on the new generation, took almost 18 minutes off the time. Just a year later he improved on the time yet again. In 1913, Edgar Lloyd, another runner who became one of the grand old men of English ultrarunning, set up a time of 6:13:58 at Stamford Bridge, a record that was to stand for almost 40 years! The 50-mile track record moved into the 5-hour range then and remained there from 1952 and 1975, when Cavin Woodward ran a 4:58:33 at the Tipton track, doing better than 6 minutes per mile. The current record of 4:53:28, held at present by Don Ritchie, is about the equivalent of a 5:50-per-mile pace.

It is only fair to note here several factors. Records are kept for track runs only, since road courses are not so consistently reliable if one is keeping records from around the world, and not so easily compared one to another. The downhill and uphill combinations, as well as the differences between running on a concrete, dirt or asphalt surface, can considerably affect the effort and strain involved in any given race. Of course, track records are more than bland statistics that reflect the very best that might be expected. The sometimes rain-soaked cinder tracks of England are very different to struggle through than the equally difficult problem of coping with a tropical sun and oceanside humidity at the track belonging to the Savages running club in Durban, South Africa. So, too, the now-forgotten track records set up by Jackie Mekler and Wally Hayward at 6,000 feet above sea level in Johannesburg, where the thin air puts more stress on the oxygen-carrying capacity of runners.

You have only to glance at the old photographs hung up in the clubhouses, now turned brown from age, or leaf through the works of the illustrated artists who sketched these events, to realize how very different a world it was a hundred years ago. The heavy leather shoes; the knee-and-elbow-length running costumes that more nearly resemble antique bathing costumes than track suits suited for easy action of arms and legs; the smoke-filled arenas—such inconveniences must have hampered performance, to say nothing of the welter of odd training fashions and costumes that flourished in those days.

Some of the conventional wisdoms seem to have survived unaltered from the time of the Greeks—both good and bad. It is not quite so simple as casting a sigh of pity for such benighted ways. Even today's runners might learn a little from early examples. There was a generally popular reliance on meat as a source of energy, although it is now well established that carbohydrates figure as a much more fundamental and ongoing source of energy during a run. For the most part there was a very firm mistrust of imbibing water or other liquids during runs—needless to say a hazardous and stressful condition for any athlete to undergo, particularly in hot weather. Other areas are a little cloudier in terms of their pernicious effects. Smoking cigarettes and cigars occasionally was not viewed as being particularly harmful. And in spite of the warnings in U.S. running magazines about the effect of alcohol or heavily sugared and salted diets, the English and South Africans are great beer and ale drinkers. The English in particular have a yen for sweets and cakes and sugared goodies that is never slaked.

Nutrition Important in Early Day Events

Diet is always a matter of controversy . . . we have covered this with current day facts in another chapter for your merits of following a sound nutrition program. It is interesting to see how differently ultrarunners from that distant Victorian generation down through ours have handled themselves. The long-dead Len Hurst (he passed away in 1937 at the age of 66) was one of the record holders on the London-Brighton course. His 1903 time held up for 21 years until the exceptional Arthur Newton came along. Hurst had great abilities: when he was 22 he ran 183 miles in 30 hours, and at the age of 24 he ran 151 miles to win a 20-hour race, a truly exceptional feat. He was fond of occasional mustard baths and massage. He liked to drink a pint of bitter ale before eating, claiming that it aided his digestion. He also imbibed egg-and-sherry concoctions during competition. Today's ultrarunners have sometimes taken a nip of one potent drink or another (usually with great discretion) and swear by the swift kick onward it gave them.

In America, for some reason, massage is not nearly so highly regarded as abroad, although this old accompaniment to very long races probably can be extremely beneficial. Yet Americans have shown much greater interest in stretching exercises before and after runs than their foreign colleagues, although this is slowly changing. Both Jackie Mekler and Wally Hayward, two of South Africa's greatest megarunners, told me that one of the things they now consider most important for longevity in running is a good stretching program.

A final notation on the differences in conditions between ultrarunners in the last century and in the more recent part of this one, has a peculiarly apt significance—stemming from what one might call the blazed-trail mentality. Most people take as a goal what everyone else around them believes in as well. They follow the markings of whomever has gone along before them in the forest, and they go just that far. If they are ambitious they look a little beyond and cut out for themselves another bit of trail. Most records in ultrarunning improve in small steps, and in spite of all the gradual improvement in training and running gear I cannot help wondering if to some degree—not a measurable kind of thing at all—runners think that at best they can improve on a record very slightly and so aim for the slight improvement. There is a kind of confidence one can have, knowing that 100 miles in 12 hours has been done by one or two older men—ah, if they could, we think, then maybe we can move along a little faster. There is for many, although not all, a gradual increase in self-assurance as longer and longer distances are completed at faster and faster speeds. The very best runners often experience changes when they begin to win races, or at least to hold up at the top of an international pack. Then, suddenly, their own times begin to come down as they realize they don't need to back off from the cutting edge and that they can sustain more than they thought, can *be* better runners than they ever imagined. It is not merely the miles and miles' worth of ever mightier muscle mitochondria and glycogen deposits in the legs, but a connection that links body to mind and heart. Optimism and hope about his or her ability is what guides the runner on to his very best achievements.

Jackie Mekler of South Africa once put it this way: you must think positively and clearly with every step of a race. Let go of that inspired focus, he suggests, and you will falter both mentally and physically. Not only does this apply to one's personal development I believe, but to the development of every generation of runners that comes along. It is perhaps why so much variation in training and coaches leads to excellent results in different ways. Belief in the rightness of the preparation matters at least as much as the actual thing done—perhaps. Which leads me to say that I hope that the current generation of ultrarunners—or any that follows—doesn't develop a subtle disdain or the slower efforts of their predecessors. Even if future running times cease to improve because of the finite improvability of the human body in relation to given laws of mass, gravity and energy—even then, would it not be most generous and realistic to judge the past in terms of effort expended?

Not a great deal happened in the world of ultras after the 1880's. About 40 years passed with little that is noteworthy occurring. Interest in the standard marathon (26.2 miles) flourished and perhaps some of the professional money then available drew off younger, talented runners.

Women Also Ran Ultramarathons

The 1923 Comrades was remarkable as well for the meteoric appearance of ultrarunning's first woman runner in modern times, a Miss Frances Hayward. The 2,000 spectators at the start kept asking: "Where is the lady?" until at last she appeared, wearing "a businesslike green gymnasium uniform." *The Natal Witness* account continues: "Miss Hayward made a steady pace, dropping to a walk on the hills and at Thorneybush she was last but one, a good mile behind the others. She looked cheerful and fit."

If her entry had been official Miss Hayward would have finished 28th among the eventual 31 finishers (there were 37 dropouts), but her official entry was canceled although officials did not discourage her appearance. It was the same conservative attitude by male officials around the world that continues to absurdly misread women's capabilities right up to the present day. (Women were not permitted to run Comrades officially until 1975.) The press and the public cared little for such niceties, however, and her time of 11:35:00 was widely praised:

> In finishing the course in well under the stipulated 12 hours, she accomplished a very fine feat indeed, and one that reflects great credit on her powers of endurance. She did what over 38 men in the race failed to perform, and the champions of women's equality will no doubt extract great satisfaction from that fact. Miss Hayward walked a good deal of the way, but she finished well and something should be said of the magnificent reception she received from the people of Durban . . . The streets were packed with people all anxious to catch a glimpse of this plucky little girl.
>
> The crowd, numbering thousands, literally swamped her, and it was only by the aid of a mounted constable that she was able to reach Lords at all, whilst the cheering and the noise were deafening . . . A word is also due to F. W. Rodgers, who ran with her all the way from Maritzburg to Durban, and coached her through. The two finished in a dead heat at Lords, and the sporting manner in which Rodgers stuck to his partner was certainly fine.

A few more details have survived about this woman pioneer. She wore specially made shoes of leather with suede tops, and had warm tea and oranges for sustenance along the route. Although she loved golf, tennis and swimming, long walks fascinated Miss Hayward and she trained for Comrades for three months, doing 8 miles every day and 26 on Sundays. It isn't clear whether she

10,600 feet above sea level 37½ miles later. Looking into the Haleakala Crater, Bob Johnson, co-author.

Dr. Paul Bragg and friend & health confident, hotel developer Conrad Hilton, chat before a health meal prepared under the supervision of Patricia Bragg at the Brentwood, California home of Mr. Hilton.

walked, or ran, or combined the two in her jaunts.

"Now that I have done it," she said in an interview after the race, "I think it is too much. It is the last 10 miles that kill. I personally feel quite fit and should have no hesitation in taking part in a 44-mile run."

She was asked whether a 44-miler would attract other women runners.

"Oh, yes, I am sure of it," she replied. "I have been informed that when my entry was announced there were eight applications for my address from girls who expressed a desire to train with me."

The First Woman Ultramarathoner

Since 1923 when Frances Hayward donned her green jumper to run in South Africa's Comrades race, few women have followed her example, until very recently. The reasons are so obvious as to hardly bear enumeration. Clearly expectation, myth and lack of opportunity had an immense amount to do with it. Innate physical limitations that would make it dangerous or difficult for women to carry off long distances simply do not exist. All the same, in relative terms, very few women do run ultras nowadays but many of them come out about middle ground in the men's fields—or better. Undoubtedly the improvement in standards for women in ultra running will rise dramatically in the next ten years. The theory that women are better suited for long distance or ultra running because they carry extra stores of body fat has been advanced by Ernest Van Aaken, a German coach and researcher, and Joan Ullyot, a San Francisco exercise physiologist and marathoner. However recent research by David Costill, an American researcher in exercise physiology, calls their surmise into dispute and suggests that men may, in fact, burn body fats more efficiently than women.

Martin Thompson, an Australian ultrarunner who has been doing research in exercise physiology in England, says that there is "nothing to suggest metabolically that Van Aaken's right on. The leanest marathon runner has enough to go from here to wherever. Extra fat would be working against male or female runners, since much of it is metabolically inert in terms of propulsion across the ground. What he and Ullyot have said is very much hypothesis, but I've heard it cited frequently. Something almost becomes unwritten law because it's stated over and over."

Regardless of whether or not the researchers come to an agreement, women are beginning to appear in ultras more and more frequently. There were over a dozen women in the 1979 Comrades 54-mile race in South Africa. And in the U.S. dozens of women have now run in ultra races. As for England, it's a sorry record of unofficial lady ghosts who detect just enough tolerance beneath the official frowns to compete, with the unwritten proviso that it just not happen too frequently. The one class event which would appeal most to women marathoners in England is the London-Brighton 55-mile race which will finally allow official women entrants for the first time in the fall of 1980.

Europe and Scandinavia have a small but apparently fairly consistent tiny minority of women ultrarunners. When we consider the very recent absurdities that took place in the road-running scene in the U.S. (irate officials in various states refusing to let women run in the 1960's—even in five-mile races), the tremendous change in attitudes seems fabulous, however overdue. The long hangover about women's "frailty" dies hard, however. To this date, women are still not able to run races longer than 1,500 meters in the Olympic Games. Women's ultrarunning is very much a wide open frontier, just as marathons were for women in 1970, and the comparatively soft times posted by women are beginning to tighten up. The next five or ten years are likely to see more women and far better times on the roads and tracks.

The ultra clan in the U.S., at any rate, is relaxed about the women who happen to be in the race. It's just fine if whoever wants to run, runs.

Ultramarathon Training

If you have come up through the marathon training method offered in this book, you will be well prepared to advance into the mystical area beyond the 26.2 mile marathon. The ultra-marathon of 50 kilometers (50 miles), 100 kilometers (100 miles) or beyond into maximum distances for 24 hour period, etc.

The training method remains the same . . . easy days alternating with hard days, striving for long slow distance, with a weekly time trial thrown in to enable a runner to learn to relax at a fast pace.

The sharpening procedures described in the Marathon Chapter of increased speed into and a little beyond the aerobic condition for a brief period is followed by a slow down period of easy jogging. This sharpening experience should commence about six weeks prior to an event as this period of time is considered a "peaking" point in training for an important event.

A person who has completed a number of marathons has attained a physical condition that would carry them through an Ultramarathon of 50 miles, but probably would fail if they tried, due to the lack of knowledge of the art of mixing walking and running. The proper fluid intake and mostly the psychological orientation required for such an event is important. Otherwise the marathon training and experience you have under your belt will serve you well.

Miles Per Week Now Becomes the Most Important Training Factor

As in the marathon, it is not required that you run the full distance of your first ultramarathon in your training routine in one day. You will build distance in your increase in weekly mileage to be able to take on the longer distances. Psychologically, it might help to put your mind at rest if you maintained constant action on foot for an extended period of time, say 6 to 8 hours for a 50 mile ultra. This will help alleviate the fear of not finishing a run that could last many hours.

The actual miles per week varies with the individual as does his strength, and the opportunity to train extended periods. Project your hard-and-easy-day routine you used in marathon training to include increased mileage of up to 80 miles the first month of training, with a goal of 100 miles or better for at least two months prior to a 50 mile ultra and 120 miles per week for two months prior to a 100 mile ultramarathon.

The Importance of Ultramarathon Training for the Triathlete

The training triathlete should achieve the level of training required to compete in an ultramara-thon. The advanced training concepts given in this chapter, going beyond the marathon training, is the minimum level of weekly and monthly training a triathlete should be into eight weeks prior to a full triathlon such as the Ironman World's Championship in Kona, Hawaii.

The running segment of the triathlon is the most debilitating. An athlete that has achieved a training schedule of 100 plus miles per week for eight weeks will excell in the marathon of the triathlon. The fat fuel conversion mechanism that takes over after the glycogen is expended has been put into action in an ultramarathon of at least 6 hours duration or 50 miles. This is one way that a triathlete can train his body to utilize this important source of go power.

Walking in the Ultramarathon

The art of mixing walking with running is one of the ultramarathoner's most important skills. A runner who can race the marathon in 3:15 would have great difficulty running more than thirty-five miles at a continuous jog, regardless of how slow the pace was. However, the same runner could run for fifteen minutes, then walk for five; run fifteen, walk five, etc., and complete sixty miles in good form. The athlete who can run the marathon in 2:35 can probably run fifty miles at a steady, seven minute per mile pace. But even runners of this class can profit from walking. They find that **a blend of walking and running allows them to cover great distances without generating fatigue!** Finally, even the greatest runners in the world cannot run continuously for periods approaching 48 hours. Races lasting two days and more are beginning to appear on road racing schedules, and they present yet another running challenge. Here even the most gifted athletes must employ walking for optimum results.

What do I mean by walking? I don't mean race walking of the heel and toe variety; I mean ordinary brisk walking. Most marathoners will find that they can walk for extended periods at a speed of about 3.5 miles per hour. With practice, walking speeds close to 4.5 miles per hour are possible without employing race walking technique. The great Edward Payson Weston, America's greatest walker ever, did not use race walking form. He often poked fun at race walkers and said in an article in the *Saturday Evening Post*, "Heel and toe walking isn't really walking at all, but is straight-legged running. And there is nothing natural about it."

Most Effective Walking For Triathletes

Dr. George Sheehan has suggested that the most efficient walking for runners might be that of a race walker who cheats. He suggests . . . that utilizing the race walker's style, but in addition, bending the knee slightly on impact (a violation of race walking rules termed *creeping*), is the most economical walking style. I am a trained runner, not a walker, and I don't have final answers to these questions. The reader should experiment to uncover the walking form which works best for him!

The exact division of an ultramarathon into pre-set walking and running segments will depend upon the circumstances of the race. In a track effort, it is best to measure these segments in laps. When I first covered one hundred miles I used a quarter mile cinder track and ran seven laps, then walked one; ran seven, walked one, etc. When on the road, it is more convenient to gauge these segments by time rather than by distance. When a group of us ran from Philadelphia to Atlantic City in the summer of 1977 (62 miles in 10.5 hours) we ran slowly for 15 minutes, then walked for five; ran 15, walked five, etc.

Few runners have tried walking in races. Walking is viewed by runners as something you do when you can no longer run. Sometimes, the poorly paced marathoner will "hit the wall" in the last few miles of the race. Such a runner may find that stopping to walk causes the legs to knot up, preventing further running. They have lost the rhythm of continuous running, and once this rhythm is lost, it is not easily regained. For this reason, the marathoner will be skeptical about the usefulness of walking.

The marathoner knows only this one rhythm of continuous running; there are other rhythms of which he has no knowledge. The body becomes used to the rhythmic pattern that is established while the runner is fresh. For this reason it is essential to begin the walking segments of an ultra in the very *beginning* of the run while the runner is still feeling very good! Let us assume that a mixture of 10 minutes running to five minutes walking is selected before the run starts. After the first 10 minutes of running the runner **must stop and walk for five minutes, even though this feels most unnatural.** It is very hard to stop because the runner is fresh and just beginning to get warmed up. Nevertheless he must establish the rhythm at the start. After an hour, stopping will no longer seem unusual, and the rhythm of running and walking will have been established.

After several hours of "mixing" in this fashion, fatigue of a mild nature will slowly settle in. At this point runners find that when they begin a running segment, the body feels reluctant to resume. This sensation leaves after about 30 seconds. As the runner approaches the end of his running segment, he will again find his body growing reluctant to run. This is a sign that the runner's inner clock has grasped the appropriate rhythm and is preparing the body for the walking phase.

How fast can you cover 50 miles while walking and running? Let us suppose you are on a quarter mile track and choose to run seven laps and walk one. Also, assume that you walk comfortably at four minutes per lap (3.75 mph). If you run at a speed of 7:30 per mile for the seven lap segment you will cover 50 miles in seven hours and eight minutes, a very good time. If you run at a speed of eight minutes to the mile then the 50 miles will be complete in seven hours and thirty minutes. If you run at nine minutes to the mile, you will do the 50 miles in eight hours and thirteen minutes.

Suppose now that you need more walking. You select a ratio of three laps running to one lap walking. Again, you walk at four minutes per lap, but you jog the three laps at a comfortable nine minutes to the mile. You will complete 50 miles in eight hours 58 minutes. One hundred miles would pass in 17 hours and 56 minutes, a time bettered by only a few Americans.

Should the runner take long, continuous walks as part of training? I doubt that these would be necessary for races shorter than 24 hours. Finally, I should mention that walking is useful not only as a means of greatly extending the distance that a runner can go on foot; it is also a marvelous restorative exercise by itself. After a hard day of training, a brisk walk of 30 minutes to an hour in the evening will accelerate the recovery process by stimulating the circulation. Walking places only one-third the pressure on tendons of the foot compared with running. Edward Payson Weston described walking as a gentle massage and claimed that many ailments could be cured through its employment.

Drinks That Will Go the Distance

Liquid intake for the ultramarathoner is very important, just as in the marathon. If you become thirsty, it is too late. Before the liquid can enter the system and come to the skin's surface to cool the body down, you could suffer serious dehydration. A good rule of thumb for hot weather is 10 to 12 ounces of liquid every 15 minutes, half of that in cold weather. If you feel the need to urinate frequently, you know you are taking too much liquid.

There are many exotic electrolite liquids on the market, some runners believe in them, some like iced or hot tea, fruit juices, etc., some with large quantities of sugar. Extended training sessions are the best time to test for what is right for you . . . what your system can handle and to get the best results with!

To Eat or Not to Eat

As with a marathon it is best to go out on an ultramarathon on an empty stomach with no food intake for at least 3 hours prior to the run. As the run progresses, you may try quartered oranges on the run, bananas, dates, peeled apples, peanut butter sandwiches, and various fruits. Care should be taken to see that the food intake is easily digestible.

The Hawaiian Ultramarathon Experience

I had the great pleasure of completing my first ultramarathon in Hawaii, the distance was 50 miles. By this time, I had three marathons under my belt and had attended World Class Runner Max Telford's Ultramarathon Training Sessions at 7:00 a.m. every Sunday morning at the Kapiolani Park Bandstand in Honolulu.

This ultra was run on a 4 mile circuit in Hawaii Kai. The fifty-mile start was for 4 a.m. By dawn, the area had started to warm up, and by 9:00 a.m., it was a steam bath; 90% humidity, not a breath of tradewind and a scorching sun. Each runner was responsible for his food support which made it practical to have your vehicle well supplied with food and drinks of all kinds. Every lap offered an opportunity to take on food fuel.

Max Telford established a record in this ultra for 100 miles. Some of the better runners attempted to go the last four mile lap with Max but unfortunately could not keep up the Telford pace.

Maui Hawaii's Outstanding Ultra," The Run To The Sun"

A year later, I had the pleasure of running what I consider the hardest established 37½ mile distance run known today. This is the "Run to the Sun" on the island of Maui. Starting at sea level the course takes you past the Kahalui Airport right up the slopes of Haleakalau to the volcano crater lookout. This is a steady grade from sea level to 10,600 ft. elevation. Max Telford placed first in this run with a time in the neighborhood of 5 hours. Here again we were required to provide our own support vehicle. I recall consuming 3 gallons of water in this run without one relief stop.

I consumed volumes of food, fruit and sandwiches. The temperature range was from a humid, tropical 90 degrees at sea level to a windy raining 40 degrees at the top . . . requiring a large selection of wet weather and cold weather running gear.

Ultramarathoning is an alternate "beyond-marathon" sport for the avid runner who does not have the desire to compete in the multisport events such as the Triathlon. Or for the runner that simply cannot stand the cold water conditioning required to compete in rough water lake or ocean swims. The serious runner today is lost in the crowds of marathoners. Ultramarathoning offers an option to train and excell in what is beyond the reach of many marathoners.

The Ultramarathon is a more relaxing endeavour when you include the mandatory walking interval. On the "Run to the Sun," the walking interval offered an opportunity to see the beautiful scenes of sea and sky and island, smell the land, experience the swirling clouds and become one with nature! Ultra-marathoning is a joy . . . enjoy your training and try one soon!!!

The American Indian Distance Runner

In the 1860s a Fox runner (our name for Mesquakie) ran over 400 miles from Greey Bay, Wisconsin to warn Sauk Indians along the Missouri River of an enemy attack. His name wasn't recorded but he is said to have been in his mid-fifties. He probably carried a dried buffalo heart. He was the last Mesquakie to hold the post of *a'chapawa,* ceremonial runner.

Until the 1920s information about this courier corps was kept secret, part of Mesquakie religion to be hidden from white men's eyes. But anthropologist Truman Michelson retrieved an account of the last ceremonial runner's investiture into the brotherhood. Then he discovered references which suggested similar systems among the Sauk, Kickapoo, Menominee, Creek, Kansa, Omaha and Osage.

The Michelson document describes Mesquakie runners who lived like messenger-monks. Carrying special bowls and spoons, hosted far and wide as tribal emissaries, they alone could deliver the deciding vote in deadlocked councils. Vowing celibacy, observing strict dietary rules, promising to be truthful, they dedicated their lives to the office. In their heyday they banded in teams of three. The leader, from the Bear clan, had wind-medicine power. The member from the War Chief clan possessed deer power. The Eagle clan runner received power from the hummingbird. They were reputedly good-natured and fearless. "It was impossible for them to be unwilling," Michelson was told. "Even if they came to rivers they would cross them if they were ordered." Their very presence brought a kind of blessing. "They foresaw everything, so where these Indians had a town, (it) would be proper and not evil."

Fasting—an Indian Runner's Ritual

Near Shallow Water (not far from St. Louis) the Fox boy who would become the last ceremonial runner was in the thirteenth day of a fast when a hummingbird spoke to him, "Today I bless you so. You will be very fast. You will call yourself, 'ceremonial runner man.' They will send you on errands no matter how far off. So I give you (the quality of) willingness. I shall also give you the quality of tranquil braveness. You will be exactly as I am."

With the "holy gift" of speed came the power of invisibility. The hummingbird's code was

Paul Bragg at his outside gym in Desert Hot Springs, California...a suburb of famous Palm Springs. It has the best naturally hot mineral water available in Southern California. Dr. Bragg helped pioneer the town through his world-wide health crusades for he always spoke of the therapeutic values of the clear desert air, the hot mineral water, and the 365 days of sunshine.

Patricia Bragg enjoys yoga and all areas of fitness exercise each morning while vacationing at her seaside home at the base of Diamond Head. Monday through Saturday, 9-10:30 a.m. at famous Waikiki Beach (Fort DeRussy area), Honolulu, she leads 100 to 150 persons at the free Bragg Exercise Classes which are in their 13th year.

strict: "You must live morally in the future." Sexual activity would despoil and weaken him. He must not jest idly with people on his mission, nor use bad words, nor steal, nor mock. Eat only turtle dove or quail, he was told, and always be clean.

For durability and power he must exchange his regular deerskin moccasins for footwear of buffalo hide. A strip of hide around his waist would remind him of his messages. He should not wear red, nor collect firewood from riverbanks where hummingbirds might be nesting. In gratitude for "this mystic power" he must burn tobacco. He must carve a special runner's bowl and spoon to use his entire life, tan a bedroll from a spotted deer's skin, and sleep on the south side of his host's *wikiup*. On runs he should carry the dried buffalo heart.

On the fourth day of instructions two hummingbirds had the boy strip down. When he was standing with the river up to his neck, they circled above his head until the earth "fell fast and whirled." The birds blew into his mouth four times, so strongly that he could not speak, as if to permanently expand his lungs for the work ahead. They said, "Perhaps this day you are the last ceremonial runner," and then they flew off.

At home the boy took a sweat bath, picked up a spotted deer hide, and soon amazed everyone by his effortless running at top speed. From village to village he delivered council declarations in record time. He burned tobacco to the forces of nature and remained clean and pure. When he was an old man and close to death, the last runner warned: "Later on there will be many people who will ruin you."

Courier-Runners . . . Held High Esteem

Far to the south and north of Pueblo country, details of courier-runner traditions have endured. Among peoples who developed foot messenger systems for knitting together vast territories were the Mesquakie of Iowa, the Chemehuevi of California, and the Inca of Peru. As one examines these systems it becomes clear that their runners were more than functionary athletes. They were communicators of culture; their units were absorbed into social and religious life. They were highly regarded as safekeepers of accurate information. Their status was high for they helped to keep their worlds intact and in touch.

Indian Women Also Ran

Part-Sky-Woman's career was launched when her "spontaneous vision" of a cloud bestowed its lightness, speed and strength upon her. That spring the Hudson Bay Trading Co. Post at Fort Francis sponsored races and offered ribbons, shawls and silks as prizes for the mile—a half-mile out and back. After a private session with her cloud, Part-Sky-Woman ran off with the three top awards.

For eight years she repeated the feat. Jealous rivals tried unsuccessfully to wheedle her secret from her. When she failed to appear the tenth year, a Chippewa woman from the United States named Bird Woman took the honors. But the next year Part-Sky-Woman staged a comeback. Before the race she smudged her moccasins to protect her legs from evil. As she and Bird Woman were running neck and neck "Part-Sky-Woman could hear that Bird Woman was out of breath, and the woman said, 'I guess you will beat me,' and Part-Sky-Woman answered, 'I don't know. I do not care to win this race!' Once the woman had sprinted ahead of her, Part-Sky-Woman addressed the shadow of her guardian cloud, "Now is the time to help me out, you that told me I would have fun. It would be shameful if I got beat." Right away she felt her body light as a feather, and, as if she were running on air, she passed the woman.

We don't know if Part-Sky-Woman employed any earthly aids to gain strength, but one Chippewa technique has been recorded to make runners feel "light-footed." Around their ankles they tied thin bags filled with lead shot. In 1888 a champion runner walked twenty-three miles after dinner wearing these weights, and the next morning won a foot race of a hundred yards in ten and a quarter seconds.

The story continues as one of Part-Sky-Woman's frustrated opponents slashes her face with a crooked knife. But the champion will not be cowed. The Hudson's Bay trader promotes her in races held in the white town of Kenora; she handily whips a featured white woman, a white man, and the trader rakes in a profit. There she is spotted by a young Indian who marries her. For four years she again abandons the field. Then her old wound becomes infected, as if her rivals are still bent upon revenge. Part-Sky-Woman appears to take this as a challenge, and, the story goes, returns to running and field hockey and never loses! She proclaims: "It's alright if I have to talk through my nose because of what the old Indians did to me. Only if they break my legs will I not be able to run anymore." But no one will compete against her now for she had proven herself to be a *manido,* a superhuman spirit.

Indian Competition Running

Whenever the Chiricahua Apache planned a lengthy stay at a campsite they would pace off a footracing track about two hundred "steps" long. When the race was underway, old men kept time by counting for their runners; one Apache remembered a runner making the distance by the count of eleven. The starters did not crouch but braced themselves, and were launched by a "One, Two, Go" signal. Among both the Chiricahua and Mescalero Apache of the Southwest, women raced men for short distances. Visiting the Mescalero in the 1860s, Major John C. Cremony observed the mile, 100-yard, and 300-yard races; he was struck by a lovely seventeen-year-old who easily outran all her male competitors in the half-mile.

Indians also enjoyed specialty races. Along the Northwest Coast canoeing generally replaced running as the popular contest. But the Kwakiutl invented—besides regular running and walking races—one-legged hopping heats as well as forward and backward somersault races, from one end of their seaside villages to the other.

Old age was rarely a barrier to running! Tarahumaras and Hopis still run well beyond their sixties! The Navajo held an "old man's race," along with regular eight-mile races and girls' races. Unlike the white man's "on your mark, get set, go," they began their runs with a 1-2-3-4 count. As in a folktale brought to life, oldtimers sometimes demonstrated how experience could outdo untutored vigor. The Cheyenne Wooden Leg liked to tell how Chief Little Wolf, a famous long-distance man in his youth, whipped the Sioux. The Oglala Sioux and the Cheyenne were moving camp together, and a Cheyenne goaded, "It appears that the Cheyennes must go a little more slowly in order not to run away from their friends the Sioux." There was some more of this back and forth until a Sioux challenged Little Wolf to a foot race. Tipis were pitched and everyone came out for the fun.

Little Wolf was well over fifty; the Sioux was in his prime. Blankets and other goods were wagered; a three-to-four mile track was measured. At the crack of a pistol, both dashed towards the tipis. Up to the last mile, remembered Wooden Leg, the young man held first place, but he was at full throttle. When he started to falter, Little Wolf inched up and came in a good hundred yards ahead.

Taos Relays

Because so much Pueblo racing is embedded in rites from which outsiders are excluded, first-hand accounts, outside of the Taos relays, are not common. During her work at Jemez Pueblo Elsie Clews Parsons awoke one September morning to glimpse the flowing hair and rippling breechclouts of the harvest racers arriving from Red Rock, but most of her Jemez material remains second-hand. In the 1930s, however, an Albuquerque writer named Clee Woods, close to some Jemez families, was allowed a more relaxed look at the harvest runs.

At Jemez nearly every season featured its running event. In spring, before the irrigation ditches were opened, kick-stick races were held—as at Cochiti. Over spring and summer there were hardy retreats and training sessions in the mountains. At the same time relay races were staged along

North Street. In winter, the runner kachina, Black Paint All Over, arrived to challenge able-bodied men and give them good luck in hunting. Rigorous training anticipated the five-to-six mile races of September and October.

They began outside the village, where runners collected before sunrise. Joe Sando writes, "A selected person would stand about fifty yards in front of a row of runners holding a trophy, a green cornstalk. Directing the stalk in the four directions, he prayed to each, ending with the south. Prayer sticks tied to the stalk gave it power, made it a trophy.

"He cried out four times, finally pointing east, and everyone broke after the man with the cornstalk. The fastest man earns his day of glory by overtaking the man with this trophy. But he may only carry it a few yards before another overtakes him. Thus you have dashmen followed by those who may be good at different distances, as in our American races—220,880, mile, and so forth—until by the time the runners are reaching the village, the long distance experts are closing in.

"As in any race one has to use strategy to accomplish whatever you plan. The man in best condition for longer distances is generally the one who finally takes the trophy to his home. The cornstalk is five to six feet long and awkward to handle while trying to speed. One learns to switch from right to left hand in carrying it. For the shorter distances, usually the same day, an ear of corn wrapped with fir branches is used. It's easier to carry, like a relay baton."

Although these ritual runs were dedicated toward a robust harvest, when Clee Woods relived them it was purely as a sports event.

Ultramarathon Bibliography

Ultramarathon, James E. Shapiro. Bantam Books, New York, 1980.
Ultramarathoning, Tom Osler and Ed Dodd. World Publications, Box 366, Mountain View, Ca., 94040, 1979.
Indian Running, Peter Nabokov, Capra Press, P. O. Box 2068, Santa Barbara, Ca., 93102.

Perhaps one of the most dramatic happenings in the history of the Ironman Triathlon World Championship is the finish-line scene in February 1982. Twenty-five yards away from apparent victory, Julie Moss of California fell to her knees and began to crawl. Seconds before reaching the finish line, Moss looked up to see Kathleen McCartney run past her to victory.

Photo by Jim Loedding

Claire St. Arnaud and Lotus Super Pro Aerodynamic . . . ABC T.V. Wide World of Sports flag flying over Ironman scene, with Kona coffee and Pakalolo plantations in background . . . Author, Bob Johnson . . . Attila Lehel, Honolulu participant in the '82 4 mile Rough Water Invitational Swim . . . Winner of 4 mile Invitational Swim . . . Ruth Yih—she learned how to run the marathon in 10 months training through the Honolulu Marathon Clinic. Ruth has run 3 marathons and a number of 1/2 marathons and 10 K's . . . Diane Giebel's son, Cyle . . . The first 1/2 Triathlon, finishing time . . . 13 mile run on a twisted knee . . . Transition rooms at the Ironman . . . Ground "Zero" at the Ironman . . . Just a few more hours, should I just catch the plane now or should I stay and face the pain . . . "Attila the Hun" surviving the 4 mile Rough Water Swim through 2 miles of head-on 6 ft. seas . . . Winner of the '81 Honolulu Marathon.

IX

Combined Swim, Bike, Run Triathlon Training

Sally Edwards placed 2nd in the 1981 Triathlon and tied for 3rd place with friend Lynn Brooks in the 1982 event.

Patricia Bragg and fellow director Alfred Apaka of the Bragg Health and Happiness exercise class at Fort De Russy, Waikiki. Alfred Sr. is the father of the late Alfred Apaka, famous Hawaiian vocalist.

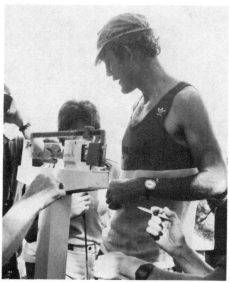

John Howard, placed 3rd in the 1980 Triathlon and first in the 1981 event, shown here weighing in, a requirement in the earlier events to make sure that contestants weight does not drop too low.

Finishing the swim, coming through the chute for finishing time.

BOOK IX

Combined Swim, Bike, Run Triathlon Training

Combining Swim, Bike and Run Training

During the year that you have been with us you have been training for three events: to Swim 2.4 miles in 12 months training, to Bike 112 miles in 12 months training, and to Run a full 26.2 mile marathon in 10 months training.

Let's assume you went into this program without a specialty sport, meaning a sport that you were strong in or excelled in. Let's further assume that you started your training programs for all three of these events simultaneously. Merging the training routines where possible daily and completing a workout on each event at least every other day.

This embodies the ideal training scheduling for the beginning triathlete. The daily training schedules laid out for each of theses events in this book make it possible for the beginner in each event to merge his training in all three events to also include 4 Long Slow Distance training days and 3 Strength training days per week in each event. The Nautilus strength training can be combined for Swim, Bike and Run, except in the case of specificity strength training as it differs for each event. For example the Bounding hill climbing, striding and fartleck speed play required for the runner should be set aside and completed independently. As should the Bike sprints and time trials.

Our testing and training is based on the aerobic formula of an 85% maximum heart rate for all three events. If you have maintained an accurate log of your progress from the start of your training you will notice that your steady or resting heart rate has dropped at least 10 points in this year's training. Your log will also show you that your timed monthly progress test has substantially improved in all three sports modes.

As stated earlier there are many training logs on the market from which to choose, some specifically are designed for the training triathlete. Fleet Feet of Sacramento puts out an excellent one. If you have followed the week-by-week and month-by-month training schedules set forth in the Swim, Bike and Run chapters you will have reached a peak in your physical ability. Care should be taken not to peak too soon and progress into an overtrained state. Care should also be taken to build your distances and strengths to the maximum one week before the Triathlon. Monthly distance schedules were set out in the biking book. We are now ready to talk about the week preceeding the Triathlon.

The Week We Have Been Training a Year For

A maintenance of your sharp condition involves just what you have been doing only much less. Keep limber, stretching exercises, Light Nautilus workouts every other day, a bike spin of 15 to 20 miles per day, plenty of tempo, a daily swim of 800 to a thousand meters with some 200 sprints, and a 10 Kilometer run every other day, including some speed play.

Now is *not* the time to experiment with: (1) Equipment. You have been using it daily and are comfortable with it the way it is. Maintain all bike equipment in good order; (2) Shoes. Now is not the time to break in a new pair of running shoes, nor is it the time to have the old pair fall apart. You should have at least 200 miles on the shoes you will run the marathon in; (3) Do not start a new vitamin-mineral formula, special food supplements, liquid concoctions. In other words maintain the status quo from now until the Triathlon is over, then change your game plan for the next one a year away and train with it, experiment with it, change it all you want. Again, do not experiment with anything at this late date.

The Day You Have Trained a Year For

Some Triathletes prefer to rise at 2 or 3 A.M., put away a huge breakfast and be fully stoked up and food digested when the cannon goes off at 7:00 A.M. Still others prefer to have some fruit or a light continental breakfast at least an hour before the start time. Most knowledgeable triathletes prefer to have something before the starting time. But this is an individual decision based, again, on what you feel comfortable with.

Do not leave last-minute duties for the morning of the Triathlon; have all problems resolved so there will not be a last minute scurrying around to find this or that, to repair the main chain ring of your bicycle. There is enough tension around without creating more. Be at the starting point at least an hour early for the check-in. Become bored waiting for the gun to go off, plan your getaway strategy carefully and this will start a relaxed mode that will get you out into clear water, while all those about you are thrashing for swimming space.

Transition of Swim to Bike

It has become apparent that there is distance against your competition to be made while in the transition mode between events. Kim Buschong was 3rd out of the water by one minute in the 1982 Spring Ironman but first on the bike course. He had planned his transition to gain that minute or two over the competition. A trend has been established at the USTS Triathlons of not changing. This is well and good for a short bike ride, but 112 miles of bike seat requires that all of the salt water be washed off before putting on bike shorts. A new one-garment concept is becoming popular, a special spandex suit with a leg length longer than a brief without chamois, that can be used in all three events. If you really need that seat padding offered by the chamois then put it on the seat, and save valuable minutes and miles in the transitions. This is being designed in both men's and women's styles. Sounds exciting!

This one suit (call it a Triathlon uni-suit) will enable a triathlete to take a good shower, suit and all, proceed to his bike where all of his foot gear, top, gloves and helmet are laid out, ready to jump into.

Another item from down under, New Zealand, is the Shampers, made of chamois with a knitted top. These substitute for sox and are excellent for both biking and running, thereby doing away with the need to change sox after the bike ride. If you get caught in a downpour as you most likely will be at the Ironman in Kona, your feet will be a pound or two lighter without heavy sox holding a large quantity of water. These comfortable sox substitutes have been available in Hawaii for some time and have become a must-have accessory for bikers and runners. Here again saving a few minutes in the Bike to Run transition.

Bike to Run Transition

If you were set up with the uni-suit and shampers the only delay would be removing bike shoes and putting on running shoes and you are on your way. One item that all runners need and with this fast change concept, might not have time for, is Vaseline. I have found that a small ziplock plastic bag of vaseline in my running shorts pocket is a lifesaver a few miles into the run. Leg chafing is a pain we can do without, as is nipple abrasion for both men and women. You will be very popular, a few miles out, with those who were not thoughtful enough to include this item in their running gear.

Recuperation

Many triathletes sleep the clock around after the Triathlon; almost all are hobbling Sunday, up and down Alii Drive, making last-minute gift purchases before departing for home on Monday morning. Ice is the best therapy for sore and burning muscles, tendons and joints. Of course, take advantage of every offer for a massage both during the run and after the finish of the Triathlon. If you have trained well your aches and pains will be at a minimum and you will be fully healed within a few days. Maintain stretching using the after run and bike chart in the Manual for a guide. This will work the lactic acid out of the tissues and relieve the soreness. See you next year on the Swim, Bike or Run. See you, that is, if you make your application promptly upon notice that applications are being taken for the next event. Write ahead of time and get on their list!

Triathlon Check List

SWIM

Swim Cap — bright color usually issued as part of the registration fee. Should the Triathlete feel that he has need for 2 to help ward off hypothermia as described in the Cold Water Swimming Chapter by Jack LaLanne, then he might have to furnish one of his own. **Ear Plugs** — extended periods in rough water swims can cause ear infections. Here again, do what feels comfortable. **Nose Clamp** — For medical reasons some swimmers have need for this device. **Vaseline** — for abrasions around suit straps and leg seams. Latisimus to tricept friction can be aleviated with a layer of vaseline.

BIKE

Bicycle — one bicycle of your choice fully set up, in top mechanical condition, new tires and tubes if used, new brake pads, straight wheels. **Tire pump, two waterbottles** (round) with holders clamped to the frame, **tool kit**, complete with tire repair kit, **spare brake cable and Derailleur cable** (the longest size), **one sew-up tire or tube** in the kit and **one sew-up tire or tube** in the middle pocket of your jersey. Excellent time and distance insurance. **Munchies**, as needed; many bikers eat constantly on something. The best carrier for this supply is the belt pack that can be rotated from rear to front.

RUN

Running Shoes that you have run at least 200 miles in, but are not so old that they will disintegrate 5 miles into the marathon, **vaseline** packed into a zip-lock plastic bag, **reflective material**, on shorts and shoes, front and back if you will be running at night, **sun visor or sweat band**.

The Biker's Edge

With a strong biking background you have a definite "edge" on the competition in a full triathlon, for there is a three- to five-hour variable between a trained and a novice bicyclist. If the top distance road racing biker can swim the distance in a reasonable time, he can make up what little he might have lost in the swim during the 112 miles of biking. As you start the run, you feel that you certainly are not going to go the distance at a full marathon pace. The top competitors are, but the rest of us, by this time, have all but lost our competitive spirit; we would be happy just to finish!

Finishing a triathlon is the ultimate individual physical achievement in distance competition: you have just completed the equivalent of two marathons. Do not take "just finishing" lightly. Pacing is the name of the game . . . take on an ultramarathon mode, run and walk it, stop and eat, have a massage, take a nap, but finish!

A biker's leg and lung power will carry him through the marathon in a moderate time to turn in an excellent finishing time against top marathoners and swimmers. This condition holds true in the early days of the growing popularity of the triathlon. As the runner and swimmer build the bike muscle power one or two seasons hence, multi-sport events will come of age as a tremendously exciting spectator sport with highly-competitive "cliff hang" finishes to thrill the crowds.

As it now stands, the triathlon is the ultimate in participating sports. You are good at what you have excelled in during the past, whether swimming, biking or running.

If you have enjoyed training in your specialty sport you are really going to enjoy multi-sport training because there certainly is no monotony! There is always a change of pace in training modes; you are never "skunked" by the weather with indoor pools, stationary bikes, and bike rollers readily available.

The triathlon-biathlons are the ultimate in participating sports in combination. Start bringing it all together now, and have the physical emotional thrill of a lifetime.

Ironman 1982 Woman's Division record holder . . .Julie Leach of Newport Beach, California, clings to her Triathlete husband Bill Leach (right) moments after setting a new record time of 10:54:08 for the 140.6-mile swim-bike-run event on Hawaii's Kona Coast. Leach also won the 1982 U.S. Ironman Triathlon Championship event in Los Angeles.

Photo by Noël Black

514

The Omega Triathlon Training Test

Throughout all of the training for swim, bike and run, we will use only a good stop watch and the heart rate. This will not only be your training chart or schedule but will be your testing equipment used to record monthly gains in each of the three sports involved. The Omega Triathlon Test involves going a given time period at a maximum aerobic rate and recording the distance covered in your training log. The time period is set for each event precisely in order to maintain the maximum aerobic state at the optimum heart rate beyond a sprint and into a middle distance mode.

Starting with a 4-month background in each sport, you should be able to maintain 20 minutes swimming or about 800 meters, 40 minutes biking equating to 15 miles and 10 minutes running, approximately 1 mile. This is your test . . . you are not concerned about averages for age groups, body weight, etc. . . . only your own month-by-month progress.

An Alternative Method of Progressive Performance Testing

In addition to Dr. Kenneth Cooper's 12 minute timed test, there is a "Mets" test created by Dr. Thomas Faheys. The Mets measurement of energy required to maintain basic life support is calculated on the basis of the oxygen requirement for a given measurement of weight times the individual's total weight. This is a very comprehensive formula.

For those of a more clinical or scientific mind I would advise the investigation of the Mets system of performance testing. The wonderful triathlon training manual developed by Sally Edwards goes into this system thoroughly. For the serious triathlete, Sally's book is a must for your training library. Sally has racked up an awesome record of athletic achievements in marathon and ultramarathon running, topping it all off with 2nd place woman overall in 1981 and tied for third place woman overall in the February 1982 Ironman World Triathlon. Sally holds a degree in sports education from University of California at Berkeley. In addition to her training manual, Fleet Feet Press, 2410 J Street, Sacramento, California 95816, also publishes a Triathlon Training Log and How to Organize a Triathlon.

Our tried and proven system of performance testing is based on the heart rate during a sustained aerobic effort for a period of minutes. This period varies with the mode: 20 minutes swimming, 40 minutes biking and 10 minutes running. We are not concerned with age, weight, comparison tables, etc., only maintaining a maximum aerobic pace at our 85% optimum heart rate for the given period of time and recording the distance covered. Each event is preceeded with a warm-up period bringing the BPM heart rate up to the optimum rate and then commence the timing over the course.

The running test distance would be easier to measure on a school track of 440 yards or 400 meters; the swimming test should be made in a pool with a swimming clock; and the biking test may be made against a mileage indicator or a bike computer. (A bike computer that has the capability of recording heart rate would be priceless in this test.)

Following is the heart rate graph that will give you your minimum optimum and maximum heart rate. The optimum rate, representing 85% of maximum, is our key rate to be used in training and in testing. You will notice that the anaerobic barrier exists somewhere between the optimum and maximum heart rate. This varies with each individual.

After 3 or 4 months training in any of the three modes you will be able to determine your optimum rate without the use of a stop watch and taking the pulse rate. It is important, while training or testing that we be true to ourselves and maintain the maximum aerobic condition, especially so in the Omega Triathlon test, as this is only for your rate of progress and not against your peers by age or weight.

Heart Rate Graph
The Omega Triathlon Training and Testing Formula

It is important that the BPM (Beats Per Minute) be taken during or as soon as possible after the aerobic effort for a limited period of time. The heart rate of 10 beats for 6 seconds, by adding a 0, gives 100 BPM. For a more exact count, 14 beats for 10 seconds gives 84 BPM, or ⅙ of an hour times 14 BPM.

THE PULSE TEST: HOW HARD TO TRAIN
WOMEN

Age	Minimum	Aerobic Optimum	Anaerobic Maximum
25	130	157	185
30	126	153	185
35	123	149	175
40	119	145	170
45	116	140	165
50	112	136	160
55	109	132	155
60	105	128	150
65	102	123	145
70	98	110	140
75	95	114	135

MEN

Age	Minimum	Aerobic Optimum	Anaerobic Maximum
25	137	166	195
30	133	162	190
35	130	157	185
40	126	153	180
45	123	149	175
50	119	145	170
55	116	140	165
60	112	136	160
65	109	132	155
70	105	128	150
75	102	123	145

The calculation for the maximum heart rate is computed by taking the age from a figure of 220 for men but adding 20 to the age of women before computing the maximum rate. The optimum rate is based on 85% of the maximum rate. The minimum rate is based on 70% of the maximum rate.

The anaerobic barrier or threshold exists between the optimum and maximum heart rate and is evidenced by oxygen debt followed by muscular soreness as the result of insufficient oxygen in the blood stream to remove the lactic acid build-up in the muscle tissues. The Omega formula is predicated on the fact that triathletes working in performance testing and training, whether it be swim, bike, or run, **should** maintain a maximum aerobic, non-oxygen debt level, and constantly push the anaerobic threshold.

———————————

The swiftest traveler is he that goes afoot. —Thoreau

USTS —
U.S. Triathlon Series
Sample Rules and Instructions

GENERAL RULES AND DEFINITIONS

Concept — The Triathlon is a three-sport event which, in the case of the United States Triathlon Series, consists of a 1.5K swim, a 40K bike, and a 10K run. It is an individual sport requiring equal skill in three separate events in order to excell.

Competitors in the USTS may not, in any way, seek or accept aid or assistance from anyone on or off the course after the race has started. To do so will result in immediate disqualification. The only exceptions to this rule (and every good rule has an exception) is the food and drink available at official aid stations, aid from officials in the transition area, official medical aid, and water, wherever it may be found on the course.

The event has three categories; men's, women's and relay. The winner in each category is the person or team who completes the course in the lowest elasped time. The lowest elapsed times for men and women overall of the races in either the California or the Northwest Regional will decide the California and Northwest Champions.

DEFINITIONS AND RULES

Assistance — Any solicitation or acceptance of help from anyone on or off the course, including race officials. Racers, escorts, support vehicles, helpers, sags, drafts and mechanical aid will all be considered forms of assistance. Two or more competitors **running** together will not be considered assistance.

Aid Stations — Food, water and medical aid tables located in the transition area and out on the bike and run course. Aid offered midway in the bike course and at miles, 2, 4, 6, 8, & finish on the run course.

Race Numbers — Four numbers; one on the swim cap, one on the front of the bike, one worn on the front of the cyclist and one worn on the front of the runner. Numbers must be attached to the front of the competitor and plainly visible at all times while on the course.

Withdrawal — A competitor voluntarily dropping out of the competition must notify the nearest check point or an official in the transition area.

Dead Heat — Where two competitors in the same race involuntarily finish less than .01 seconds apart. The competitors will share the place finish and split the prize, if any, for that place. The next place finish will be the next number (i.e., tied for third, next finisher is 4th.)

Intentional Tie — Where two competitors in the same race attempt to finish together. The competitors will be asked to decide who gets which place.

Warning — Where a race official informs a competitor that she/he is in violation of the rules. Two warnings constitute grounds for disqualification.

Disqualification — Where the race director, on the recommendation of an official and of the event coordinator, removes a competitor from the event. Grounds for disqualification include violation of the assistance rule, course shortening or acting in a manner that violates the basic rules of good sportsmanship.

Course Shortening — Any intentional cutting or shortening of the course. Grounds for immediate disqualification.

Pace Runner-Escort — Any person not entered in the race who attempts to aid a runner or cyclist by accompanying them during their race.

EQUIPMENT NEEDED FOR THE EVENT

	Required Items	Recommended Items	
SWIM:			
	Clothes	Goggles	
	Official swim cap	Towel	
BIKE:			
	Bicycle	Frame Pump	Water bottle
	Bicycle helmet	Bike tools	Bicycling clothing and shoes
	Clothes	Spare tub or sew-up	Sunscreen
RUN:			
	Clothes	Shoes	
		Hat	
		Sunscreen	

TRANSITIONS

A transition is the act of switching from one sport to another while the clock is running. It takes place in a Transition Area which is comprised of the changing corrals, the showers, Bike Bag Area, The Bike Holding Area, and the Bike and Run Relay Area.

A. SWIM TO BIKE TRANSITION:

After passing the swim gate at the end of the swim, where your # and time are recorded, you will be handed your bike bag. Proceed to the shower area (if you wish) or directly to the changing corrals. After changing into your bicycle clothing put your swim gear into the bag and hand it to a volunteer outside the changing corral. Follow the officials' instructions into and out of the Bicycle Holding Area.

B. BIKE TO RUN TRANSITION:

Follow the chalk arrows and officials' instructions back into the Bicycle Holding Area. Get off your bike at the Entrance to the Bicycle Holding Area and return it to its numbered spot. Take your Run Bag and proceed to the changing corral. When changed give the bag with your bike gear to a volunteer. Follow officials' instructions and exit onto the run course only through the Run Gate.

3) RELAY TEAMS:

Swimmers will be handed wrist bands as they pass through the Swim Gate. Relay cyclists should be waiting with their bikes in the Bicycle Relay Area. Swimmers pass the wristband to the cyclists. Cyclists should **not sprint** until they are out of the Transition Area. Cyclists in front have the right of way if any collisions between cyclists occur in the Transition Area. Runners must wait in the designated Run Relay Area for the handoff from the cyclists. Handoffs outside of the Designated Relay Area will result in disqualification.

PRE-RACE NIGHT PREPARATION

1) CLOTHING BAGS AND SWIM CAPS:

Mark each bag with your race #. Make it large and readable. Mark the opposite side of the bag from the logo. Mark your cap on the front and back with your race #.

2) RACE NUMBERS:

You will receive 3 numbers; a bike number, a run number (w/name tag) and a small number for your bicycle. You will also receive 4 pins and elastic string. Place your run # (w/name tag) on the front of your running jersey or shorts. Your bike # (w/out name tag) should go on your bike jersey or riding shorts. Competitor using one suit for the entire event should make appropriate adjustment (use your run #). REMEMBER YOUR NUMBER MUST BE VISIBLE AT ALL TIMES!! The small bicycle number should be attached to the handlebars and headset with the elastic string.

3) RUN AND BIKE GEAR:

Place all of your bike gear (except helmet) in your bike bag. (Your helmet can hang from your bike.) Place all of your run gear in your run bag. Make sure you can tell between them because they will go to separate places. If you have special food or liquid needs, place it in the appropriate bag. Once the race starts you are on your own. No unofficial aid or help is allowed.

EVENT RULES

SWIM

1) No buoyancy suits or devices; fins, paddles, snorkles or artificial propulsion or flotation devices are not allowed.
2) Swim goggles or face masks may be worn.
3) No escorts of any kind will be permitted.
4) Swimmers must wear official numbered swim caps (provided at pre-race check-in) while in the water and until they are checked through the swim transition gate at the end of the swim.

BIKE

1) Bicycle helmets of the type generally accepted in bicycle racing must be worn at all times during the bicycle race.
2) Any form of self-propelled bicycle may be used. Recumbants, tandems or any devises designed exclusively to reduce air resistance are not allowed.
3) No drafting of another bicycle or of a motor vehicle is allowed. No cyclist shall follow behind another cyclist closer than 2 bicycle lengths ahead or 7 feet to the side. Cyclists must overtake riders in front of them or stay 2 lengths behind. Cyclists observed drafting will be given one warning and disqualified upon the second occurrence.
4) Cyclists receiving aid (other than water) from unofficial sources will be disqualified. No individual support crews or vehicles allowed anywhere on the course.
5) Cyclists are responsible for obeying local traffic laws including stop signs, red lights and riding to the right of the center line.
6) Cyclist race numbers must be worn on the front of the cyclist and on the bike and must be clearly visible at all times.
7) Cyclists may walk the bike, if necessary.
8) Cyclists shall be responsible for insuring that their bicycles meet maximum safety standards to the satisfaction of race officials. All bicycles must be certified by approved checkers or by race officials before the race start. Bike checks will be held during the week prior to the event at local sites listed in your local race instructions. Bikes will be checked for:
   a. Functional brakes
   b. Tight headset, handlebars and seat
   c. Condition of tires, rims and spokes
   d. Handlebar ends properly plugged.
9) Bring tools necessary to make required adjustments to the check-in.
10) Cyclists must follow the directions and instructions of race officials.

RUN

1) Runners may run, walk or crawl the course.
2) Pace or escort runners are not allowed.
3) Race numbers must be worn on the front and be plainly visible at all times.
4) Runners must follow the direction and instructions of race officials.

Before supper walk a little; after supper do the same —Erasmus

Every mountain means at least two valleys. —Anon

1985 QUALIFYING TIMES

A finish time in the 1984 Ironman Triathlon World Championship in the following age-group categories will automatically qualify a participant for re-entry in the 1985 Ironman. These times will NOT be retroactive to Ironman events prior to 1984.

Men		Women	
18-24	11:20	18-24	11:30
25-29	11:05	25-29	11:45
30-34	11:20	30-34	12:15
35-39	11:35	35-39	12:15
40-44	12:15	40-44	13:15
45-49	12:30	45-49	15:00
50-54	13:15	50-54	17:00
55-59	15:30	55-59	17:00
60+	16:15	60+	17:00

The oldest and youngest of the Feb. '82 Ironman in Kona, Hawaii. Bob Johnson the oldest and co-author of this training manual and youngest Rodney Faust, 14 has completed 4 Ironman Triathlons to date. His fastest time was 13:36.

A man can do nothing better than to eat and drink and find satisfaction in his work. This too, I see, is from the hand of God, for without Him, who can eat or find enjoyment? To the man who pleases Him, God gives wisdom, knowledge and happiness . . . Ecc. 2: 24-26 (NIV)

Aerodynamic Principles Create New Bicycling Concepts

The Aerodynamic Era

Now another breakthrough of historical dimensions has revolutionized the bicycle industry — the aerodynamic bicycle. The whole bicycle's effectiveness is completely restructured to provide energy efficient cycling never before accomplished. The past great achievements in the bicycle's structure were identified by the contribution they made to comfort and speed. These elements took up most of the bicycle industry's time and effort in trying to improve the bicycle. By concentrating on reducing human effort, in the case of the derailleur, and increasing power output, in the case of light weight components, the industry considered these to be the most important areas for improvement.

Recently, however, Lotus, through intensive wind tunnel tests and related research identified another area in need of much improvement — air resistance. Air resistance is now the biggest obstacle that stands in the way of the bicycle's progress with road resistance having already been dealt with my making progressively lighter components. By overcoming air resistance, the rider is able to win races and break time trial records, and most important all categories of cyclists benefit from the extra comfort derived from using energy more productively. This area was long neglected in the bicycle's development and now Lotus has researched and implemented the means to combat air resistance through aerodynamic components to suit all cyclists. This achievement signifies another great landmark in the 200 years of the bicycle's history. 1980 will long be remembered as the beginning of an exciting new era of improvement for the bicycle and Lotus is proud to have pioneered the aerodynamic system components concept which will drastically improve cycling for cyclists the world over.

The Aerodynamic Bicycle and the Ironman World Triathlon

For most of the year the northeast trade winds blow 15 to 35 miles per hour, with a vengence in the Hawaiian Islands. They are a cool blessing to every one except an Ironman Triathlon contestant.

The 112 mile Ironman bicycle course is traveled 96 miles perpendicular to the wind direction, out and back. This includes 18 miles of hillclimb and hard head wind to the turn-around point at Havi, followed by 18 miles of free down hill and down wind sailing, to the harbor at Kawaihae.

This 96 miles of strong lateral wind direction combined with a 15 to 20 mile per hour ground speed equates to a devastating head wind for over 96 miles. This is the un-expected torture waiting for the Triathlete at Kona.

All wind resisting accesories should be removed from the bicycle, including front handbar travel bags, computers, seat hanging spare sew-up and tool kit, except the type that straps tightly under the seat in a fore and aft position. The bike tire pump should be clamped or taped to the top tube, not the down tube.

Now we come to the bike. If the Lotus and Shimano claim is true and the wind resistance bike for bike can be reduced by 21.7 percent with this revolutionary principle. I would say that the aerodynamic concept for bicycle equipment is the choice to make for the next Ironman World Triathlon.

You never know when an adventure is going to happen. —Christopher Morley

Swimming identification number being inked on a girl participant.

Girl contestant, starting on the 35 kilometer segment of the San Diego USTS Triathlon.

Julie Moss, on the right, star of Wide World of Sports TV Production of the 82' February Ironman World Triathlon, Kona, Hawaii, 2nd Place woman Finisher.

Kemp Aaburg, 80th place winner of the 82' February Ironman Triathlon giving instructions to a young triathlete.

Dr. Patricia Bragg Ph.D. is active in Life Extension, Physical Fitness, and Preventive Medicine. She is a symbol of perpetual youth, a living and sparkling example of hers and her father, Dr. Paul C. Bragg's precepts. She continues the Bragg Crusade world-wide with Health Science books, tapes, Bragg health and fitness seminars and lectures. In the past two years, Patricia has been a guest on over 300 radio talk shows and T.V. appearances nationwide. Patricia has super high energy and her lectures and seminars are life changing . . . never to be forgotten by those who hear them and benefit from her powerful health message.

Request for Bragg Health and Fitness Seminars or lectures to your corporation, women's, men's, youth and/or church groups, etc. Also for radio or T.V. talk shows requests . . . Please write to:

Health Science, Box 7, Santa Barbara, CA 93102 or call (805) 968-1028.

Bob Johnson, on the right, listens to Percy Cerutty, world famous running trainer to Olympic stars, at his Portse, Melbourne, Australian training camp.

X

The History and Future
of the Triathlon

The start of the 1979 Triathlon, a roaring gale was blowing but the event took place as scheduled from the beach in front of the Kaimana hotel, Diamond Head.

Over 1,000 top athletes from around the globe participated in the Oct. 1984 Ironman Triathlon World Championship in Hawaii. The Ironman begins with a 2.4-mile roughwater ocean swim, immediately followed by a 112-mile bike race and a 26.2-mile marathon run to the finish line.

Photo by Noel Black

1

The History of the
Ironman World Championship Triathlon

An Exclusive Club

It's an exclusive club — this Ironman fraternity. It's not something you can train for in a couple of months. You need to have a good aerobic running base of at least two or three years. The material rewards seem meager; no prize money, little fame, a pat on the back and finally a trophy made of nuts and bolts.

O Lord, Give Us the Strength to Endure Today

These words or a similar pre-race invocation are recited for the triathlon contest in the morning hours in Hawaii. What strength is needed? Fortitude of the mind and physical strength to endure three demanding events in one day: a 2.4 mile, rough-water open-ocean swim, a 112-mile bike ride and a 26.2-mile marathon run (total of 140.6 miles), all by man and woman power.

In the Beginning

Gathered together after a running relay, a group of extremely fit men were arguing about what would be the best test of endurance — the Waikiki Rough Water Swim, the 112-mile bike race around Oahu, or the Honolulu Marathon. John Collins, a 42 year old Navy Commander, suggested combining the three premier island endurance events into one long gruelling race. Everyone laughed, but the seed was planted.

That is one version, another is heard around the Saturday morning breakfast table after the weekly swim of the Waikiki Swim Club in Honolulu. The thought might have germinated after the "Around the Island" relay but according to the long time distance swimmers of the club, the plan went together at the awards banquet of the Waikiki Rough Water Swim in the fall of 1977. The same spirited contestants were present and the beer and enthusiasm were flowing. Of such ingredients are wild dreams made. Six months later, Collins and 14 men competed in the first Ironman Triathlon.

THE FIRST TRIATHLON—1978

"Three (huff) Races in One (puff) Day"
"2.4-mile swim, 112-mile ride, 26-mile run"

These were the headlines for the Honolulu Advertiser's article on the first triathlon.

In February, 1978, 15 triathletes gathered to participate in the Ironman Triathlon. It was a day marked by driving rain, sea breezes and an event launched at 7:19 a.m. and finished by Haller about 7:06 p.m. He recorded a time of 11 hours, 46 minutes and 58 seconds. His time in the swim was 80:40, with a bike time of 6:56, and a run of 3:30.

The 1978 events began as an experiment and included a mixed bunch of casual entrants. One fellow could barely tread water. Another bought a bicycle and learned to ride it the day before the race. During the run, a contestant stopped at McDonald's for a soft drink. The man who won the swim had a bad knee from an old karate injury and needed eight hours to complete the marathon. Organizer John Collins did not foresee that Gordon Haller and a college student named John Dunbar would bite the athletic bullet and almost kill themselves the first contest.

The preposterous dimensions of the event, the first Swim, Bike and Run Triathlon, held the athletic community of Honolulu spellbound. Normally not taken aback by gargantual feats, when it comes to distance running or swimming, Honolulu marathon runners, 30-mile Molokai Channelswimmers, canoe paddlers and local bicycle club members could not believe something like this could happen in paradise. To attempt to cover 140.638 miles by three modes of self-propelled methods over land and water in one day, back to back, certainly had to be something out of a Superman Comic Book. In fact, one of the early contestants felt the same way about it and appeared on the wind swept beach in a Superman costume ready for the swim.

It Was Haller and Dunbar All the Way

Dunbar splashed out of the ocean with a 20-minute lead over Haller. As Haller chased him the rest of the day, Dunbar slowly crumbled. Haller caught him four different times and finally passed him near the end of the marathon. Meanwhile, Dunbar was hallucinating, running into parked cars, and accused his support driver of trying to poison him by suggesting he drink beer when the water supply ran out.

One of those is enough to do in most mortals. But except for some cramping in the back of his legs and a numbness of his posterior in the bicycle ride, Haller was amazingly fresh.

He finished roughly 33½ minutes in front of John Dunbar (12:20:27), a Chaminade University student who had led the pack by 13 minutes through the first two events.

They were the frontrunners among a field of 15, which had only one dropout early in the day. And the dropout — Ralph Yawata — retired because of his handler's car failure rather than because of fatigue.

When Haller ran out of the Aloha Tower checkpoint for the start of the marathon a little under 13 minutes behind Dunbar, he felt he had the Triathlon won.

"Since I'm a whole lot faster than he is in the marathon, I should be all right," Haller said, leaving the tower.

And he was right. Haller had finished eighth in the swim at 80 minutes, 40 seconds, then picked up some steam with the best time in the bike ride at 6:56. But it was his 3:30 clocking in the marathon (ticked off at 3:29 by his Nautilus handlers) that made the difference.

"I caught him at 17, 20 and 21 miles," Haller said. He had rubdown and rest stops at the 17- and 20-mile marks, allowing Dunbar to stay with him, then finally went ahead to stay at 21 miles out.

Sports Illustrated calls the Triathlon "Probably the Most Physically Demanding Test of Endurance Held Anywhere in the World!!!

Haller stated: "I ran the last five miles pretty quick," he said, still breathing easily. "I started to get a little cramp behind my knee about a mile out (from the finish of the bike race). And I had some trouble there early in the marathon."

It appeared he might make a runaway of the final event early. He chopped his deficit from 13 minutes to three on the downhill side of Diamond Head going out, but the cramping stopped him just before the corner of Kahala Avenue, where the course turns alongside Waialae Country Club and the deficit went back to eight minutes.

"Agony and torture, that describes it perfectly."

The pain was most severe on the return route alongside Waialae, but Dunbar managed to dig down deeply enough to sprint the final 50 yards to the Kapiolani Park finish line.

Haller's victory was not a fluke by any means.

"He's really been training for this," said Johnny Faerber, another fine distance runner who didn't enter the event this time. "He's a bike rider; I think that's what it takes."

Of course, both Haller and Dunbar are pretty fair marathon runners, too. Haller was 10th in the 1976 Honolulu Marathon and ran a 2:27 marathon at Washington, D.C. In November 1977.

"Heck, I've been running since I was eight months old, so my mom says," Haller said while getting a rubdown with Absorbine Jr. and mineral oil minutes after the finish.

"Actually, I got into it competitively in the first grade but I didn't run my first marathon until my senior year of college," he said. That was at Pacific University of Forest Grove, Ore. "I did a lot of bike riding, swimming and running one after the other while I was in the Navy out here (1972-1974), but never this long or this fast,"

He's biked the distance in as little as 5½ hours.

Traffic bothered him most in the bicycle race.

"It was pretty bad out there on the North Shore," Haller said. "I had to go out on the sand, but I probably had my worst time at the finish, went around the corner a little too fast and almost flipped over."

John King did, or rather he was forced off the road and into a heap. He wasn't injured but it took a couple of hours to get his bicycle back in running condition.

"Riding a bike? Hey, that's my transportation," Haller said.

But a Triathlon?

"Well, it's only recently that I've really flipped out!" he said.

And that's the kind of event this was. If ever there was a case of mind over matter, it was tried yesterday.

The following is an interview with Commander Collins prior to the Running of the first Ironman Triathlon

Have you ever heard the story about the *Triathlon*?

Don't feel bad. Neither had I until this week, and after hearing the punch line it took five minutes of total rest to get over it.

You see, the Hawaiian Iron-man Triathlon seems to be an inhumane attempt to tax the body beyond all comprehension and award the survivor — if any — with a trophy.

So what is it? It is three events.
- A 2.4-mile rough water, open ocean swim.
- A 112-mile bicycle ride.
- A 26-mile, 385-yard marathon run.

"Oh, I see," I said, listening with some reservations to Navy Cmdr. John Collins' enthusiastic description. "And you probably plan to try one a day over a three-day period?"

"Nope," said John. "We'll do 'em all together, the swim first, the bike ride second and the run last . . . all of 'em on Feb. 18."

Not strangely, this Triathlon will *not* be sponsored by the American Heart Association, the Marathon Clinic or Dr. Jack Scaff. It's Collins' brainchild, another one of those "because it's there" expeditions.

"We started talking about the idea after that around-the-island (running) relay last year," Collins said, the same one during which a few long-distance devotees ran 50 miles individually.

"We got into one of those Primo Beer arguments and tried to dream up the ultimate test," he said.

By that time I got the feeling that this guy was really serious. And he was.

Collins was reciting the terms — $5 entry fee, competition as a combination participant - committee member to try to take care of some of the problems of liability, orange stocking-cap sort of hats for the swim, etc. — I was thinking of the chafed inner thighs and the punctured lungs that would be strewn over the course of this extravaganza.

"We really do think it's possible," he said. "My wife and I (Judy, the gal who attempted the Lanai-to-Maui swim) are both going to compete. She'll slow down for me in the swim and I'll slow down for her — but won't have to much — in the marathon. We hope to do the whole thing in about 13½ or 14 hours."

"Once you are working in the aerobic region — processing oxygen as fast as you need it — there's not much you can't do," he said. "It's like running your first marathon. That first one is really scary. After about 14½ miles, you think you're going to die. But the next time and the next time, you learn you're not dying when you think you are."

That must be the consolation. All runners meet it, and all express the exhilaration that fights with the pain for their attention.

"There's a real crisis of will; an awful lot of it is mental," he said. "But take Tom Knoll. Last year he ran 100 miles one week and turned right around the next week and ran the 25 kilometers."

Knoll is one of the people who will be in the field. Experienced distance runner and better-than-average swimmer Johnny Faerber is another.

This might not sound like the working mind of a 42-year-old, but that's how old Cmdr. Collins is. He's also a design superintendent at the Pearl Harbor Shipyard.

In that vein, Collins plans to have trophies ready for everyone who finishes the grind. How about the purple heart or the medal of honor?

"No, I'm making them out of nuts and bolts," he said, "just going to braze 'em up." Iron-man . . . right!

But it still gets down to the bottom line. How many are going to try it?

"We could have as many as 45 or as few as 20, depending on how enthusiastic the people are on that day," Collins predicted.

1979 NAUTILUS TRIATHLON

He was taking the gale head-on now, but at least the stinging rain had stopped and his mind was still working. Keep concentrating, Tom Warren told himself. Still 20 miles to go, most of it into that awful wind, the same gale he had been fighting for 120 miles and almost nine hours. The bass drum in his leg was getting louder, and his head flopped sideways.

Up ahead stood a man and his wife, paunchy, middle-aged Hawaiian tourists, watching a spectacle outside their ken. Past the astonished couple the runner stumbled, shirtless, eyes down, concentrating to avoid delusion and shock. Finally the tourist could be quiet no longer. "Go, Iron Man!" he shouted. "Go, Iron Man!" Tom Warren, age 35, shuffled off. Still 20 miles to go. And the others were back there chasing him.

The athlete had been stung by a jellyfish and partially blinded by salt water. He had been lost and confused. Physically he was a mess. But still he kept on in this, the Hawaiian Iron Man Triathlon, an event that involved swimming 2.4 miles in perilously stormy seas, then bicycling 112 miles around the island of Oahu, followed by a 26.2-mile marathon run. A fellow in a Superman outfit was among the competitors. They all shared a common reason for being there, a very compelling reason (some called it a curse): an addiction to inordinate amounts of exercise.

That morning 15 people, including a woman, had ignored the boundaries of sanity and started the contest. It was a Sunday in January, the stormy season for Honolulu and the middle of one of the worst stretches of weather in recent years. In six days, five feet of rain had fallen in Hilo on the nearby big island of Hawaii. Now the waters off Waikiki boiled and frothed, stirred by winds of 40 miles per hour. A Navy officer of two decades of seagoing experience could not get his boat out of the harbor. That meant there would be only one rescue vessel in seas of four to six feet during the swim from the War Memorial Natatorium to Hilton Channel. The competitors were undeterred. This was a legal way to prove their toughness.

The vote was, go High Seas or No.

The vote was 13-3 to race. A balking, apprehensive woman entrant wondered why. "Everybody has to make their own decision," yelled a man in a rain slicker, one hand holding the hat on his head. "It's just like life." The woman walked away. She had dropped out of school and trained for a year to be in the contest. Still, she figured her life was worth more than that.

The Iron Man contest was born when someone wondered what would happen if endurance tests in swimming, bicycling and running were piled on one another in a single event. Twelve people finished the 1978 Triathlon. Three did not. One fellow turned delirious and quit. Another inexplicably said that he would run only 14 miles in the marathon. And the third wrecked his bike. He was unhurt, naturally, being an Iron Man, but his fretful father persuaded him to retire. All finishers received five-inch-high trophies made of nuts and bolts, each with a hole in the top, or, you might say, the head.

It would seem not much of an award for so great an effort, but the significance of the event is that there is no apparent significance. No prize money is involved, and little fame; last year's winner, bearded Gordon Haller, a 28-year-old retired taxi driver, was delighted to read a short race report of his arduous accomplishment.

A Gusty Raining Morning on Kaimano Beach

Haller huddled in a rain jacket. And Tom Warren paced nervously. Warren had arrived as an unknown quantity from San Diego, where he owns a bar called Tug's Tavern. His trip cost $1,000, suggesting he could be just as serious about the event as Gordon Haller or John Dunbar. "Some people would take the $1,000 and buy furniture, but this is something you'll have with you for the rest of your life," Warren said.

The contest rules stipulated that each swimmer be escorted by a paddler. Finding one certainly would be no problem, since it is assumed that any young able-bodied man in Hawaii can handle himself in water.

Ocean swimming is not like swimming in a pool, where Haller had trained diligently for 12 months. Last year in calm seas he managed the ocean swim in about 80 minutes. This time he hoped to lop off 20 minutes, improve significantly in the other events and complete the contest in 10 hours or less. In Oregon a few weeks before, he did half a triathlon at a 9:12 overall pace.

Ian Emberson the swimmer, first out of the water

First out of the ocean was Ian Emberson, a 27-year-old restaurant manager for a Honolulu hotel. His time was 62 minutes and 35 seconds, a pace of 2.3 miles per hour. For comparison, distance swimmer Lynne Cox averaged 2.1 miles per hour on her most recent English Channel (20-mile) swim. Old Tom Warren finished four minutes later. Then in quick succession John Dunbar and Mike Collins, son of the Commander, arrived. The 16-year-old Collins was so debilitated that it would take him 14½ hours to complete the bike ride. Dunbar was thoroughly chilled, his body shaking and his arms and legs flopping about uncontrollably. A tourist looked on worriedly and said, "Doesn't he need rest?" As Dunbar climbed on his bicycle to take after Emberson and Warren, Haller was still hidden somewhere back in the swells of the ocean.

After the early finishers scrambled out of the water, the mood of Haller's support crew grew somber. Lyn Lemaire, a 27-year-old Bostonian and the only woman competing, emerged at the 76-minute mark. At length the defending champion was sighted, barely moving.

On superficial inspection the triumvirate of Warren, Haller and Dunbar might appear to be the same person, one fanatic inhabiting three bodies. However, there are differences. Warren is able to combine a lust for training with the successful operation of his tavern, while Haller would be content never to work another day. Dunbar is somewhere in the middle. Believing that physical conditioning can become a cult activity, he vowed that this Iron Man contest would be his last, win or lose.

Commander Collins had postponed the race one day, then had delayed the scheduled 7 a.m. start, afraid not only that someone might drown in the turbulent passage but that during the 112-mile bike segment a sudden squall might unseat a rider. Warren was thinking of the wind, too. He planned to use it to his advantage on the bike leg, figuring he could ride it down the entire back side of the island, using his body as a sail. For this purpose he had installed an unusually high gear on his bike. He hoped to leave the younger fellows like Haller and Dunbar so far behind that they never would recover.

With starting time near, German martial music blared from Dunbar's van as he changed from his Superman costume into swim trunks. At the water's edge, Cowman, wearing his horned hat, knelt before the ocean. And gave up a prayer to his god, for traveling mercies and a safe passage over the raging sea.

Triathletes are from all walks of life

Among the Iron Man entries was an individual with a master's degree in exercise physiology, another with a degree in accounting, a fellow applying to law school, a research anesthesiologist, the treasurer of a San Francisco leasing company and Haller with his physics degree. Disparate as their backgrounds were, they shared a common bond. Henry Forrest, a Marine stationed in Jacksonville, N.C., had hitched rides on military transport planes to get to Honolulu. Until the 1978 Iron Man Triathlon, he had not ridden a bike since the fourth grade and had become lost during the race. He hoped to improve on his performance this year.

Pedaling along during the first part of the bike race, Warren reflected that this would be a momentous day. His presence near the lead was surprising. A businessman closing in on middle age, he had less time for training than the unemployed Haller and Dunbar. When Dunbar, disgusted at the event's one-day postponement, had impulsively announced on Saturday that he would challenge Haller to do the course that day — just the two of them, man against man — off to the side stood Warren, unnoticed. No one thought to challenge the saloonkeeper. So Warren went down to a Waikiki bar, drank beer in solitude and watched a week-old television replay of the Hula Bowl.

After a dozen miles of bicycling, Warren caught Emberson on a steep hill overlooking the Pacific, a point where the wind was so bad Warren's support car was almost blown off the road. Emberson swims five miles a day and carries his ocean gear to work, just in case conditions are conducive to swimming the channel between Oahu and Molokai, a 26-mile trip. But he is not a cyclist and had run only one marathon, and gave up the lead to Warren.

Going down the length of the island, Dunbar trailed Warren by 15 minutes, then 30. He thought, "When is he going to stop?" Warren, the man who does sit-ups in saunas, was dreaming of cool rides through the evenings back home and thinking, "If I don't stop, nobody can catch me." His eyes watered from saltwater irritation, no big problem; Warren does not feel pain as most people do. He won't allow himself to. Yet his feet are so tender that he has tried running races wearing women's nylon ankle socks to prevent blisters. It didn't help. Warren claimed to be in only mediocre shape, "but sometimes it's more fun that way," which is to say the challenge is greater.

Turning back toward Honolulu, Warren's path took him up Route 99, a tortuously steep grade that arrows through pineapple and sugar-cane fields, and directly into the wind. On this stretch Ian Emberson balanced almost motionless, making virtually no forward progress against the gale. Warren began the six-mile climb with a 30-minute lead over Lemaire and a bit more over Dunbar, but the pursuers took an alternate route that was more sheltered and made up great chunks of time. The woman cyclist closed to within five minutes. "Where's the girl?" Warren kept shouting. He started pumping harder.

Ken Shirk, the Cowman Keeps Up the Pace

Tom Warren lay on the grass and talked as onlookers stood in awe. When he tried to rise he held out a shaky arm and a slight man in his late 60s pulled him to his feet. A little later there was a minor commotion. Cowman was jogging by, just starting the first phase of the marathon. He had taken almost 2½ hours in the ocean and just under nine hours on his bike. His real name is Ken Shirk. When he works, it is in construction, usually in Lake Tahoe. As he passed he let out a weird, loud yodel.

Of the 15 entries, 12 finished. A Naval physician from San Diego, Frank Day, wrenched his knee in the swim and had to quit midway in the marathon. And two youngsters, Dave Heffernan and Dennis Cahill, had assorted mishaps and retired from their agony in the run. Emberson was third in 12 hours and 23 minutes. Haller needed 12:31, strengthening as the day progressed and as he got farther from the debacle of the swim. His marathon time was fastest of the group, eight minutes faster than Warren's. Lyn Lemaire finished fifth overall in 12:55. She ran hard at the finish. Henry Forrest improved his overall time by 35 minutes, sir. Cowman finished in 16 hours and 41 minutes, his horns in place.

1980 NAUTILUS TRIATHLON

With a widely published article in March, 1979, issue of "Sports Illustrated," coverage of ABC's Wide World of Sports and sponsored by Nautilus Fitness Centre, the 1980 Triathlon proved to be exciting and had grown dramatically. With the increase of media exposure, there was a substantial increase in the number of participants — from 15 to 108.

"You did it! You did it, Dave!" cried an exultant and slightly tearful Vera Scott just seconds after his son, Dave, proved he was made of flesh, blood, and iron. After starting the swim at 7:55 a.m., 26-year-old Dave Scott put together a winning combination that took 9 hours, 24 minutes — 1 hour, 51 minutes faster than 1979 winner, Tom Warren. Scott, who trains 12 months a year, said he probably wouldn't be back next year because it cost him over $5,000 to participate in the event.

Thirty-year-old Robin Beck (one of the two women entries) came in with a time of 11 hours, 21 minutes. This was 1 hour and 34 minutes faster than the first woman triathlete, Lyn Lemaire's, time in the 1979 triathlon.

Kona Feb. 1982 World Triathlon

The third place finisher in 1981, Scott Tinley, lowered the triathlon record to 9:19:41, to win the 1982 Triathlon. Tinley was 53rd in the swim with a time of 1:10:45. W. F. McCarthy III won the event with 57:39. Tinley came first in the bike event with 5:05:11 and first in the marathon with 3:03:45. 1980 Triathlon winner Dave Scott placed 2nd with a time of 9:36:57. He exited the water in 58:39, completed the bike event in 5:17 and finished the marathon in 3:21:02. Closely behind him was Scott's brother Jeff Tinley, who did the swim in 1:13:02; bike, 5:27:45 and marathon in 3:12:49, to post a 9:53:16.

In the female competition, Kathleen McCartney (11:09:40) edged out Julie Moss (11:10:09) to place first, only 29 seconds ahead.

McCartney finished the swim in 1:32:00; bike 5:51:12; run 3:46:30. Moss did the swim in 1:11:00; bike, 5:53:39 and marathon in 4:05:30. Lyn Brooks and Sally Edwards (who finished 2nd last year) tied for third with 11:51:00.

Growing old isn't so bad—when you consider the alternative.

MAURICE CHEVALIER

Gordon Haller:	1978 (1st) 11:46:58	**Dave Scott:**	1980 (1st) 9:24:33
	1979 (4th) 12:31:53		1982 (2nd) 9:36:57
	1980 (6th) 10:58:15		1982 (Oct./1st) 9:08:23
	1981 (37th)		1983 (1st) 9:05:57
	1982 (finished)		1984 (1st) 8:54:20
Tom Warren:	1979 (1st) 11:15:56	**John Howard:**	1980 (3rd) 10;32:36
	1980 (4th) 10:49:16		1981 (1st) 9:38
	1981 (2nd) 10:04		1984 (6th) 9:38:37
	1982 (10th) 10:18:06	**Scott Tinley:**	1981 (3rd) 10:12
John Dunbar:	1978 (2nd) 12:20:27		1982 (1st) 9:19:41
	1979 (2nd) 12:03:56		1982 (Feb./1st) 9:19:41
			1983 (2nd) 9:06:30
			1984 (2nd) 9:18:45

New Records Being Broken by Ironmen

Since the beginning of the Triathlon in 1978, Gordon Haller's time was lowered from 11:46:58 to 8:54:20 by Dave Scott in Oct. 1984. In 1984 Chris Hinshaw had the fastest 2.4-mile rough water swim in 48 minutes and John Howard recorded the fastest 112-mile bike ride of 4:56. Dave Scott holds the fastest marathon time of 2:53.

First Woman to Complete Triathlon

The history of the women triathlete contestants has gone from the first woman in 1978 not finishing to Lyn Lemaire, the first woman triathlete to ever finish, in 1979, to over 50 women completing the race in 1982. Kathleen McCartney holds the honor of completing the triathlon in a time of 11 hours, 9 minutes and 40 seconds. Linda Sweeney posted the fastest 2.4-mile swim with a time of 1:02, Kathleen McCartney has the fastest 112-mile bike ride with a time of 5:51, and also recorded the fastest marathon time of 3:46.

Increase of Participants from '78-'84

1978:	15 contestants —	14 males,	1 female
1979:	15 contestants —	14 males,	1 female
1980:	108 contestants —	106 males,	2 females
1981:	326 contestants —	305 males,	21 females
1982:	583 contestants —	530 males,	53 females, Feb./82
1982:	775 contestants —	690 males,	85 females, Oct./82
1983:	835 contestants —	720 males,	115 females
1984:	903 contestants —	767 males,	136 females

Dave Scott leads in the 1980 Nautilus Triathlon

He did that yesterday — all day — by breaking the record in the third annual Nautilus *Triathlon*, a grueling event that consists of a 2.4-mile roughwater swim, a 112-mile bicycle race around Oahu and a 26-mile, 385-yard marathon, all performed back-to-back.

The Triathlon — billed as the "ultimate challenge" — this year drew nearly seven times as many contestants as last year, with three women and 108 men huddled together for a pre-race invocation that began, "O Lord, give us the strength to make it through today."

Diana Nyad, world-famous long distance swimmer, on hand to give commentary for ABC television, said, "The whole nature of the swim is a roughwater event. Although I understand the safety reasons, I think the water is too flat."

"I was pleased with my bike ride, but it took its toll," said a tired Scott just after finishing the marathon at Kapiolani Park last night at 5:19 p.m. "When I saw where (John) Howard was, I was real pleased. (Howard is six-time U.S. National cycling champion, three-time Olympian and was a gold medalist in the 1971 Pan American games.)

The bike race was not without its hazards, too, as cyclists maneuvered through Ala Moana and Waikiki traffic, heading out Makapuu way.

Howard, who finished third overall and probably has more experience on the road than any other contestant, said, "What we have here is an impossible event, not so much from a point of view of endurance, but you cannot run a bike race around an island with 200 stoplights.

"I can do it, but a less skillful rider could get killed. You have a potential disaster situation. If I had any less skill on the bike, I wouldn't have done the things I did," he said.

The top cyclists maintained an average pace of 24-30 miles per hour and although Scott never gave up his wide lead, Howard, who completed his swim an hour after Scott, made up his time and finished the bike portion in second place, just 25 minutes behind Scott.

No Change Rooms Here

At Aloha Tower, modesty flew out the window as riders leaped off their bikes ducked into bushes or behind towels and changed into running gear with cries to the crowd of "Turn your head!" "Where's the john?" and "Where are my shorts?"

Next, they hopped on the scales to make sure their body weight had not dropped more than 10 percent (which for health and safety reasons, would have disqualified them from further competition), and amidst cheers and applause, took off running in a diamond head direction.

Scott, who ran his first marathon last September, appeared fresh and maintained good, fluid motion.

In a surprise move, Chuck Neumann passed Howard in the final three miles before the finish, near Kahala, to take second place. Neumann seemed so fatigued and disappointed that he had not won, that he had very little to say, expect to congratulate Scott quietly.

"The marathon was really taxing," added Scott, who coaches the 400-member Masters Aquatics Swimming Club at Davis, Calif., and is three-time winner in the adult division of the annual Waikiki Roughwater Swim.

A TRIATHLON IS PEOPLE

Valerie Silk, the Ironman's Favorite Iron Lady
An Ironlady looks after the Ironman
By BILL GIESE JR., Special to West Hawaii Today

Perhaps the most prestigious of all sporting events, the Original Ironman World Triathlon, is the lovechild of one woman.

The event, which started as a joke only four years ago is now hosting some of the toughest, fittest powerhouses of athletic stamina and has attracted international press, spectators by the thousands but is still looked after by that same lady, who is in her own right, a powerhouse of efficiency and dedication.

Valerie Silk, however, does not even remotely resemble the cross-section of athletes she signs up for the 2.4-mile swim followed by a 112-mile bicycle race and topped off with a 26.2-mile marathon run. She is not a person whom one would expect to single-handedly organize such a competition.

She is a tall, slender, ultra-feminine lady whose good looks seem to cause media persons to stutter momentarily after being brought before the "big chief."

So, to answer the question usually asked quietly but not raised openly as to just how one person (especially one who looks like Valerie) gets stuck with such a mammoth task, this reporter asked her: "How did you get stuck with such a mammoth task."

"Almost by default," was her reply. "Early in 1980, I was pulling out of a management position of Nautilus Fitness Centers of Oahu, which I jointly owned with my former husband. At that time, Nautilus Centers were the sponsors of the Original Ironman and I knew what a tough time they had organizing the competition, especially since it had grown to over

180 participants. When I left the business, I decided to take the chance of organizing it myself.''

So for the rest of that year, Valerie took a dive into what looked like an exciting project. What she didn't count on was that the 1981 event had attracted 326 competitors, nearly twice as many as the year before, and that the 1982 Ironman Triathlon has attracted over 600!

"I Had No Experience"

"I had to organize things and this looked good," she remembered. "But I had never run a race before or had any background in sporting competitions. I had no idea that it would require this level of organization."

Before she took over the responsibilities, contestants were told they had to have their own aid personnel and support crews. She quickly snuffed the rule because it was too costly for the athletes, especially those from foreign countries, who spent all their crackers just to get themselves over to Hawaii.

Having accepted the responsibility of looking after all of the athletes' gear, however, she compounded her already endless task of organization.

"That change threw the race into a different light," she said. "It meant that the race would have to become responsible for the athletes and a task force would have to be organized. As the whole thing unfolded, it became obvious that it really was a potential fiasco.''

So besides corresponding with all inquiries and entrants, she had the task of organizing food and water stations placed strategically throughout the course, safety personnel, traffic control, security guards, medical teams, administrators, accomodation, banquets, timers and be available for the forever-badgering media.

"They Just Laughed."

"When all of the contestants found out that race coordinators would become responsible for handling their equipment and clothes, etc., they just laughed," Valerie said. "They thought it was a joke and all I kept hearing was that the whole affair would end up a mess.''

But it didn't. As a matter of fact that Ironman Triathlon which was supposed to end up another joke, was the most successful. It was also Kona's first.

And now that the teething period is over and all of the bugs have been worked out, the 1982 Ironman looks like a certain success.

"I am confident that it will be a success," says Silk. "The people of Kona were unreal last year in their assistance and their enthusiasm has already manifested itself again this year." Much of the pressure is off now that she has some help, especially that of Earl Yamaguchi, whom she worships for his thoroughness and dedication.

"I Get Scared."

But though all systems look like A-OK, the soft-spoken 31 year-old feels herself growing older quickly.

"Sure, I'm scared. My greatest fear is that I have forgotten to correspond with someone or have overlooked some little thing or that some of the supplies won't arrive. I keep going over and over every little thing in my head. I stay up many nights and don't sleep. Sometimes I wonder why I ever do it . . . I feel like I'm aging fast.''

Valerie says she feels like throwing in the towel almost every day but something keeps driving her.

"It's exciting and challenging and I love to talk to the contestants," she added assuredly. "I'm not the only one who's scared. They are too. Sometimes the athletes call me just for consolation. It's really neat.''

Yes, it is "neat" and most of the contestants, co-workers and members of the media (like me) think that Valerie is pretty neat too!!

Who Enters Triathlons

The scope of the contestants vary from 14-year-old Robin Tain to 73-year-old Walter Stack. The event is entered not only by typical male and female superstar athletes, but includes many other determined characters. For instance, there have been people like Robert Deuriarte, who has a polio affliction in one of his legs; John Huckaby, who was once given 6 months to live; Stephen Gaither, who had limited use of his upper body and Harry Cordellos, who is blind.

Also present was "Cowman" (34-year-old bearded Ken Shirk who wears caveman pants and a buffalo hat made of fake fur with two large cow horns protruding from it), Superman and a fellow with a football helmet.

The average age of the 1982 spring Triathlete was 39. This proves that you either have to have an oil well in your back yard . . . be a drop out . . . or be comfortably retired at a young age in order to afford the cost and the time away from productive work to train for a triathlon.

Why Do They Do It

Why are athletes willing to train for and enter such a grueling contest? The only way to find out is to ask.

Basically a winning cyclist, Mike Moffitt, 21, of Kaneohe, is doing it because of the "ultimate challenge." Joe Mensching from Tucson, Ariz., said, "Why? I don't know. I've run five marathons and competed in the past on bikes. My brother Jim from Chicago was on the 1972 Olympic cycling team and I guess I'm entered because he's doing it."

Laddie Shaw, 30, from Imperial Beach, Calif., who placed fifth in the San Diego Heart Marathon is in because "John Dunbar is a personal friend of mine and he's taken second for the past two years. All I want to do is beat him."

Bill Mckean, 30, from Jamul, Calif., wants to beat both Shaw and Dunbar.

"We were all in the Navy Seals (underwater demolition teams) together, and on the U.S. Pentathalon team for the military Olympics. We're all out to beat each other. Cycling is my best event," he explained.

John Howard, 32, six-time U.S. National Cycling Champion, three-time Olympian and a gold medalist in the 1971 Pan American Games.

"To some it's like the mountain, it's just there," he said. "I don't really have a good answer for why I'm entering. It's got to be one of the foremost endurance events ever. Swimming? I can do it but I don't know how fast. I swam in high school years ago. I'm planning on doing well in this, but it's the bike ride that will do it."

Three-time winner of the run-swim-run, a master swimmer and All American swimming champion, Rick Koslowski, 27, from San Diego, is entering "to prove that a person who has a business and who can't work out five hours a day can still compete in a race like this."

Harold Irving, 32, from Pupukea, is simply in it "for myself — desire!" while Bob Babbitt, 28, from Chicago, is in "just to see if I can finish. I'm tough — especially in between each event — and especially good at stretching."

But Del Scharffenbert, 34, from Portland, Oregon, came over to win or place, not just to finish. Unfortunately I'm not a very strong swimmer, but I've been a good cyclist and runner for years."

Down-to-business Ron Seiple, 37, from Lanikai, is entering for the second time — "to win. I'm strong in all three — all equally as bad as the other — but I'll probably show best on the bike. I like that better than running."

Dan McGilvery, 25, from Boston, prefers running and recently ran across the U.S. for the Jimmy Fund. "This particular event is basically my forte," McGilvery said. "The training that goes into it and the challenge of trying to finish excites me."

Over 1,000 contestants lineup for the start of the 1st United States Triathlon Series Event.

Waiting bicycles, being held in racks, for the swimmers to emerge from the water.

Lyn Lemaire — The First Woman Triathlete to Finish — 1979

In the 1979 Triathlon, Lyn Lemaire was the first Ironwoman to complete the event. She finished with a time of 12 hours, 55 minutes, 38 seconds, and placed 5th overall. Being the American women's cycling record holder for 25 miles, she managed to move up to 2nd place in the bike event and was only 5 minutes behind leader Tom Warren. When Lemaire pedaled past Dunbar, he appeared startled, then asked a crew member, "Is she in the race?" Lemaire smugly turned and waved.

Course Change

As the sport became more popular, the number of entrants grew dramatically, and it was decided Honolulu couldn't accommodate the contestants safely. The 1981 Triathlon was moved from Honolulu to Kailua-Kona, Hawaii. The name of the event was changed, too. In prior years it was referred to as the Ironman triathlon but due to more female entrants, and the fact that Ironperson didn't seem to fit, that name was dropped from the program. In 1981, Nautilus International Triathlon became the new name.

1981 NAUTILUS INTERNATIONAL TRIATHLON

With the temperature ranging from 90-110 degrees, John Howard emerged as the victor. He led a pack of 326 contestants and posted a time of 11 hours, 38 minutes and 29 seconds. The 33-year-old Olympic cycling competitor, sponsored by Campagnola, was elated when he crossed the finish line at the Kailua pier.

"I've never done anything like this," said Howard over the cheers of the huge crowd. "I'm overjoyed; it's more of an honor than winning an Olympic gold medal." Howard, by being sponsored, was able to train eight hours a day. It became a full-time job.

The number one woman was 22-year-old Linda Sweeney of Tucson, Arizona, who finished 53rd overall in 12 hours and 35 seconds. Second was 33-year-old Sally Edwards of Sacramento, California, in a time of 12 hours and 37 minutes.

1000 Enthusiastic volunteers

In previous years triathlon contestants were required to supply their own support team; however, with the growing popularity of the sport, over 1000 volunteers from the Kailua Kona area volunteered for the 1981 Triathlon. Even more impressive was the tremendous amount of enthusiasm and energy generated by the 1000 aid and safety personnel and over 7000 spectators.

Consider the logistics of simply putting together a race of this magnitude. All volunteers — who outnumbered contestants two-to-one — had to be provided with t-shirts, food and drink. Concern for their comfort and safety was as important as for those competing. Some volunteers were patrolling the water, others were out on the highway and still others were at the marathon aid/weigh-in stations. 1,600 boxes of raisins, 2,000 cake doughnuts, 500 pounds of bananas, five cases of oranges and 2000 sandwiches were consumed by the volunteers and contestants.

1982 BUDWEISER IRONMAN WORLD TRIATHLON

Six video cameras, three production staff members, 25 crew engineers and four announcers prepared ABC's Wide World of Sports for the 1982 Triathlon. ABC said the 1981 coverage of the triathlon was the most widely watched TV show of 1981.

Scott Tinley, a 25-year old triathlete from San Diego, swam, biked and ran his way to a record-smashing victory in the 1982 Triathlon. He beat a field of 33 seconds by 5 minutes. Tinley recorded a time of 9 hours, 19 minutes and 41 seconds, while his brother Jeff Tinley came third with a time of 9 hours, 53 minutes and 16 seconds.

Scott Tinley anticipated spending about 1:05 in the water, as he had the year before, but instead he emerged in 1:10, 53rd out of the water.

Thinking he was already too far behind to win, he changed his pacing strategy and went all out on the bicycle leg. He was there to win. Somebody once told him that you go back to do the Ironman a second time only if you think you can win or you're crazy. Some people go back just for the fun of it — they get into the scene and enjoy the craziness of it all, which is fine. But if you're competing seriously, you don't go back to try and take 4th or 5th again. Tinley was 3rd in the 1981 Triathlon.

It took 80 miles of hard cycling to catch Dave Scott, whom Tinley had pegged as the man to beat. "Dave's a real nice guy," says Tinley. "I'd met him the day before the race. When I caught up to him, we talked about the wind and the heat — just general things. I think I told him I'd buy him a beer later." Tinley pulled away, but Scott overtook him at mile 90, and they finished the bike portion together. Tinley's 5:05 was 53 minutes faster than the year before.

At the start of the marathon, Tinley ran a couple of sub-6:30 miles to close the gap between himself and front-running Kim Bushong. After mile 5 of the foot race, Tinley took the lead and never relinquished it, but it wasn't until mile 18 that he said he started feeling confident of winning.

To prepare for the 1982 Triathlon, Tinley entered 14 triathlons in 1981 and was never less than 3rd. Coordinating his work (as an instructional coordinator at Mission Bay Aquatic Centre) with his training, Tinley bicycled to work, ran at lunch and swam on duty. He didn't have to pay at all for the 1982 triathlon because his sponsors provided him with money and equipment.

Insurmountable will and resilience

Julie Moss, a recent Cal Poly San Luis Obispo graduate, drew national attention to her sport with her poignant, gritty finish in Hawaii. It was covered by "Wide World of Sports" and shown several times by ABC-TV. She came across as a modern woman of insurmountable will and resilience.

Moss, 23, leading, collapsed 15 feet from the finish line, her arms and legs like noodles. As spectators and backers urged her to get up, McCartney, who had been second crossed the line. Finally, Moss rallied and, wobbling, crawled the rest of the way.

"I felt so good when I crossed the finish line," she said. "People who saw me on TV thought I was spaced out. It's off base that they thought I almost died. All I did was go beyond my limit. I hit the wall, like in a marathon, I knew everything that was going on around me. I knew I was being filmed. You just don't care what people think. You reach a point where you just want to finish."

Winner of the female entrants, Kathleen McCartney did the swim in 1:32:0, the bike in 5:51:12 and ran a 3:46:28 marathon to put together a winning combination time of 11:09:40. Second place finisher Moss swam a 1:11:0, biked 5:53:39 and ran a marathon in 4:05:30, for a total elapsed time of 11:10:09, only 29 seconds behind Kathleen McCartney. Sally Edwards and Lyn Brooks tied for third, posting 11 hours and 51 minutes.

Moss and many of the other 580 trianthletes plan to participate in the next Ironman contest held in October, 1982.

BETTER PERFORMANCE THROUGHOUT THE YEARS

1978

Gordon Haller, winner of the 1978 Triathlon, won the event with a time of 11:46:58. He completed the swim in 1:20:40 and placed eighth. Winner of the swim was Archie Hapal with a time of 57:35. Haller came first in the bike and run with times of 6:56 and 3:30, respectively. Second place finisher John Dunbar recorded a time of 12:20:27; with a swim, 60:15; bike, 7:04 and run of 4:03. The only female entrant in the 1978 Triathlon did not finish.

1979

Tom Warren won the 1979 Triathlon with a time of 11:15:56. He was second in the swim and run with times of 66:12 and 3:51 respectively. Warren recorded a 6:19 in the bike event to place first. Ian Emberson won the swimming event with a time of 62:35 and placed 3rd in the 1979 Triathlon with a time of 12:23:30. Last year's winner Gordon Haller placed 4th, with a time of 12:31:53 and won the running event in 3:43. John Dunbar once again placed second with a time of 12:03:56. He recorded 1:09:55 in the swim, 6:51 cycling, and 4:03 in the run. The only female entrant, and the first woman triathlete, Lyn Lemaire, placed a respectable 5th, with an overall time of 12:55:38. Lemaire exited the water in 1:16:20 and came in second in the bike (almost catching Tom Warren) with a time of 6:30. she ran a strong marathon to record a time of 5:10 and placed 7th in the run.

1980

In 1980, Dave Scott lowered the time to 9:24:33 and recorded a first in the swiming bike, with times of 51:00 and 5:03 respectively. He completed the marathon in 3:30:33. Scott led the whole day and was never challenged.

The 1980 Triathlon had 2 female entrants, Robin Beck and Eve Anderson. Beck finished the swim in 1:20, bike, 6:05 and the run in 3:56:24, to post an overall winning time of 11:21:24. Even Anderson finished the swim in 1:30, bike, 7:48 and marathon in 6:22:59, to post a time of 15:40:59.

1981

With the course being changed to the Big Island, and people saying the new course was tougher, John Howard put together a winning combination of 9:38 to win the 1981 Triathlon at Kona, Hawaii. Howard didn't even place in the top ten of the swim, but won the bike in 5:03 and placed 7th in the marathon with a time of 3:21. Tom Schmidt was 1st in the swim, posting a time of 51:50, while Joe Kasbohm won the marathon with a time of 2:59. These two contestants didn't finish in the top ten in the overall standings. Second-place went to 1979 winner, Tom Warren with a time of 10:04. He did the swim in :59, bike, 5:37 and came in 10th in the marathon with a time of 3:27. Third-place finisher Scott Tinley finished the swim in 1:05; bike, 5:47 and marathon in 3:19, to record 10:12.

The first female entrant was Linda Sweeney with a time of 12 hours. She did the swim in 1:02; bike, 6:53 and run in 4:04. Close behind her was Sally Edwards, who finished the swim in 1:28; bike in 6:58 and run in 4:10 to record a 12:37 time. Carolyn Brooks came in third with a overall time of 12:42 and posted a time of 1:20 in the swim, bike 7:13 and a marathon of 4:08.

However, he was not able to do it in the 1979 Triathlon. He did manage to place fourth and was getting stronger at the end, winning the marathon.

Tom Warren

Thirty five year-old Tom Warren, who won the 1979 Triathlon in 11 hours, 15 minutes and 56 seconds, is able to combine his tough training schedule with the successful operation of his tavern. He came to the 1979 Triathlon as an unknown from San Diego, at a cost of $1,000, indicating that he was just as serious about the race as were Haller and Dunbar.

Warren took the lead from Emberson near Makapu and was never threatened after that. He completed the bike race in 6 hours, 13 minutes and the marathon run in 3 hrs., 50 minutes.

"I didn't have much trouble except for a slight muscle problem on the other side of the island," he said. "I took some Gatorade and ERG and it went away."

Warren said that he has participated in similar events on the Mainland, although none were so long as this one.

A competitive swimmer at USC in the early 60's, Warren said that he did not train specifically for this event. He does a lot of bike "touring" and occasionally runs marathons. He finished the recent Honolulu Marathon in 2 hrs. 50 minutes.

Warren is a blithe, irrepressible imp who speaks in an almost breathless voice, his eyes magnified behind his glasses. He says he does a secret type of sit-up and claims the bad feature of racing is that it interrupts his training routine. "I could never associate racing with pain," he says. "It's like going to school. You have to take exams to find where you stand."

Precise Training Diaries

Most of the Iron Man contestants keep precise training diaries. To them they are canceled checks to peruse fondly. Haller logs not only every shred of physical activity, but also each morsel of food and the time it was consumed. Junk food is underlined. He records his pulse rate, his sleeping time, injuries and the quality of the day. Tom Warren not only chronicles his daily exercise but makes copies that he sends each month to friends around the country. Most of them get thrown away; some do not. Fifteen years ago Warren swam for the University of Southern California. He has a standing bet with each year's swim team that he can do more exercise mileage per month than the entire team can do in practice. Coach Peter Daland reads Warren's monthly exercise tallies to the squad. Once Warren rode his bike from San Diego to Los Angeles, rolling onto the Southern Cal campus and into the natatorium to hand-deliver the workout sheet. The swimmers applauded.

Ian Emberson

Ian Emberson placed fourth in the 1978 Triathlon and third in the 1979 event. He won the swimming race in 1979 with a time of 1:02:35.

Emberson doesn't look like an athlete. Boyish, soft-spoken and humble, the 28-year-old Hawaii Kai man could double as a scout leader, a pianist, or a student of philosophy.

At less than six-feet tall and a slight 165 pounds, you could hardly call Emberson superstar material. But a quick glance at his athletic achievements and it becomes apparent that inside that frame stands a mountain of determination and strength. Emberson is truly Hawaii's "Iron Man."

"Although I've never been formally coached, I've been running, swimming and playing sports all of my life," he explained. "I suppose I'm at my best swimming (Emberson holds, or held, freestyle swim records at the University of Hawaii and at the University of Massachusetts). Some coaches say that I have tremendous lung capacity. I guess that helps."

Although the athlete is primarily a distance swimmer, Emberson also runs marathon footraces, bicycles around Oahu, plays rugby, paddles canoes, and during his high school years in England, played cricket.

"In looking back," Emberson recalled, "my 16-hour and 40-minute Molokai to Oahu swim last May (Emberson, with Mike Miller, became the fourth and fifth persons ever to swim across the treacherous Molokai Channel) was far more difficult than either of my Triathlons. "At least in the bike and running competition of the three-stage contest you can stop, rest and massage your legs.

"But in the Molokai swim, with that fast-flowing current, you must keep swimming. If Mike and I would have arrived at Sandy Beach (Oahu) 25 minutes later than we did, the current would have swept us back to Molokai."

Haller and Dunbar

In the early years of the triathlon, Haller and Dunbar were two very keen competitors, each with his own personality make-up.

Twenty five-year-old Dunbar, a blond, open-faced fellow was very good-natured and shy around strangers. He ran in a women's race in 1977 wearing a T-shirt that read TOKEN. But there is a serious side to Dunbar. When people mime his hardened competitive spirit, they clench their fists and make chomping, biting gestures, evidently comparing him with an implacable snapping turtle.

In the Navy Dunbar had been a member of the Seals, an elite underwater demolition group. On ambush training patrols, Seals are not allowed to swat mosquitoes, and during 23 weeks of schooling they are at times in mud all but three hours a day: that is when they sleep. One of the tough parts is log training, when a group of men run with a 300-pound log on their shoulders, shouting, "Kill." Seals are supposed to have the highest divorce rate, as well as dropout rate, in the military, but they think it unfair to them to be considered only as zealots who, on bets, bite heads off chickens or eat glass. They say they are looking for challenges.

At the 1979 Triathlon, John Dunbar arrived at the starting line wearing a Superman costume sewn by the sister of one of his support crew.

Dunbar's rival, Haller, also was in the Navy. "The Seals aren't so tough," he says. "There were a few in my unit and I was tougher than they were."

Haller grew up in Forest Grove, Ore. as a studious, bashful sort. He took a degree in physics at Pacific University. Since then he has raised a beard, learned to modulate his voice at radio broadcast school, taken a speed-reading course, let his hair grow, studied the power of positive thinking, shed his timid ways and resculpted his body on exercise equipment. Around strangers he wears tight T shirts and subtly pops his muscles. Old friends don't recognize him. The revamped Haller finds joy in odd accomplishments, he is, for example, an expert on TV cartoon trivia. Someday he hopes to run cross-country — that is to say, across the entire country, the continental United States. Meanwhile, his average yearly income runs between $4,000 and $5,000. He gave up driving a cab and now repairs roofs. More exercise to be had doing that.

Competing is Haller's real profession; he will sign entry blanks the rest of his life. "I'm good at it," he says. "If you've got a talent, don't waste it. Also, I like the feeling of power." During the months preceding the defense of his Iron Man title Haller trained back home in Oregon, running and swimming through fog, cold, rain, ice and snow, and pedaling his bicycle indoors on rollers. He drove 80 miles round trip several times weekly to exercise on Nautilus equipment. He has seen the movie *Superman* twice. A favorite scene is when the man of steel scans Lois Lane's lungs for cancer. Haller will not date a girl who smokes. He says he is happy.

Plagued by Injuries & Sickness

Some people associate times of their lives with popular songs or love affairs. Haller does it with injuries. Thus, 1972 was the year he sprained his ankle four times. And he will never forget 1969. He was sick then for nine months, a siege precipitated by his exaggerated regimen. He was working out three times a day, had two girl friends, was staying up all night to study for exams and was preparing to run the quarter mile and half mile in a track meet. In succession he had mononucleosis, strep throat, hepatitis, dysentery, tonsillitis and trench mouth. His legs became paralyzed. "Then I really got sick," he says. His convulsions were so severe that he suffered a double hernia. "It was a good time to lay back and reflect on life — what was left of it." Haller lost 28 pounds in one week. "At the end of the week, Neil Armstrong walked on the moon and I ate my first meal," he recalls.

Haller played the trumpet to ease the boredom of convalescence. Then his face became partially paralyzed. But worse, he felt, was the deterioration of his athletic skills. Frantically he fought against it. "I liked my crutches because they were building up my triceps," he says. Haller sneaked a rubber inner tube under his bedcovers and surreptitiously exercised with it, and, when nobody was home, he slipped outside and ran around the block. His time was 3:12, a minor disappointment. He rested and slept for three days, then did it again in 2:52. There is a big star in Haller's workout log for Jan. 5, 1970, the day the doctors pronounced him cured.

Haller Loses His Escort Paddler

During the 1979 Triathlon, Haller's escort paddler had to be rescued due to the roughness of the ocean waters. This left him at a disadvantage, and his strength was sapped as he zig-zagged, trying to stay on course.

Ten yards from shore, in water so shallow he could have stood, he weakly splashed in place. Finally he got up, stumbled and almost fell. "Is that all there is?" he wheezed. His time was 112 minutes.

There were those who expected Haller to quit, in exasperation if not in exhaustion. Winning seemed no more than a remote possibility. But Haller is convinced he is tougher than a Seal. He showered, changed clothes, swallowed some high-energy liquid nourishment and wobbled off after Warren, Dunbar and the others. Last year the bearded athlete had passed wilting rivals throughout the bike race.

John Howard

John Howard was training eight hours a day before his '81 victory. Now he's getting a divorce. "Another casualty of the Ironman," he says somewhat ruefully. "You can't really expect anyone to put up with a program like mine."

John Howard took up cycling while still a high school student in Springfield, Missouri in the mid-'60s. Back then, cycling was an activity that took considerable nerve. High school students didn't ride bikes; they cruised in their Chevies and Fords and GTOs and threw beer bottles at guys like Howard who were so rash or unorthodox as to venture onto the roads in any conveyance other than the highest powered maroon metal flake monstrosities of fuel consumpion.

But Howard also was a boxer, a skill which no doubt offered him some comfort during the dark ages before enlightenment and the new super-lightweight, high-strength alloy bike frames. It was as a young boxer, inexperienced but talented and carelessly overmatched with an older veteran of the ring, that Howard discovered the hard way that he doesn't like to lose.

In 1980 it took Howard 1:51 to complete the Ironman's 2.4-mile swim segment, which is not the sort of time you write home to Mother about. He finished the 112-mile bike race in 5:28, however, much faster than anyone else in the contest. But then he was forced to walk the last five miles of the marathon because of leg pains. He finished third overall, with a total time of 10:36.

After losing to Dave Scott in 1980, Howard devoted himself to a victory in 1981.

Typical Howard Day

A typical Howard day, when he was at the peak of his conditioning, would begin at about 5:00 a.m. with 30 minutes to an hour of yoga, then an eight- to 10-mile run. Howard would take the rest of the morning off to recuperate, and then at 1:00 p.m. he'd get on his bike and ride between 35 and 110 miles. Howard says his daily biking was more for recuperation and recreation than conditioning. He wasn't really pushing himself.

At about 4:00 p.m. he'd lift weights for upper body strength and then sometime between 4:30 and 6:00 he'd do an easy 2,000 yards in a pool at a swim club near where he was living at the time in Houston.

However, this 2,000 yards was just a warm-up, and he completed another 2,000-4,000 yards with a swim team every night at 7 p.m.

The next year, of course, he redeemed himself in spectacular fashion. he cut his swim time by 40 minutes and his marathon time from 4:13 to 3:22. It took him about 30 minutes longer to complete the bike part, but the event had been moved from Oahu to Kona that year, and the course, though the same distance, was more difficult. His total winning time was 9:38, and there now are people who think that John Howard is the greatest endurance athlete in America.

Howard isn't sure if there's another triathlon in his future. At 34, he may not necessarily be in his prime for that sort of thing, and there are a few other achievements he'd like to get out of the way soon, like breaking Lon ("Marathon Lon") Haldeman's cross-country cycling record of 10 days, 23 hours and 11 minutes.

Scott Tinley

After a third place finish in the 1981 Triathlon, Scott Tinley won the 1982 Triathlon with a record time of 9 hours, 19 minutes, and 41 seconds.

The second of eight children, Tinley grew up in the Los Angeles area "with a pool in the back yard and bicycles in the garage." He played little league baseball and flag football as a youth, after which his only experience with organized competition came in high school, where he ran track and cross country.

After high school, Tinley moved to San Diego and competed in 10 ks, half marathons, and marathons. After two years of this he saw a magazine article about fellow San Diegan Tom Warren's 1979 Ironman victory.

"When I first read about it, I said 'Well this is nuts!'" But it still sounded like a lot of fun. All the triathlons I had done were fun, and I thought the Ironman must be even better. I wanted to give it a try."

By this time Tinley was, in his own mind, a triathlete. His best marathon to date is a 2:35 — good, but not fast enough to win. He's sure he'd lose any race in a pool, because he can't execute a decent flip turn. And he's never even considered entering a bicycle race, although he probably would turn in a respectable performance. But mention the combined contest where overall fitness, endurance, strategy, and training become more important, and his interest is up.

Reluctant to Reveal Training

Tinley is reluctant to reveal much about his training, and for two good reasons. First, he feels, there is the danger that less capable athletes may attempt to emulate the front runners and end up hurting themselves. Even a well-conditioned runner risks injury in the water or on the bicycle simply because the same muscles are stressed differently from one event to the other. Equally important, Tinley believes, is the edge that his particular training techniques have given him and his brother Jeff over the competition in Hawaii and elsewhere. If they know something the other triathletes don't, shouldn't they keep it to themselves?

1982 — Triathlete
A Sioux Indian Named Claire
John Christensen—Honolulu Newspaper Agency—Feb. 1982

Claire St. Arnaud (san areKNOW), 44, is a 6-foot, 180-pound blacksmith from Center, Neb., who also breeds and breaks horses. He is here to compete next week, Saturday, in the Ironman Triathlon in Kailua-Kona.

The Triathlon is a one-day gala which includes a 2.4-mile ocean swim, a 112-mile bicycle ride and 26.2-mile marathon. St. Arnaud rightfully calls it "the Boston Marathon of endurance sports."

St. Arnaud figures he's trained hard for the Ironman. By anyone else's standards, he already is an Ironman.

His problems begin at his front door. Center, Neb., population 111, is about 150 miles northwest of Omaha in the northeast corner of the state. His 160-acre ranch is seven miles and another consciousness level away.

He has no running water and no indoor plumbing. He splits and hauls his own firewood, as well as water and feed for his horses. This, mind you, in an area where the winter wind-chill factor wrestles the mercury down to 70 below. Where St. Arnaud lives, shoveling snow is an Olympic event.

545

There is plenty of room to run, of course, but no paved roads to ride a 10-speed bike on and the nearest swimming pool is 55 miles away. To train, St. Arnaud had to travel.

Last summer he drove to a health board meeting in Washington state and then stayed on through the fall to train. During the day he rode his bike and ran in the mountains. At night, he wrapped himself in blankets and slept on a picnic table.

This would go on for three or four days, and then he'd stop and shoe horses for a day or so to earn money. He also picked apples and hauled hay. "I've been down to my last twenty cents a few times," he says.

St. Arnaud returned home for a month and then went to Tucson to train with a cycling coach. He cycled and ran in the desert, shoed horses for money and slept in a stable.

During this six months, incidentally, one horse kicked him in the forehead and another got him in the shoulder. A third stepped on his foot and broke two of his toes. St. Arnaud kept on training.

"It's incredible what the body can do," he says.

St. Arnaud has run "20 or 21" marathons — including Boston and Pike's Peak — and once ran marathons on three successive weekends. He says he runs because he enjoys it, even the occasional 40-mile training run.

St. Arnaud is a Sioux Indian, a once-proud tribe known for its horsemanship. Today the Sioux live on reservations and suffer, he says, from a terrible self-image. There is alcoholism, disease and violence. The average Sioux male dies before he is 48. The suicide rate among 12-and 13-year-olds is frighteningly high.

St. Arnaud has a college degree. He is an Army veteran and worked in the so-called civilized world for several years before "retreating" to his grandfather's farm and what he felt was a better lifestyle. You would think he would be a source of local pride. He isn't.

His tribe shuns him as a recluse. It neither understands nor values athletics, nor does it grasp what he is trying to prove. At 44, he is an old man by their standards. The guy ought to be babbling and eating mush.

"I'd be lying if I didn't say I'm doing this for me," he says, "I love the challenge. But I think it's high time the Indians learned to take care of themselves. I want them to see that what I'm doing is possible. They need an Indian hero like (distance runner) Billy Mills or Jim Thorpe."

He figures the training, the equipment and the travel have cost him at least $10,000, and that doesn't include lost wages.

Friends started a fund to send him here, and all they got was $200. Calls to the governor, the congressional delegation and legislators — he is the only Nebraskan entered — netted nothing. Only a month and a half ago, a statewide campaign quickly raised $100,000 to send the University of Nebraska band to the Orange Bowl.

St. Arnaud is here only because his girlfriend (she teaches Head Start kids on the reservation) put his ticket on her American Express card. The Oklahoma State Horseshoeing School, where he learned blacksmithing, paid his $85 entry fee. They'll figure out later how to pay it back.

He is staying with a benefactor and another invited him to use the Outrigger Canoe Club. But things aren't necessarily getting better. Until three weeks ago, he'd never been in the ocean. Two weeks ago, a car knocked him off his bike, bruising his spine.

Not everybody has it this tough. Some of the better-known athletes in the Triathlon have sponsors and now that ABC-TV has assumed control, someday there may be support for everyone.

St. Arnaud could use it, although he says he's out here for the chance to compete with top athletes. "I'm not out here for money," he says. "I'm here for the sport."

St. Arnaud expects to put in 10 or 12 hours of continuous effort. No whistles, no time outs, no cheering crowds, no boos, either. Win or lose, his reward is a T-shirt and a hot meal.

Claire's participation in the 1982 spring Ironman Worlds Triathlon, was plagued from the start. Upon arriving at his Bicycle, A Lotus Aerodynamic, one of the best on the staging pier at Kona, Hawaii, on Saturday morning just prior to the start of the Ironman Triathlon, he found both sew up tires had been removed from the rims. This was accomplished in spite of the tight security guarding over $1 million dollars worth of top quality bicycles. Fortunately there was sufficient time to replace the tires before the Swim cannon went off. Into the bike race, Claire began to blow out tires, and continued to blow out tires until he had blown out 6 tires. The resulting delays in finding extra spares cost him over 4 hours. Claire has tremendous power in his legs and it was discovered that the stems were pulling out of the tires through his torque power on the wheels. Later it was decided that a substance had been applied to the glue on the rims. Needless to say, Claire was terribly disappointed, not by the troubles out on the course or the dissapation of the effort and money required to be a participant in the triathlon but most of all why someone would single him out of all of the triathletes, to play such an unsportsmanlike trick on him. In spite of the delays on the road, Claire turned in a sub-10-hour time net, with the tire repair time subtracted from his finish time.

Having had very little time in the ocean to train for the 2.4 mile swim he finished the swim in around 2 hours. But more than made it up in the bike ride, (less the 4 hour tire repair delay) and the marathon in which he excells.

Claire had arrived in Honolulu about 6 weeks prior to the Ironman without the ability to swim over 50 yards. Members of the Outrigger Canoe Club and fellow Training Triathletes assisted him in extending his swimming distance sufficiently to be able to go the distance in the Kona, Triathlon.

Claire was the only triathlete from Nebraska, the only full blooded American Indian to have participated in the Hawaii Triathlons to that date. His purpose was to set an example for the young American Indians to follow. To take them out of alcohol, drugs and self pity and get them involved in the sport of their forefathers, the great Indian runners of the past.

At 44 years of age, Claire claims to be 90 years of age. He qualifies this statement by proving that the American Indians life expectancy is less than 50 years old. This is due in part to the life style that they have reduced themselves to due to lack of will, and self determination, resulting in indulging in poor living habits, alcohol and drugs.

Many in Hawaii who met Claire, met an American Indian for the first time. His candor and straight forwardness, regarding the plight of the American Indian certainly left an indellible mark on their hearts and minds. If the White man ever carried any mixed feelings about the Native Americans this old Indian saying should certainly hold true, "Never judge a man until you have walked from sunrise to sunset in his moccasins."

A freelance Television Company of Kona is preparing a Television Special, depicting Clair's participation in the Ironman Triathlon. This combined with scenes of his life on the Sioux Indian Reservation in northern Nebraska, will be instrumental in showing all of the American Indian nations that they can be proud to be an Indian and to become involved in self improvement, and reject self pity, so Clair believes.

Former Pipeline Surfer
Kemp Aaberg Courts A New Wipeout

By JOHN ZANT
News-Press Sports Writer

Kemp Aaberg just can't resist a wonderful opportunity to get his breath taken away.

Years ago, it was surfing. Aaberg started riding the waves in 1956, before the words to the song — "Everybody's gone surfin' . . ." — became a reality. He often appeared in surfing magazines and movies, swooping down the sheer blue walls of those giant waves in Hawaii.

Aaberg's explanation for his stardom is modest and simple: "Because I was there."

He's 42 now, but he hasn't gone away. Aaberg has returned to the cutting edge of recreational challenge. He's in Hawaii this week, not to take on the big, big waves, but to attempt the long, long triathlon.

Aaberg is one of over 500 superbly conditioned athletes who will embark tomorrow on the fifth annual Ironman World Triathlon in Kona. It starts with a 2.4-mile open ocean swim, followed by a 112-mile bicycle race and then by a 26.2-mile marathon run. There are no prescribed rest stops; the object is to do the whole thing as fast as you can.

"I'm really curious about the triathlon," said Aaberg, who's been training for a year between his night shifts at UPS in Goleta. "It's a unique sport. Instead of being ambitious and competitive, you have to be steady, smooth and economical.

"It's gruelling. It takes every single bit of energy out of you. It'll leave you all wrung out like a washrag. You have to dig deeper and deeper into yourself to stay smooth and keep going for it."

Surfing was a different experience for Aaberg. Instead of gradually peeling back his layers of determination until there's nothing left, he had to summon his courage all at once when a mountainous wave rolled toward him.

"You had to dig away to find your confidence when it looked terrifying," said Aaberg. "You can't panic in the face of a big dragon at Waimea. There's an immediate thrill in riding a vicious wave and getting away with it in elegant fashion."

Aaberg lived in Pacific Palisades when he started his surfing career. He attended UCSB in the early '60s. Then he moved to Australia, where he worked as a PE teacher, and eventually worked his way around Europe doing odd jobs. He settled down in Santa Barbara in 1975.

Always a fitness buff, Aaberg took up running several years ago. Sometimes the surf was flat, but he was always able to run. Last October, he finished seventh in the Santa Barbara Marathon in a time of 2:56:23. He was first in the 40-49 age group.

Aaberg will be shooting for age-group honors in the Ironman Triathlon. His intention is to remain steady and balanced the entire way.

"Hot swimmers can outswim you; hot bikers can outpedal you; hot runners can outrun you," he said. "But the combination of all three events is a great equalizer. The person who knows how to pace himself will be in the best shape. He'll be able to walk over bodies on the road during the marathon."

The idea for Ironman Triathlon originated in 1977 when John Collins, a Navy commander, was downing a few brews with his buddies, and they started thinking up ultimate physical challenges. They decided to combine swimming, bicycling and running, three popular sports in Hawaii. The next year, Collins and 14 other people tried it for the first time. Only 12 finished.

Now, the Ironman Triathlon attracts hundreds of participants and will be covered by ABC's Wide World of Sports.

Aaberg is one of several Santa Barbara-Goleta athletes attempting this year's Ironman Triathlon. They include Ken Askew, who finished 25th last year. Askew, 28, tried out for the Olympic kayaking team in 1980. He's a carpenter who reportedly will stay in Hawaii to work on a ranch after the triathlon.

Dr. Allen Thomashefsky of Santa Barbara is participating in the triathlon as a way of setting an example of preventative medicine.

"Some doctors don't practice what they preach," said Dr. Thomashefsky, 38. "I see this as a great opportunity. There are not many things I've done full out. There's been no space in my life the past year for getting sick or having my relationships not working."

Kemp Aaberg, who once enjoyed solititude on top of the waves, sees the triathlon as another way of getting inside one's self. "There aren't coaches for this sort of thing," he said. "It takes self-discipline and a long-term commitment."

The Ironman World Championship Triathlon, held February 1982, proved that Kemp Aaberg could take anything the sizzling course had to offer. Kemp finished 72nd place overall as follows; the Swim in 1:15:30 and burned up the bike course on his Lotus Super Pro Aerodynamic Bicycle in the fast time of 6:7:38 and a marathon of 4:8:4. In the 40 to 44 year age group Kemp placed 4th out of 54 contestants in this crowded field. Training has not stopped for Aaburg. His sights are on the October 82 Ironman, and he certainly should be the one to watch.

Robert Deuriarte

Thirty seven year-old Robert Deuriarte finished the 1980 Triathlon in 19 hours and 11 minutes. You ask, so what's so special about this fellow? If you look closely, this 130-pound marthon man will tell you why he gets runner's adrenalin flowing. For unlike most of us who have two good legs for running, Deuriarte, because of polio affliction as a youngster, has only one.

"The fact that I finished the Triathlon still hasn't sunk in," said the 37-year-old Deuriarte."

With his polio-afflicted leg providing only 15 percent of his biking power. Deuriarte still nearly outpedaled his vehicular support crew.

"I really enoyed the bike run," he said. "I strapped my right foot on the pedal and took off with my good leg spinning.

He completed the around-Oahu course in eight hours and 12 minutes — well under his 10-hour prediction. His support crew in the car didn't catch him until far along the Windward Coast.

Training For The Triathlon

Deuriarte, who has been dragging and pushing his matchstick-sized right leg over 4,000 racing and training miles during the past two and a half years, has completed 11 marathon (26.2-miles) distance events. His left leg is probably the strongest one in town.

Although biking gives the spunky athlete 15 percent usage out of his polio limb, Deuriarte estimates that while running, he has only five percent usage, and while swimming, his right leg affords no power at all.

"My swimming is all arms and shoulders," he explained. "I just drag both legs behind me in the water. I find if I use my good leg for propulsion, I end up swimming in circles."

Incredible Huck

Eight years ago John Huckaby was 52 years old and overweight, suffering from a bad heart condition and high blood pressure. He was told to make out a will and take it easy.

The doctors gave him six months to live.

At age 60, he was the oldest finisher in the 1980 Triathlon.

In 1979, Huckaby completed 18 marathons; including six "ultra marathons" — runs over 50 miles. In May he ran the original Greek marathon course near Athens three times (78.6 miles) non-stop; in June he became the oldest runner ever to finish the grueling 8.3 mile uphill White Face Mountain course at Lake Placid; and in July he completed "The Ultimate Challenge," a 100-mile run over the Sierra Nevada mountains between Squaw Valley and Auburn, California. Running at night over narrow wilderness trails he carried a noisemaker to ward off rattlesnakes common to the area.

Huckaby is a rapid-fire talker who gulps down 31 different vitamins a day, wears "Incredible Huck" T-shirts and brags about every scar on his muscular re-born body. Now a self-styled vegetarian evangelist, he would probably be unbearable if he took himself serious.

Almost Drowned

Six months before the 1980 triathlon, John Huckaby didn't even know how to swim a stroke. When decided to enter the Honolulu competition, he picked up a book on swimming and started to learn at home.

He found the book tough going and, after practicing for a week on the living room floor, decided to actually get in the water. Huckaby jumped into the YMCA pool, sank to the bottom and panicked. The lifeguard slipped a boat hook under his swimming shorts and pulled him out.

"Don't let anyone tell you," he says, "that you can learn to swim by reading a book. I went right home and threw that book away."

During the Nautilus Triathlon, Huckaby almost drowned during the rough-water competition. Washed ashore twice during the swim, it took him over three hours to cover the 2.4 miles.

"Because I hadn't had much practice in the open ocean, the current was too strong for me. I wasn't able to do a decent scissors kick. Once I found myself in water so shallow that my belly was stuck in the sand."

After swimming, biking and running, Huckaby recorded a total time of 21 hours, 51 minutes, and 32 seconds, more than double the time of the first place finisher. It took him over 21 hours to complete the course and he still had enough energy to sprint the final 100 yards.

No wonder his fellow marathoners call him "The Incredible Huck."

"I got that nickname a couple of years ago," he explains with no modesty at all, "when I ran two marathons in two days, in Buffalo and New York City. During the Buffalo race I tripped over a road marker and broke my ankle but I got up and kept going. Nobody could believe it. I've never dropped out of a marathon for any reason."

"Not bad," he says, "for an old man like me. Next month I'm running the Mardi Gras Marathon in New Orleans and in April there's the Boston Marathon. The Thompson vitamin people want to sponsor me on a run of 5,000 miles from Long Island to Alaska but my boss refuses to let me take off five months from work. I'll have to wait on that until I retire."

Huckaby says he "hit the wall" around Hawaii Kai and began staggering off the road. Tears started flowing from his eyes and he feared that he would black out if he ran any farther. He remembered that he had some caffein tablets and popped them into his mouth.

"All I could think of was that if I didn't finish the marathon run my friends would be disappointed. I'd never given up before. The caffein tablets must have worked because suddenly I was wide awake.

"I just kept running down the road, trying to disassociate my mind from the pain in my body. Finally I saw the finish line and sprinted across it. The last thing I remember was people applauding."

"The thing you have to remember," he says, "is that I'm doing all of this for fun. Of course, the only thing I like better than running is wrestling on the sofa with my wife."

But Huckaby's life wasn't always thus. In 1972, he was a chubby 225-pounder, stuck to his desk as a Griffiss Air Force Base electronics engineer in Rome, N.Y. He even hated to walk.

One day at work, Huckaby took a heart and blood pressure screening administered by the Rome Heart Association. The cardiogram revealed that he had fibrilation of the heart and that there was danger of a fatal attack. His doctors told him to get used to the thought of dying.

A friend at work suggested he start dieting and take short daily walks for exercise. He slowly lost weight — 85 pounds worth — and his six-month life expectancy turned into two years.

"During one of my walks," he says, "I got caught in a rainstorm. I ran about 100 yards to shelter before I realized what I'd done. Since I was still alive I ran again the next day. The third day I ran a little farther and just kept increasing my distance from then on."

Huckaby joined a local YMCA jogging club, The Roman Runners, and began running eight miles a day during his lunch hour at work and several more in the evenings.

He worked his way up from three mile "races" to the marathon contests, always concentrating more on edurance than speed records. The Nautilus Triathlon was the 35th marathon he's completed in the last two and a half years.

"This race," he explains, "was harder than all the rest because it included swimming and bicycling events. Until last July, I didn't even know how to swim a stroke."

After finishing his swim, Huckaby took a fast shower, changed into warm clothes and climbed aboard a new Peugeot (his Triathlon sponsor) bicycle. He had participated in one previous bicycle race but had never worn toe-clips on the pedals before.

"Somebody gave me a quick explanation on how to work those rat traps," he explains, "but I never got my coordination down. You release them by reaching down and flicking a buckle. The bike always fell over, though, before I got my feet out."

Huckaby had three major spills during the 112-mile bicycle race and has the scrapes and bruises to prove it. Once, on Kamehemeha Highway, a car stopped unexpectedly in front of him and he swerved toward the shoulder of the road. The bike slipped on the loose dirt, hit a guardrail, and sailed over the top. He landed in a 15-foot gravel ditch.

Later, near Haleiwa, his brakes stuck and he slid down a cement embankment on his left thigh. When the bystanders lifted up the bike his feet were still caught in the toe-clips.

"I finished the bicycle race at about 10 in the evening," he says, "and somebody at the Aloha Tower massaged my legs for an hour. I put on my jogging clothes and took off on the regular Honolulu Marathon course to Kapiolani Park."

He came in last but eight of the 103 younger starters were forced to drop out of the race.

WOMEN IN THE TRIATHLON

Eve Anderson

"The turtle is my special friend, I figure 'slow but sure' we're gonna get there. 'I'm at my best swimming," said 42-year-old Anderson, a 10-handicap golfer, who plays tennis, swims to Rabbit Island, bikes and runs for miles at the drop of a starter's flag, "but bicycling should be the most fun.

"I didn't begin any serious training for the Triathlon until I recovered from my Alaskan hike (Anderson climbed a couple mountains and then skied 150 miles across several glaciers) last summer. It seems that whenever I tackle something like this I'm always late in starting my training," she sighed.

Anderson's Triathlon training is not very consistent or regimented.

"There were days that I would mix all three activities, plus, play a round of golf, or a few sets of tennis," the Punahou School and Mills College graduate explained. "With so many outdoor activities, I feel that I've been training all of my life. To toughen my leg muscles, I'm even climbing and trimming our 100 coconut trees."

Nancy Kummens

"I've always been athletically inclined, but never gone after it," she said. "I always felt there was something missing. Last year I ran the marathon and it seemed like no big thing for me. Then I saw the triathalon and thought 'go for it' just for the challenge."

Like many others, Kummens was impressed by last year's entrants. "When I saw those people running the last several yards before Diamond Head, it hit me like a bomb and I wanted to do it."

Triathalons consume a lot in terms of time. Best on a bicycle, Kummens trains anywhere from six to eight hours each day.

"I guess I should take a day off now and then, I do push myself hard," she said. "But that's just the way I've been ever since I started training last January. I have a hard time resting."

This inhibits her social life a lot. "I don't socialize that much and I don't go out in the evenings," she said. "I'm in bed early and get up early, 4:30 a.m., and on the road either riding or running by at least 5:30." A training dairy serves as her constant companion along with running shoes, bicycle and bathing suit.

Occasionally fatigue hits in the form of depression but the side benefits are she's lost 15 pounds and she has determined a goal for the future.

"I had visions of myself doing this and then saying 'now what am I going to do?' Why not use the triathalon in a positive way? So afterwards I'd like to get back into teaching exercises. I'm taking lifesaving now and multi-media first aid. I'll study for my water safety instructors test and I'd like to teach swimming to handicapped people or children," she said.

"Some people think I'm kinda nuts, but I have a few really close friends who've been very supportive. My family thinks I'm running from reality but I like to think I'm doing it because I want to. How do I dream of doing. I think I'll do well."

 ## Hawaii 1981: Making It Look Easy

Sally Edwards

Sally Edwards . . . an athlete, par excellence and at the same time a business woman and author/publisher was far ahead of sports writers with her publication of "Triathlon — A Triple Fitness Sport," followed by "Fleet Feet Training Log for Runners, Swimmers, Cyclists, Triathletes." Sally and her friend Lyn Brooks together finished 95th overall in the 1982 Ironman, and tied for third in the womens division, much to the amazement of the timing officials.

Imagine yourself a slim 33 year-old woman standing on the Kailua-Kona beach among heavily muscled women and men who tower in height and flex with prowess, each clad only in a swatch of spandex nylon. The dim light of early morning barely illuminates a boat with orange sails more than a mile offshore. You are about to swim to that boat and back, attempting the first leg of Hawaii's 1981 Iron Man World Triathlon. A T.V. crew is taking in the scene, as the announcer gives final instructions. Your muscles quiver as you anticipate the day ahead. The race is about to begin.

Sally is co-owner of the Fleet Feet sports store and franchise operation, fitness is her business. As a woman, she feels athletic activity is part of her liberation. Sally's personal and professional interests are entwined in a lifestyle that makes the running trail her office and her office a place to savor life.

For three years she had anticipated that morning in Hawaii. The path to that sandy beach began with a simple interest in sports which eventually developed into a passion — obsession, some would say. Graduate school at Berkeley in physical education gave her an academic foundation in fitness with a master's thesis appropriately written on the causes of muscle fatigue. Then came Ken Cooper with his aerobic revolution of the late 1960's and she was off and running. Eventually she entered a road race. She did well and discovered she liked the competition; she liked to win.

The races became more frequent and longer. First, 7 miles then 10, 20, and the 26.2 mile marathon. Next, a 50-miler, the 75, and then Western States 100 Mile Endurance Run. Next came the Levi Ride-and-Tie with another sportswoman and a horse soon after that her first triathlon. She met both success and failure in these contests, enticed ever onward by her need to progress, to meet each new challenge, to build with each effort a foundation for confronting the next one. She acquired a unique kind of self-understanding which is constructed from both triumph and disappointment.

That morning standing on the Pacific beach she found herself reciting some of the hard-earned principles ingrained by these previous competitions: don't feel intimidated by the starting field; don't wander into the deadly rip-tide of reasons to fail — "Why didn't I prepare more," and "They look in better shape," and "I should have lost more body fat." She switched off doubt and changed her focus to admiring the physiques of men and women confident they could power themselves through the choppy ocean for 2.4 miles, then pedal for 112 miles in muggy heat and then run a 26.2 mile marathon to the third and last finish line.

Never before had she tried to do what she would attempt today. Her swimming career had consisted of no more than laps in the YMCA pool, yet here was the ocean — deep, salty, rough, without lanes and full of creatures. A predictable nervousness caused her to shiver despite the tropical warmth. Can one prepare fully for the unfamiliar? Was her anxiety shared by her tanned and muscled competitors?

The start was minutes away. Some of the men strode confidently into the ocean and swam to the starting line where they tred water while awaiting signal blast from the starting cannon. A power boat full of film crews and celebrities took position as the countdown continued. The sun had just risen.

141 Miles To Go

She knew that anything could go wrong in the 141 miles ahead. Many little mistakes, glitches, and fateful intrusions might crop up along the way. The tropical sun was a potential problem, shining all day on a skin paled by Sacramento's fog. For the swim, her strategy had been to apply zinc oxide to the back of her knees, the most exposed part of the body during the first event; that done, the slick residue on her fingers caused the strap on her swim goggles to slip through its buckles. Frantically, with only seconds to the start, she approached the head of the swim race who loaned her another set of goggles. This time she carefully avoided smearing them with the grease on her hands.

The cannon boomed, the race was on. Quickly hugging her closest friend, business partner and sister triathlete, Elizabeth Jansen, they both walked into the water together. The hard chargers were already in motion, arms flying, water splashing. They looked like a school of sardines, its wake widening as more entered the ocean, three hundred-fifty in all.

She tried to keep up with Elizabeth, but her friend was the more powerful swimmer and a tenacious competitor. Elizabeth pulled away. No shortage of other bodies in the crowded water, with the fast ones swimming over the backs of the slow, the slow ones flutter kicking in the faces of the fast. Sally's new goggles did not fit well, and she had to stop frequently and tread water as she adjusted them, each time smearing the lenses with more grease. Her target, the boat with two orange sails, became but a colorful blur.

A succession of outrigger canoes spaced 500 yards apart defined the path of the swim. Aboard the canoes were volunteer lifeguards with surf boards, ready to haul in swimmers in difficulty. A large white fishing boat marked the half-way point. She would pass it twice . . . once on the way out and once on the way back into shore. At the end of the string of canoes loomed the large glass-bottomed tourist boat with orange sails.

One Half Way Point

She felt relieved when she reached the turnaround. The boat was crammed with spectators and photographers yelling encouragement to swimmers who could hear only garble and splash. Next to her, a swimmer did not complete the turn around the boat and headed out toward the open sea. Another reminder of a hard-won lesson, she thought: Do not follow those in front; follow your own inclinations. She circled the boat, and began to swim with the canoes again to her right, holding close to the line defining the shortest distance between the two most important points of the moment — her body and the shore.

Past the halfway mark, the weight of doubt sloughed off into the salty water. Accomplishment of this goal was certain; now maybe she could pick up the pace. Breathing harder, feeling pain high across her shoulders, concentrating on her strict mental discipline, she began to stroke faster and moved up through the field. Then in the distance she saw through her smeared goggles a few contestants walking up the boat ramp. The finish was imminent.

Time for a "here-and-now" check of all systems. She asked her body how it was doing. The different systems answered one at a time. Feet and legs? Not working hard yet. Arms? Tired but sturdy enough to hold onto handlebars. Eyes? Unaffected by salt water. The goggles were working. Kinesthetics? All motions smoothly in cadence, muscles working with, not against, each other. Endurance? Pace strong, fires burning steadily, no sign of fatigue. Just keep moving in good form and you'll get there.

She completed the initial leg of the Hawaii "gruelathon." Quite a contrast to her first triathlon in Lodi, California, three years earlier. Then, the events had been much shorter and in different sequence. The footrace had been first, a mere three miles, followed by a seven-mile bicycle race and then a swim through a swampy frog pond the Lodi locals called a lake. She had led the run and been the first woman off her bicycle. but though she had begun the two-thirds of a mile swim with a five minute lead, she had ended up the fifth female finisher. Each sweep of her stroke had reaped a harvest of pond lilies. She did not like swimming through a swamp. But she liked finishing fifth even less.

Remembering that Lodi triathlon, she prepared to stagger up the boat ramp as her sense of balance re-adjusted to land, her inner ear heard and balanced those wobbly legs. As she pulled herself out of the water and regained her dry land footing, she broke into a trot. In fresh water showers she joined those same muscled bodies she had so admired an hour and twenty-eight minutes earlier. She, as well as they, had just swum 2.4 miles through the Pacific Ocean.

The shower was quick. No time for idle relaxation! The race was still on; the clock would not stop until the end. Briskly but carefully she washed the sand and salt out of her hair. If any salt remained, she might sweat it into her eyes later. As she left the shower, a volunteer passed her the blue bag printed with the large number 104, the same number scrawled in felt pen on her shoulders for identification during the swim. Everything read 104 that day, it seemed, even the temperature.

Dressing quickly, she swigged a cup of water and grabbed two bananas before sighting bicycle 104 racked in space 104. Hers was easy to find since most of the 350 racks were empty. The machine, a French LeJeune, was a beauty. She had borrowed it from a friend in lieu of purchasing her own for $1,000 or more. The frame was 25" for its 6'3" owner. She did not know about the disadvantages of having the wrong bike size. She did know that it was light, fast, and red.

The crowd had kept up its enthusiasm. The first cyclists had raced away forty minutes earlier, but their claps and vells resounded strongly in her heart and made her feel like a winner as she set off. She looked at her watch. It read 1 hour 27 minutes.

The second race was underway; she knew that, with luck, it would be long into the hot afternoon before she would dismount. There were seven women in front of her — Shawn Wilson, a fellow Sacramentan, was in the lead. This was to be expected since Shawn was a swimmer. But her strongest event was over.

Hawaii Is Heating Up

At first the morning was cool, a beautiful time for a leisurely bike ride through town. This course though stretched far out from Kona along a black asphalt highway laid atop a bleak black lava flow. The blackness of road and stone gradually absorbed the sun's heat and soon the landscape shimmered. She felt like a little pat of butter in an immense black cast-iron frying pan. She was not fully confident on a bike. She had never participated in a bicycle race and knew little about repairs or maintenance, technique, or training. Yet she was able to shake her doubts. Here-and-now is all that matters, she told herself. No gain from wallowing in excuses to fail.

No pit crews were allowed, since self-reliance was an essential part of this triathlon mystique. Contestants had to be responsible for their own food, equipment and repairs. She had tucked two extra sew-up tires under the bicycle saddle and had learned the week before how to change a flat. Fortunately her new knowledge never had to be tested. Her friend Elizabeth, with tougher high-pressure clinchers, had all the tire problems — two flats at mile 65 on the black asphalt highway in the black lava desert in 100 + degree heat. It was a stroke of bad luck, but the determined Elizabeth had by no means finished playing out her hand.

It was noon as she reached the turn-around point in the small town of Hawi. Spectators and aid station volunteers cared for the contestantas. Here all competitors had to stop for a mandatory weight check. Sally dismounted her red Lejeune and ate yet another banana. Someone announced that she had gained two pounds. She knew the scales were not accurate as the effects of lost body fluids should have been a weight loss not gain. At the weigh station was a selection of foods: bananas, oranges and donuts. Oranges are too high in acid for easy digestion and deep-fried donuts are high in fat, a poor food source for high performance. She would have preferred her special diet of baby food or a sandwich. So, for hours she ate only bananas, all day and into the night. Boring, bland bananas.

She passed four women riders during the arduous trip. Her spirits were high as she rode through the afternoon passing landscape of black lava fields with waves of heat bouncing off them. The constant exposure to the sun took its toll: dehydration. As John Howard, the first place man, was beginning the marathon race along the same road, she was fourteen miles out and still pedalling. He was wearing a bicycle cap and was shining shirtless in the sunlight from the water he poured over his body.

Her only thought at the end of the bike leg was to get it over with. Her rear felt like the bicycle seat had been shoved inside. Her shoulders were ached from the inaccustomed tension of hoisting her head up for seven hours. Her quadriceps prime bicycle muscles sputtered spastically. She was just plain tired. The pain subsided when she concentrated on it, a technique learned from Shiatsu therapy for years of sciatic nerve problems in her hips. Only one steep but short hill before entering the parking lot of the Kona Surf Resort Hotel, one long grind in the lowest gear to the crest, then a coast down the hill. One hundred and twelve miles finished in 6 hours and 58 minutes.

The bicycle race, the longest segment of the Hawaii Triathlon in both time and distance, was over. The first male finisher, John Howard, had been a Pan American gold medal winner in cycling. He completed the course in five hours and three minutes. The fastest woman in six hours and thirty-five minutes, was Shawn Wilson. Shawn's speed was holding out.

At the finish, there were no flags or lines to cross. The 112 mile bike race simply petered out in a parking lot by the tennis courts. Her mother and friends were there applauding. After seven hours in a fixed position, the muscles always pulling in a fixed way, her bottom fixed to the seat, she dismounted. As she waddled to the scales to be weighed again, she knew her bicycle seat would be a companion for life. No point in eating any more disgusting bananas — she was plugged up at the other end for good.

Race rules state that a contestant must be within 10 percent of starting weight at each weigh station. Sally started at 124 pounds and finished at 120 pounds. A tough way to stay trim. Someone handed her plastic bag number 104. This one held her running clothes. A woman volunteer accompanied her to the dressing room. She told the volunteer she was rather in a rush, lacked modesty, and would appreciate help in stripping and dressing. The volunteer even laced up her NIKE racing shoes as Sally stuffed down another unacceptable banana.

26.2 Miles to Go

She strode out of the parking lot to start the 26.2 mile marathon at 3 o'clock. She knew there were three women in front of her. But running was her forte. Within a mile she passed the third place woman and advanced with gusto upon second place. To her surprise, that second place person was Shawn from Sacramento and she was walking. Shawn had never run a marathon before. The two walked and chatted. The encounter was a good excuse to rest at a walking pace; Sally was already deep into her reserve tank, glycogen low.

After a few minutes, Sally broke into a slow run leaving Shawn behind. The landscape rolled by, almost unseen. Moving more slowly than on her bicycle, she noticed the heat more. It seemed to rise from the hot pavement, through her feet and into her upperbody.

Her legs were shot, no more strength. The bicycle race was claiming its toll. The hours of fast, constant pedaling and running had drained her energy dry. The legs said walk; the will said run. She compromised by alternating mile runs with one-minute walks. The compromise worked; her stomach improved. Near mile six, she began to have a sharp abdominal pain that jarred with every step. It was a dry heave kind of pain. Her stomach was on the verge of rebellion. Probably bananas and bicycle seats. She passed the halfway point of the run at about 5 p.m. Thirteen miles still lay ahead but there was still a woman ahead. Linda Sweeney was from Tucson, Arizona, a 22 year old marathoner with a personal record at that distance two minutes faster than Sally's own best mark of 2:53. Linda had been thirty minutes ahead at the end of the swim. Halfway through the marathon, still the same.

As the sun started to set, Sally reached the last "weigh-in" station. Her weight was stable now at 121 lbs. The changes in the light from hot afternoon brightness to the reddening sky towards the inevitable night would take their toll as the feet were slowing with the sinking sun. She learned that the woman ahead had not faltered her pace. There was nothing left that Sally could utilize to pick up the pace.

Monkeys of Fatigue on Her Back

Her spirits deteriorated as that monkey, fatigue, was on her back. The marathon, her specialty, was now her worst event because it was last. Darkness added to her gloom making her feel alone, isolated. It was night time now and with two miles left to the finish her mind was asking the same question a thousand times over — "Why are you doing this to yourself? You can stop, you know." At that point she knew she would have to reach inside, deep down inside, and grab those extra calories of courage necessary to endure. It is a long reach and it comes close to touching the soul. In this moment of crisis, some crack; others find that no matter how hard the struggle, they can continue to the end. At the 25-mile marker she knew she could finish the race. The last mile would be her personal victory lap. She would finish her first ultra-distance triathlon, the ultimate test of all-around fitness. No matter the place

She remembered the scene at the pier where the race had begun in the early morning. Now it was dark, the thick dark of a Hawaiian night. She was wearing an orange reflective bib to keep her visible to passing motorists on that long, lonely black highway. Suddenly, she entered a gauntlet of cheering spectators. They lined the street approaching the pier where the marathon would finish. "Second woman," they were yelling. She remembered one of her rules: a trick in her bag. No matter how tired or how sore, no matter the terrible shape of your feet and bottom (the bicycle seat would finish with her), you try to make it look easy. The spectators are there not only to encourage you, but they are also curious to see the faces of the dying. As an experienced gladiator in the arena of endurance sports, she knew she must make the ordeal look effortless, as if she had just begun. a smile spread across her face, a real smile happy with the feeling of the finisher. Her spine straightened, her pace quickened, her feet skipped over the pavement. The crowd was applauding. A thousand candlewatts of light showered down from a tower as the T.V. crew captured the glory of her triumph. The clock stopped—a moment to last a lifetime. A mental picture clicked 12:33:15. She crossed the finish line at 8:30 p.m. with a marathon split time of 4 hours and 10 minutes.

the finish line at 8:30 p.m. with a marathon split time of 4 hours and 10 minutes.

Two women placed a flower lei around her neck, kissed her in congratulation, and led her to a grassy area where she could sit. She had wondered during each leg of the race how it would feel to finally stop and sit. And now she knew what only another 141 mile triathlon finisher could know. The last event was now over, and she could rest. Masseuses were working on several prone triathletes, and waited her turn. When the volunteer masseuse asked where the pain was, she could have read off the index to Gray's Anatomy.

Her next concern was Elizabeth. The race was not over until it was over for them both. Her friend, though she had lost much time on her luckless bicycle ride, had vowed to continue on through the marathon. She hiked those 26.2 miles in seven hours and fifty-two minutes. Elizabeth finished 18 hours and 43 minutes after the triathlon had begun. The crowd was gone, the film crew was home in bed, the masseuses had left long before, the flower leis had all been distributed. But the clock and the finish banner were there. Elizabeth, too, remembered the trick in the bag: she stood up straight, her feet started running, the smile spread across her face. She made it look real easy, but I knew better.

Robin Beck

Robin Beck, 30, from Salt Lake City Utah, was the first woman to finish the 1980 Triathlon, with a time of 11 hours, 21 minutes. She was entering "just for the fun of it because it's an endurance event," she said. "Having them all together makes it more convenient and I'm interested in seeing how much I can endure."

Beck, a former downhill skier and bicycle racer, feels that the bike leg and the footrace won't give her as much trouble as the swim.

"I know pretty much how to train for the bike event and the run (Beck's fastest marathon time is three hours and four minutes)," said the 120-pound athlete, "but the swim training leaves me puzzled. To be on the safe side, I swam laps — three miles, three times a week — in a small pool. That sure takes a lot of lap-counting."

Beck's weekly training included running 80 miles; biking 225 miles, and swimming nine to 10 miles.

Kathlene McCartney

This 'Ironman' has an unusual name: Kathleen. If you watched the finals of the women's "Ironman" triathlon competition from Hawaii last winter on ABC's *Wide world of Sports,* you'll recall the dramatic conclusion.

Fifteen yards from the finish, leader Julie Mos collapsed.

As Moss, tears streaking down her face, crawled toward the finish line, another competitor, unshaken by a day of ocean swimming (2.4 miles), bicycling (112 miles) and running (26.2 miles), made her way around the group encouraging Moss and was the first woman to finish.

That was Kathleen McCartney, 23, of Newport Beach. She had trailed Moss throughout until those final 15 yards.

Coupled with that triumph in Hawaii, and more recently one in San Diego, McCartney now is regarded as the No. 1 triathlete in the country.

"This is a sport, just like anything else," McCartney says. "It's a real challenge and people like being in shape."

While the "Ironman" competition lures the best athletes in the world, the shorter distances of the triathlon series appeals to many others.

"People can compete for three or four hours and they can relate to that," McCartney says. "Not everybody can do an 'Ironman' competition."

McCartney says her ultimate goal is to win the Hawaii "Ironman" competition again.

"These triathlons are good preparation for it," she says.

With weekends "completely booked" until the next "Ironman" competition in October, McCartney said she isn't worried about burning out. "In the long run, I think this much training will do me good."

Kathlene McCartney, Women's division leader of the Ironman in 1982.

Photo Credit: Carol Hogan

The Dolphin Swimming Club, on the shores of San Francisco Bay, Jack LaLanne has just completed his Alcatraz Swim and posed with friend Patricia Bragg.

Dr. Paul Bragg congratulates Jack LaLanne for his San Francisco Bay swim at Jack's 60th birthday party.

1982 Iron Boar In Training
Pig at bay in the Bay or Triathlete meets new obstacle.

By PEGGY McCAMANT
West Hawaii Today Staff Writer

Triathlon competitors have to contend with a lot. Long hours of practice, a strict training regimen, aching muscles, sore feet, hot sun, wild pig attacks in Kailua Bay . . .

Pig attacks?

While not in the normal realm of competition, one triathlete did add this experience to his list of rigors. Richard Carlson of Las Vegas was practising for the open-water swim in Kailua Bay, accompanied by his brother Jack, a Kona resident, Jack, on a surfboard, was swimming alongside his brother when suddenly, he said, something bit his swim fin. The "something" was a very large black pig.

Jack struck the pig with the board to keep it away from him, he said, "then the pig went for Richard." The animal was biting at the board, both brothers said, and then tried toclimb up on top of Richard to get out of the water.

After getting the pig, literally, off their backs with the surfboard and by waving their arms, the pig turned and headed for shore.

One man in a kayak, hailed by Richard's son Mike who had witnessed the commotion and thought his father was drowning, paddled out to help. He herded the pig away from other swimmers and in toward the rocks at the base of the seawall.

No one knows where the pig came from. It was first spotted, reports say, swimming straight into the bay from the open ocean. Local Hawaiians claimed it, and within minutes it was prepared for a Hawaiian style Imu, or roasting pit, a portion reserved for Pig PuPus— Hawaiian appetizers and served on the Kailua Pier to training triathletes. It is only fair to report that the Iron Boar was a lady.

Ironman World Triathlon Event Times— Hawaii— 1978

2.4 Mile Rough Water Swim
1. John Dunbar, 60.15
2. Ian Emberson, 62.30
3. Harold Irving, 65.30
4. Ralph Yawane, 69.15
5. Gordon Haller, 80.40
6. John Collins, 82.35
7. Ron Henrisckson, 95.35
8. Henry Forrest, 96.42
9. Frank Day, 1:04.20
10. John King, 1:22.20

112-Mile Bicycle Race
1. Dunbar, 7:04
2. (tie) Lewis and Dunbar, 7:47
3. Happai, 8:06
4. Knoll, 8:19
5. Day, 8:45.9
6. Forrest, 9:10.11
7. Collins, 9:15
8. Irving, 11:04
9. King, 11:13

Top Finishers

1. Dunbar, 12:20:27
2. Orlowski, 13:59:13
3. Day, 14:04:35
4. Knoll, 14:45:11.7
5. Forrest, 15:30:14

Ironman World Triathlon Event Times— 1979

Overall Finish
1. Tom Warren, 11:15:56
2. John Dunbar, 12:03.56
3. Ian Emberson, 12:23.30
4. Gordon Haller, 12:31.53
5. Lyn Lemaire, 12:55.39
6. Ron Seipie, 13:43.7
7. Henry Forrest, 14:55.08
8. Cowman Shirk, 16:41.02.9
9. (tie) Jim Well, Buck Swannick
   and Jay Cassell, 21:45.12
12. Mike Collins, 24:25.58

Swimming
1. Emberson, 1:02.35
2. Warren, 1:06.15
3. Dunbar, 1:09.55
4. Lemaire, 1:16
5. Haller, 1:51.59
6. Seiple, 1:58.47
7. Forrest, 2:09.49
8. Shirk, 2:27.35

Bicycling
1. Warren, 6:19
2. Lemaire, 6:30
3. Seiple, 6:47
4. Dunbar, 6:51.5
5. Emberkson, 6:53
6. Haller, 6:57
7. Forrest, 8:12
8. Shirk, 8:53

Distance Running
1. Haller, 3:43.2
2. Warren, 3:51
3. Dunbar, 4:03
4. Emberson, 4:28
5. Forrest, 8:12
6. Seiple, 4:57.7
7. Lemaire, 5:10.8
8. Shirk, 5:20

Ironman World Triathlon Event Times—Kona, Hawaii 1981

Top 10 Finishers

PLACE	NAME	SWIM	BIKE	RUN	TOTAL
1	John Howard	1:11	5:03	3:23	9:38
2	Tom Warren	:59	5:37	3:27	10:04
3	Scott Tinley	1:05	5:47	3:19	10:12
4	Thomas Boughey	:56	5:57	3:30	10:23
5	Dennis Hansen	1:03	6:01	3:21	10:26
6	Dante Dettamanti	1:01	5:36	3:41	10:29
7	James Butterfield	1:27	5:58	3:05	10:31
8	Jonathan Durst	:58	5:33	4:02	10:34
9	Conrad Kress	1:02	5:49	3:46	10:38
10	Ronald Krueper	1:02	6:00	3:25	10:39

Top 10 Women Finishers

PLACE	NAME	SWIM	BIKE	RUN	TOTAL
1	Linda Sweeney	1:02	6:53	4:04	12:00
2	Sally Edwards	1:28	6:58	4:10	12:37
3	Carolyn Brooks	1:20	7:13	4:08	12:42
4	Cynthia Marks	1:11	7:33	4:16	13:00
5	Kika Walker	1:08	7:21	5:03	13:33
6	Nancy Kummen	1:51	6:26	5:16	13:34
7	Georgia Gatch	1:05	7:23	5:51	14:21
8	Carol LaPlant	1:45	7:43	4:54	14:24
9	Christa Obara	2:10	7:48	4:44	14:44
10	Patricia Specht	1:57	7:41	5:11	14:50

Ironman World Triathlon Event Times—Kona, Hawaii February 6, 1982
Top 10 Finishers

PLACE	NAME	SWIM	BIKE	RUN	TOTAL
1	Scott Tinley	1:11	5: 5	3: 3	9:19
2	Dave Scott	0:58	5:17	3:21	9:36
3	Jeff Tinley	1:13	5:28	3:12	9:53
4	Mark Sisson	1:18	5:21	3:18	9:57
5	Reed Gregerson	1: 5	5:32	3:25	10: 2
6	Jeff Jones	1: 3	5:33	3:34	10:10
7	Greg Reddan	1: 4	5:53	3:16	10:13
8	Kim Bushong	0:58	5: 8	4: 9	10:15
9	Thomas C. Boughey	1: 2	5:40	3:35	10:17
10	Tom Warren	1: 4	5:26	3:48	10:18

Top 10 Women Finishers

PLACE	NAME	SWIM	BIKE	RUN	TOTAL
1	Kathleen McCartney	1:32	5:51	3:46	11: 9
2	Julie D. Moss	1:11	5:54	4: 5	11:10
3	Lyn Brooks	1:20	6:38	3:53	11:51
4	Sally Edwards	1:37	6:30	3:44	11:51
5	Cheryl Lloyd	1:23	6: 2	4:32	11:57
6	Claire McCarty	1:20	6:21	4:16	11:57
7	Cherry Stockton	1:44	6: 7	4: 9	12: 0
8	Eva Oberth	1:20	6:27	4:26	12:13
9	Darlene Ann Drumm	1:15	6:32	4:32	12:19
10	Shawn Wilson	1: 1	6:26	4:58	12:25

Ironman World Triathlon Event Times—Kona, Hawaii 1983
Top 10 Finishers

PLACE	NAME	SWIM	BIKE	RUN	TOTAL
1	Dave Scott	:50	5:10	3:04	9:05
2	Scott Tinley	:57	5:03	3:05	9:06
3	Mark Allen	:52	5:13	3:15	9:21
4	Marc Thompson	1:01	5:20	3:26	9:49
5	Robert Roller	:53	5:32	3:30	9:56
6	Mark MacIntyre	1:03	5:52	3:00	9:57
7	Bob Curtis	1:00	5:23	3:38	10:01
8	Thomas Boughey	:50	5:36	3:34	10:01
9	Mac Martin	:59	5:25	3:39	10:04
10	Kurt Madden	:57	5:43	3:23	10:05

Top 10 Women Finishers

PLACE	NAME	SWIM	BIKE	RUN	TOTAL
1	Sylviane Puntous	1:00	6:20	3:22	10:43
2	Patricia Puntous	1:00	6:26	3:22	10:49
3	Eva Ueltzen	1:02	6:05	3:53	11:01
4	Kathie Rivers	1:05	6:12	3:52	11:10
5	Sally Edwards	1:17	6:29	3:20	11:16
6	Jann Girard	:53	6:37	3:49	11:20
7	Annie Dandoy	1:12	6:15	3:53	11:22
8	Eaine Alrutz	1:05	6:20	4:00	11:25
9	Sue Kinsey	1:03	6:20	4:01	11:25
10	Jenny La Mott	:55	6:19	4:13	11:29

Top 10 Finishers

PLACE	NAME	SWIM	BIKE	RUN	TOTAL
1	Dave Scott	:50	5:10	2:53	8:54
2	Scott Tinley	:55	5:18	3:03	9:18
3	Grant Boswell	:53	5:15	3:15	9:23
4	Rob Barel	:53	5:10	3:23	9:27
5	Mark Allen	:50	4:59	3:45	9:35
6	John Howard	1:07	4:56	3:33	9:38
7	David Evans	:59	5:21	3:23	9:43
8	Chris Hinshaw	:48	5:20	3:39	9:48
9	Steve Sine	1:03	5:39	3:14	9:56
10	Scott Skultety	:58	5:33	3:26	9:59

Top 10 Women Finishers

PLACE	NAME	SWIM	BIKE	RUN	TOTAL
1	Sylviane Puntous	1:00	5:50	3:33	10:25
2	Patricia Puntous	1:00	5:50	3:36	10:27
3	Julie Olson	1:00	5:37	3:59	10:38
4	Joanne Ernst	1:04	5:49	3:46	10:40
5	Moira Hornby	1:05	6:12	3:44	11:03
6	Jennifer Hinshaw	:50	5:58	4:15	11:05
7	Juliana Harrisonbrening	1:00	5:54	4:10	11:06
8	Karen McKeachie	1:09	6:10	3:48	11:07
9	Jacqueline Shaw	1:03	5:41	4:27	11:12
10	Anne Dandoy	1:10	6:08	4:02	11:21

Bibliography

History of the Triathlon Bibliography   *West Hawaii Today Newspaper*, Kailua Kona, Hawaii
Triathlon The Triple Fitness Sport, Sally Edwards, Fleet Feet Press, 1982, 2410 J St., Sacramento, Ca. 95816
Honolulu's Newspaper Syndicate, Honolulu Advertiser, Honolulu Star Bulletin, Kapiolani Blvd., Honolulu Hi
Santa Barbara News Press, Santa Barbara Ca.   *Sports Illustrated*, March, 1979 issue

Joanne Ernst, top woman triathlete from Palo Alto, California . . . finished 4th (10:40:32) in the womens' division of the Oct., 1984 Ironman Triathlon in Kona, Hawaii.

Photo by Mike Plant

2

The Future of the Triathlon

The Triathlon History

In February, 1977, Navy Captain John Collins was sitting around with several of his very fit friends having an argument about who was the fittest: the cyclist, the runner, or the swimmer. One beer led to another. Before long someone suggested the best way to settle the question would be to combine the Waikiki Rough Water Swim (2.4 miles) with the Around the Island of Oahu 112-mile bike, and then run the 26.2 mile Honolulu marathon course.

"Everyone laughed," recalled Collins. But a year later, Collins and 14 of his friends competed in the first Ironman Triathlon. The next year, in 1979, some 100 or so crazies showed up in Hawaii. In 1980 it was 350. In February, 1982, about 590 triathletes took the challenge. In October of 1982, the number reached 850 . . . with over 400 applicants waiting. It's good reason to always get your application in early for any event you are considering — play it safe so you will not be left out by getting a letter saying, "Sorry, participant limit has been reached."

The original Ironman has captured the imagination of fit people everywhere. Mini triathlons and other endurance events, all patterned after the original, are popping up all over the country.

The Multi-Sport Future

Multi-sport events will very likely become more common in the future. Endurance athletics came into its own with the renaissance of the marathon in the late 1970's, and the multi-sport endurance contest is the next logical step. Already there is talk of an Olympic triathlon, and there is some public enthusiasm for a demonstration triathlon at the 1984 Olympics in Los Angeles.

Throughout the country, increasing numbers of runners are turning to multi-sport contests which combine running with one or more other sports. The most famous, and the first held of these events is the Ironman Triathlon in Kailua-Kona, Hawaii, which is comprised of a 2.4 mile ocean swim, 112 mile bicycle dash across a sizzling lava desert, and a 26.2 mile marathon. But the Ironman is only one of many types of events demanding multi-skills of varying intensity.

There are some social events such as the "Renaissance-Man Octathlon" — the sort of event where in one continuous exertion one (1) runs a footrace, (2) play a game of Monopoly, (3) skis a slalom course, (4) parses a Latin sentence, (5) swims the rapids, (6) speedreads the *Wall Street Journal,* (7) runs a steeplechase, and (8) solves a set of trigonometry problems.

But more related to the Ironman type of event is the Iowa Triathlon which matches the Ironman inch for inch. There is also the Warriors Path Triathlon in Kingsport, Tennessee, which is exactly half the distance of the standard Ironman race. These half-distance events, incidentally, are known among the devotees as "tinman" triathlons.

"Escape from Alcatraz" is another rigorous multi-sport event. This triathlon is a 1.4-mile swim in the 54-degree waters and tricky currents of the San Francisco Bay, followed by a stiff 15-mile bike race across the Golden Gate Bridge to Mill Valley, and capped off by running the 14.5-mile Double Dipsea. The Double Dipsea alone is quite a formidable race: 5000 vertical feet over the ridges of Mt. Tamalpais to Stinson Beach, then back up and back down to the finish line.

There are many more of these Multi-Sport events scattered throughout America. The monthly calendars of local track clubs now frequently boast biathlons and triathlons which are permutations of such endurance sports as bicycling, swimming, horseback riding, cross country skiing, canoeing, and kayaking, as well as running. On the national scale, the multi-sport contests have been appearing in the sports calendars in steadily larger numbers.

Ian Emberson placed 3rd overall in the 1979 Ironman. Lyn Lemaire, the first woman Triathlete, placed 5th overall.   **Photo Credit: Ian Emberson**

3

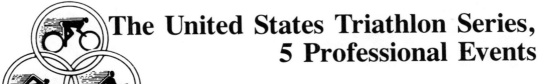

The United States Triathlon Series, 5 Professional Events

The United States Triathlon Series, 5 Professional Events

These professional triathlons have drawn a large contingent of contestants; solo participants for the most part with a few relay teams entered. San Diego, Los Angeles, and San Francisco were filled to capacity with nearly 1,000 contestants for each event. The Los Angeles Triathlon, held in the Marine Stadium area of the Long Beach Harbor, was the largest triathlon held to date with close to 1,100 participants.

Jim Curl, Director of the U.S. Triathlon Series, said there was full advance registration for the Portland and Seattle events. These professional triathlons have been well planned and administered by local volunteer staffs. Jim is enthusiastic about the future of the sport and USTS is planning for '85 in a big way with anywhere from 10 to 15 additional cities scheduled. Triathlons will commence in early spring in the south and work north as the season warms up. The present distances of 1.5Km swim, 40Km. bike, and a 10Km. run will remain the same according to Mr. Curl.

You may contact Jim Curl c/o USTS, Box 1438, Davis, CA 95617 for future USTS triathlon events in your area.

The Concept

The United States Triathlon Series (USTS) was the brainchild of Carl Thomas, former All-American swimmer and water polo player at UCLA who is now vice president of marketing for Speedo International Ltd., the U.S. division of the world's leading manufacturer of competitive swimwear, and of Jim Curl of Endurance Sports Productions in Davis, California, who organized the series around Thomas' original concept.

Also you may contact Carl Thomas, now President of Federation International Triathlon (FIT), 101 First Street, Los Altos, CA 94022. Triathlons...are heading for the Olympics - when we get there, they will be the most popular!!!

"We feel the triathlon, at our distances and format, creates an interesting challenge to individuals who are more committed to fitness than the weekend athlete," said Thomas.

Planning began late in 1981 with the confirmation of co-sponsors Nautilus Sports/Medical Industries and Mizuno running shoes. Meetings were held with top triathletes such as Scott Tinley, Dave Scott and Sally Edwards to determine the distances for the USTS. Then, under Curl's and Thomas' direction, sites were set in each city, volunteer groups contacted and a million and one details were ironed out.

"This has been a classic case of a dream coming together through the efforts of a great number of people who believe in triathlons," said Thomas.

The Beginning

The USTS is the first city-to-city triathlon series in the country. Thomas believes the prospects are excellent for expanding the series next year from five cities to as many as 20 across the United States, with regional winners competing for a USTS National Champion title.

Splashing into 54 degree Pacific Ocean water for the 2,000 meter swim.

Ground Zero, for all of the Ironman Triathlon action. This apex of Alli Drive and Kona Bay is the start finish of the Swim, the start of the Bike course and the finish of the Marathon and the Triathlon.

Running Is Still The Basic Triathlon Sport

None of this multi-sport activity will supplant running as a major participation sport. For one thing, most amateur athletes lack the time for serious training in more than one sport. Running will always be a highly efficient way for people, whose time is precious, to stay in condition. Few activities burn as many calories per minute as running. Thus, the overall health benefits of running are excelled by few, if any, other sports.

For another thing, the running event seems to be a fixed feature of most multi-sport contests. There will always be running specialists who will tear up the course at a 10K or marathon. However, in the future many runners are going to branch out into other sports that they can pursue for variety or to compensate for periods when they suffer from a running injury. (One can often bicycle or swim when pain and doctor's orders prevent running.) If one already practices those other sports, it will be natural to combine them with running in a triathlon or biathlon.

The Triathlon and the Olympics

Consideration is being given at this early date to establish the triathlon as an Olympic competitive sport by proposing an exhibition triathlon at the 1984 Los Angeles Olympic games. At this point, the interest in triathlon as an international competitive sport is intense, spearheaded by the Ironman World Triathlon Championships in Kona, Hawaii each year.

A.B.C.'s "Wide World of Sports" coverage of this event has given international exposure to the triathlon as a competitive sport. To date, Health Science Publishing has received orders for the Triathlon Training Manual from all foreign countries including Saudi Arabia, South Africa, most European countries, South and Central America, Canada, Australia, New Zealand, etc. . . . Video cassettes are available in most European countries of the past Ironman World Triathlon Championships.

The Ironman Original World Triathlon Championship . . .
Late Fall Date More Perfect For Triathletes

The date change of the Ironman Triathlon to late fall gives training and competing triathletes full spring and summer training seasons to prepare adequately for this event. The mid-winter date previously used, although affording good weather in Hawaii at that time of the year, made it extremely difficult for training triathletes from colder climates to fill out their training times sufficiently due to the colder weather.

The Ironman Original World Triathlon has also oriented itself into the position, date wise, to qualify as the Triathlon World Championship event of the year being held at the end of the World Triathlon Season. The interest in this event has peaked with a full quota of entries and a waiting list of over 400 disappointed applications for October 9, 1982. The only limit to the number of contestants for the Kailua-Kona Triathlon event seems to be space. The staging area at the Kona Harbor dock seems to be the only limiting factor.

Volunteers for this event are tremendous not only in numbers but for enthusiasm. The support committee indicates that there are over 1,000 standby volunteers enthusiastically waiting to be chosen to do any menial task just for the privilege of being on the support team. For the participating triathlete in Kona, the welcome mat is out everywhere you go. Residents willingly "adopt" a triathlete and consider it an honor and an "in" status to have a triathlete reside in their home during the event.

Tourists (many not so physically fit) stand gaping on the sidewalks of Alii Drive as the endless display of muscular, trim and top conditioned Ironmen and Ironwomen stroll, bicycle and swim by. Nowhere on earth, at any given time, could you find this many finely tuned and conditioned physical specimens as in evidence at Kailua-Kona, Hawaii on Triathlon Week. The energy flows, the air is charged with electricity, and the casual spectator feels drained by the aura of it all! The triathlon as a multiple fitness endurance sport is excellent. The personal challenge to the competitor is there, the spectator interest is high and the future is limited only in the minds of men!

TOTAL HEALTH FOR THE TOTAL PERSON

In a broad sense, "Total Health for the Total Person" is a combination of physical, mental, emotional, social, and spiritual components. The ability of the individual to function effectively in his environment depends on how smoothly these components function as a whole. Of all the qualities that comprise an integrated personality, a well-developed, totally fit body is one of the most desirable.

A person may be said to be totally physically fit if they function as a total personality with efficiency and without pain or discomfort of any kind. That is to have a Painless, Tireless, Ageless body, possessing sufficient muscular strength and endurance to maintain an effective posture, successfully carries on the duties imposed by the environment, meets emergencies satisfactorily and has enough energy for recreation and social obligations after the "work day" has ended, meets the requirements for his environment through efficient functioning of his sense organs, possesses the resilience to recover rapidly from fatigue, tension, stress and strain without the aid of stimulants, and enjoys natural sleep at night and feels fit and alert in the morning for the job ahead.

Keeping the body totally fit and functional is no job for the uninformed or the careless person. It requires an understanding of the body, sound health and eating practices, and disciplined living. The results of such a regimen can be measured in happiness, radiant health, agelessness, peace of mind, in the joy of living and high achievement.

Our sincere blessings to you dear friends, who make our lives so worthwhile and fulfilled by reading our teachings on natural living as our Creator laid down for us all to follow . . . Yes—he wants us all to follow the simple path of natural living and this is what we teach in our books and health crusades world-wide. Our prayers reach out to you for the best in health and happiness for you and your loved ones. This is the birthright He gives us all . . . but we must follow the laws He has laid down for us, so we can reap this precious health, physically, mentally and spiritually!

Patricia Bragg

My dear friend, I pray that everything may go well with you, and that you may be in good health—as I know you are well in spirit.   3 John:2

Top left: Dave Scott leaving water during '80 Nautilus Ironman, Honolulu, Hawaii . . . Kemp Aaburg, Santa Barbara top swimmer, biker and sub 3 hour marathon runner seems in quandry about the whole thing . . . John Howard on finishing 3rd in the '80 Ironman Triathlon . . . Dave Scott biking around the island in '80 Ironman. Note his support vehicle piloted by his father following close by . . . Biker's legs belonging to Dale James on the right, top contender in the Oct./82 Ironman . . . Mr. Shimano himself, Feb./82 Ironman . . . Claire St. Arnaud's Lotus Super Pro Aerodynamic being checked over by Dave Bending at the Team Lotus Open Air Repair Shop . . . John Howard in transition from Bike to Run at the Aloha Tower, Honolulu. Shannon Sullivan is his support crew.

Photo Credit: Carol Hogan

TRIATHLONS - A FAMILY AFFAIR FOR TERRY AND DUNCAN THOMAS

Yes - winning can be also - there's no doubting the amazing Thomases - Terry (left) and her ironman husband Duncan - both winners in the Oct. 1984 Santa Barbara, California Triathlon (800 triathletes competing). Terry laughlingly said she started competing in the demanding swim, bike, run sport so she could see her husband more! Duncan also won in 1982, and was 2nd in 1983.

Photo by Rafael Maldonado

Now I see the secret of the making of the best persons, it is to grow in the open air, and eat and sleep with the earth. — *Walt Whitman*

In health there is liberty. Health is the first of all liberties, happiness gives us the energy which is the basis of health. — *Miel*

570

INDEX

INDEX

INDEX

INDEX

INDEX

INDEX

TRIATHLETE
TRAINING IDEAS:

TRIATHLETE
TRAINING IDEAS:

TRIATHLETE
TRAINING IDEAS:

TRIATHLON
PERSONAL TIMES:

TRIATHLON
PERSONAL TIMES:

FELLOW TRIATHLETE ADDRESSES:

FELLOW TRIATHLETE ADDRESSES:

TRIATHLETE AUTOGRAPHS

TRIATHLETE AUTOGRAPHS

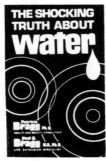

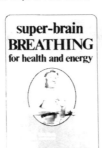

Bragg

Live Longer — Healthier — Stronger
Self - Improvement Library

Let Legendary PAUL C. BRAGG, World Health Crusader, Pioneer Nutritionist, Originator of Health Stores and Beloved Sage to Millions and PATRICIA BRAGG, Health and Fitness Educator, Show You the Simple Path to a Greater, Longer, More Vital Life — "High Health" Physically, Mentally and Spiritually!

BRAGG "HOW-TO, SELF-HEALTH" BOOKS

Remember . . . The Gift of a Bragg Book is a Gift of Life!

Bragg

Live Longer — Healthier — Stronger
Self - Improvement Library

Let Legendary **PAUL C. BRAGG**, World Health Crusader, Pioneer Nutritionist, Originator of Health Stores and Beloved Sage to Millions and **PATRICIA BRAGG**, Health and Fitness Educator, Show You the Simple Path to a Greater, Longer, More Vital Life — "High Health" Physically, Mentally and Spiritually!

BRAGG "HOW-TO, SELF-HEALTH" BOOKS

Prices subject to change without notice

Remember . . . The Gift of a Bragg Book is a Gift of Life!

Buy these Bragg books today for yourself, family and friends. Purchase or order at your health store or better book stores. If unavailable in your area, you may obtain from Health Science. When ordering please add for postage and handling — $1.00 for first, 50¢ for each additional book. Remittance in U.S. funds only. California residents add sales tax.

Please send Free Health Fitness Bulletins to these friends and relatives:

● _____
Name

_____
Address

_____
City   State   Zip Code

● _____
Name

_____
Address

_____
City   State   Zip Code

● _____
Name

_____
Address

_____
City   State   Zip Code

● _____
Name

_____
Address

_____
City   State   Zip Code

● _____
Name

_____
Address

_____
City   State   Zip Code

PLEASE SEND NAMES TO:

HEALTH SCIENCE Box 7, Santa Barbara, California 93102 U.S.A.

PLEASE CUT ALONG DOTTED LINE

Bragg

Live Longer — Healthier — Stronger
Self - Improvement Library

Let Legendary PAUL C. BRAGG, World Health Crusader, Pioneer Nutritionist, Originator of Health Stores and Beloved Sage to Millions and PATRICIA BRAGG, Health and Fitness Educator, Show You the Simple Path to a Greater, Longer, More Vital Life — "High Health" Physically, Mentally and Spiritually!

BRAGG "HOW-TO, SELF-HEALTH" BOOKS

Please send Free Health Fitness Bulletins to these friends and relatives:

● _____
Name

_____
Address

_____
City   State   Zip Code

● _____
Name

_____
Address

_____
City   State   Zip Code

● _____
Name

_____
Address

_____
City   State   Zip Code

● _____
Name

_____
Address

_____
City   State   Zip Code

● _____
Name

_____
Address

_____
City   State   Zip Code

PLEASE SEND NAMES TO:

HEALTH SCIENCE Box 7, Santa Barbara, California 93102 U.S.A.

PLEASE CUT ALONG DOTTED LINE

Co-author, Bob Johnson, right, ... attended Jack LaLanne's birthday feat of pulling a 1,000 lb. boat from Alcatraz Island to the Dolphin Club, San Francisco Bay shoreline hand and foot-cuffed in 50 degree water.

Facing the camera center is Jim Cotton, founder of the Waikiki Rough water swim. This group is going ashore on the island of Lanai to start the Maui Channel relay terminating in Lahaina Harbor, Maui.

Finishers of the Maui Channel Relay.

PATRICIA BRAGG, Ph.D.
Life Extension Specialist

Author, T.V. and Radio Personality, Health and Fitness Lecturer—Patricia Bragg is dedicated to perpetuating the legacy left by her father, the late Dr. Paul C. Bragg, of spreading the Gospel (good news) of health, nutrition and total fitness, through the Bragg Health Crusades. As co-author of this Triathlon Manual, her contributions can change your life both spiritually and physically, just as she has done for thousands of her health students around the world. Patricia is a health confidant of movie stars, champion athletes, and leaders of business and industry. Through this book she wishes to reach into the lives of training triathletes, in an inspiring health-giving way.

BOB JOHNSON
USTS Regional Champion Triathlete

Bob's writing background is extensive and includes...editor of a world-wide yacht racing publication, editor of a health and fitness periodical with a 200,000 North American circulation, and author of a number of health and fitness books.

Bob started his Triathlon participation, as many have, as a marathoner and ultra-marathoner at age 57, then into Triathlons, having participated in eight to date including two Ironman World Triathlons. At 62, Bob held the Regional Championship in the over 55 age group in the United States Triathlon Series Professional Triathlons, having won two of the first three held on the west coast.

Bob is retired, having been active in real estate development in Beverly Hills and the Carmel area of California for over 40 years.

As a volunteer Christian Courier, Bob served in the Eastern European Communist countries and Mainland China, delivering the Christian word to the oppressed peoples of these countries, and was imprisoned in Russia for his Christian faith.

Bob wishes to join Patricia in reaching the training triathlete with a physical and spiritual message that will change their lives for the better.

HEALTH SCIENCE
Box 7 • Santa Barbara, California 93102, U.S.A.

Printed in U.S.A.

Biker with Dillingham Memorial Fountain in the background—Diamond Head area of Honolulu . . . USTS Triathlon, Author's transition equipment . . . Early A.M. at Del Valle Lake, site of San Francisco USTS Triathlon . . . Point "Zero" for Ironman World Triathlon . . . Bikes . . . Swim Course, turnaround course marker is glass bottom catamaran on the right . . . Claire St. Arnaud, 6 photos and coming out of the water . . . Claire is a Sioux Indian from Nebraska, a ferrier (blacksmith) by trade, he shoed horses all the way to Kona . . . Ground "Zero" . . . Team Lotus Repair Shop . . . Dave Bending, Open Air Bike Shop.